ALGEBRA ONE

ALGEBRA ONE

Joseph N. Payne

Floyd F. Zamboni

Francis G. Lankford, Jr.

HARCOURT, BRACE & WORLD, INC.

New York   Chicago   San Francisco   Atlanta   Dallas

ABOUT THE AUTHORS

JOSEPH N. PAYNE
Professor of Education,
Coordinator of Mathematics and
Department Chairman at the University School,
University of Michigan, Ann Arbor, Michigan

FLOYD F. ZAMBONI
Teacher of Mathematics,
Jefferson County Schools,
Jefferson County, Colorado

FRANCIS G. LANKFORD, JR.
Professor of Education,
Director, Office of Institutional Analysis,
University of Virginia, Charlottesville, Virginia

ABOUT THE COVER

The cover shows a photograph taken by Sheldon S. Rose.
He created the moiré pattern using four films of the same
basic design, each in a different color. He placed the
films one on top of the other and then photographed
the result through a textured sheet of glass.

Regular Edition   ISBN 0-15-354180-6
With Alternate Answers ISBN 0-15-354181-4

Contents

CHAPTER 1

SETS AND NUMBERS

Much of mathematics has been created by man to describe things in his environment. You use mathematics to count and tell the number of things, to describe shapes, to calculate distances and dimensions, to solve problems.

In this chapter you will review the ideas of sets and subsets. You will look at sets of numbers and relations between them, and review the postulates for operating with sets and numbers. Working with equations will be introduced.

For how many of the following questions do you know the answer?

● What do the set of horses and the set of telephone poles in the photographs have in common?

● Name some other sets in the photographs at the left. Does each set have a finite number of elements or an infinite number of elements? Can you count the stars in the center photograph? If you lived long enough, could you count the grains of sand on the beach in the lower right photograph? What is an infinite set?

● What are you doing when you count? How can you tell if two sets have the same number of elements?

● Can you name the part that one telephone pole is in relation to the whole set? Is the answer one of the whole numbers?

● Look at the diagram of the square. Can you count the number of units in the length of each side? Can you tell the length of the diagonal, as marked with the same units?

● Can you find something in one of the photographs that makes you think of a set of points that is a triangle? a line?

When you have studied this chapter, you will know the answers to all these questions and to many more.

1–1 Sets and Elements

Long ago a mathematician and scientist named Galileo Galilei (1564–1646) noticed something very odd. He wrote a list of numbers used for counting, which today are called the **natural numbers** or **counting numbers.**

$$1, 2, 3, 4, 5, 6, 7, 8, 9, 10, 11, 12, \cdots$$

(The three dots mean that the list can be continued in the same way. The natural numbers continue without bound.) Underneath this list, Galileo wrote the product of each number with itself, which is called the **square** of the number. The square of 3, written as 3×3 or 3^2, is 9.

$$1, 2, 3, \quad 4, \quad 5, \quad 6, \quad 7, \quad 8, \quad 9, \quad 10, \quad 11, \quad 12, \cdots$$
$$1, 4, 9, 16, 25, 36, 49, 64, 81, 100, 121, 144, \cdots$$

Galileo noticed that the square numbers seem to be farther and farther apart as the numbers get larger. But there seem to be just as many square numbers as there are natural numbers. In fact, for each natural number there is one and only one square number, and for each square number there is one and only one natural number, called a **square root.** The natural-number square root of 16, which is 4, is written as $\sqrt{16}$.

The **even natural numbers** can also be matched, one to one, with the natural numbers.

$$1, 2, 3, 4, \quad 5, \quad 6, \quad 7, \quad 8, \quad 9, 10, 11, 12, \cdots$$
$$2, 4, 6, 8, 10, 12, 14, 16, 18, 20, 22, 24, \cdots$$

Do there seem to be as many even numbers as there are natural numbers? Can you show a similar matching for the **odd numbers,** 1, 3, 5, 7, 9, 11, $\cdots$, with the natural numbers?

Galileo did not know how to explain this mystery. Many years later, at the end of the nineteenth century, a mathematician named Georg Cantor investigated the problem thoroughly and, in the process of explaining it, invented a new branch of mathematics that is useful in many ways. Cantor's new mathematics is called **set theory,** and in the beginning of this book, you will learn enough about sets to understand Galileo's mystery.

A **set** is a well-defined collection of objects called **elements.** You think of the collection as a single thing. When you think of the boys and girls in your room as a set of persons, you think of *one* group.

Well-defined means that you can tell if any given object belongs or does not belong to the set, that is, whether or not it is an element of the set. If the set under consideration is the set of green vegetables, then you know *spinach* is an element of the set, but *carrot* is not. The set is well defined.

The idea that an element belongs to a given set is used so often that a special symbol is used to express it.

> The symbol $\in$ means **is an element of**, and $\notin$ means **is not an element of.**

Are the following two statements correct? The first statement is read "*Spinach* is an element of the set of green vegetables."

Spinach $\in$ The set of green vegetables.
Carrot $\notin$ The set of green vegetables.

Look at the examples in the table below showing the ways that a set may be indicated, or named. The **rule method** denotes the set by using words, formulas, or properties. The **roster method** denotes the set by listing the elements of the set in braces, { }. No matter how a set is denoted, it must be well defined.

	Rule method	Roster method
Numbers	W = The set of whole numbers.	$W = \{0, 1, 2, 3, \cdots\}$
Points	P = The set of points A, B, and C. B A C	$P = \{A, B, C\}$
Teams	T = The set of baseball teams in the American League.	T = {Tigers, Indians, Twins, Orioles, Yankees, Senators, Red Sox, Angels, Athletics, White Sox}
No elements	$\emptyset$ = The empty set, or the null set.	$\emptyset = \{ \ \}$

In the examples the letters W, P, and T are names for the sets. In the last example the symbol $\emptyset$ is the name for the **empty set,** the set that has no members at all. The set of men 17 feet tall is the empty set, or { }. Is the set of purple spots on this page also the empty set?

Both W and {0, 1, 2, 3, · · ·} denote the same collection, as is indicated by the equals sign.

Sets are used in geometry as well as in algebra. For instance, a line segment is defined in terms of sets. Line segment AB, $\overline{AB}$, is defined as the set of points A and B and all the points between them. In this case, no braces are used, because $\overline{AB}$ has been defined as a set.

Now try these

— Refer to the examples in the table on page 3, and replace the ● with $\in$ or $\notin$ to make true sentences.

1. 2 ● W   2. B ● P
3. Orioles ● T   4. $6\frac{1}{2}$ ● W
5. $\sqrt{2}$ ● W   6. Line segment AB ● P
7. Triangle ABC ● P   8. Angels ● T
9. 1 ● $\emptyset$ 10. Yankees ● $\emptyset$

Answers: **1.** $\in$ **2.** $\in$ **3.** $\in$ **4.** $\notin$ **5.** $\notin$ **6.** $\notin$ **7.** $\notin$ **8.** $\in$ **9.** $\notin$ **10.** $\notin$

Checkpoint

1. What is the difference between the rule and the roster methods for describing a set?
2. What do the symbols $\in$ and $\notin$ mean?
3. What symbol is used to name the empty set?
4. When is a collection a well-defined set?

Exercises

A — The sets W, P, T, and $\emptyset$ used in the sentences below are from the examples in the table on page 3. Read each mathematical sentence and tell whether it is *True* or *False*.

1. $3 \in W$ 2. $2\frac{1}{2} \notin W$
3. $D \in P$ 4. $C \in P$
5. White Sox $\notin$ T   6. $97 \in W$
7. Cardinals $\notin$ T   8. $86\frac{1}{2} \in W$
9. $a \in \emptyset$ 10. $0 \notin \emptyset$

— Write the members of each of the following sets by the roster method. A few elements of some sets are shown.

11. The set of odd whole numbers less than 16.

$$\{1, 3, 5, \underline{?}, \underline{?}, \underline{?}, \underline{?}, \underline{?}\}$$

12. The squares of all whole numbers less than 6.

$$\{0, 1, 4, \underline{?}, \underline{?}, \underline{?}\}$$

13. The whole-number square root, $\sqrt{\ }$, of each number in your answer to Exercise 12.

$$\{0, 1, 2, \underline{?}, \underline{?}, \underline{?}\}$$

14. The natural numbers from 2 through 37 that are exactly divisible by 7.

$$\{7, 14, \underline{?}, \underline{?}, \underline{?}\}$$

15. The consecutive, odd whole numbers from 30 to 40.

$$\{31, 33, \underline{?}, \underline{?}, \underline{?}\}$$

16. The set of *prime numbers* less than 20. (A **prime number** is a whole number greater than 1 that has only one pair of whole-number factors, itself and 1.)

$$\{2, 3, 5, \underline{?}, \underline{?}, \underline{?}, \underline{?}, \underline{?}\}$$

17. The set of all *composite numbers* less than 20. (A **composite number** is a whole number greater than 1 and not prime; that is, it has more than one pair of factors: $6 = 6 \times 1$ or 3×2.)

$$\{4, 6, 8, 9, \underline{?}, \underline{?}, \underline{?}, \underline{?}, \underline{?}, \underline{?}\}$$

18. The set of line segments connecting the points A, B, and C.

$$\{\overline{AB}, \overline{BC}, \underline{?}\}$$

A
B
C

19. The set of line segments that are the five sides of pentagon $PQRST$.

$$\{\overline{PQ}, \overline{QR}, \underline{?}, \underline{?}, \underline{?}\}$$

20. The set of vertices (points of intersection of sides) of pentagon $PQRST$.

$$\{P, Q, \underline{?}, \underline{?}, \underline{?}\}$$

Pentagon PQRST

21. The set of teachers in your classroom.

22. The set of infants in your classroom.

Replace each ● with ∈ or ∉ to make true sentences. (A **multiple** of a number is any of the products of the given number and some other whole number.)

N = The set of natural numbers.   {1, 2, 3, 4, 5, · · ·}
W = The set of whole numbers.   {0, 1, 2, 3, 4, · · ·}
E = The set of even whole numbers.   {0, 2, 4, 6, 8, · · ·}
D = The set of odd whole numbers.   {1, 3, 5, 7, 9, · · ·}
M = The set of whole numbers that
    are multiples of 3.   {0, 3, 6, 9, 12, · · ·}

23. 5 ● N   **24.** 7 ● M   **25.** 8 ● W

26. 15 ● M   **27.** 7 ● E   **28.** 198 ● D

29. $8\frac{1}{2}$ ● N   **30.** $\sqrt{9}$ ● W   **31.** $(2\frac{1}{2} + \frac{1}{2})$ ● W

32. (8×2) ● W   **33.** $(8 \div 3)$ ● W   **34.** $(16 \div 9)$ ● N

35. $(15 + 6)$ ● N   **36.** $(9 + 7)$ ● D   **37.** $(12 + 96)$ ● E

B   **38.** List the members of the set of all whole numbers less than 20, each of which is named by a two-digit numeral whose tens digit exceeds the units digit by one.

39. What element is in the set {0}? Does ∅ have any elements?

C   **40.** List the members of the set of whole numbers that are square roots of whole numbers less than 25.

41. List the members of the set of prime numbers between 100 and 200. How many elements does this set have?

1–2   Subsets

Study the following examples that illustrate the meaning of **subset.**

EXAMPLE 1. Think of set P as the set of people in the illustration, G as the set of girls, and B as the set of boys. Name the elements of set P; of set G; of set B. Is each element of G also an element of P?

Since each element of the set of girls is an element of the set of people, the set of girls is a *subset* of the set of people.

> **Definition**   A set G is a <u>subset</u> of a set P if and only if every element of set G is an element of set P.

The symbol ⊆ means *is a subset of.* The sentence G ⊆ P is read "G is a subset of P."

Is B ⊆ P true? Explain, using the definition of subset.

EXAMPLE 2. Here is Galileo's problem, which was stated on page 2, written with the notation of sets.

N = {1, 2, 3, 4, 5, 6, 7, 8, 9, 10, 11, 12, · · ·}
S = {1, 4, 9, 16, 25, 36, 49, 64, 81, 100, 121, 144, · · ·}

Is every element of S also an element of N? Which is true, N ⊆ S or S ⊆ N? Every element of S is an element of N, so S ⊆ N is true.

EXAMPLE 3. Let X be the set of points of the rectangle *ABCD*. Think of the subset of points $\overline{AB}$. Is each point of $\overline{AB}$ an element of X? Then is $\overline{AB}$ ⊆ X true?

Since each point of the segment *AB* is also a point of the rectangle, the segment *AB* is a subset of X, and $\overline{AB}$ ⊆ X is true.

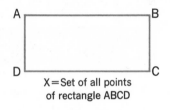
X = Set of all points of rectangle ABCD

EXAMPLE 4. Name the members of sets N, L, and M. Is each member of L also a member of N? Is each member of M also a member of N?

N = {0, 1, 2, 3, 4, 5, 6, 7, 8, 9}
L = {2, 3, 4}   M = {6}

Each member of L and of M is a member of N.

Tell why these sentences are true.

a. L ⊆ N   b. M ⊆ N

The symbol for *is not a subset of* is ⊄.

Tell why the following are true.

c. L ⊄ M   d. N ⊄ M
e. N ⊄ L   f. M ⊄ L

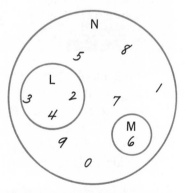

Now answer this question. Is each member of set N a member of N? Then, by the definition of subset, the truth of the following statement should be obvious.

Every set is a subset of itself.

Thus, the sentences $P \subseteq P$, $N \subseteq N$, and $X \subseteq X$ are true, where P, N, and X are the sets in Examples 1–3 on pages 6 and 7.

Look at Example 1 again. Suppose you are to choose a subset of P to come to your party. Name the members of three subsets that you might invite. Do you think that one of your subsets could include no person of set P? If you invited no person from set P, you would invite the empty set. If you listed all the possible subsets of people that you invite, it would be sensible to include the empty set. Are there any elements in the empty set that are not in set P? Therefore, you can conclude that the following is true.

The empty set is a subset of every set.

Using the sets from Examples 1–3, these sentences are true: $\emptyset \subseteq P$, $\emptyset \subseteq G$, $\emptyset \subseteq B$, $\emptyset \subseteq X$, $\emptyset \subseteq N$, $\emptyset \subseteq L$, $\emptyset \subseteq M$. The same sentences can be written using braces: $\{ \ \} \subseteq P$, $\{ \ \} \subseteq G$, and so forth.

Let set A be $\{1, 2, 3\}$. If $B = \{1, 2\}$, is B a subset of A? Does B contain all the elements of A? Then B is a **proper subset** of A.

Definition   A proper subset of A is any subset of A except the subset A itself.

The symbol $\subset$ means *is a proper subset of*. The symbol for *is not a proper subset of* is $\not\subset$.

Suppose sets A and B are as shown at the right. Is $A \subseteq B$ a true statement? $B \subseteq A$? Are the members of A exactly the same as the members of B? This leads to the definition of **equal sets**.

$A = \{1, 2, 3, 4\}$

$B = \{4, 3, 1, 2\}$

Definition   Set A is equal to set B if and only if A is a subset of B and B is a subset of A.

The definition can be stated in mathematical symbols as follows.

A = B if and only if A ⊆ B and B ⊆ A.

Checkpoint

1. When is set B a subset of set A? When is set B not a subset of set A?

2. Is set A always a subset of A? a proper subset of A?

3. Is the empty set a subset of any set?

4. When is it true that set S is equal to set T?

5. When is set S a proper subset of set T?

Exercises

A —— If A = {3, 5, 12, 15, 17}, list the elements for each of the following subsets of set A.

1. The subset of A whose elements are exactly divisible by 5.

2. The subset of A whose elements are exactly divisible by 3.

3. The subset of A whose elements are exactly divisible by 1.

4. The subset of A whose elements are prime numbers.

—— If T = {1, 3, 4, 8, 10, 16}, list the elements for each of the following subsets of T.

5. The subset of T consisting of even whole numbers.

6. The subset of T consisting of odd whole numbers named by two-digit numerals.

7. The subset of T consisting of all elements of T that are perfect-square whole numbers. (4 is a perfect square because 2 × 2 = 4 is true, but 5 is not a perfect square because 5 is not the square of any whole number.)

—— What is the number of elements in each of these sets?

8. The set of natural numbers that divide 36 with zero as a remainder.

9. The set of even natural numbers less than 40.

10. The set of prime numbers between 40 and 50.

11. The set of digits used in our decimal system.

— Tell whether each sentence is true or false. (Refer to the diagram below for Exercises 12–16.)

12. $\overline{AB}$ is a subset of $\overline{AF}$.

13. $\overline{AF} \subseteq \overline{AF}$

14. $A \subset \overline{AB}$

15. $\emptyset \subset \overline{AF}$

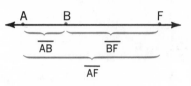

16. $\overline{AF} \not\subseteq \overline{AB}$

17. The set {rectangle, square, parallelogram, rhombus} is a subset of the set of quadrilaterals.

18. {0} is a subset of the set of natural numbers.

19. {0} is a subset of the set of whole numbers.

20. The set of natural numbers is a subset of the set of whole numbers.

21. For every set A, $A \subseteq A$ is true.

22. For every set A, $\emptyset \subseteq A$ is true.

23. For every set A, $A \subseteq \emptyset$ is true.

— Replace ● with = or ≠ in each of the following to make the sentence true.

24. A ● B if A = {a, b, c} and B = {a, b}.

25. C ● D if C = {2, 3, 5, 7} and D = {2, 5, 7, 3}.

26. R ● T if R = {$\frac{1}{2}$, $\frac{1}{10}$, $\frac{1}{5}$} and T = {0.5, 0.1, 0.2}.
(*Hint:* Think of R and T as sets of numbers, not as sets of numerals.)

27. J ● $\emptyset$ if J is the set of natural numbers greater than 5 and less than 6.

28. {0} ● $\emptyset$ (*Hint:* How many members are in {0}? in $\emptyset$?)

— Classify the first set of each of the following as either a proper subset of the second set or equal to the second set.

29. {3, 6, 9, 15} and the set of natural numbers between 1 and 18 that are exactly divisible by 3.

30. The set of odd whole numbers less than 10 and {1, 3, 5, 7, 9}.

31. The set of prime numbers less than 12 and {2, 3, 5, 7, 11}.

32. The set of numbers represented by the numerals on a 12-hour clock and {1, 2, 3, 4, 5, 6, 7, 8, 9, 10, 11, 12}.

33. The set of whole numbers greater than 3 and less than 10, and {4, 5, 6, 7, 8, 9, 10}.

—— Does a subset relationship exist between X and Y for each of the following? If so, write a sentence using $\subset$ or $\subseteq$.

34. X = {0, 1, 3, 5, 7}; Y = {1, 5, 7}

35. X = {a, b}; Y = {a, b, e}

36. X = the set of all natural numbers less than 20; Y = the set of prime numbers less than 25.

37. X = the set of natural numbers greater than 3 and less than 9; Y = the set of natural numbers less than 8.

—— Given the following three sets, indicate *True* or *False* for each statement.

$$A = \{1, 3, 5, 7\}$$
$$B = \{1, 7\}$$
$$C = \{1, 3, 5, 7, 9, 11\}$$

38. B $\subseteq$ C	**39.** A $\subseteq$ B	**40.** C $\subseteq$ C
41. B $\subseteq$ A	**42.** C $\subseteq$ A	**43.** A $\subseteq$ C

B —— Tell whether or not set A is a subset of set B.

44. A = {0, 5} and B = {0}

45. A = ø and B = {0}

46. A is the set of all natural numbers and B is the set of all natural numbers that may be divided evenly by 10.

C **47.** To prove that ø $\subseteq$ N is true for every set N, you reason indirectly. Answer the questions that follow to understand the proof.

a. Either ø $\subseteq$ N or ø $\not\subseteq$ N is true. How do you know this?

b. Suppose ø $\not\subseteq$ N is true. What does this imply? Since N is well defined, you know all the elements in N. Then there is at least one element in ø that is not in N. Why?

c. Does ø have any elements? Why?

d. In **b**, you found that there is an element in ø. From **c** you know that ø has no elements. Could both be true?

e. Does the supposition that ø $\not\subseteq$ N is true lead to contradictory statements? What are they? Then the supposition ø $\not\subseteq$ N is false.

f. In **a** you saw that either ø $\subseteq$ N or ø $\not\subseteq$ N is true. If ø $\not\subseteq$ N is false, then must ø $\subseteq$ N be true?

This is proof that ø $\subseteq$ N is true for every set N.

1–3 Equivalent Sets and Infinite Sets

Consider sets A and B. Although A and B are not equal sets, they have something in common. Can you match each element of A with just one element in B so that each element of B is matched with exactly one element of A? Then the two sets are in **one-to-one correspondence**.

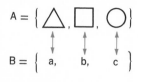

Definition Two sets, J and K, are in one-to-one correspondence if each element in J is matched with exactly one element in K and if each element in K is matched with exactly one element in J, and no members are left over.

In Galileo's problem, set S is a proper subset of set N.

$$N = \{1, 2, 3, \ 4, \ 5, \ 6, \ 7, \ 8, \ 9, \ 10, \ 11, \ 12, \cdots\}$$
$$S = \{1, 4, 9, 16, 25, 36, 49, 64, 81, 100, 121, 144, \cdots\}$$

Do sets N and S appear to have the same number of elements? Are they in one-to-one correspondence? Can you name the number of elements in sets N and S?

Definition Equivalent sets are sets that can be placed in one-to-one correspondence.

From the definition, you can tell that N and S are **equivalent sets** and that A and B are equivalent. If B = {a, b, c} and X = {b, c, a}, are B and X equal sets? Are B and X equivalent sets? Why are all equal sets also equivalent sets?

If R = {0, 6, 27} and Q = {270, 6}, are R and Q equal? Are they equivalent? R and Q are **nonequivalent** sets.

Now look again at the equivalent sets B and X. What number property do the two sets share?

Two equivalent sets have the same number of elements.

Sets B and X each have three elements. You can think of the number 3 as the common property of all sets equivalent to B or X, such as set A. Since N and S are equivalent, they have the same number of elements. But you cannot name a natural number, such as 3, or 6, or 100, to identify that number. The difference between set A and set N is that A is **finite** and N is **infinite.**

Look at some other examples of finite and infinite sets.

Finite sets

a. The set of students in your class.

b. The set of cities in the U.S.

c. The set of molecules in your body.

d. The set of whole numbers, zero through one trillion.

e. The set of grains of sand on the beach.

f. The set of stars in the Milky Way.

g. The set of atoms in the earth.

h. The set of pages in this book.

Infinite sets

i. The set of whole numbers.

j. The set of even numbers.

k. The set of points on a line segment.

l. The set of multiples of ten.

m. The set of prime numbers.

n. The set of composite numbers.

o. The set of lines that contain a given point.

p. The set of numbers named with 1 as the numerator and a natural number as the denominator, that is, $\frac{1}{1}, \frac{1}{2}, \frac{1}{3}, \cdots$.

Definition   A <u>finite set</u> has elements that can be counted, with the counting coming to an end. The empty set is a finite set.

This does not mean that the physical job of counting the elements can be done by any one person or by many persons. It merely means that it is mathematically possible.

Definition   All sets that are not finite sets are <u>infinite sets.</u>

It is impossible to count the elements of an infinite set with the counting coming to an end. Look at each infinite set in the list above, and tell why it is infinite. (*Hint:* If there is a new element beyond any given element in a set, the set is infinite.) While you cannot count the elements of an infinite set with the counting coming to an end, you can tell if two infinite sets are equivalent.

Look again at the set of natural numbers and the set of even numbers. The set of even numbers is a proper subset of the set of natural numbers. Are these two sets equal? Are they equivalent? Are they finite or are they infinite?

$$N = \{1, 2, 3, 4, \; 5, \; 6, \; 7, \cdots, \quad n, \quad \cdots\}$$
$$E = \{2, 4, 6, 8, 10, 12, 14, \cdots, 2 \times n, \cdots\}$$

If n represents any natural number, what does $2 \times n$ represent? In these sets what even number matches 5? 7? 25? 1000? any natural number denoted by n? For each natural number, can you name one and only one even number that matches it?

What natural number matches the even number 4? 12? 50? 1,000,000? any even number $2 \times n$? For each even number, can you name one and only one natural number that matches it? Then the sets N and E are equivalent: they have the same number of elements.

> **Definition**   The name for the number of elements in the set of natural numbers and in all sets equivalent to the natural numbers is <u>aleph-null</u>. The symbol for the number is $\aleph_0$.

It may seem strange to match the elements of a set with a proper subset of itself. But it can be done with infinite sets. In fact, this matching property can be used to define *infinite sets*. Why can you not place a finite set in one-to-one correspondence with a proper subset of itself?

Checkpoint

1. When are two sets said to be in one-to-one correspondence?
2. When are two sets equivalent sets?
3. When are two sets nonequivalent sets?
4. What is a finite set?
5. What is an infinite set?
6. When do two sets have the same number of elements?
7. How many elements are in the set of natural numbers?

Exercises

A — Write *Equivalent* or *Nonequivalent* for each pair of sets in Exercises 1–11. Also, identify each set as *Finite* or *Infinite*.

1. $\{1, 2, 3\}$ and $\{6, 7, 8\}$

2. $\{3, 4, 5, 6\}$ and $\{\frac{1}{4}, \frac{1}{5}, \frac{1}{6}, \frac{1}{7}\}$

3. The set of even whole numbers between 40 and 50 and the set of even whole numbers between 50 and 60.

4. The set of odd whole numbers less than 25 and the set of prime numbers less than 25.

5. The set of natural numbers that are exact divisors of 36 and the set of digits in the decimal system.

6. The set of vertices of triangle ABC and the set of line segments that form the triangle.

7. The set of vertices of any polygon and the set of sides of the polygon.

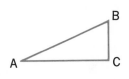

8. The set of teachers in your school and the set of adult females in your school.

9. The set of pages in this book and the set of natural numbers 1 through 576.

10. The set of fingers on a normal hand and $\{1, 2, 3, 4, 5\}$.

11. The set of all circles and the set of centers of all circles.

12. The graph shows the set of whole numbers matched with certain points on a line. Is each number matched with exactly one point? Is the given set of points on the line equivalent to the set of whole numbers?

$$\overleftrightarrow{\underset{0\quad 1\quad 2\quad 3\quad 4\quad 5\quad 6}{\bullet\ \ \bullet\ \ \bullet\ \ \bullet\ \ \bullet\ \ \bullet\ \ \bullet}}$$

13. The drawing shows one way that sets C and D can be placed in one-to-one correspondence. Make drawings to show five other ways that this can be done.

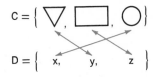

B **14.** Indicate a 1–1 correspondence between the even natural numbers, E, and the odd natural numbers, D. Describe a pattern that indicates how the elements in D are to be matched with the elements in E. What conclusion can you draw about these two sets? How many members has each set?

15. Indicate a 1–1 (one-to-one) correspondence between

$$N = \{1, 2, 3, 4, 5, 6, \cdots\}$$

and

$$B = \{100, 101, 102, 103, 104, 105, 106, \cdots\}.$$

Describe a pattern that indicates how the elements in B can be matched with the elements in N. What can you conclude about these two sets? How many members has each set?

C **16.** Is the set of numbers $F = \{\frac{1}{2}, \frac{1}{3}, \frac{1}{4}, \frac{1}{5}, \cdots, \frac{1}{n+1}, \cdots\}$ equivalent to the set of natural numbers? How many members has F?

1–4 Variables and Expressions

If you buy a given number of five-cent stamps, the total cost is 5 times the number of stamps. The number of stamps can be any number in the set $W = \{0, 1, 2, 3, \cdots\}$.. To represent any number in the set, you can use a symbol such as n, x, or $\square$. Such symbols are called **variables.**

> **Definition** A <u>variable</u> is a symbol (usually a letter) that may represent any element in a given set. The given set is called the <u>replacement set</u> for the variable.

The expressions $3 \times n$, $3 \cdot n$, and $3n$ mean "3 times any number chosen from the replacement set." What would $5\square$ mean? In the diagram at the right, the box, $\square$, is the variable and the numbers shown on the strip form the replacement set.

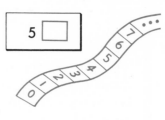

If $\square$ is replaced by 2, then $5\square$ names 5×2, or 10. Tell the numbers that complete the following table.

Number from replacement set	0	1	2	3	4	5	6	7	$\cdots$	n
$5\square$ is	0	5	10	15	?	?	?	?	$\cdots$	?

The set that results from $5\square$ is the set of multiples of 5.

16   CHAPTER 1

The replacement set in this example of buying any number of stamps is a finite set of whole numbers. Why would it not make sense to have $6\frac{1}{2}$ in the replacement set? The replacement set is often determined by the nature of the problem; other times, the choice of the replacement set is arbitrary. Sometimes the replacement set is called the *universal set*.

EXAMPLE. Suppose that each table in a furniture store has 4 legs and that n represents the number of tables. Then $4n$ represents the total number of legs. What replacement set is sensible?

The sensible replacement set is $\{0, 1, 2, 3, 4, \cdots, n\}$ because there must be a whole number of tables.

The group of symbols $2 + 5x$ is an **algebraic expression.** An algebraic expression is made up of one or more terms joined by $+$ or $-$. A **term** is the product and/or quotient of numerals and variables, for example, $\frac{1}{2}xy$, $3mn^2$, $\frac{a}{2b}$. Any one of the factors of the term is a **coefficient** of the other factors. Thus, in the term $\frac{1}{2}xy$, $\frac{1}{2}$ is the coefficient of xy; x is the coefficient of $\frac{1}{2}y$; and y is the coefficient of $\frac{1}{2}x$. But *coefficient* usually means **numerical coefficient.** So when you are asked for the coefficient of an expression such as $3mn^2$, it is 3.

An algebraic expression names a number when the variable is replaced by an element in the replacement set. To find the number named by $2 + 5x$, you need to know whether it means "Add 2 and 5, and then multiply x by the sum" or "Multiply x by 5, and then add the product to 2." Punctuation marks can be used to make the meaning of the expression $2 + 5x$ clear. The most common punctuation marks in algebra are parentheses. Look at the expressions $(2 + 5)x$ and $2 + (5x)$.

The expression $(2 + 5)x$ means "Add 2 and 5, and then multiply x by the sum." Complete this table. If the replacement set were W, what would be the set of values for $(2 + 5)x$?

x	0	1	2	3	4	5	6
$(2 + 5)x$	0	7	14	21	?	?	?

The expression $2 + (5x)$ means " Multiply x by 5, and then add the product to 2." Complete this table. If the replacement set for x were the set of multiples of 5, what would be the set of values for $2 + (5x)$?

x	0	5	10	15	20	25
$2 + (5x)$	2	27	52	77	?	?

An agreement is usually made on the **order of operation** so that you will be able to write the expressions more easily. Unless parentheses or other grouping symbols show clearly that something else is to be done, the standard agreement on the order of operations is as follows.

First multiply and/or divide in the order that the operations appear; then add and/or subtract in the order that these operations appear.

Thus, for $2 + 5x$, you multiply first, and then add, and no parentheses are necessary.

Note that the set of values for x and the set of values for $2 + 5x$ are equivalent.

$$\{0, \quad 5, 10, 15, \quad 20, \cdots\}$$
$$\{2, 27, 52, 77, 102, \cdots\}$$

Each value of x is matched with just one value of $2 + 5x$, and each value of $2 + 5x$ is matched with just one value of x.

Now try these

▬ Write a single numeral for each expression.

1. $3 + 5 \cdot 2$ **2.** $5 \cdot 6 - 2$ **3.** $(5 + 3) \cdot 8$

4. $5 + 3(6 + 4)$ **5.** $6 + 3 \cdot 5 + 8 - 2 \cdot 3 + 6 - 4 - 1$

6. What numbers may result from $1 + 3n$ if the replacement set for n is $\{0, 1, 2, 3, 4, \cdots\}$?

Answers: **1.** 13   **2.** 28   **3.** 64   **4.** 35   **5.** 24   **6.** $\{1, 4, 7, 10, 13, \cdots\}$

Checkpoint

1. What is a variable? What is the connection between a variable and a replacement set?

2. What is an algebraic expression? When does an expression such as $2 + 5x$ name a number?

3. What agreement is made on the order of operations in an algebraic expression?

Exercises

A — If t is a variable whose replacement set is $\{1, 3, 5, 7\}$, find the set of numbers named by each of the following.

1. $4t$ **2.** t^2 **3.** $t - 1$ **4.** $\frac{t+1}{2}$

— If n is a variable whose replacement set is the set of whole numbers, W, list the set of numbers named by each of the following.

5. $2n$ **6.** $2n + 1$ **7.** $2n + 2$

8. $3n$ **9.** $n + \frac{1}{2}$ **10.** $2n + \frac{1}{2}$

11. $\frac{n}{2} + 7$ **12.** $5(n + 3)$ **13.** $\frac{3+n}{2}$

14. $3n(5 + n)$ **15.** $\frac{n}{2}$ **16.** $\frac{n}{3} + \frac{2}{3}n$

17. If the replacement set is W, which of the following names all the even numbers? the odd numbers? the multiples of 3? none of these?

a. $3n$ **b.** $2n$ **c.** $2n + 1$ **d.** $3n + 1$

— If the replacement set for the variable t is $\{0, 1, 2, 5\}$, what is the least number represented by each of the following?

18. t **19.** $t + t + t$ **20.** $t + 2$

21. $2t$ **22.** $t - t$ **23.** $t \cdot t$

B — For which variables is a finite set of whole numbers the replacement set?

24. n represents the number of pounds of candy you buy at $.89 a pound. $\}$ $.89n$ is the total cost.

25. l represents the number of inches in the length of a rectangle whose width is 5 inches. $\}$ $5l$ is the number of square inches in the area of the rectangular region.

26. x represents the number of people in your class. $\}$ $10x$ is the total number of fingers on all the people in the class.

— If $p = 3t$ is true and the replacement set for t is $\{1, 2, 3\}$, what is the greatest number represented by each of the following?

27. $p + 5$ **28.** $p \div t$ **29.** $4 + t$

30. $5t$ **31.** $4t - p$ **32.** $7p - 4t$

33. $p - 3$ **34.** $p - p$ **35.** $4(p + t)$

— List the replacement set necessary so that each of the following names a whole number.

36. $a + 2$ **37.** $x \div 2$ **38.** $x \div x$

39. $0 \div a$ **40.** $\frac{b}{2} + \frac{1}{2}$ **41.** $(3x + 9) \div 2$

1–5   Sentences

You know that "I am an algebra student" is a true English sentence about you and algebra.   The following are true *mathematical* sentences with a brief description of each.

a. $5 + 2 = 7$ A sentence using =, *is equal to*, is an **equality,** or an **equation.**

b. $8 > 5$ A sentence using >, *is greater than,* is an **inequality.**

c. $15 + 6 < 25$ A sentence using <, *is less than,* is an **inequality.**

d. $15 \neq 4$ A sentence using $\neq$, *is not equal to,* is an **inequality.**

The symbol = means "is identical to" or "names the same thing as."   The sentence $5 + 3 = 10$ is false because $5 + 3$ and 10 do not name the same number.   The sentence can be made true by changing the symbol to $\neq$: $5 + 3 \neq 10$.   (Note that a line through any symbol means "not.")

The relations *is greater than* and *is less than* can be visualized on the **number line.**   To make a number line, match 0 with a point of a horizontal line, and choose a point to the right to match 1; then mark off congruent (equal in measure) segments to locate points for successive whole numbers.   The number is called the **coordinate** of the corresponding point.   The arrows at the ends indicate that the numbers go on indefinitely in both directions.

$$\xleftarrow{\quad \bullet \quad \bullet \quad \bullet \quad \bullet \quad \bullet \quad \bullet \quad \bullet \quad \bullet \quad} \rightarrow$$
$$0 \quad 1 \quad 2 \quad 3 \quad 4 \quad 5 \quad 6 \quad 7$$

To compare numbers using the number line, note the following.

A given number is less than any number to its right.

A given number is greater than any number to its left.

Pick a number and place your pencil at the corresponding point. Name numbers that are greater than the one you chose; name some that are less than the one you chose.

The idea of using the number line to compare two numbers can be stated as an equation. For example, you can say that $8 > 5$ is true because there is a counting number, 3, that added to 5 makes 8; that is, $8 > 5$ is true because $8 = 5 + 3$ is true. The definition is as follows.

Definition If a and b are whole numbers, then $a > b$ means that there is a natural number c such that $b + c = a$ is true. If $a > b$ is true, then $b < a$ is true.

Look at sentences **e–h** below. You cannot tell whether they are true or false until elements of the replacement set are substituted for the variable. They are **open sentences.**

Definition The <u>solution set</u> of an open sentence is the set of numbers that make the sentence true.

Substitute elements of the replacement set, U, to explain how the solution set was obtained.

Sentence	Replacement set	Solution set
e. $x + 2 > 4$	$U = \{0, 2, 4, 6\}$	$\{4, 6\}$
f. $x + x = 0$	$U = \{0, 1, 2, 3, 4, \cdots\}$	$\{0\}$
g. $x + 3 > x$	$U = \{0, 1, 2, 3, 4, \cdots\}$	$\{0, 1, 2, 3, 4, \cdots\}$
h. $4 \div 3 = x$	$U = \{0, 1, 2, 3, 4, \cdots\}$	$\emptyset$

The graphs of sentences **e–h** are shown below.

e.
```
←•—•—•—•—●—•—●—•—•—•→
  0 1 2 3 4 5 6 7 8 9
```

f.
```
←●—•—•—•—•—•—•—•—•—•→
  0 1 2 3 4 5 6 7 8 9
```

g.
```
←●—●—●—●—●—●—●—●—●—●→
  0 1 2 3 4 5 6 7 8 9
```

h.
```
←•—•—•—•—•—•—•—•—•—•→
  0 1 2 3 4 5 6 7 8 9
```

The **graph of an open sentence** is the set of points on the number line whose coordinates make the sentence true. The graph of **e** is two points, and of **f**, one point. The graph of **g** is all the points on the number line (the arrow shows that the graph continues indefinitely). The graph of **h** is no points because the solution set is empty.

Checkpoint

1. How is = defined? <? >?

2. When is a sentence an equality? an inequality?

3. What is the coordinate of a point on a line?

4. What is the graph of an open sentence?

Exercises

A — Write *True* or *False* to describe each sentence.

1. $3 + 4 = 4 + 3$ 　　　　　　　　**2.** $4 \cdot 3 = 3 \cdot 4$

3. $3 + (3 + 10) = (3 + 5) + 10$ 　**4.** $(4 + \frac{1}{5}) + \frac{4}{5} > 4 + (\frac{1}{5} + \frac{4}{5})$

5. $(2 \cdot 3) \cdot 5 < 2 \cdot (3 \cdot 6)$ 　　**6.** $18 + 96 = 95 + 18$

7. $632 + 49 = 49 + 632$ 　　　　**8.** $0 \cdot 632 > 632$

9. $0 + 632 = 632$ 　　　　　　　**10.** $1 \cdot 3\frac{1}{2} = 3\frac{1}{2}$

11. $12 + 44 < 43 + 12$ 　　　　　**12.** $27 \cdot 9 > 9 \cdot 26$

— If the replacement set is U = {2, 4, 6, 8, 10}, list the elements in the solution set of each of the following sentences.

13. $x + 2 < 10$ 　　　　　　　　**14.** $n \neq 3 + 5$

15. $a + 2 = 2 + a$ 　　　　　　　**16.** $3x > 15$

17. $w + w = 8$ 　　　　　　　　　**18.** $t = 8$

19. $x \neq 2 + x$ 　　　　　　　　　**20.** $w + 5 = 7$

21. Which of the above sentences are equations? Which sentences are inequalities?

22. Look at the following. The replacement set is U.

$$U = \{1, 3, 5, 7\}$$
$$3x + 1 > 16$$

$3(1) + 1 > 16$ 　　　　　　$3(3) + 1 > 16$

$3(5) + 1 > 16$ 　　　　　　$3(7) + 1 > 16$

a. Which of the above inequalities is an open sentence?

b. Identify the replacement set.

c. Which sentences are true? Which are false?

d. List the elements of the solution set of the open sentence.

23. Write *True* or *False* to describe the sentence that results when x is replaced by 3.

    a. $3x = 9$ **b.** $x + 9 = 11$ **c.** $x - 1 = 2$

        d. $\frac{x}{2} = 1\frac{1}{2}$ **e.** $3x - x = 7$

—— If the replacement set is $U = \{0, 1, 2, 3, 4, 5, \cdots\}$, write the solution set by the roster method.

24. $x + 3 > 15$	**25.** $x + 2 = 10$
26. $x + 2 > 10$	**27.** $10 + x = 30$
28. $10 + x < 30$	**29.** $x + 3 < x + 4$
30. $x + 1 < 5$	**31.** $3x \not< 9$
32. $x + 5 \neq 6$	**33.** $25 < 2x + 3x$

B —— If x is a variable whose replacement set is $\{1, 2, 3, 4, 5, 6\}$, find the solution set for each of the open sentences below.

34. $\frac{x}{2} = 1$	**35.** $x^2 = 25$	**36.** $\frac{x}{10} < 1$
37. $x \not< 5 - 2$	**38.** $3x \not> \frac{x^2}{2}$	

—— Suppose that the replacement set for x and y is the set of whole numbers. Tell whether each of the following sentences is *True* or *False*. If the sentence is false, give an example that proves it is false. The symbol $\forall x \, \forall y$ means that for every pair of members chosen for x and for y, the sentence is true.

39. $\forall x \, \forall y \quad x + y = y + x$

40. $\forall x \, \forall y \quad (x + y) + x = x + (y + x)$

41. $\forall x \, \forall y \quad x + y$ is one and only one whole number.

42. $\forall x \, \forall y \quad xy$ is one and only one whole number.

43. $\forall x \, \forall y \quad x + y > x + x$

44. $\forall x \, \forall y \quad x \cdot y > x \cdot x$

45. $\forall x \quad 1 \cdot x = x$

46. $\forall y \quad 0 + y = y$

47. $\forall x \quad$ There is a whole number a such that $xa = 0$.

48. $\forall x \quad$ There is a whole number a such that $x + a = x$.

49. $\forall x \quad$ There is a whole number a such that $xa = 1$.

1–6 The Set of Fractional Numbers

Tell why the set of whole numbers is not sufficient to answer these questions.

a. What is the measure of $\overline{AB}$ when $\overline{AC}$ measures one unit?

b. What part of the square region is shaded?

c. What number is the quotient $4 \div 5$?

Fractional numbers can be used for the answers.

For **a,** does the natural number 3 name the number of parts of equal length in $\overline{AC}$, the entire segment? Does the whole number 2 name the number of parts of equal length in $\overline{AB}$, the segment being considered? Then what does the **ordered pair** (2, 3) name? Is the fractional number $\frac{2}{3}$ the measure of $\overline{AB}$?

For **b,** what does 4 name; what does 2 name? What does the ordered pair (2, 4) tell about the shaded region in **b?** Does the fractional number $\frac{2}{4}$ describe the shaded part of the region in relation to the whole region?

What do the ordered pair (4, 5) and $4 \div 5$ have in common? Is the fractional number $\frac{4}{5}$ the quotient of 4 divided by 5?

The pairs of numbers (2, 3), (2, 4), and (4, 5) are called *ordered pairs* because the numbers are given in a particular order: 2 out of 3 parts, 2 out of 4 parts, and so forth.

In **a,** you compared 2 to 3; in **b,** you compared 2 to 4; in **c,** you compared 4 to 5. Each of these comparisons is a **ratio** of a whole number to a natural number. The ratio is the quotient of two numbers. Why must the second number be a natural number? This leads to the formulation of a definition for fractional numbers.

> **Definition** A fractional number is a number that can be named as the ratio $\frac{x}{y}$, where $x \in W$ and $y \in N$.

As you know, when the fractional number is named by a ratio $\frac{x}{y}$, the name is a **fraction,** x being the **numerator** and y the **denominator.**

Can you name 10 as the ratio of 10 to 1, or as $\frac{10}{1}$, or as $\frac{20}{2}$? Can you name any whole number as a fraction?

> **The set of whole numbers is a subset of the set of fractional numbers.**

What does the ordered pair (1, 2) tell about A at the right? What does (2, 4) tell about B? What does (4, 8) tell about C? Do the fractions $\frac{1}{2}$, $\frac{2}{4}$, and $\frac{4}{8}$ name the same part of the unit segment? Then the fractions $\frac{1}{2}$, $\frac{2}{4}$, and $\frac{4}{8}$ are names for one fractional number; they are **equivalent fractions.** The names $\frac{1}{2}$, $\frac{2}{4}$, $\frac{4}{8}$, and other names for the same fractional number are shown matched with one point on the number line. Does the number have five other names? a thousand other names? a million other names?

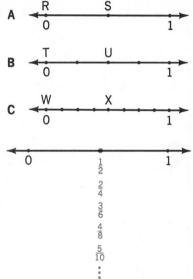

Another way of naming fractional numbers that are named as tenths, hundredths, thousandths, and so forth, is by decimals. As you recall, the places after the decimal point are called tenths, hundredths, and so forth. Thus, $\frac{3}{10} = 0.3$, $\frac{46}{100} = 0.46$, $\frac{79}{1000} = 0.079$, and $\frac{129}{100} = 1.29$ are true. Notice that 0.2, 0.20, 0.200, and so forth, all name the same fractional number. Why?

The set of names for any fractional number is an infinite set. Each fraction names an ordered pair — a whole number and a natural number.

Checkpoint

1. What is a fractional number?
2. What is an ordered pair?
3. What is a fraction?
4. What are equivalent fractions?
5. How many equivalent fractions can there be in a set?

Exercises

A **1.** Give five names for the fractional number $\frac{7}{8}$.

2. What fractional number is the coordinate of each lettered point?

—— Name each fractional number shown below in three ways.

3. $\frac{2}{7}$ **4.** 62   **5.** 6.7   **6.** 0.000001

7. 3.82   **8.** 13.205   **9.** 0.623   **10.** $\frac{23}{5}$

—— Write a numeral for the variable to make each sentence true.

11. $\frac{1}{2} = \frac{n}{16}$ **12.** $0.14 = \frac{t}{100}$ **13.** $2.001 = \frac{y}{1000}$ **14.** $\frac{1}{4} = \frac{5}{x}$

—— Graph each of the following sets on a number line.

15. $\{0, \frac{1}{3}, \frac{2}{3}, 1, \frac{4}{3}, \frac{5}{3}, 2\}$ **16.** $\{0, 0.5, 1, 1.5, 2\}$

17. Classify each number in Exercises 15 and 16 as a whole number, W, a natural number, N, or a fractional number, F. Some numbers may be classified in more than one way.

B **18.** Show a one-to-one correspondence between the set of natural numbers and the set of fractional names for $\frac{1}{2}$.

$$\{\tfrac{1}{2}, \tfrac{2}{4}, \tfrac{3}{6}, \tfrac{4}{8}, \cdots\}$$

What is the number of elements in the given set of names?

1–7   Addition, Multiplication, and Equality

Probably you recall that fractional numbers showing the same denominator can be added by merely adding the numerators.

Definition   When a and c are whole numbers and b is a counting number, then the following is true.

$$\frac{a}{b} + \frac{c}{b} = \frac{a + c}{b}$$

Thus, $\frac{7}{12} + \frac{4}{12}$ is equal to $\frac{11}{12}$. But can you add $\frac{7}{12}$ and $\frac{1}{3}$? You can if you recognize that $\frac{1}{3}$ is just another name for $\frac{4}{12}$.

It is not always easy to recognize names with common denominators for fractional numbers. Here multiplication can be useful. Recall that the product of two fractional numbers is the product of their numerators divided by the product of their denominators.

> **Definition** If a and c are whole numbers and b and d are natural numbers, then the following is true.
>
> $$\frac{a}{b} \cdot \frac{c}{d} = \frac{ac}{bd}$$

You may use the definition of multiplication when you rename a fractional number by multiplying it by a name for 1.

EXAMPLE 1. Do $\frac{35}{77}$ and $\frac{5}{11}$ name the same fractional number?

$$\frac{35}{77} \overset{?}{=} \frac{5}{11}$$
$$\overset{?}{=} \frac{5}{11} \cdot 1, \text{ or } \frac{5}{11} \cdot \frac{7}{7}$$
$$\frac{35}{77} = \frac{35}{77}$$

This shows that $\frac{35}{77}$ and $\frac{5}{11}$ do name the same fractional number.

Here is another way to check equality for fractional numbers.

> **Definition** When $a, c \in W$ and $b, d \in N$, $\frac{a}{b} = \frac{c}{d}$ is true if and only if $ad = bc$ is true.

EXAMPLE 2. Do $\frac{2}{3}$ and $\frac{8}{12}$ name the same fractional number?
Examine the products $2 \cdot 12$ and $3 \cdot 8$. Is it true that $2 \cdot 12$ equals $3 \cdot 8$? Then $\frac{2}{3}$ and $\frac{8}{12}$ do name the same fractional number.

If you must add two fractional numbers, you may need to find equivalent fractions with a common denominator.

EXAMPLE 3. Add $\frac{1}{5}$ and $\frac{3}{8}$.
You must find equivalent fractions for each number. Note that 40 is a multiple of each denominator. Therefore, each given number can be multiplied by a name for 1 to have a denominator of 40, and the problem may be rewritten.

$$\frac{1}{5} + \frac{3}{8} = \frac{1}{5} \cdot \frac{8}{8} + \frac{3}{8} \cdot \frac{5}{5}$$
$$= \frac{8}{40} + \frac{15}{40} = \frac{23}{40}$$

You know that $\frac{1}{2}$ is greater than $\frac{1}{3}$. How can you tell which of *any* two fractional numbers is greater; that is, how can you order them?

EXAMPLE 4. Which is greater, $\frac{5}{11}$ or $\frac{4}{10}$?

Examine the products $5 \cdot 10$ and $11 \cdot 4$. Is $5 \cdot 10 > 11 \cdot 4$ true? If so, then $\frac{5}{11} > \frac{4}{10}$ is true.

> **Definition** When $a, c \in W$ and $b, d \in N$, $\frac{a}{b} > \frac{c}{d}$ is true if and only if $ad > bc$ is true, and $\frac{a}{b} < \frac{c}{d}$ is true if and only if $ad < bc$ is true.

Use the definition to show that these sentences are true.

a. $\frac{4}{5} > \frac{1}{5}$ b. $\frac{3}{11} > \frac{2}{10}$ c. $\frac{9}{10} < \frac{8}{8}$

Between some pairs of whole numbers, it is impossible to find another number of the same set. This means that the set of whole numbers is **discrete.** This is not true of the fractional numbers. The fractional numbers are not discrete.

Between any two fractional numbers, another fractional number can be found. Between $\frac{1}{2}$ and $\frac{7}{8}$, the fractional number $\frac{11}{16}$ can be inserted. Between $\frac{11}{16}$ and $\frac{7}{8}$, you can insert $\frac{3}{4}$. This property of fractional numbers is the **density property.** A set is *dense* if there is always another member of the set between any two members.

The density property can be illustrated by using the number line. For example, between A and B, there is another point, C, that is halfway between A and B. If A matches 0 and B matches 1, then C matches $\frac{1}{2}$.

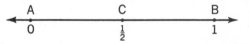

If you look at points A and C, you will see there is a point halfway between them, call it D, and it matches $\frac{1}{4}$; there is a point halfway between A and D that matches $\frac{1}{8}$; and so on.

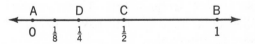

This pattern continues indefinitely for any pair of different fractional numbers.

Exercises

A   **1.** Which is true?

  a. $\frac{12}{17} > \frac{7}{9}$ **b.** $\frac{12}{17} < \frac{7}{9}$ **c.** $\frac{12}{17} = \frac{7}{9}$

2. Insert one fractional number between $\frac{5}{7}$ and $\frac{6}{8}$.

—— Add or multiply as directed.

3. $\frac{3}{5} + \frac{4}{5}$ **4.** $\frac{3}{4} \times \frac{2}{7}$ **5.** $\frac{1}{8} + \frac{1}{2}$

6. $\frac{7}{15} + \frac{2}{15}$ **7.** $\frac{2}{3} \times \frac{8}{8}$ **8.** $\frac{2}{3} + \frac{2}{15}$

9. $\frac{2}{3} + \frac{3}{4}$ **10.** $\frac{1}{6} \times \frac{1}{4}$ **11.** $\frac{1}{6} + \frac{1}{4}$

12. $\frac{3}{20} + \frac{2}{10}$ **13.** $\frac{5}{10} + \frac{19}{100}$ **14.** $0.3 + 0.4$

15. $0.25 + 0.5$ **16.** 0.25×2.4 **17.** 1.02×2.37

—— The **mixed form** of a fractional number is one in which the number is named as the sum of a whole number and a fraction, without writing the addition sign. For example, $2\frac{1}{4}$ is a mixed form for the number also named by $\frac{9}{4}$ or by 2.25. Rename each of the following as mixed forms.

18. $\frac{5}{3}$ **19.** $\frac{72}{5}$ **20.** 2.5   **21.** 7.309

—— Replace each ● by one of the symbols $<$, $>$, or $=$ to make each sentence below true. You should be able to do most of these without computation.

22. $\frac{2}{3}$ ● $\frac{4}{6}$ **23.** $\frac{111}{50}$ ● $\frac{112}{50}$

24. $\frac{5}{7}$ ● $\frac{5}{8}$ **25.** $8 + 2\frac{1}{2}$ ● $12 - 1\frac{1}{2}$

26. $6\frac{3}{4} - 6\frac{3}{4}$ ● 0   **27.** $15\frac{1}{2}$ ● 15.4998

28. $3 \times 4\frac{1}{2}$ ● $4\frac{1}{2} \times 3$ **29.** 2.0001 ● 2.00001

30. $6 \div 7$ ● $\frac{6}{7}$ **31.** $\frac{1}{2} \div 7$ ● $\frac{1}{2} \div 5$

32. $\frac{2}{3} \div 4$ ● $\frac{2}{3} \times \frac{1}{4}$ **33.** $\frac{5}{6} \div \frac{2}{5}$ ● $\frac{5}{6} \times \frac{2}{5}$

—— The variables m, x, y, and z represent fractional numbers between 0 and 20. The numbers are arranged as shown at the right. Replace the ● with $<$, $>$, or $=$ to make true sentences.

34. m ● 20   **35.** 0 ● x **36.** x ● m **37.** m ● y

38. m ● z **39.** z ● y **40.** m ● x **41.** 20 ● y

42. x ● x **43.** $3m$ ● 0 **44.** $5y$ ● 0 **45.** $\frac{1}{4}m$ ● 20

■ What set of numbers is represented when the variable is replaced in turn by each element of the replacement set $\{\frac{1}{2}, 2\frac{1}{4}, 8\}$?

46. $2n$ **47.** $3n + 1$ **48.** n^2 **49.** $3n^2$

50. $\frac{n}{2}$ **51.** $\frac{2}{n}$ **52.** $\frac{n+2}{4}$ **53.** $\frac{4}{n+1}$

■ If the replacement set is $\{0.2, 0.3, 0.4\}$, what set of numbers is named by each expression in column **a**? in column **b**?

a	b
54. $4n + 3n$	$7n$
55. $n^2 + n^2$	$2n^2$
56. $(4n + 3n) + 2n^2$	$7n + 2n^2$

57. The division example shows how the decimal name for $\frac{1}{7}$ is found. What digit replaces the question mark? The numerals in color show the remainders. What will be the next six remainders? Then, what will be the next six digits in the quotient?

Is $\frac{1}{7} = 0.\overline{142857142857}$ true if the bar means that the block of digits beneath the bar is repeated over and over? The decimal name for a number such as $\frac{1}{7}$ is a **repeating decimal**.

The decimal name for $\frac{1}{8}$ is 0.125. This is a **terminating decimal**.

$$\begin{array}{r} 0.142857? \\ 7)\overline{1.0000000} \cdots \\ \underline{7} \\ 30 \\ \underline{28} \\ 20 \\ \underline{14} \\ 60 \\ \underline{56} \\ 40 \\ \underline{35} \\ 50 \\ \underline{49} \\ 10 \end{array}$$

■ Name each fractional number below with a decimal. Use a bar to indicate a block of digits that repeats.

58. $\frac{3}{7}$ **59.** $\frac{9}{25}$ **60.** $\frac{1}{3}$ **61.** $\frac{1}{9}$ **62.** $\frac{2}{11}$ **63.** $\frac{11}{20}$

B ■ The example at the right shows how the repeating decimal $x = 0.12\overline{12}$ can be expressed as a fractional number. Express each of the following in the same way.

64. $0.3\overline{3}$ **65.** $0.3\overline{23}$

66. $635.1\overline{51}$ **67.** $0.83\overline{3}$

68. $0.123\overline{123}$ (*Hint:* Multiply by 1000 instead of 100. Why?)

69. $6.87\overline{2872}$

$$x = 0.12\overline{12}$$
$$100x = 100(0.12\overline{12})$$
$$= 12.12\overline{12}$$

Subtract.
$$100x = 12.12\overline{12}$$
$$\underline{x = 0.12\overline{12}}$$
$$99x = 12$$
$$x = \tfrac{12}{99}, \text{ or } \tfrac{4}{33}$$

1–8 Postulates for Addition and Multiplication

From your previous school work, you have probably learned the properties of the operations on the fractional numbers. The properties provide reasons for much of your work in algebra. These properties are assumptions that are made about the operations of addition and multiplication. An assumption is called a **postulate.** The postulates are named and summarized in the table.

Read each postulate and its name. The symbol $\forall x$ is read "for every x" and the symbol $\forall x \; \forall y$ is read "for every x and every y."

Postulates for Addition and Multiplication of Fractional Numbers

Postulate	Name
1–1 $\forall x \in F$ $\forall y \in F$ $x + y$ is a **fractional number and only one fractional number.**	Closure postulate for addition.
1–2 $\forall x \in F$ $\forall y \in F$ xy is a **fractional number and only one fractional number.**	Closure postulate for multiplication.
1–3 $\forall x \in F$ $\forall y \in F$ $\quad x + y = y + x$	Commutative postulate for addition.
1–4 $\forall x \in F$ $\forall y \in F$ $\quad xy = yx$	Commutative postulate for multiplication.
1–5 $\forall x \in F$ $\forall y \in F$ $\forall z \in F$ $x + (y + z) = (x + y) + z$	Associative postulate for addition.
1–6 $\forall x \in F$ $\forall y \in F$ $\forall z \in F$ $x(yz) = (xy)z$	Associative postulate for multiplication.
1–7 $\forall x \in F$ $\forall y \in F$ $\forall z \in F$ $x \cdot (y + z) = (xy) + (xz)$	Distributive postulate for multiplication over addition.
1–8 $\forall x \in F$ $x + 0 = 0 + x = x$	Additive identity postulate (postulate for 0 in addition).
1–9 $\forall x \in F$ $\quad 1 \cdot x = x \cdot 1 = x$	Multiplicative identity postulate (postulate for 1 in multiplication).
1–10 $\forall x \in F$ $x \neq 0$, **there** exists y in F such that $xy = 1$.	Multiplicative inverse postulate.

Note that if two fractional numbers are multiplicative inverses, their product is the identity element for multiplication, 1. The multiplicative inverse of a fractional number x can be expressed as $\frac{1}{x}$.

a. $x = 2$

$\frac{1}{x} = \frac{1}{2}$

$2 \cdot \frac{1}{2} = 1$

b. $x = \frac{3}{4}$

$\frac{1}{x} = \frac{1}{\frac{3}{4}}$, or $\frac{4}{3}$

$\frac{3}{4} \cdot \frac{4}{3} = 1$

Another name for the multiplicative inverse is **reciprocal.**

You should be able to explain each postulate in your own words and give an example like those below.

	Postulate	Example
1–1	Closure postulate for addition.	$(\frac{1}{4} + \frac{1}{8})$, or $\frac{3}{8}$, is a fractional number and only one fractional number.
1–2	Closure postulate for multiplication.	$(4 \cdot \frac{1}{5})$, or $\frac{4}{5}$, is one and only one fractional number.
1–3	Commutative postulate for addition.	$19 + 0.5 = 0.5 + 19$
1–4	Commutative postulate for multiplication.	$0.5 \cdot 0.6 = 0.6 \cdot 0.5$
1–5	Associative postulate for addition.	$(\frac{1}{3} + \frac{1}{5}) + \frac{1}{2} = \frac{1}{3} + (\frac{1}{5} + \frac{1}{2})$
1–6	Associative postulate for multiplication.	$(\frac{2}{5} \cdot \frac{7}{9}) \cdot \frac{5}{3} = \frac{2}{5} \cdot (\frac{7}{9} \cdot \frac{5}{3})$
1–7	Distributive postulate for multiplication over addition.	$3(20 + 4) = (3 \cdot 20) + (3 \cdot 4)$
1–8	Additive identity postulate.	$\frac{196}{9} + 0 = 0 + \frac{196}{9} = \frac{196}{9}$
1–9	Multiplicative identity postulate.	$1 \cdot 15\frac{1}{2} = 15\frac{1}{2} \cdot 1 = 15\frac{1}{2}$
1–10	Multiplicative inverse postulate.	$6 \cdot \frac{1}{6} = \frac{1}{6} \cdot 6 = 1$

Checkpoint

1. Which postulate deals with the order of addends? of factors?

2. Do the associative postulates state anything about the order of the addends? Why are these postulates sometimes called the "grouping" postulates?

3. Which one postulate does not hold for whole numbers?

4. Under what conditions is a set of numbers closed?

5. What is meant by *identity element*?

Exercises

A —— In each of the following, write the numeral for the number that makes the sentence true. Then name the postulate that the completed sentence illustrates.

1. $12 \cdot \frac{4}{5} = \frac{4}{5} \cdot n$ **2.** $6(2 + x) = (6 \cdot 2) + (6 \cdot 1)$

3. $5 + 10 = a + 5$ **4.** $\frac{1}{6} \cdot (\frac{1}{5} \cdot \frac{1}{4}) = (c \cdot \frac{1}{5}) \cdot \frac{1}{4}$

5. $4 + 6 = 6 + b$ **6.** $\frac{7}{3} \cdot (\frac{9}{2} \cdot \frac{6}{5}) = (\frac{7}{3} \cdot \frac{9}{2}) \cdot m$

7. $\frac{2}{3} \cdot h = 1$ **8.** $9 + (3 + 1) = (x + 3) + 1$

—— Write the name of the postulate that is a reason why each sentence is true.

9. $6 + 8 = 8 + 6$ **10.** $(10 \cdot 5) \cdot 4 = 10 \cdot (5 \cdot 4)$

11. $3(10) = (10)3$ **12.** $8 \cdot (2 + \frac{1}{2}) = (8 \cdot 2) + (8 \cdot \frac{1}{2})$

13. $(6 \cdot 0)5 = 6(0 \cdot 5)$ **14.** $(1 + 3) + (6 \cdot 7) = (3 + 1) + (6 \cdot 7)$

15. $\frac{2}{3} \cdot 1\frac{1}{2} = 1$ **16.** $(6 \cdot 3) + (8 \cdot 2) = (8 \cdot 2) + (6 \cdot 3)$

17. $(6 + 0) + \frac{2}{3} = 6 + \frac{2}{3}$ **18.** $(6 + \frac{1}{3}) + (\frac{4}{3} \cdot 2) = (\frac{1}{3} + 6) + (\frac{4}{3} \cdot 2)$

19. $6 \cdot 1 = 6$ **20.** $8(\frac{1}{2} + 3) = (8 \cdot \frac{1}{2}) + (8 \cdot 3)$

21. $0 + 0 = 0$ **22.** $(3 \cdot 4) + (3 \cdot 5) = 3 \cdot (4 + 5)$

23. $8 + 100 = 100 + 8$ **24.** $\frac{3}{2} \cdot 9 + \frac{3}{2} \cdot 30 = \frac{3}{2}(9 + 30)$

B —— A combination of postulates is needed as reasons why each of the following is true. Write the names of the postulates.

25. $8(5 \cdot 6) = 6(8 \cdot 5)$ **26.** $(3 \cdot 2) + (3 \cdot 7) = 3(7 + 2)$

27. $\frac{9}{2} + \frac{5}{2} = \frac{1}{2}(5 + 9)$ **28.** $6(2 + 1) = 6 + (6 \cdot 2)$

29. $8(1 \cdot \frac{4}{5}) = \frac{32}{5}$ **30.** $6 + (0.75 + \frac{1}{3}) = \frac{1}{3} + (6 + 0.75)$

31. $\frac{2}{7}(3\frac{1}{2}) + 10 = 10 + 1$ **32.** $2 \cdot 3 \cdot (1 + 4) = [(2 \cdot 1) + (2 \cdot 4)]3$

C —— In the following exercises, there is hidden one true sentence showing that the distributive postulate holds for the given operations. Can you find this true sentence?

Example. Addition is distributive with respect to subtraction.

To express this sentence algebraically, you replace $\cdot$ by $+$ and $+$ by $-$ in the pattern $a \cdot (b + c) = ab + ac$. Thus, an example expressing the meaning of the above sentence might be $6 + (3 - 2) = (6 + 3) - (6 + 2)$. It is apparent that this sentence is not true. Therefore, you conclude that addition is not distributive with respect to subtraction.

33. Division is distributive with respect to division.

34. Division is distributive with respect to multiplication.

35. Division is distributive with respect to subtraction.
36. Subtraction is distributive with respect to addition.
37. Addition is distributive with respect to addition.
38. Subtraction is distributive with respect to subtraction.
39. Multiplication is distributive with respect to subtraction.

1–9 Using the Postulates

There are three more postulates, the Postulates of Equality, for which you will find frequent use.

Postulate	Name
1–11 $\forall a \in F$ $a = a$	Reflexive postulate.
1–12 $\forall a \in F$ $\forall b \in F$ **If $a = b$, then $b = a$.**	Symmetric postulate.
1–13 $\forall a \in F$ $\forall b \in F$ $\forall c \in F$ **If $a = b$ and $b = c$, then $a = c$.**	Transitive postulate.

You can use these postulates with the postulates for addition and multiplication to simplify written computation or even to allow computation to be done mentally. For instance, the associative postulate makes it easier to find the following sum.

$$(13 + 97) + 3 = 13 + (97 + 3)$$
$$= 13 + \quad 100$$
$$= 113$$

You may be familiar with using the distributive postulate to simplify multiplication.

$$21 \times 13 = 21(10 + 3)$$
$$= (21 \times 10) + (21 \times 3)$$
$$= \quad 210 \quad + \quad 63$$
$$= 273$$

Sometimes, it is better to reverse the steps and simplify in the following way, since by the symmetric postulate, the distributive postulate can be reversed.

$$(10 \times 14) + (10 \times 4) = 10(14 + 4)$$
$$= 10 \times 18$$
$$= 180$$

The distributive postulate, $x \cdot (y + z) = xy + xz$, is often called the **left distributive postulate.** Can you complete the following proof of the **right distributive property,** $(y + z) \cdot x = yx + zx$?

Statements	Reasons
1. $(y + z) \cdot x = x \cdot (y + z)$	1. Commutative postulate.
2. $x \cdot (y + z) = xy + xz$	2. ?
3. $(y + z) \cdot x = xy + xz$	3. Transitive postulate.
4. $(y + z) \cdot x = yx + zx$	4. ?

Why is $(y + z) \cdot x = yx + zx$ called the *right distributive property*? Many other uses of the postulates will be shown in the Exercises.

Exercises

A —— Make use of the commutative and associative postulates of addition and multiplication to find the simplified name for each given expression. You should be able to write the answers with no other written work.

1. $(2 + 29) + 1$ **2.** $(18 + 6) + 14$

3. $(5365 + 1150) + 1850$ **4.** $(879 + 13) + 21$

5. $0.3(8 \cdot 10)$ **6.** $\frac{1}{5}(3 \cdot 100)$

7. $2(5 \cdot 19)$ **8.** $25(4 \cdot 12)$

9. $250(4 \cdot 12)$ **10.** $125(8 \cdot 65)$

11. $4(26 \cdot 25)$ **12.** $0.5(362 \cdot 2)$

13. A frame is $3 + x$ units long and 5 units wide. The area of the region enclosed by the frame is found by multiplying $3 + x$ by 5.

$$\text{Area} = 5(3 + x)$$
$$= 15 + \underline{\ ?\ }$$

What is the other addend in the sum for the area? Find the area inside the frame when x is replaced by 7; by 19; by 265.

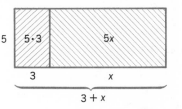

—— Use the distributive postulate to name each number with a single numeral.

14. $3 \cdot (10 + 6)$ **15.** $3 \cdot (20 + 9)$ **16.** $2 \cdot (9 + \frac{1}{2})$

17. $8 \cdot (200 + 6)$ **18.** $20 \cdot (40 + 7)$ **19.** $\frac{3}{4} \cdot (3000 + 8)$

—— Reverse the steps of simplification, using the distributive postulate.

20. $8(3) + 8(4)$ **21.** $10(9) + 10(0.2)$

22. $67(8) + 67(2)$ **23.** $86(97) + 86(3)$

—— Use the distributive postulate to perform these computations. Do as much work mentally as you can.

Example. $8(32) = \underline{\ ?\ }$

$$8(32) = 8(30 + 2) = 240 + 16 = 256$$

24. $3(21)$ **25.** $\frac{1}{4}(102)$ **26.** $11(205)$

27. $9(1009)$ **28.** $5(86)$ **29.** $9(1200)$

30. $5(52)$ **31.** $6(4\frac{2}{3})$ **32.** $12(72)$

—— Use the right distributive property to name each algebraic expression below as an expression with no addition signs.

Examples. $5x + 8x = (5 + 8) \cdot x$
$$= 13x$$

$$15y^2 + 8y^2 = (15 + 8) \cdot y^2$$
$$= 23y^2$$

33. $3a + 7a$ **34.** $15y + 18y$

35. $14(xy) + 2(xy)$ **36.** $17m + 18m$

37. $635a + 22a$ **38.** $5 \cdot (x \cdot x) + 6 \cdot (x \cdot x)$

39. $15x^2 + 2x^2$ **40.** $13y^2 + 26y^2$

—— Simplify both expressions in each item below.

41. $5 - (4 - 1)$ and $(5 - 4) - 1$

42. $30 - (10 - 6)$ and $(30 - 10) - 6$

43. $25 - (11 - 2)$ and $(25 - 11) - 2$

44. $2832 - (2762 - 13)$ and $(2832 - 2762) - 13$

45. According to your answers for Exercises 41–44, does the associative postulate hold for subtraction?

—— Simplify both expressions in each item below.

46. $20 \div (4 \div 2)$ and $(20 \div 4) \div 2$

47. $144 \div (45 \div 9)$ and $(144 \div 45) \div 9$

48. $(35 \div 7) \div 5$ and $35 \div (7 \div 5)$

49. $10 \div (20 \div 4)$ and $(10 \div 20) \div 4$

50. According to your answers for Exercises 46–49, does the associative postulate hold for division?

51. Does the commutative postulate hold for subtraction? for division? Illustrate.

B —— There is a transitive postulate that applies to "is greater than" and "is less than," in addition to the one for "is equal to." Use the following elements in the order given with =, >, or < to make true sentences in "if . . . then" form.

Example. 1, 2, 3

$$\text{If } 1 < 2 \text{ and } 2 < 3, \text{ then } 1 < 3.$$

52. $\frac{1}{2}, \frac{1}{3}, \frac{1}{9}$ **53.** $4 + 5, 9, 5 + 4$

54. 0.25, 0.2, 0.02   **55.** 1 ounce, 1 pound, 1 ton

56. 100, 10^2, $199 - 99$ **57.** 25 pennies, 5 nickels, 1 quarter

58. $\frac{2}{7}, \frac{3}{8}, \frac{4}{10}$ **59.** 6 inches, $\frac{1}{2}$ foot, $\frac{1}{6}$ yard

60. The formula for the area of a triangle is $A = \frac{1}{2}bh$, where A is the number of square units of area, b is the number of units in the base, and h is the number of units in the altitude. Have you ever made mistakes in finding $\frac{1}{2}bh$ by multiplying $\frac{1}{2}$ by b and $\frac{1}{2}$ by h? If you have a clear understanding of the associative postulate of multiplication, you will not make such errors.

$$A = (\tfrac{1}{2}b)h \quad \text{OR} \quad A = \tfrac{1}{2}(bh)$$

Given $b = 10$ and $h = 6$.

$$A = (\tfrac{1}{2} \cdot 10)6 \qquad A = \tfrac{1}{2}(10 \cdot 6)$$
$$= 5 \cdot 6 \qquad\qquad = \tfrac{1}{2}(60)$$
$$= 30 \text{ square units} \quad = 30 \text{ square units}$$

When b is 10 and h is 5, $A = (\frac{1}{2}b)h$ is easier. But when b is 7 and h is 9, $A = \frac{1}{2}(bh)$ is easier. Explain.

Use the commutative postulate to show that $\frac{1}{2}(hb)$ and $(\frac{1}{2}h)b$ can also be used. When would it be sensible to use them?

61. A desk top is $x + y$ units long. Its width is r units. Its area may be written $r(\underline{\,?\,} + \underline{\,?\,})$. Use the distributive postulate and express the area of the desk top in a different way.

—— Whether or not closure under an operation exists depends on both the set of elements in question and the operation used. Indicate which sets are closed under the specified operation. If the set is not closed, give a **counterexample** that shows this.

62. {0, 1, 2, 3}; addition.

63. {0, 1}; multiplication.

64. $\{0, 1\}$; addition.

65. $\{2\}$; subtraction.

66. $\{0, 1\}$; division.

67. $\{0\}$; division.

68. The set of all natural numbers that are multiples of 3; addition.

69. The set of all whole numbers that are multiples of 5; multiplication.

70. The set of natural numbers; subtraction.

71. The set of natural numbers; division.

72. The set of even whole numbers; multiplication.

73. The whole numbers; division.

1–10 Pythagorean Theorem and Irrational Numbers

The triangle at the right is called a right triangle because it has one 90-degree angle. The side s, opposite the right angle, is called the **hypotenuse.** The other two sides are called **legs.** Each of the legs is the same length, one unit. What is the measure of the hypotenuse?

Make a number line, using the length of the legs of the right triangle as the unit. You can match the length of the hypotenuse with a point on the number line, but is there a fractional number that names this point?

Now look at another right triangle. The sides are marked off in units.

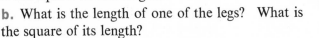

a. What is the length of the hypotenuse? What is the square of this length?

b. What is the length of one of the legs? What is the square of its length?

c. What is the length of the other leg? the square of its length?

d. Add the squares of the lengths of the legs together. How does this sum compare to the square of the hypotenuse? Is $9 + 16 = 5^2$ a true statement?

Look at the section of tile floor pictured here. All the triangles are right triangles. How does the sum of the areas of the squares on the two shorter segments of the shaded triangle compare with the area of the square on the longer side of the triangle? Is the sum of the two small squares outlined in color the same as the large square outlined in color?

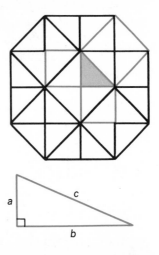

The relationship between the lengths of the legs of a right triangle and the length of the hypotenuse is known as the Pythagorean theorem. Proving the theorem would take more algebra than you know now, but you can still use it. Refer to the figure at the right as you read Theorem 1–1.

Theorem 1–1 (Pythagorean Theorem)   If a, b, and c are the measures of the three sides of a right triangle, then $a^2 + b^2 = c^2$ is true, provided that c is the length of the hypotenuse.

Note how the theorem is used in the example below.

EXAMPLE. The sides of a right triangle are 5 units and 12 units. Find h, the length of the hypotenuse.

To find h, use the Pythagorean theorem $a^2 + b^2 = c^2$, replacing a by 5, b by 12, and c by h.

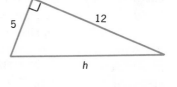

$$5^2 + 12^2 = h^2$$
$$25 + 144 = h^2$$
$$169 = h^2$$

Check $5^2 + 12^2 = 13^2$
$25 + 144 = 169$

Since $169 = h \cdot h$ is true, h is 13.

Now s, the measure of the hypotenuse in the triangle at the beginning of the section, can be found. Use the Pythagorean theorem, replacing a by 1, b by 1, and c by s.

$$1^2 + 1^2 = s^2$$
$$1 + 1 = s^2$$
$$2 = s^2$$
$$\sqrt{2} = s$$

The symbol $\sqrt{2}$ denotes the number s, such that $s \cdot s = 2$ is true, or $\sqrt{2} \cdot \sqrt{2} = 2$ is true. Likewise, $\sqrt{16}$ denotes the number x, such that $x \cdot x = 16$ is true. Since $4 \cdot 4$ equals 16, x is 4, or $\sqrt{16}$ is 4.

Recall that $\sqrt{x}$ denotes a number such that $\sqrt{x} \cdot \sqrt{x}$ is x. Is there a fractional number s for $\sqrt{2}$ such that $s \cdot s$ is 2? Try $1\frac{1}{2}$.

$$\tfrac{3}{2} \cdot \tfrac{3}{2} = \tfrac{9}{4}, \quad \text{or} \quad 2\tfrac{1}{4}$$

So $1\frac{1}{2}$ is too large. Try $1\frac{1}{4}$.

$$\tfrac{5}{4} \cdot \tfrac{5}{4} = \tfrac{25}{16}, \quad \text{or} \quad 1\tfrac{9}{16}$$

You can see that $1\frac{1}{4}$ is too small. You can try a few more examples, but you will find that there is no fractional number for $\sqrt{2}$.

Look at the members of the following set.

$$\{\sqrt{2},\ \sqrt{3},\ \sqrt{5},\ \sqrt{6},\ \sqrt{7},\ \sqrt{8},\ \sqrt{10},\ \sqrt{11},\ \sqrt{12},\ \sqrt{13},\ \sqrt{14},\ \sqrt{15},\ \sqrt{17}\}$$

None of these numbers can be expressed as a fractional number, yet each of them matches a point on the number line, as was shown for $\sqrt{2}$ at the beginning of the section. The members of the above set are members of the set of **irrational numbers.**

> **Definition** An <u>irrational number</u> is one that cannot be expressed in the form of a ratio, $\frac{a}{b}$ ($a \in W$, $b \in N$).

You cannot name an irrational number with a fractional number, or a terminating or a repeating decimal. You can, however, approximate irrational numbers by using decimals. (See the table on page 546.) A decimal approximation for $\sqrt{2}$ to the nearest thousandth, is $\sqrt{2} \approx 1.414$, where $\approx$ means "is approximately equal to." How does the computation at the right prove that $\sqrt{2} = 1.414$ is false?

$$
\begin{array}{r}
1.4\,1\,4 \\
\times\ 1.4\,1\,4 \\
\hline
5\,6\,5\,6 \\
1\,4\,1\,4 \\
5\,6\,5\,6 \\
1\,4\,1\,4 \\
\hline
1.9\,9\,9\,3\,9\,6
\end{array}
$$

Now try these

— Which of the following numbers are fractional, F, and which are irrational, Ir? If the number is fractional, express it without the $\sqrt{\ }$.

1. $\sqrt{25}$ **2.** $\sqrt{24}$ **3.** $\sqrt{\tfrac{25}{9}}$ **4.** $\sqrt{81}$ **5.** $\sqrt{\tfrac{16}{36}}$ **6.** $\sqrt{11}$

7. If the two legs of a right triangle are 3 and 7, how long is the hypotenuse?

Answers: **1.** F; 5 **2.** Ir **3.** F; $\tfrac{5}{3}$ **4.** F; 9 **5.** F; $\tfrac{4}{6}$ **6.** Ir **7.** $\sqrt{58}$

1. What does the Pythagorean theorem tell you about the relationship between the lengths of the sides of a right triangle?

2. What is an irrational number?

Exercises

A — Find the length c (a fractional number) of the hypotenuse of a right triangle, where a and b are the lengths of the other two sides.

	a	b	c
1.	6	8	_?_
2.	12	9	_?_
3.	12	5	_?_
4.	10	24	_?_
5.	15	20	_?_

— In each of the following exercises, c is an irrational number. Name the number for c by using a square root sign. Then use the table, and give a decimal approximation to the nearest thousandth.

	a	b	c
6.	1	1	_?_ ≈ _?_
7.	2	1	_?_ ≈ _?_
8.	2	3	_?_ ≈ _?_
9.	2	2	_?_ ≈ _?_
10.	3	3	_?_ ≈ _?_
11.	4	5	_?_ ≈ _?_
12.	10	11	_?_ ≈ _?_
13.	5	10	_?_ ≈ _?_
14.	2	4	_?_ ≈ _?_

B — Replace n with the smallest possible whole number to make a true statement.

15. $6 < \sqrt{39} < n$ **16.** $7 < \sqrt{63} < n$

17. $3 < \sqrt{12} < n$ **18.** $15 < \sqrt{229} < n$

— Replace x with the largest possible whole number to make a true statement.

19. $x < \sqrt{223} < 15$ **20.** $x < \sqrt{441} < 22$

21. $x < \sqrt{189} < 14$ **22.** $x < \sqrt{625} < 26$

23. If the hypotenuse of a right triangle is 35 units long and one of its sides is 25 units long, how long is its other side? Leave the answer in radical form.

24. The hypotenuse of an isosceles right triangle (a right triangle with two equal sides) is 2 units. How long are its sides?

25. How high is a fence if the brace that supports it is 7 feet long and its ends are 3 feet from the foot of the fence and 3 feet from the top of the fence? Express the answer using $\sqrt{}$.

26. If the elements of {0, 1, 4, 9, 16, 25, 36, $\cdots$} are called perfect squares, make a rule about which natural numbers have square roots that are irrational numbers.

C **27.** The figure shows a series of right triangles, each with an altitude of 1 unit. The hypotenuse of the first triangle becomes the base of the next triangle, and so on. Find the length of each hypotenuse, naming each irrational number with a square root sign.

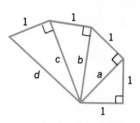

28. The diagonal of a square is 2 units long. How long are its sides?

29. Look at the diagram at the right. If you walk at the speed of 8 feet per second, how much longer will it take you to walk from A to B and then from B to C, than directly from A to C?

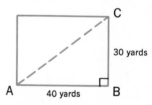

CHAPTER REVIEW

1. Know the meaning of and be able to use each of the following words or phrases. The number shown after each word or phrase indicates where it is introduced, in case you need to review.

natural number (*2*)	whole number (*3*)
square (*2*)	empty set (*3*)
square root (*2*)	prime number (*5*)
set (*2*)	composite number (*5*)
element (*2*)	subset (*6*)
rule method (*3*)	proper subset (*8*)
roster method (*3*)	equal sets (*8*)

one-to-one correspondence (*12*)
equivalent sets (*12*)
finite set (*13*)
infinite set (*13*)
aleph-null (*14*)
variable (*16*)
replacement set (*16*)
algebraic expression (*17*)
term (*17*)
coefficient (*17*)
order of operation (*18*)
equation (*20*)
inequality (*20*)
number line (*20*)
coordinate (*20*)
open sentence (*21*)
solution set (*21*)
fractional number (*24*)
ordered pair (*24*)
ratio (*24*)

fraction (*24*)
equivalent fractions (*25*)
discrete (*28*)
dense (*28*)
mixed form (*29*)
repeating decimal (*30*)
terminating decimal (*30*)
postulate (*31*)
closure (*31*)
commutativity (*31*)
associativity (*31*)
distributivity (*31*)
identity element (*31*)
multiplicative inverse
    element, or reciprocal (*32*)
reflexive postulate (*34*)
symmetric postulate (*34*)
transitive postulate (*34*)
Pythagorean theorem (*39*)
irrational number (*40*)

2. Which of the following phrases describes a set: "the younger generation" or "teenagers"? Why?

3. Is the set of whole numbers finite or infinite? the set of even numbers? Is there a one-to-one correspondence between the whole numbers and the even numbers? Are the two sets equal? equivalent? Explain your answers.

4. What is the meaning of each of the following symbols?

    a. $\in$ **b.** $\notin$ **c.** $\subset$ **d.** $\not\subset$ **e.** $\subseteq$ **f.** $\nsubseteq$ **g.** $\emptyset$

5. Write a rule to denote each of the following sets.

    a. $G = \{3, 6, 9, 12, \cdots\}$ **b.** $H = \{2, 7, 12, 17, \cdots\}$
    c. $J = \{4, 6, 8, 10, 12, 14\}$ **d.** $K = \{63, 70, 77, 84, 91, 98\}$

6. You are given the following sets.

    W = {whole numbers}   N = {natural numbers}
    P = {prime numbers}   E = {even whole numbers}
    O = {odd whole numbers}   C = {composite numbers}

Replace ● by $\subseteq$ or $\nsubseteq$ to make each a true sentence.

    a. N ● W   **b.** W ● N   **c.** $\{2, 4, 6, \cdots\}$ ● P
    d. $\emptyset$ ● N   **e.** C ● E   **f.** $\{31, 37, 23, 29\}$ ● P

7. If the replacement set is X = {0, 1, 2, 3, 4, 5}, what set of numbers is named by each of the following expressions?

a. $7 + 3w$ **b.** $\dfrac{5w + 2}{2}$ **c.** $\dfrac{3w}{4} + \dfrac{5}{2w}$

8. If the replacement set is W = {0, 1, 2, $\cdots$}, give the solution set for each of the following and represent it on a number line.

a. $x + 5 = 17$ **b.** $x + x = 2x$ **c.** $x + 9 > 7$

d. $x + 7 < 5$ **e.** $3x + 2x = 24$ **f.** $x = x^2$

9. What is the postulate represented by each of the following?

a. $\forall a \; \forall b \quad a + b = b + a$ **b.** $\forall a \; \forall b \quad ab = ba$

c. $\forall a \quad 1 \cdot a = a \cdot 1 = a$ **d.** $\forall a \quad 0 + a = a + 0 = a$

e. $\forall a \; \forall b \; \forall c \quad (a + b) + c = a + (b + c)$

f. $\forall a \; \forall b \; \forall c \quad (ab)c = a(bc)$

10. If $\dfrac{a}{b}$ represents a fractional number, why may the replacement set for b not include 0?

11. What does it mean to say that the set of whole numbers is discrete and the set of fractional numbers is dense?

12. Replace ● with >, <, or = to make each sentence true.

a. $\frac{7}{9}$ ● $\frac{56}{72}$ **b.** $\frac{1}{2} + \frac{1}{5}$ ● $3\frac{1}{2} \times \frac{1}{5}$ **c.** $17\frac{2}{3}$ ● $\frac{52}{3}$

d. $\frac{5}{11}$ ● $\frac{25}{56}$ **e.** $\frac{9}{11} - \frac{1}{3}$ ● $\frac{4}{4} \cdot \frac{3}{4} + \frac{5}{16}$ **f.** 0.1251 ● $\frac{1}{8}$

—— Give a reason for each step in the following.

13. $3\frac{5}{8} + \frac{7}{8} = 3\frac{5}{8} + (\frac{3}{8} + \frac{4}{8}) = (3\frac{5}{8} + \frac{3}{8}) + \frac{4}{8} = 4 + \frac{1}{2} = 4\frac{1}{2}$

14. $7\frac{2}{3} \cdot 5 = 5 \cdot 7\frac{2}{3} = 5(7 + \frac{2}{3}) = (5 \cdot 7) + (5 \cdot \frac{2}{3}) = 35 + \frac{10}{3} = 38\frac{1}{3}$

15. $27 \cdot 8 = (20 + 7) \cdot 8 = 8 \cdot (20 + 7) = (8 \cdot 20) + (8 \cdot 7) = 216$

16. Which of the following are irrational numbers?

a. $\frac{17}{21}$ **b.** $.66\overline{6}$ **c.** $11\frac{1}{3}$ **d.** $\sqrt{81}$ **e.** $\sqrt{77}$

—— In each of the following, x and y are legs of a right triangle and h is the hypotenuse. Find the missing side.

17. $x = 13$ $y = 20$ $h = \underline{\ ?\ }$

18. $x = 9$ $y = 12$ $h = \underline{\ ?\ }$

19. $x = 36$ $y = \underline{\ ?\ }$ $h = 60$

20. $x = \underline{\ ?\ }$ $y = 12$ $h = 15$

CHAPTER TEST

— Write the members of the following sets by the roster method.

1. The set of whole numbers.

2. The set of perfect-square numbers.

3. The set of prime numbers greater than 5 and less than 25.

4. The set of even whole numbers greater than 4 and less than the square of 4.

— Refer to the diagram at the right and write *True* or *False* to describe the following sentences.

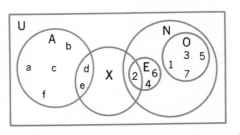

5. $d \in A$ **6.** $X \subseteq A$

7. $E \nsubseteq A$ **8.** $4 \notin N$

9. $X \subset X$ **10.** $A \subseteq \emptyset$

11. $O \subset N$ **12.** $N \subseteq A$

13. $c \subset U$ **14.** X is equivalent to E.

— Give the postulate or property that is the reason for each of the following statements.

Statements	Reasons
15. $2(3 + 1) + 6(\frac{1}{6}) = 6 + 2 + 6(\frac{1}{6})$	?
16. $\qquad = 2 + 6 + 6(\frac{1}{6})$	?
17. $\qquad = (2 + 6) + 1$	?
18. $\qquad = 1 + (2 + 6)$	?

19. Write a single numeral for each of the following.

   a. $\dfrac{2(3 + 4) - 13}{6}$ **b.** $2 + 6 \times 5 - 4 \div 2$

20. If the replacement set is $\{0, 1, 2, 3, 4, 5, 6\}$, give the solution set for each of the following.

   a. $\dfrac{x^2}{3} < 8$ **b.** $x + 5 = 4$ **c.** $2x - 4 = \dfrac{x}{2} - 1$

21. Name each of the following fractions with a decimal. Use a bar to indicate a block of digits that repeats.

   a. $\frac{1}{6}$ **b.** $\frac{2}{5}$ **c.** $\frac{1}{13}$

22. The lengths of two sides of a triangle are $2\frac{1}{2}$ and 6. Find the length of the hypotenuse.

23. Which of the following sets are closed under multiplication?

    a. $\{0, 1, 2, 3, \cdots\}$ **b.** $\{0, 1\}$ **c.** $\{0, 1, \frac{1}{2}, \frac{1}{4}\}$

24. One leg and the hypotenuse of a right triangle measure $\sqrt{192}$ units and 16 units, respectively. How long is the other leg?

—— Refer to the number line below and write $>$, $<$, or $=$ to make the following sentences true.

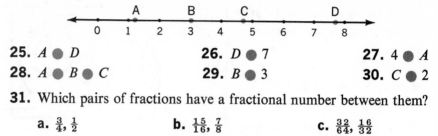

25. $A \bullet D$ **26.** $D \bullet 7$ **27.** $4 \bullet A$

28. $A \bullet B \bullet C$ **29.** $B \bullet 3$ **30.** $C \bullet 2$

31. Which pairs of fractions have a fractional number between them?

    a. $\frac{3}{4}, \frac{1}{2}$ **b.** $\frac{15}{16}, \frac{7}{8}$ **c.** $\frac{32}{64}, \frac{16}{32}$

—— Tell whether or not the following statements are true.

32. $\forall x \in W \quad x^2 - 2x = x(x - 2)$ **33.** $\forall y \in W \quad y + \frac{y}{2} = 2y$

ENRICHMENT

Finite Fields

For the set $X = \{a, b, c, \cdots\}$, the following postulates are true with respect to two operations, $*$ and $\circ$.

  ① $(a * b) \in X$ and $(a \circ b) \in X$ [Closure.]

  ② $(a * b) = (b * a)$ and $(a \circ b) = (b \circ a)$ [Commutativity.]

  ③ $(a * b) * c = a * (b * c)$ and

      $(a \circ b) \circ c = a \circ (b \circ c)$ [Associativity.]

  ④ $a \circ (b * c) = (a \circ b) * (a \circ c)$ [Distributivity.]

  ⑤ There exists an element z such that, for every

      $a \in X$, $a * z = a$, and there exists an element e

      $(e \neq z)$ such that, for every $a \in X$, $a \circ e = a$.   [Identity elements.]

  ⑥ For every $a \in X$, there exists an element i

      such that $a * i = z$, and for every $a \in X$ except

      z, there exists an element l such that $a \circ l = e$.   [Inverse elements.]

The set X that has these properties with respect to two operations $*$ and $\circ$ is a **field.** Examine the set $S = \{E, O\}$ with the two operations $+$ and $\times$ as defined in the following tables.

$+$	E	O
E	E	O
O	O	E

$\times$	E	O
E	E	E
O	E	O

You must check all six postulates to be sure the set is a field.

① Is S closed under addition and multiplication? Only E and O appear in the tables, so S is closed.

② Is S commutative under addition and multiplication?

$$E + O = O = O + E \qquad E \times O = E = O \times E$$

Hence, S is commutative.

You can also check for commutativity by the "diagonal-line test." If you compare the two halves of each chart, you see that they are exactly alike. (This is especially convenient with larger sets.)

③ To check associativity, you must check all the combinations for both operations, as shown below for addition.

$$E + (O + O) = (E + O) + O \qquad O + (E + E) = (O + E) + E$$
$$E + (O + E) = (E + O) + E \qquad O + (E + O) = (O + E) + O$$
$$E + (E + O) = (E + E) + O \qquad O + (O + E) = (O + O) + E$$
$$E + (E + E) = (E + E) + E \qquad O + (O + O) = (O + O) + O$$

Check $E + (O + O) = (E + O) + O$.

$$E + (O + O) = (E + O) + O$$
$$E + \quad E \quad = \quad O \quad + O$$
$$E = E$$

Check $E \times (O \times O) = (E \times O) \times O$.

$$E \times (O \times O) = (E \times O) \times O$$
$$E \times \quad O \quad = \quad E \quad \times O$$
$$E = E$$

Check the other combinations to be sure S is associative.

④ All possible combinations must also be checked to be sure S is distributive with respect to $+$ and $\times$. One is checked for you.

$$E \times (O + O) = (E \times O) + (E \times O)$$
$$E \times \quad E \quad = \quad E \quad + \quad E$$
$$E = E$$

⑤ Look at the tables to find the identity elements. The identity element for + is E.

$$O + E = O \qquad E + E = E$$

The identity element for $\times$ is O.

$$E \times O = E \qquad O \times O = O$$

⑥ Check for the inverse elements.

Is there an element that added to E gives E? Is there an element that added to O gives E?

Is there an element for every element of S except E (that leaves O) such that O times that element is O?

Thus, S under the operations defined in the tables is a field.

Exercises

1. Below are tables defining + and $\times$ for S = $\{i, j, k, l\}$.

+	i	j	k	l
i	k	l	i	j
j	l	k	j	i
k	i	j	k	l
l	j	i	l	k

$\times$	i	j	k	l
i	i	j	k	l
j	k	k	k	k
k	k	k	k	k
l	i	j	k	l

a. Is S closed under +? under $\times$?

b. Is S commutative under +? under $\times$?

c. Are the associative and distributive postulates satisfied?

d. Does each element have a multiplicative inverse? Explain.

e. Is k the additive identity element? Explain.

f. Can you find a product of two numbers, neither of which is the identity element, that is equal to the identity element? How does this differ from the whole numbers?

g. Is S with + and $\times$ as defined here a field? Why?

2. Below is an addition table and part of a multiplication table for a field of elements.

+	a	b	c	d
a	a	b	c	d
b	b	a	d	c
c	c	d	a	b
d	d	c	b	a

$\times$	a	b	c	d
a	a	a	a	a
b	a	?	c	d
c	a	?	?	b
d	a	d	b	?

Using the field postulates, fill in the rest of the multiplication table. (*Hint:* Since distributivity holds, the equation $(c \times c) + (c \times d) = c \times (c + d)$ is valid. The product $c \times c$ is unknown, but you can determine its value by evaluating the rest of the equation. Use a similar equation to determine $d \times d$.)

3. Is T = {0, 1, 2} a field under addition and multiplication as defined below?

+	0	1	2
0	0	1	2
1	1	2	0
2	2	0	1

×	0	1	2
0	2	0	1
1	0	1	2
2	1	2	0

4. Is T = {0, 1, 2} a field with addition and multiplication as defined below?

+	0	1	2
0	0	1	2
1	1	2	0
2	2	0	1

×	0	1	2
0	0	0	0
1	0	1	2
2	0	2	1

THE GROWTH OF MATHEMATICS

The Invention of Numbers

It is difficult to trace the development of mathematics before the Greeks. But as all primitive peoples today have some conception of the natural numbers, it is assumed that early man did also. Out of necessity, he would have wanted to keep a record of his animals and other possessions and used the idea of a one-to-one correspondence to match them with a handful of pebbles or a string of beads. Then the natural numbers would have logically developed. But as society changed from one of hunters to one of farmers and traders, numbers for parts of things were needed and this probably marked the invention of the positive rational numbers. No definite evidence of this exists, for the societies involved did not have writings. But since a number is an idea, not a symbol, numbers could be used before the development of numerals.

The Greeks discovered the irrational numbers in connection with measuring the diagonal of a square but refused to call them numbers. And in the seventeenth century, what are called imaginary numbers met with resistance, as had all extensions of the number system.

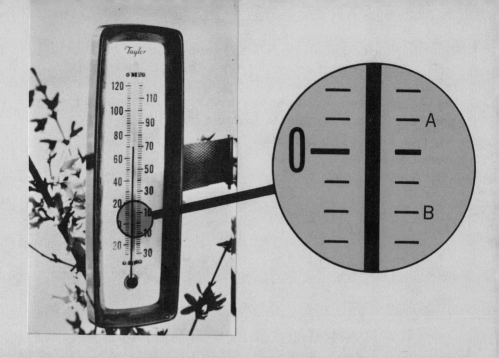

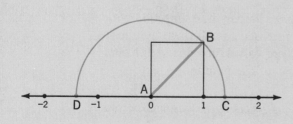

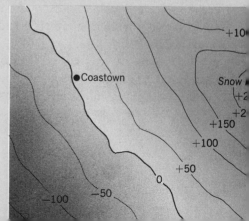

CHAPTER 2

THE SET OF REAL NUMBERS

Not every problem can be solved with the numbers you have used so far in this book. You must learn how to operate with a more general system of numbers to progress very far in algebra. You must also learn other interpretations for the numbers that you already know. The following questions give some ideas about the real numbers.

● You have used 0 to mean "not any." However, does 0 on the thermometer mean that there is no temperature or no heat? On the thermometer, 0 matches a point that represents a temperature. With this reference point, you may measure temperature as degrees *above zero* or *below zero*. On the enlarged portion of the thermometer, which number matches A? B? What are the numbers called?

● Is the use of zero on the thermometer similar to the use of zero on a number line? To indicate direction from zero, you use the words *positive* and *negative*. Is *positive* up or down? right or left? Is *negative* up or down? right or left?

● On the number line in the lower left corner, $\overline{AC}$ and $\overline{AD}$ have the same length as $\overline{AB}$. What number matches point C? point D? What *kind* of number matches point C? point D?

● On the map, what do the plus and minus signs indicate?

● In football, there are gains of so many yards and losses of so many yards. How many yards must a team travel to have a first down? What is the reference point from which the yards are measured? On the football field shown, how many yards must the team travel to make a first down? What number must be added to $^-3$ so the sum is $^+10$? How can you use directed line segments to find the sum?

● How do you add, subtract, multiply, or divide any two positive real numbers? any two negative real numbers? a positive and a negative real number?

2–1   The Real Numbers

A set of points is often used as a geometric model for a number system. The diagrams below show certain sets of numbers matched with sets of points on the line. Answer the questions.

Whole Numbers

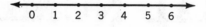

a. How do you locate the point for 10? for 99? for 100?

b. Are any points remaining on the line after each whole number is matched with a point?

Just as there are numbers "below zero" on a thermometer, there are also numbers matched with the points on a line to the left of 0.

Integers

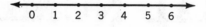

c. How do you locate the point for $^+10$? for $^+25$? $^-10$? $^-25$?

The raised signs are used to indicate whether the number is a positive integer or a negative integer. The number $^+10$ is named **positive** 10; the number $^-10$ is named **negative** 10. The set of **integers** includes the positive and the negative integers and 0. Often the raised sign $^+$ is omitted in designating a positive number. The symbol 25 also means *positive 25.*

$$^+25 = 25$$

When no sign is attached to a numeral, the number named by the numeral is positive or it is 0.

d. Are any points remaining on the line after each integer is matched with a point?

Rational Numbers

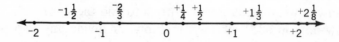

e. Where is the point for $^+\frac{1}{8}$ located? for $^-\frac{1}{8}$? $62\frac{1}{5}$? $^-62\frac{1}{5}$?

f. If a, b, and c are natural numbers and if $\frac{b}{c} < 1$, where do you locate the point for $\left(a + \frac{b}{c}\right)$? for $^-\left(a + \frac{b}{c}\right)$?

The raised signs indicate positive and negative rational numbers. Just as for the integers, if there is no sign, the number is positive. The set of **rational numbers** includes numbers of the form $\frac{a}{b}$, where a is any integer and b is any nonzero integer.

g. Are any points remaining on the line after each rational number is matched with a point?

The correct answer to **g** is that there are more points on the line than can be matched with the rational numbers. The members in the following set are not rational. They are *irrational numbers*.

$$\{\sqrt{2},\ ^-\sqrt{2},\ \sqrt{3},\ ^-\sqrt{3},\ \sqrt{5},\ \pi,\ ^-\pi,\ \sqrt[3]{72}\}$$

The union of the set of rational numbers and the set of irrational numbers is the set of **real numbers**. If you ask "Are there any points left on the line after matching each *real* number with a point?" the answer is "No." The irrational numbers are just those numbers that can be matched with the points on the line left over after the "rational points" are removed. Each point on the number line is matched with a number from the set of real numbers.

The relationship between real numbers and points on a line is an important assumption of algebra. It is Postulate 1 of Chapter 2.

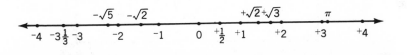
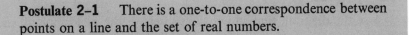

Postulate 2–1 There is a one-to-one correspondence between points on a line and the set of real numbers.

The point for $\sqrt{2}$ can be found by using the diagonal of the **unit square** (a square whose sides each measure one unit) as the radius of a circle. With 0 as the center, the points of intersection of the circle and the number line locate $^+\sqrt{2}$ and $^-\sqrt{2}$.

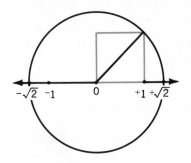

The point for π can be located by "rolling" a **unit circle** (a circle whose radius measures one unit) along the line, beginning at 0. After one half revolution to the right, as shown below, point A will match π. How could the point for $^-\pi$ be located on the number line?

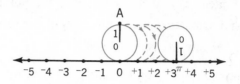

To summarize, the set of real numbers includes all the numbers you have studied so far. The diagram below shows some important relationships between subsets of real numbers.

R = The set of real numbers.

Ir = The set of irrational numbers.

Q = The set of rational numbers.

I = The set of integers.

W = The set of whole numbers.

N = The set of natural numbers.

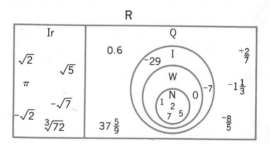

Now try these

—— Use the diagram that shows the subsets of the real numbers and tell whether each sentence is *True* or *False*.

1. $\sqrt{2} \in R$ **2.** $\sqrt{2} \in Q$ **3.** $\sqrt{2} \in I$ **4.** $\sqrt{2} \in W$

5. $^-9 \in R$ **6.** $^-9 \in Q$ **7.** $^-9 \in I$ **8.** $^-9 \in W$

9. $17 \in R$ **10.** $17 \in Q$ **11.** $17 \in Ir$ **12.** $17 \in N$

13. $Ir \subseteq R$ **14.** $R \subseteq Ir$ **15.** $Q \subseteq Ir$ **16.** $Q \subseteq R$

17. $I \subseteq Q$ **18.** $I \subseteq Ir$ **19.** $N \subseteq I$ **20.** $N \subseteq W$

Answers: **1.** True.   **2.** False.   **3.** False.   **4.** False.   **5.** True.   **6.** True.   **7.** True. **8.** False.   **9.** True.   **10.** True.   **11.** False.   **12.** True.   **13.** True. **14.** False.   **15.** False.   **16.** True.   **17.** True.   **18.** False.   **19.** True. **20.** True.

Exercises

A ▬ Write *True* or *False* to describe each sentence.

1. $7 \in R$ **2.** $^-6\frac{1}{2} \in Q$ **3.** $^-7\frac{1}{2} \in Ir$ **4.** $8\frac{1}{2} \notin Q$

5. $^-\sqrt{3} \notin I$ **6.** $8 \in N$ **7.** $^-100 \in W$ **8.** $^-100 \in I$

9. $^-100 \in Ir$ **10.** $^-100 \in R$ **11.** $\pi \in Ir$ **12.** $\pi \in Q$

13. $0 \in I$ **14.** $0 \in N$ **15.** $0 \in W$ **16.** $I \subseteq N$

17. $R \subseteq Q$ **18.** $Q \subseteq I$ **19.** $W \subseteq R$ **20.** $Ir \subseteq Q$

21. $W \subseteq Q$ **22.** $Q \subseteq W$ **23.** $R \subseteq I$ **24.** $N \subseteq Ir$

25. All rational numbers are real numbers.

26. All real numbers are rational numbers.

27. Some real numbers are rational numbers.

28. All integers are rational numbers.

29. No rational number is also an irrational number.

30. There exists a whole number that is not a natural number.

31. Rewrite the definition of $a > b$ on page 21 so that it is true for all real numbers.

▬ Using the letters N, W, I, Q, Ir, and R to stand for the sets of numbers, classify each of the following numbers. Some may belong to more than one set.

32. 28   **33.** 0

34. π **35.** $0.\overline{15}$

36. 2.6738   **37.** $^-2$

38. 25   **39.** $\frac{22}{7}$

40. $\frac{10}{5}$ **41.** $^-3\frac{1}{3}$

42. If an elevation on a government map is labeled $^-97$ to indicate that a point is 97 feet below sea level, how would you describe a point that is labeled $^+203$ on the same map?

43. Inspectors used to mark packages $^+2$ to indicate that the package was two pounds over the amount stated on the bill. How do you think they marked a package that was a half pound underweight? (Some historians think that the marks used by such inspectors were the actual origin of the present plus and minus signs.)

44. In launching a satellite, the time 2 minutes, or 120 seconds, before liftoff is known as $^-120$. What is the time $1\frac{1}{2}$ minutes after liftoff called?

B —— Use the Pythagorean theorem to find the length of the hypotenuse, c, of a right triangle. Make a drawing of each triangle as shown. Use a compass to locate points on the line for c and ^-c.

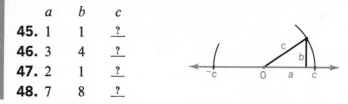

	a	b	c
45.	1	1	?
46.	3	4	?
47.	2	1	?
48.	7	8	?

C **49.** Which values for c in Exercises 45–48 are rational and which are irrational? Find other values for a and b that will give rational values for c.

2–2 Negatives and Absolute Value

On the number line below, the numbers $^+3$ and $^-3$ have something in common, as do $^-4\frac{1}{5}$ and $^+4\frac{1}{5}$. Can you identify the common characteristic of the numbers in such pairs?

$$-4\tfrac{1}{5} \quad \tfrac{-7}{2} \quad -\sqrt{6} \quad -1\tfrac{2}{3} \qquad\qquad +1\tfrac{2}{3} \quad +\sqrt{6} \quad \tfrac{+7}{2} \quad +4\tfrac{1}{5}$$

$$\overset{\text{-5} \quad\text{-4}\quad\text{-3}\quad\text{-2}\quad\text{-1}\quad 0 \quad\text{+1}\quad\text{+2}\quad\text{+3}\quad\text{+4}\quad\text{+5}}{\longleftrightarrow}$$

The real numbers $^+3$ and $^-3$ are on opposite sides of 0, both the same distance from 0.

> **Definition**   Two distinct numbers that may be matched with points on the number line on opposite sides of 0, both the same distance from 0, are called <u>opposites</u> of each other. Another name for <u>opposite of</u> is <u>negative of</u>. The number 0 is its own opposite.

The dash – in front of a numeral or an expression means **the negative of**. For example, $-(^+3\frac{1}{4})$ means the negative of $^+3\frac{1}{4}$ and is read "the negative of positive three and one fourth." The dash means "negative of," but the *raised* dash means just "negative." Since $^-3\frac{1}{4}$ is the negative of $^+3\frac{1}{4}$, you can write the following.

$$-(^+3\tfrac{1}{4}) = {}^-3\tfrac{1}{4}$$

Read the following sentences and tell why each is true.

a. $-(^{+}1\frac{2}{3}) = ^{-}1\frac{2}{3}$ b. $-(^{-}4) = ^{+}4$ c. $^{-}2 = -(2)$

d. $-(\frac{7}{2}) = ^{-}\frac{7}{2}$ e. $-(^{+}\sqrt{6}) = ^{-}\sqrt{6}$ f. $-0 = 0$

If x represents a positive real number, does $-x$ represent a positive or a negative number? If x represents a negative number, is $-x$ positive or negative?

The numbers $^{-}5$ and $^{+}5$ are negatives of each other. Each is 5 units from zero. The number of units a number is from zero, disregarding direction, is called the **absolute value** of the number. The absolute value of $^{-}5$ is 5; also, the absolute value of $^{+}5$ is 5. Two vertical marks, $|\ |$, indicate absolute value. You write $|^{-}5|$ to mean the absolute value of $^{-}5$. Thus, the sentence $|^{-}5| = 5$ is true. Read the following sentences and tell why each is true.

g. $|^{-}6\frac{1}{2}| = ^{+}6\frac{1}{2}$, or $6\frac{1}{2}$ h. $|^{+}4\frac{1}{4}| = ^{+}4\frac{1}{4}$, or $4\frac{1}{4}$

i. $|100| = ^{+}100$, or 100 j. $|0| = 0$

The definition for $|x|$ must be stated so that $|x|$ names a positive number when $x < 0$ or when $x > 0$.

> **Definition**   The <u>absolute value</u> of a real number x, symbolized by $|x|$, is the greater of the two numbers x and $-x$, $x \neq 0$. If x is 0, then $|x|$ is also 0.

How does the definition assure you that $|x|$ is positive when $x < 0$? when $x > 0$? Use the definition to explain **g–j** above.

Checkpoint

1. What is the negative of a given real number?

2. What symbol denotes *is the negative of*?

3. What is meant by *the absolute value of a real number*? What symbol denotes absolute value?

Exercises

A —— What is the negative of each real number?

1. $^{-}3$ **2.** $^{+}\frac{1}{2}$ **3.** $^{+}0.321$ **4.** $^{-}\frac{3}{2}$

5. $\sqrt{7}$ **6.** 0 **7.** $^{-}\pi$ **8.** $^{+}12{,}597$

—— What is the absolute value of each real number?

9. $^+6$ **10.** $^-6$ **11.** $^-3\frac{1}{2}$ **12.** $^-\pi$

13. $^-19.5$ **14.** 15   **15.** $^-25$ **16.** 0

17. $^-16$ **18.** $^-100$ **19.** 695   **20.** $^-462$

21. $^-72.5$ **22.** 22,000   **23.** $^+37.75$ **24.** $^-7.25$

25. $^-\sqrt{2}$ **26.** $\sqrt{5}$ **27.** 86.75   **28.** $^+\sqrt{7}$

29. What are the two numbers that have an absolute value of 10? Is there a number that has an absolute value of $^-10$? Explain.

—— Write *True* or *False* to describe each of the following sentences.

30. $|^+8| = 8$ **31.** $|^-231| = 231$ **32.** $|^-663| = |663|$

33. $|^+9| > 9$ **34.** $|^-235| > |^+235|$ **35.** $|^-35| > {}^-35$

36. $|^-27| < 17$ **37.** $|17.9| < |^-17.9|$ **38.** $|^-0.01| < |^-0.001|$

39. $|^-\frac{1}{3}| < \frac{1}{4}$ **40.** $\frac{2}{3} < |^-\frac{3}{4}|$ **41.** $|\frac{1}{8}| < {}^-\frac{1}{7}$

—— Rename each number without using the signs for "negative of" or "absolute value of."

42. $-(^+5)$ **43.** $-(^-9)$ **44.** -3.14 **45.** $-(^-3.14)$

46. $-|^+5|$ **47.** $-|^-9|$ **48.** $-|3.14|$ **49.** $-|-3.14|$

—— Replace each ● with $<$, $>$, or $=$ to make true sentences.

50. $|^+0.23| ● |^-3.7|$ **51.** $|^-6| ● |^+6|$ **52.** $|^-\frac{1}{2}| ● |^+\frac{1}{3}|$

53. $|^+0.01| ● |^-0.001|$ **54.** $|0| ● |^-1|$ **55.** $|^-\frac{1}{6}| ● |^+\frac{1}{7}|$

56. $|^-1| ● |^+1|$ **57.** $|0| ● -|0|$ **58.** $|^-3| ● |^-\frac{1}{4}|$

59. $|^-3| ● |^+4|$ **60.** $|-2| ● |^-2|$ **61.** $|^-5| ● |^-5|$

—— Find the real number that makes each sentence true.

62. $|^-2| = x$ **63.** $|^-7| = a$ **64.** $|^+4.6| = m$

65. $|^-2\frac{2}{3}| = y$ **66.** $-|9| = b$ **67.** $a = |^-96|$

68. $-(^-3) = x$ **69.** $-(^-9) = y$ **70.** $-(^+3) = m$

71. $a = -(^-9\frac{1}{2})$ **72.** $q = -(0)$ **73.** $-a = {}^+6$

74. $-m = {}^-6$ **75.** $-a = 8$ **76.** $-m = {}^-14\frac{1}{5}$

B —— Is each sentence in Exercises 77–91 *True* or *False*?

R = The set of real numbers.
P = The set of positive real numbers.
I = The set of integers.
Ne = The set of negative real numbers.

77. $I \subseteq R$ **78.** $R \not\subseteq I$ **79.** $P \not\subseteq R$

80. $Ne \subseteq R$ **81.** $^+4\frac{1}{2} \in P$ **82.** $^-9\frac{1}{2} \in Ne$

83. $6\frac{2}{3} \notin R$ **84.** $0 \in P$ **85.** $0 \notin Ne$

86. $0 \in R$ **87.** $-(^-6) \in P$ **88.** $-(^+6\frac{1}{2}) \in P$

89. $-(^-96) \notin Ne$ **90.** $-(^-6\frac{1}{4}) \in I$ **91.** $Ne \subseteq I$

C 92. Is the following sentence true? Why or why not?

$$\forall x \in R \quad -[-(x)] = x$$

2–3   Vectors

You have been using real numbers to locate points on a line with reference to a point labeled 0. Numbers such as $^+3$ and $^-3$ can describe temperatures above or below zero.

There is another useful model for the real numbers. It uses the notion of "change." The number $^+3$ denotes a *rise* of 3° in temperature or a change of $^+3$. The real number $^-5$ denotes a drop of 5° or a change of $^-5$. The real numbers $^+3$ and $^-5$ denote both the amount of change and the direction of the change. Thus, if the temperature is 6°, as in the diagram, and there are changes of $^+3$ and $^-5$, what is the final temperature?

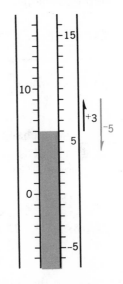

The geometric models for changes of $^+3$ and $^-5$ shown in the diagram are **vectors**. In the figure the black line segment marked with a half arrowhead is the vector $^+3$. The vector for $^-5$ is shown in red.

Every line segment has two endpoints. For a vector, one endpoint is called the **initial point** and the other is called the **terminal point**. A vector has direction, whereas a line segment has no direction. The half arrowhead shows the terminal point of the vector, indicating its direction. To identify a vector m, a half arrowhead is placed over the variable: $\vec{m}$.

Definition   A <u>vector</u> is a directed line segment.

Where does the vector that shows $^+3$ begin? Where does it end? Is the direction up or down? Where does the vector that shows $^-5$ begin? Where does it end? What is its direction?

All the vectors below show a change of ⁺3, a change of 3 to the right.

The vectors below show a change of ⁻5, a change of 5 to the left.

These drawings show that the change can be from any beginning position.

To find the sum of two vectors, think of combining the two changes into one change.

EXAMPLE 1. Draw a vector that is the sum of $\overrightarrow{a}$ and $\overrightarrow{b}$.

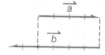

① Begin with $\overrightarrow{a}$. It shows a change of 4 units to the right.

② Think of $\overrightarrow{b}$ as starting at the end of $\overrightarrow{a}$. It shows a change of 6 units to the left.

③ The sum is the vector that shows the total change. The total change is 2 units to the left.

sum

Do you get the same result if you start with $\overrightarrow{b}$?

EXAMPLE 2. Draw a vector that is the sum of the two vectors shown.

Place the initial point of the second at the terminal point of the first. The sum is the vector shown in black.

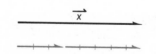

The first vector shows a change of 3 units to the right; the second shows a change of 5 more units to the right. Thus, the sum, marked $\overrightarrow{x}$ to show it is a vector, shows a total change of 8 units to the right.

Checkpoint

1. What is the difference between a line segment and a vector?

2. How do you draw a vector that is a model for $^+7$? for $^-10$? for a if $a > 0$? for $-a$ if $a > 0$?

Exercises

A **1.** If $^+3$ represents a gain of \$3, _?_ represents a loss of \$5.

2. If $^+\frac{3}{4}$ on a chart indicates that a stock on the stock market increased in value by \$.75, what does $^-\frac{1}{2}$ mean on the same chart?

3. Could the area of a rectangular region be represented by a negative number? Could the change in area of a rectangular region when one dimension is changed be represented by a negative number?

4. Would you use a positive number or a negative number to record the altitude of a landmark that is two hundred feet below sea level? How would you record the change in altitude when traveling from that landmark to a lake that is one hundred feet below sea level?

5. Positive and negative numbers are sometimes called *directed numbers*. Can you explain why this name might be used?

—— The vectors $\vec{a}$ and $\vec{b}$ in the exercises below represent two vectors to be added. The vector shown in black is the sum of $\vec{a}$ and $\vec{b}$. What is the length and direction of each vector?

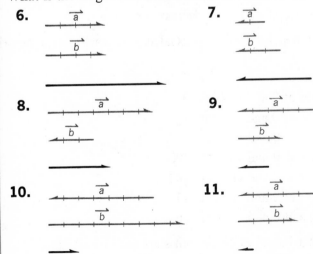

6. $\vec{a}$

    $\vec{b}$

7. $\vec{a}$

    $\vec{b}$

8. $\vec{a}$

    $\vec{b}$

9. $\vec{a}$

    $\vec{b}$

10. $\vec{a}$

    $\vec{b}$

11. $\vec{a}$

    $\vec{b}$

▬ Draw a vector that is the sum of the two shown. Give the real number that is associated with each of the three vectors.

12.

13.

14.

15.

16.

17.

18. The drawing shows the results of two football plays.
One play: Gain of 7 yards.
Next play: Gain of 5 yards.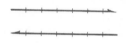
What is the result of the two plays?

What do you need to know to be sure the team made a first down?

19. The two vectors show a gain of 7 and a loss of 7. What is the sum of the two vectors?

▬ Draw vectors to find the result of the following.

20. Gain of 7; then a loss of 4.

21. Loss of $6\frac{1}{2}$; then a loss of $7\frac{1}{2}$.

22. Gain of $8\frac{3}{4}$; then a gain of $7\frac{1}{4}$.

23. Loss of 5; then a gain of 9.

24. Increase of 8; then a decrease of 17.

25. Decrease of 6; then a decrease of $3\frac{1}{2}$.

▬ What real number is associated with each vector described below?

26. Begins at 0 and ends at $^+3$.

27. Begins at 0 and ends at $^-3$.

28. Begins at 0 and ends at $^-2\frac{1}{2}$.

29. Begins at 0 and ends at $^-\sqrt{2}$.

30. Begins at 0 and ends at $^+100$.

31. Begins at 0 and ends at $^-100$.

32. Begins at 0 and ends at $^-17$.

33. Begins at 0 and ends at $^-16\frac{5}{9}$.

34. Repeat Exercises 26–33, but start each vector at $^-2$.

B ── If vector $\vec{a}$ is 9 units long and vector $\vec{b}$ is 7 units long, what is the sum of the two vectors if the following is true?

35. Both $\vec{a}$ and $\vec{b}$ are *to the left.*

36. Both $\vec{a}$ and $\vec{b}$ are *to the right.*

37. $\vec{a}$ is *to the left* and $\vec{b}$ is *to the right.*

38. $\vec{b}$ is *to the left* and $\vec{a}$ is *to the right.*

C ── The length of vector a is represented as $|\vec{a}|$. For example, the length of the vector $^-8$ is $|{^-8}|$, or 8. What is the sum of $\vec{a}$ and $\vec{b}$ when the following conditions hold?

39. Both are *to the left.*

40. Both are *to the right.*

41. $\vec{a}$ is *to the left*, $\vec{b}$ is *to the right*, and $|\vec{a}| > |\vec{b}|$.

42. $\vec{a}$ is *to the left*, $\vec{b}$ is *to the right*, and $|\vec{a}| < |\vec{b}|$.

43. $\vec{a}$ is *to the right*, $\vec{b}$ is *to the left*, and $|\vec{a}| > |\vec{b}|$.

44. $\vec{a}$ is *to the right*, $\vec{b}$ is *to the left*, and $|\vec{a}| < |\vec{b}|$.

2–4 Postulates for Addition of Real Numbers

The set of real numbers is a mathematical model of the set of vectors. You know how to add vectors. If the real numbers are to be an accurate model, the **sum of two real numbers** should be defined so that it corresponds to the sum of the two matching vectors. Experience with vectors should convince you that when addition is defined in this way, the real numbers have the properties of the fractional numbers, which were listed on page 31. You assume that this is true. Four postulates for addition of real numbers are summarized below.

Postulates for Addition of Real Numbers	Name
2–2 $\forall x \in R$ $\forall y \in R$ $x + y$ **is one and only one real number.**	Closure postulate.
2–3 $\forall x \in R$ $\forall y \in R$ $x + y = y + x$	Commutative postulate.
2–4 $\forall x \in R$ $\forall y \in R$ $\forall z \in R$ $(x + y) + z = x + (y + z)$	Associative postulate.
2–5 $\forall x \in R$ $x + 0 = 0 + x = x$, **and** 0 **is the only real number with this property.**	Identity postulate.

Besides the given four postulates for addition of real numbers, one more can be stated. The example below illustrates Postulate 2–6.

EXAMPLE. What number added to ⁺6 gives 0?

Think of ⁺6 as a "gain of 6." Then a "loss of 6" puts you back at 0. Thus, adding ⁻6 to ⁺6 gives a sum of 0. Are ⁺6 and ⁻6 opposites of each other?

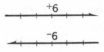

Could you answer the question in the example if the number had been ⁺9? if it had been ⁻3? if it had been x? For each real number x, there is another real number $-x$, the negative of x, such that their sum is 0. The sentence $x + (-x) = 0$ is always true. This is Postulate 2–6.

Postulates for Addition of Real Numbers	Name
2–6 $\forall x \in R$ **there exists** $-x \in R$ **such that** $x + (-x) = 0$ **is true. For each x there is one and only one** $-x$.	Additive inverse postulate.

If two numbers such as $\frac{3}{2}$ and $\frac{2}{3}$ are *multiplicative inverses*, then their product is 1: $\frac{3}{2} \times \frac{2}{3} = 1$. If two numbers are *additive inverses*, what is their sum?

You can simplify the way you write the numerals for the real numbers by writing 6 for ⁺6 in most cases. Similarly, since the negative of 6 is shown by the symbol −6, you may write −6 instead of ⁻6. Tell why these sentences are true.

a. $-7\frac{1}{2} = {}^-7\frac{1}{2}$ b. $-\sqrt{2} = {}^-\sqrt{2}$ c. $-100 = {}^-100$

In general, if a is a positive number, $-a$ is a negative number. In fact, the *negative of a* when a is positive is equal to the number *negative a*. Hereafter, the sign for "negative of" will be used to indicate negative numbers. You may read −6 usually as "negative 6," although in some circumstances it may be more appropriate to say "the negative of 6." Similarly, +6 will sometimes be used to mean ⁺6.

Checkpoint

1. Is the negative of a real number always a negative number? Explain.

2. Explain why any negative number may be written as the negative of a positive number.

3. Explain why the set of real numbers is closed under addition.

Exercises

A ▬ If the sentence is true, give the name of the postulate that it illustrates. If the sentence is false, write a true sentence by changing one of the real numbers, and then name the postulate. The sign for addition is in color to remind you that it is not the sign for a positive number.

1. $6 + (-2) = (-2) + 6$

2. $3 + (-3) = 0$

3. $(3 + 4) + (-5) = 3 + [4 + (-5)]$

4. $-11 + 0 = -11$

5. $-9 + (-11) = 11 + (-9)$

6. $-27 + 27 = 0$

7. $(5 + 9) + (-8) = (-8) + (5 + 9)$

8. $0 + (-5) = -5$

9. $-\pi + \pi = 0$

10. $-\sqrt{2} + \sqrt{2} = 0$

▬ Find a real number that will replace x so that the sentence is true.

11. $-4 + 3 = x + (-4)$

12. $5 + x = 0$

13. $(7 + x) + (-9) = 7 + [(-2) + (-9)]$

14. $x + (-3) = 0$

15. $9 + (-9) = x$

16. $-11 + x = -11$

17. $x + 0 = -29$

18. $-44 + x = 0$

19. $x + \frac{3}{4} = 0$

20. $-0.2 + x = 0$

B ▬ Which postulate for addition of real numbers is a mathematical model of the given situation in Exercises 21–23? Write a mathematical sentence to illustrate each.

21. Two hours later than 11 A.M. is the same time as eleven hours later than 2 A.M.

22. A party of mountain climbers traveled the same distance down the mountain as they did in climbing to its peak, and they arrived where they had started. The mountain peak was 5247 feet above their camp.

23. The price of stock in the Acme Apex Corporation dropped an eighth of a dollar on Monday and it stayed at that level on Tuesday. The net change over the two days was $-\frac{1}{8}$.

24. Make up your own examples of physical situations for which Postulates 2–3, 2–4, and 2–5 for addition might serve as the mathematical models.

2–5 Addition of Real Numbers

Negative numbers often occur in applications. For example, if a plane is traveling 400 miles an hour into a head wind of 80 miles an hour, the ground speed of the plane is $400 + (-80)$. To solve such a problem and find the answer as 320, you need to know how to add positive and negative numbers.

The examples below show how the postulates of addition can be used to find sums. The sign for addition, +, is written in color for a while to stress that it is the sign of the operation.

Sum of Two Negative Numbers

EXAMPLE 1. Find the sum of -4 and -3.

Think of -4 as a "loss of 4" and of -3 as a "loss of 3," as shown in the vector diagram.

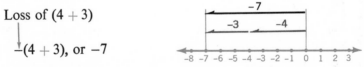

Loss of $(4 + 3)$

$\downarrow$

$-(4 + 3)$, or -7

The sum of -4 and -3 is -7.

Draw vector diagrams for each true sentence below. Can you discover a pattern?

a. $-5 + (-7) = -12$ b. $-6\frac{1}{2} + (-8\frac{1}{2}) = -15$

c. $-11 + (-8) = -19$ d. $-5.2 + (-8.1) = -13.3$

e. $-15 + (-20) = -35$ f. $-4 + (-99) = -103$

Now try to state a rule for adding two negative numbers.

You can prove the rule for adding any two negative numbers by using the postulates for addition, as outlined in Exercise 77 on pages 70 and 71. The proof is left as an exercise. A statement proved from postulates and definitions is a **theorem.**

Theorem 2–1   The sum of two negative numbers is a negative number. The sum is the negative of the sum of their absolute values.

If $-a < 0$ and $-b < 0$, then $(-a) + (-b) = -(|a| + |b|)$.

Use the theorem to check sentences **a–f** above. Then see if you can find the numbers to replace x and make sentences **g–j** true.

g. $(-12) + (-23) = x$ **h.** $(-6.1) + (-6) = x$

i. $(-8\frac{1}{2}) + (-8\frac{1}{2}) = x$ **j.** $(-325) + (-163) = x$

Sum of a Positive Number and a Negative Number

EXAMPLE 2. Find n if $-14 + 8 = n$ is true.

One way is to use the vector diagram below. A vector for -14 begins at 0 and extends 14 units to the left. Then a vector for $+8$ is drawn, beginning at the terminal point of the vector for -14.

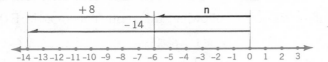

The sum is n, the total change. So n is -6.

Here is another way to find the sum. Begin by thinking of -14 as $-6 + (-8)$ so that you can use the additive inverse postulate.

Statements	Reasons
1. $-14 + 8 = [-6 + (-8)] + 8$	1. Theorem 2–1.
2. $\qquad = -6 + (-8 + 8)$	2. Associative postulate.
3. $\qquad = -6 + 0$	3. Additive inverse postulate.
4. $\qquad = -6$	4. Identity postulate.

The sum, n, is -6.

The outline above shows how you can think of the 8 matching with part of the -14, leaving -6 in the part not matched.

Verify each of the following, using either method in Example 2.

k. $-16 + 5 = -11$ **l.** $-12 + 9 = -3$ **m.** $-50 + 8 = -42$

n. $-7 + 4\frac{1}{2} = -3\frac{1}{2}$ **o.** $16 + (-17) = -1$ **p.** $20.4 + (-31.4) = -11$

If the absolute value of the negative number is greater than the absolute value of the positive number, is the sum a positive or a negative number?

EXAMPLE 3. Find n if $-11 + 17 = n$ is true.

The diagram shows one way. You can think of a "loss of 11" and a "gain of 17." The result is a "gain of 6."

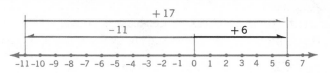

Here is another way.

Statements	Reasons
1. $-11 + 17 = -11 + (11 + 6)$	**1.** Renaming 17 as $11 + 6$.
2. $\qquad = (-11 + 11) + 6$	**2.** Associative postulate.
3. $\qquad = \quad 0 \quad + 6$	**3.** Additive inverse postulate.
4. $\qquad = 6$	**4.** Identity postulate.

Verify each of the following, using either method in Example 3.

q. $12 + (-7) = 5$ **r.** $45 + (-35) = 10$ **s.** $65 + (-52) = 13$

t. $-2\frac{1}{2} + 4\frac{1}{2} = 2$ **u.** $-1.2 + 7.2 = 6$ **v.** $-4.2 + 15 = 10.8$

If the absolute value of the positive number is greater than the absolute value of the negative number, is the sum a positive or a negative number?

Now try to make a rule for adding any positive and any negative number.

Here is the way that one algebra student made a generalization. To add a positive and a negative number,

① find the absolute value of each number and subtract the smaller absolute value from the greater;

② if the absolute value of the positive number is greater, the sum is the result in step 1;

③ if the absolute value of the negative number is greater, the sum is the negative of the result in step 1.

This generalization is Theorem 2–2. In algebraic symbols, it is stated as follows.

> **Theorem 2–2** If $x < 0$ and $y > 0$, then $x + y = -(|x| - y)$ when $|x| > y$, and $x + y = y - |x|$ when $|x| < y$.

Now try these

—— Find the sums.

1. $-3 + (-4)$ **2.** $-9 + (-5)$ **3.** $-3 + 4$
4. $3 + (-4)$ **5.** $-9 + 5$ **6.** $9 + (-5)$
7. $3 + 4$ **8.** $-12 + 18$ **9.** $5 + (-5)$

Answers: **1.** -7 **2.** -14 **3.** 1 **4.** -1 **5.** -4 **6.** 4 **7.** 7 **8.** 6 **9.** 0

Exercises

A —— Name each sum with a single numeral.

1. $-3 + (6)$ **2.** $3 + 6$ **3.** $(-3) + (-6)$
4. $3 + (-6)$ **5.** $9 + (-6)$ **6.** $(-9) + 6$
7. $2 + (-5)$ **8.** $(-7) + (-2)$ **9.** $(-4) + (-9)$
10. $7 + 5$ **11.** $(-3) + 7$ **12.** $(-10) + (-3)$
13. $6 + (-2)$ **14.** $(-9) + (-6)$ **15.** $8 + (-3)$
16. $6 + 2$ **17.** $(-10) + (-4)$ **18.** $-8 + 3$
19. $9 + 0$ **20.** $0 + 9$ **21.** $(-9) + 8$
22. $7 + (-3)$ **23.** $8 + (-7)$ **24.** $(-3) + (-7)$
25. $9 + 6$ **26.** $(-6) + 3$ **27.** $5 + (-6)$
28. $(-3) + 7$ **29.** $(-9) + 0$ **30.** $0 + (-9)$
31. $2\frac{3}{4} + (-1\frac{1}{2})$ **32.** $(-\frac{3}{5}) + (-\frac{2}{3})$ **33.** $7 + 4\frac{1}{2}$
34. $-9\frac{1}{3} + 6\frac{3}{4}$ **35.** $(-6\frac{5}{12}) + 8\frac{1}{6}$ **36.** $8.6 + (-3.7)$
37. $(-4.5) + 2.4$ **38.** $8.0 + (-3.2)$ **39.** $(-6.0) + (-7.2)$
40. $8.2 + 6.4$ **41.** $1.3 + (-0.7)$ **42.** $2.4 + (-4.5)$
43. $(-3.7) + 8.6$ **44.** $(-4.0) + 0.7$ **45.** $(-1.6) + (-6.0)$
46. $[5 + (-8)] + [9 + (-2)]$ **47.** $[5 + (-7)] + [(-8) + (-3)]$
48. $[-8 + 9] + [7 + (-5)]$ **49.** $[7 + 4] + [(-9) + 8]$
50. $[-12 + (29)] + [37 + (-18)]$ **51.** $[(-15) + 2] + [37 + (-22)]$

52. Find the sum of the numbers named in each row and in each column.

						Row sums
-3	7	-2	1	0	4	?
-2	5	8	0	-3	7	?
-9	3	5	6	-4	-10	?
-6	-8	-6	-5	-5	9	?
10	-7	6	7	4	-7	?
Column sums	?	?	?	?	?	?

Add the row sums and the column sums. The two results should be the same.

— Evaluate each of the following expressions.

53. $|3| + |15|$ **54.** $|-3| + |-9|$ **55.** $|23| + |-18|$

56. $|-15| + |14|$ **57.** $|6| + |-8|$ **58.** $|-4| + |8|$

59. $|-9| + |9|$ **60.** $|9| + |-12|$ **61.** $|0| + |0|$

62. $|\frac{1}{2}| + |\frac{2}{3}|$ **63.** $|0.2| + |-0.37|$ **64.** $|-235| + |16|$

B — Find the real number that can replace the variable to make a true sentence.

65. $x + 5 = 12$ **66.** $6 + y = -2$ **67.** $-8 + 22 = n$

68. $10 + t = 1$ **69.** $a + (-7) = -17$ **70.** $-14 + u = 42$

71. $7 + c = 0$ **72.** $m + 10 = 20$ **73.** $13 + z = 9$

74. $v + 14 = 2$ **75.** $16 + 18 = r$ **76.** $g + 7 = 3$

C   **77.** Some of you may like to see how to prove that $-4 + (-3) = -(4 + 3)$ is true, using the postulates for addition. To prove it, you must show that $-4 + (-3)$ is the negative of $(4 + 3)$, or that the sum of $-4 + (-3)$ and $(4 + 3)$ is 0.

Complete the following by giving the reason why each statement is true.

Statements	Reasons
1. $[-4 + (-3)] + (4 + 3) = -4 + [(-3) + 4] + 3$	1. ?
2. $\qquad = -4 + [4 + (-3)] + 3$	2. ?
3. $\qquad = (-4 + 4) + [(-3) + 3]$	3. ?
4. $\qquad = \quad 0 \quad + \quad 0$	4. ?
5. $\qquad = 0$	5. ?

Once you know that the sum is 0, you know that $-4 + (-3)$ and $(4 + 3)$ are inverses. What part of the additive inverse postulate tells you that if $-4 + (-3)$ is the negative of $(4 + 3)$, then $-4 + (-3)$ must be the same number as $-(4 + 3)$? Hence, $-4 + (-3) = -(4 + 3)$ is true.

━━ Prove that each of the following sentences is true.

78. $-9 + (-15) = -24$ **79.** $-9 + 7 = -2$ **80.** $-9 + 17 = 8$

81. Prove that $-a + (-b) = -(a + b)$ is true $a \in R$, $b \in R$.

82. Prove that $-(-a) = a$ by using the additive inverse postulate.

2–6   Subtraction of Real Numbers

If you bought a shirt for $2.49 and gave the salesman a five-dollar bill, he would give you your change (the difference between $5.00 and $2.49) probably by counting it out, saying, "$2.49, $2.50, $2.75, $3.00, $4.00, $5.00." What he has really done is added as follows.

$$2.49 + 0.01 + 0.25 + 0.25 + 1.00 + 1.00 = 5.00$$

In other words, to find $5.00 - $2.49, the salesman thought "$2.49 *plus* some amount equals $5.00."

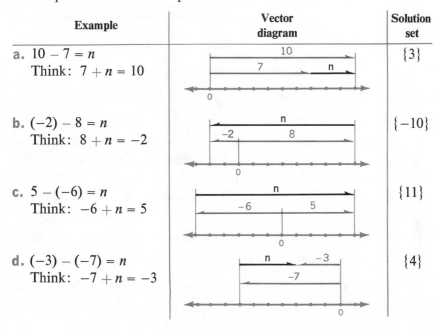

Example	Vector diagram	Solution set
a. $10 - 7 = n$ Think: $7 + n = 10$		$\{3\}$
b. $(-2) - 8 = n$ Think: $8 + n = -2$		$\{-10\}$
c. $5 - (-6) = n$ Think: $-6 + n = 5$		$\{11\}$
d. $(-3) - (-7) = n$ Think: $-7 + n = -3$		$\{4\}$

These examples suggest the following definition of subtraction for real numbers a and b.

Definition To <u>subtract</u> b from a, written $a - b$, means to find the number c such that $b + c = a$.

$\forall a \in R$ $\forall b \in R$ $a - b = c$ if and only if $b + c = a$

Now try these

— Use the definition of subtraction to find the solution set for each sentence. The replacement set is the set of real numbers. Draw a vector diagram for each.

1. $9 - 3 = n$ **2.** $6 - (-1) = x$ **3.** $(-8) - 3 = n$

4. $(-9) - (-5) = m$ **5.** $(-18) - 13 = n$ **6.** $(-17) - 11 = y$

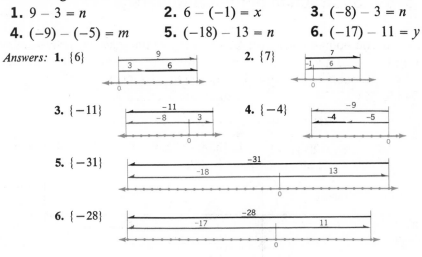

Answers: **1.** $\{6\}$

2. $\{7\}$

3. $\{-11\}$

4. $\{-4\}$

5. $\{-31\}$

6. $\{-28\}$

Exercises

A — Use the definition of subtraction to find the solution set for each sentence. Draw vector diagrams for Exercises 1–5. The replacement set for each variable is the set of real numbers.

1. $-19 - (-10) = n$ **2.** $-17 - 8 = b$ **3.** $-15 - (-11) = a$

4. $13 - 6 = x$ **5.** $15 - (-9) = c$ **6.** $-18 - (-13) = t$

7. $7.5 - (-4.5) = u$ **8.** $-2\frac{1}{2} - 3\frac{1}{2} = y$ **9.** $-4.4 - (-3.6) = v$

10. $4.01 - 6.36 = f$ **11.** $-45 - 81 = r$ **12.** $-8\frac{1}{4} - (-12\frac{3}{4}) = g$

13. A football team gained 3 yards on one play and lost 5 yards on the next. What was the total change in position?

14. A stock lost $1\frac{1}{2}$ dollars on Wednesday and another $\frac{3}{4}$ dollar on Thursday. What was the total change for the two days?

15. A stock lost $1\frac{1}{4}$ dollars on Tuesday, and by the closing of the exchange on Wednesday, it was down $2\frac{3}{4}$ dollars from its opening on Tuesday morning. What happened on Wednesday?

16. An airplane traveling 385 miles per hour ran into a head wind of 72 mph. What was its speed with respect to the ground?

17. An airplane traveling 410 miles per hour found it had a ground speed of only 385 miles per hour. If it was traveling directly into the wind, how fast was the wind?

B **18.** A football team is on its own 12-yard line. On the first play, it gains 7 yards. After the second play, it is on its own 9-yard line. What happened during the second play?

19. The Texas Rio Molasses Corporation stock stood at $91\frac{1}{8}$ at the opening of trading on Monday. It lost $3\frac{1}{2}$ dollars on Monday, and by the closing Tuesday, it was at $90\frac{1}{4}$. What happened Tuesday?

2–7 Using the Postulates in Subtraction

The definition of subtraction may be used directly to solve simple problems, but for more complicated situations, you need a quicker way to deal with subtraction of real numbers. Have you noticed a way of simplifying subtraction by rewriting it as addition? You might be able to guess that the subtraction example $4 - (-7)$ has the same answer as the addition example $4 + 7$. Here is a way to show this is the case.

EXAMPLE. Show that $4 - (-7)$ is the same as $4 + 7$.
You can set your work up as a formal chain of statements.

	Statements	*Reasons*
1.	$4 - (-7) = n$	1. Given.
2.	$(-7) + n = 4$	2. Definition of subtraction.
3.	$7 + [(-7) + n] = 7 + 4$	3. Closure postulate.
4.	$[7 + (-7)] + n = 7 + 4$	4. Associative postulate.
5.	$0 + n = 7 + 4$	5. Additive inverse postulate.
6.	$n = 7 + 4$	6. Identity postulate.
7.	$7 + 4 = 4 + 7$	7. Commutative postulate.

The chain of statements shows that the following sentence is true.

$$4 - (-7) = 4 + (+7)$$
To subtract -7, add $+7$.

The proof for any real numbers, a and b, follows the same pattern as in the example. The proof of the general theorem is left as an exercise. It is stated in words and mathematical symbols as follows.

Theorem 2–3 To subtract any real number b from any real number a, add the additive inverse of b to a.

$$\forall a \in R \quad \forall b \in R \quad a - b = a + (-b)$$

Exercises

A —— Name each difference with a single numeral.

1. $5 - 11$	**2.** $-8 - (-6)$	**3.** $-4 - 5$
4. $-5 - 1$	**5.** $-6 - 2$	**6.** $4 - (-6)$
7. $-6 + 4$	**8.** $-6 + (-4)$	**9.** $-4 - 6$
10. $-8 - 3$	**11.** $-4 - 8$	**12.** $-6 - (-7)$
13. $16 - (-15)$	**14.** $-24 - 12$	**15.** $15 - 15$
16. $-9 - 3$	**17.** $-9 - 10$	**18.** $-10 - 10$
19. $-2.4 + 9.4$	**20.** $0 - (-7.8)$	**21.** $-7.8 - 0$
22. $\frac{1}{2} - (-\frac{1}{2})$	**23.** $\frac{5}{3} - (-\frac{2}{3})$	**24.** $-54 - (-14)$
25. $-64 - 74$	**26.** $12.3 - 6.7$	**27.** $-12.3 - 6.7$
28. $12.3 - (-6.7)$	**29.** $6.7 + 12.3$	**30.** $-12.3 - (-6.7)$
31. $-6.7 + 12.3$	**32.** $-6.7 - (-12.3)$	**33.** $6.7 - (-12.3)$
34. $-\frac{1}{2} - (-\frac{1}{2})$	**35.** $-\sqrt{2} - \sqrt{2}$	**36.** $\sqrt{3} - (-\sqrt{3})$

—— Label each of the following as *True* or *False*. The replacement set for a and b is R.

37. $-6 + (-2) = 4$
38. $-\frac{2}{3} - (-\frac{2}{3}) = \frac{1}{3}$
39. $-4 - (-2) = -2 - (-4)$
40. $|0| = 0.24 - (-0.24)$
41. $8 - (-8) = 0$
42. $6 - 2 = 6 + (-2)$
43. $|-8 + (-2)| = |-8| - |-2|$
44. $|8 - 2| = |2 - 8|$
45. $|8 - (-2)| = |8| - |-2|$
46. $|8 - 2| = |8| - |2|$
47. $|2 - 8| = |2| - |8|$
48. $-3 + (-3) = -6$
49. $a - b = a + (-b)$
50. $|a - b| = |b - a|$

B —— The formula for converting a temperature expressed in degrees Fahrenheit to a temperature expressed in degrees Celsius (centigrade) is $C = \frac{5}{9}(F - 32)$, where C represents the number of degrees Celsius and F represents the number of degrees Fahrenheit. For each of the following temperatures expressed in degrees Fahrenheit, find the temperature in degrees Celsius.

51. 70° **52.** 32° **53.** 50° **54.** 100°

C **55.** Use the method in the Example on page 73 to prove that $a - b = a + (-b)$ is true for all real replacements for a and b.

56. Prove that $|a - b| = |b - a|$ is true for all real replacements for a and b. (*Hint:* You will have to consider several cases.)

2–8 Multiplication of Real Numbers

You know that there are certain postulates that are true for multiplication of *positive* numbers. Since the set of positive numbers is a subset of the set of real numbers, it is reasonable to expect that those postulates also apply to the set of real numbers.

Recall that xy means the same as $x \cdot y$, $x(y)$, and $x \times y$.

Postulates for Multiplication of Real Numbers	Name
2–7 $\forall x \in R$ $\forall y \in R$ xy **is one and only one real number.**	Closure postulate.
2–8 $\forall x \in R$ $\forall y \in R$ $xy = yx$	Commutative postulate.
2–9 $\forall x \in R$ $\forall y \in R$ $\forall z \in R$ $(xy)z = x(yz)$	Associative postulate.
2–10 $\forall x \in R$ $x \cdot 1 = 1 \cdot x = x$, **where 1 is the only number with this property.**	Identity postulate.
2–11 $\forall x \in R, x \neq 0$ **there exists** $\frac{1}{x}$ **such that** $x \cdot \frac{1}{x} = \frac{1}{x} \cdot x = 1$, **where for each x there is only one number** $\frac{1}{x}$.	Inverse postulate.
2–12 $\forall x \in R$ $\forall y \in R$ $\forall z \in R$ $x(y + z) = xy + xz$	Distributive postulate for multiplication over addition.

You know how to find the product of two positive real numbers. How do you find the product of two real numbers when one is positive and one is negative? The example below shows how to find that product, but first you need the following theorem.

Theorem 2-4 The product of any real number and 0 is 0.

$$\forall x \in R \quad x \cdot 0 = 0 \cdot x = 0$$

The proof of the theorem is left as an exercise.

EXAMPLE. Show that $3(-4) = -12$.

One way to do this is to use a vector diagram on a number line.

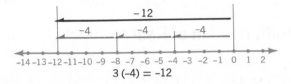

$$3(-4) = -12$$

The diagram illustrates the process of multiplication as repeated addition. You can think of −4 as being a "loss of 4" and of 3 as being "3 times." Then, 3 losses of 4 each is a total loss of 12, or −12.

You may also be interested in the proof that $3(-4) = -12$. The postulates and previously proved theorems are used as reasons.

The goal in proving the theorem is to show that $3 \cdot 4$ and $3(-4)$ have a sum of 0. If the sum is 0, then $3 \cdot 4$ and $3(-4)$ are additive inverses, and $3(-4)$ is −12, the inverse of 12.

You begin the proof of the theorem by choosing the sentence $4 + (-4) = 0$. This will lead to the desired result. (Notice that addition and subtraction will be indicated in black type from now on. You can differentiate between the signs by the way the sign is used.)

Statements	Reasons
1. $\quad 4 + (-4) = 0$	1. Additive inverse postulate.
2. $\quad 3[4 + (-4)] = 3 \cdot 0$	2. Closure postulate.
3. $\quad 3[4 + (-4)] = 0$	3. Theorem 2-4.
4. $3 \cdot 4 + 3(-4) = 0$	4. Distributive postulate.
5. Hence, $3 \cdot 4$ and $3(-4)$ are additive inverses.	5. Additive inverse postulate.
6. $3(-4) = -(3 \cdot 4)$, or −12.	6. Additive inverse postulate.

Having proved that $3(-4) = -12$ is a true sentence, you can use the commutative postulate to show that $(-4) \cdot 3$ is also equal to -12.

Use vector diagrams to show that each of the following is true. Try to make a rule for the product of a positive and a negative number.

a. $5(-4) = -20$ b. $8(-3) = -24$ c. $7(-2\frac{1}{2}) = -17\frac{1}{2}$

d. $(-5)(8) = -40$ e. $(-6)(5) = -30$ f. $(-9)(9) = -81$

The generalization for the product of a positive number and a negative number is stated as a theorem. The proof is left as an exercise.

Theorem 2–5   The product of a and $-b$ is $-ab$.

$$\forall a \in R \quad \forall b \in R \quad a(-b) = -(ab)$$

The proof of Theorem 2–6 follows directly from Theorem 2–5.

Theorem 2–6   The product of $-a$ and b is $-ab$.

$$\forall a \in R \quad \forall b \in R \quad -a(b) = -(ab)$$

Statements	Reasons
1. $-a(b) = b(-a)$	1. Commutative postulate.
2. $\quad = -(ba)$	2. Theorem 2–5.
3. $\quad = -(ab)$	3. Commutative postulate.

Now try these

— Find the products.

1. $7(-3)$ **2.** $-6 \cdot 9$ **3.** $4 \times (-8)$ **4.** $(-5)(0)$

5. $3.2(-2.1)$ **6.** $-0.5(4.6)$ **7.** $\frac{3}{4}(-\frac{2}{3})$ **8.** $(-15)(8)$

Answers: **1.** -21 **2.** -54 **3.** -32 **4.** 0 **5.** -6.72 **6.** -2.3 **7.** $-\frac{1}{2}$ **8.** -120

Exercises

A — Find the products of the following numbers.

1. 6 and -3	**2.** -5 and 2	**3.** 2 and -5
4. -2 and 5	**5.** 5 and -2	**6.** 2 and 5
7. 4 and 0	**8.** -4 and 0	**9.** -4 and 3
10. 4 and -3	**11.** $-\frac{3}{4}$ and $\frac{2}{3}$	**12.** $\frac{1}{8}$ and $-\frac{5}{6}$

Find the products as indicated.

13. $6 \cdot 3$ **14.** $-6 \cdot 3$ **15.** $-3 \cdot 6$

16. $8(-\frac{1}{4})$ **17.** $12(6)$ **18.** $12(-6)$

19. $-12(6)$ **20.** $(-1)(5)$ **21.** $8(-2.5)$

22. $\frac{2}{3}(-12)$ **23.** $3.8(-10)$ **24.** $-62(100)$

25. $-17(28)$ **26.** $2\frac{1}{5}(-\frac{3}{5})$ **27.** $33 \cdot (-\frac{1}{3})$

28. $8.1(0)$ **29.** $-5(2.4)$ **30.** $-7.2(\frac{1}{4})$

B — Recall that a Celsius (centigrade) temperature C may be found from a Fahrenheit temperature F by the formula $C = \frac{5}{9}[F + (-32)]$. Give the Celsius temperature that corresponds to each of the following Fahrenheit temperatures.

31. $7°$ **32.** $43°$ **33.** $-18°$ **34.** $212°$ **35.** $-54°$

— Using the formula $\frac{9}{5}C + 32 = F$, give the Fahrenheit temperature that corresponds to each of the following Celsius temperatures.

36. $72°$ **37.** $20°$ **38.** $0°$ **39.** $-12°$ **40.** $-2°$

41. You are familiar with the statement that distance is the product of rate and time, or $d = rt$. When you consider direction along with distance, the formula becomes a vector formula, $\vec{d} = \vec{v}t$.

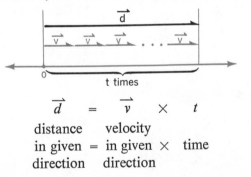

$$\vec{d} \quad = \quad \vec{v} \quad \times \quad t$$

distance   velocity
in given   =   in given ×   time
direction   direction

The time is always a positive number; it has no direction.

If traveling east or north is viewed as moving in the positive direction and traveling west or south is viewed as moving in the negative direction, find d if

a. you travel south at 10 miles per hour for $6\frac{1}{2}$ hours.

b. you travel north at 50.2 kilometers per hour for 5 hours.

c. you walk east at 200 meters per minute for 8 minutes and west at 180 meters per minute for 6 minutes.

C **42.** Show that the two formulas for converting temperatures, $\frac{9}{5}C + 32 = F$ and $C = \frac{5}{9}[F + (-32)]$, are equivalent.

── For the following proofs, copy the *Statements* column as shown, and then give the reason for each directly to the right.

43. Prove Theorem 2–4: $\forall x \in R \quad x \cdot 0 = 0 \cdot x = 0.$

Statements	*Reasons*
1. a. $x(1 + 0) = x \cdot 1 + x \cdot 0$	1. a. $\underline{?}$
b. $\quad\quad\quad = x \;\; + x \cdot 0$	b. $\underline{?}$
2. a. $x(1 + 0) = x(1)$	2. a. $\underline{?}$
b. $\quad\quad\quad\; = x$	b. $\underline{?}$
3. Therefore, $x = x + x \cdot 0.$	3. $\quad\underline{?}$
4. Hence, $x \cdot 0 = 0.$	4. $\quad\underline{?}$
5. And $0 \cdot x = 0.$	5. $\quad\underline{?}$

44. Prove Theorem 2–5: $\forall a \in R \quad \forall b \in R \quad a(-b) = -(ab).$

Statements	*Reasons*
1. $\quad\quad b + (-b) = 0$	1. $\underline{?}$
2. $\quad\quad a[b + (-b)] = a(0)$	2. $\underline{?}$
3. $\quad\quad ab + a(-b) = 0$	3. $\underline{?}$
4. Therefore, $a(-b) = -(ab).$	4. $\underline{?}$

2–9 The Product of Two Negative Numbers

To find the replacement for n that makes $-3(-4) = n$ a true sentence, you must be able to find the product of two negative numbers.

Look at the table of products shown at the right. Is the first factor in each sentence the same? What pattern do you see for the second factor in the sentences? What pattern do you see for the products?

If the pattern for the products continues, what will the last four products be? Does it make sense for $-3(-1)$ to be 3? for $-3(-2)$ to be 6? for $-3(-3)$ to be 9? for $-3(-4)$ to be 12?

Here is another way to reason about the problem. Think of -4 as a "loss of $4 a week"

$-3(4) = -12$
$-3(3) = -9$
$-3(2) = -6$
$-3(1) = -3$
$-3(0) = 0$
$-3(-1) = \underline{?}$
$-3(-2) = \underline{?}$
$-3(-3) = \underline{?}$
$-3(-4) = \underline{?}$

and of −3 as "3 weeks ago." If you have lost $4 a week for the past 3 weeks [(−4) × (−3)], then 3 weeks ago you were $12 richer (+12).

You may be interested in the way to prove that −3(−4) = 12 is true by using the postulates and previous theorems.

Statements	*Reasons*
1. $4 + (-4) = 0$	1. Additive inverse postulate.
2. $-3[4 + (-4)] = -3(0)$	2. Closure postulate.
3. $-3(4) + (-3)(-4) = 0$	3. Distributive postulate and Theorem 2–4.
4. $-12 + (-3)(-4) = 0$	4. Theorem 2–6.

Since −12 and (−3)(−4) have a sum of 0, they are additive inverses. By the additive inverse postulate, a number has only one additive inverse. Since 12 is the additive inverse of −12, then (−3)(−4) is equal to 12.

Is each of the following sentences true? Explain each one by using any of the ways of thinking in this section. As you work, try to make a rule for multiplying two negative numbers.

a. $-7(-5) = 35$ b. $-8(-2) = 16$ c. $-7\frac{1}{2}(-2) = 15$

d. $-\sqrt{2}(-\sqrt{2}) = 2$ e. $-\sqrt{3}(-\sqrt{3}) = 3$ f. $-5(-15) = 75$

g. $-0.5(-4) = 2$ h. $-0.3(-0.7) = 0.21$ i. $-\frac{3}{4}(-\frac{2}{3}) = \frac{1}{2}$

If −a is negative and −b is negative, is their product positive or negative?

The conclusion you might draw from **a–i** can be summarized as a theorem.

Theorem 2–7   The product of −a and −b is ab.

$$\forall a \in R \quad \forall b \in R \quad (-a)(-b) = ab$$

The proof is left as an exercise.

Exercises

A —— Find the products of the following numbers.

1. −2 and −5   2. −5 and −2   3. −3 and 5

4. −4 and 3   5. −4 and −3   6. 4 and −3

7. −2.5 and −0.1   8. $-\frac{1}{8}$ and $-\frac{5}{6}$ 9. $-\sqrt{5}$ and $-\sqrt{5}$

— Find the products as indicated.

10. $-6(-3)$ **11.** $-4(-5)$ **12.** $4(-5)$

13. $-4(5)$ **14.** $4(5)$ **15.** $0(-2)$

16. $-2(-9)$ **17.** $7(-1)$ **18.** $-48(-10)$

19. $-1(-1)$ **20.** $-\frac{2}{3}(-\frac{3}{2})$ **21.** $-7649(-580)$

22. $-0.5(-12)$ **23.** $-1.1(3.4)$ **24.** $-\frac{1}{9}(-\frac{3}{4})$

25. What postulate for the real numbers can you use in finding the product of three numbers?

26. Do you think the following is true?

$$[-2(4)](-3) = -2[4(-3)]$$

Why or why not? Check by multiplying both ways.

— Find the products as indicated.

27. $5(4)(-2)$ **28.** $-5(4)(-2)$ **29.** $-6(-5)(-4)$

30. $5(-4)(-2)$ **31.** $6(-4)(-5)$ **32.** $-8(-1)(2)$

33. $3(0)(-5)$ **34.** $5(-6)(-4)$ **35.** $-2(-2)(-2)$

36. $(-3)^2 = (-3)(-3)$ **37.** $(-4)^2$ **38.** $(5)^2$

39. $(-1)^2 = (-1)(-1)$ **40.** $(1)^2$ **41.** $(-1)^3$

42. What kind of number is the product when two negative numbers are multiplied? when four negative numbers are multiplied?

43. What kind of number is the product when three negative numbers are multiplied? five negative numbers?

44. For the product to be positive, must an even number of negative numbers be multiplied or an odd number of negative numbers? Explain.

45. Is the set of negative real numbers *closed* under multiplication?

— Replace ● with either $>$, $<$, or $=$ to make true statements.

46. $2(-3)$ ● $-3(2)$ **47.** $-6(-1)$ ● $-1(6)$

48. $-0.34(-6)$ ● $-0.17(-3)$ **49.** $-\frac{3}{2}(\frac{1}{2})$ ● $-\frac{1}{2}(\frac{3}{2})$

50. $-6(0)$ ● $0(6)$ **51.** $|4 \cdot 5|$ ● $|4| \cdot |5|$

52. $|-0.34 \cdot -2|$ ● $|-0.34| \cdot |-2|$ **53.** $|0 \cdot 1|$ ● $|0| \cdot |1|$

54. $|-0.2 \cdot 0.1|$ ● $|-0.2| \cdot |0.1|$ **55.** $|\frac{2}{3} \cdot \frac{1}{2}|$ ● $|\frac{2}{3}| \cdot |\frac{1}{2}|$

B — Substitute as indicated: $r = -3$, $s = 2$, $t = -7$. Express your answers as real numbers.

56. rs **57.** tr **58.** sr **59.** rst

60. $2st$ **61.** $3rs$ **62.** $\frac{1}{3}rt$ **63.** $(-4)(st)$

64. $-\frac{1}{2}(rs)$ **65.** $-2(rs)$ **66.** $\frac{1}{6}rst$ **67.** $-3rst$

68. $s(r+t)$ **69.** $r(s+2t)$ **70.** $s(t+r)$ **71.** $t(s+r)$

72. $r(s+t)$ **73.** $s(r-t)$ **74.** $s(r-2t)$ **75.** $-s(r-3t)$

76. Complete the following proof of Theorem 2–7: The product of the opposites of two numbers is equal to the product of the two numbers. Copy the statements and supply a reason for each.

	Statements	Reasons
1.	$b + (-b) = 0$	1. _?_
2.	$-a[b + (-b)] = -a(0)$	2. _?_
3.	$-a(b) + (-a)(-b) = 0$	3. _?_
4.	$-ab + (-a)(-b) = 0$	4. _?_
5.	$(-a)(-b) = ab$	5. _?_

2–10   Division of Real Numbers

Look at the pairs of sentences and solutions, and see if you can explain each.

Find c.	Think	Quotient
a. $\frac{15}{5} = c$	$5 \cdot c = 15$	3
b. $\frac{3}{9} = c$	$9 \cdot c = 3$	$\frac{1}{3}$
c. $\frac{10}{-5} = c$	$(-5) \cdot c = 10$	-2
d. $\frac{-20}{-4} = c$	$(-4) \cdot c = -20$	5

To find the quotient for $\frac{15}{5}$, you can ask, "5 times what number gives 15?" Thus, as subtraction is the inverse of addition, *division is the inverse of multiplication.* By using multiplication to define division, $\frac{15}{5}$ means to find a number such that 5 times that number is 15; that is, $\frac{15}{5}$ means $5 \cdot c = 15$.

Definition   To <u>divide</u> a by b ($b \neq 0$) find the number c such that $b \cdot c = a$ is true.

$\forall a \in R$ $\forall b \in R$ $(b \neq 0)$ $\forall c \in R$ $\frac{a}{b} = c$ if and only if $b \cdot c = a$

Another way to solve the division problem is to multiply the dividend by the reciprocal of the divisor.

EXAMPLE 1. $\frac{24}{6} = \underline{\ ?\ }$

Think: $\frac{24}{6} = 24 \times \frac{1}{6} = \underline{\ ?\ }$. The quotient is 4.

Thus, $\frac{24}{6} = 4$ is true.

EXAMPLE 2. $\frac{-24}{-6} = \underline{\ ?\ }$

Think: $-24 \cdot (-\frac{1}{6}) = \underline{\ ?\ }$. The quotient is 4.

Thus, $\frac{-24}{-6} = 4$ is true.

EXAMPLE 3. $\frac{24}{-6} = \underline{\ ?\ }$

Think: $24 \cdot (-\frac{1}{6}) = \underline{\ ?\ }$. The quotient is −4.

Thus, $\frac{24}{-6} = -4$ is true.

EXAMPLE 4. $\frac{-24}{6} = \underline{\ ?\ }$

Think: $-24 \cdot \frac{1}{6} = \underline{\ ?\ }$. The quotient is −4.

Thus, $\frac{-24}{6} = -4$ is true.

Whichever method of thinking you use, it should be clear from the examples above that the pattern for positive and negative numbers in division is the same as the pattern in multiplication. The quotient of two positive numbers is positive. The quotient of two negative numbers is positive. The quotient of a negative number and a positive number is negative.

$$a \div b = a \div b \qquad -a \div b = -(a \div b)$$
$$-a \div -b = a \div b \qquad a \div -b = -(a \div b)$$

Exercises

A — Divide as indicated.

1. $\frac{-6}{2}$ 2. $\frac{-6}{-2}$ 3. $\frac{6}{-2}$ 4. $\frac{6}{2}$

5. $\frac{-20}{5}$ 6. $\frac{-20}{-5}$ 7. $\frac{20}{5}$ 8. $\frac{20}{-5}$

9. $\frac{0}{5}$ 10. $\frac{0}{-5}$ 11. $\frac{100}{-2}$ 12. $\frac{-600}{5}$

— Divide each of the following numbers by −5.

13. 10 **14.** −5 **15.** 0 **16.** −20

17. 20 **18.** −15 **19.** −5x **20.** 5y

— The definition of division includes the condition that you cannot divide by 0. By what number can x not be replaced in each of the following? (Ask yourself what replacement for x will make the denominator 0?)

21. $\frac{6}{x}$ **22.** $\frac{8}{x-1}$ **23.** $\frac{10}{-5+x}$

24. $\frac{5}{2x-4}$ **25.** $\frac{7}{-1+3x}$ **26.** $\frac{8}{2x+12}$

— Divide as indicated.

27. $\frac{7}{10} \div 14$ **28.** $-\frac{3}{7} \div \left(-\frac{8}{21}\right)$ **29.** $-13\frac{1}{2} \div 3\frac{5}{6}$

30. $-3241 \div (-10)$ **31.** $785 \div (-100)$ **32.** $3.2 \div 1000$

33. $15.75 \div (-15)$ **34.** $-4590 \div 45$ **35.** $-6\frac{2}{3} \div 3\frac{3}{4}$

— Replace the letters by real numbers to make true sentences.

36. $\frac{-100}{-75} = a$ **37.** $\frac{c}{-8} = 12$ **38.** $\frac{\frac{1}{15}}{-\frac{1}{14}} = a$

39. $\frac{-\frac{1}{4}}{\frac{3}{8}} = b$ **40.** $\frac{-14}{\frac{2}{7}} = a$ **41.** $-\frac{-7}{c} = -21$

42. $-\frac{9}{b} = 18$ **43.** $\frac{a}{3} = 0$ **44.** $\frac{c}{2} = -6$

B — Perform the indicated operations.

45. $(3)(-5) + \left(\frac{-8}{2}\right)$ **46.** $(-3)(-4)\left[-\left(\frac{-9}{-3}\right)\right]$

47. $(7)^2 + 2(7)^2(-3)$ **48.** $(4)^3 - 5(3)(-2)$

— Find the numbers that result if the replacement set for x in each of the following expressions is {−3, −1, 0, 2}.

49. $x + 5$ **50.** $x - 5$ **51.** $2x$

52. $\frac{x-6}{2}$ **53.** $x^2 - 5$ **54.** $x^2 + x$

— Substitute as indicated and perform the operations.

$$r = 4 \qquad s = 6 \qquad t = (-3)$$
$$u = (-2) \qquad v = (-3) \qquad w = \left(-\frac{1}{2}\right)$$

55. $s + t$ **56.** $st + rw$ **57.** $tu + rs$

58. $uv + rs$ **59.** $s \div u$ **60.** $r \div u$

61. $r \div w$ **62.** $s \div t$ **63.** $sw \div t$

64. $st - r$ **65.** $rw \div u$ **66.** $3(r \div w)$

67. $\dfrac{u}{v} - \dfrac{s}{r}$ **68.** $stu \div v$ **69.** $(r \div w) + t$

70. $(sv \div w) - r$ **71.** $(svw \div t) + u$ **72.** $\dfrac{s}{u} \div \dfrac{v}{t}$

C ——— You know how to find the mean, or average, of a group of numbers by adding the numbers and then dividing the sum by the number of addends. But for a long list of large numbers, it is possible to find the mean more easily by using an *estimation*.

Example. Find the mean of 17, 20, 28, and 21.

Try 22 as the mean. The difference between each number and the mean is called the **deviation from the mean,** and the sum of the deviations from the *true* mean is always zero. If 22 is the true mean, the sum of the deviations is zero.

$$17 - 22 = -5$$
$$20 - 22 = -2$$
$$28 - 22 = 6$$
$$\underline{21 - 22 = -1}$$
$$-2$$

Since the sum of the deviation is -2, not zero, 22 is not the true mean. Can you find the true mean from the assumed mean?

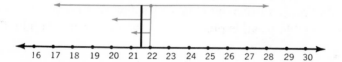

There are four deviations and each one is greater than or less than the deviation from the true mean by the same amount. In this example, the sum is -2, so each deviation is $\dfrac{-2}{4}$, or $-\frac{1}{2}$, unit different from the deviation from the true mean; that is, each is $\frac{1}{2}$ unit less than it should be. Then the true mean is $-\frac{1}{2}$ unit away from the assumed mean. So the true mean is $22 + (-\frac{1}{2})$, or $21\frac{1}{2}$. Check to see that the sum of the deviations from $21\frac{1}{2}$ is zero.

73. Use an assumed mean to find the true mean of 29, 42, 50, 37, 45, 30, 30, and 49.

74. Using 152 as an assumed mean, find the mean weight of 16 boys, whose weights are given below.

116	200	184	150
110	195	140	136
162	171	158	147
130	125	118	167

2–11 Equivalent Algebraic Expressions

Is it reasonable to suspect that the expressions $3x + 2x$ and $5x$ name the same number for every real number x? Use a line segment as a model for x.

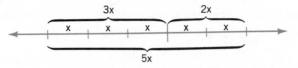

It would seem that $3x + 2x$ and $5x$ would always be equivalent.

Use the area of a rectangle as a model. What is the area of each of the smaller rectangles? What is the area of the large rectangle?

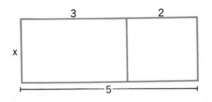

Then, $3x + 2x$ and $5x$ are again names for the same thing.

Experiment further by choosing a few real-number replacements for the variable in an expression and then compare the numbers that result.

EXAMPLE 1. Are $3x + 2x$ and $5x$ equivalent?

Replacements for x	$3x + 2x$	$5x$
2	$3(2) + 2(2) = \underline{?}$ $6 + 4 = 10$	$5(2) = 10$
-3	$3(-3) + 2(-3) = \underline{?}$ $(-9) + (-6) = -15$	$5(-3) = -15$
$\frac{1}{2}$	$3(\frac{1}{2}) + 2(\frac{1}{2}) = \underline{?}$ $1\frac{1}{2} + 1 = 2\frac{1}{2}$	$5(\frac{1}{2}) = 2\frac{1}{2}$
-0.7	$3(-0.7) + 2(-0.7) = \underline{?}$ $(-2.1) + (-1.4) = -3.5$	$5(-0.7) = -3.5$

For each of these replacements for x, $3x + 2x$ and $5x$ name the same number. Do you think there are other values of x for which $3x + 2x$ and $5x$ name the same number?

> **Definition** Two algebraic expressions are equivalent expressions if and only if the expressions name the same number for every replacement of the variables for which the expressions are defined.

If you find that each of several randomly chosen replacements gives the same numbers for the two algebraic expressions, you may reasonably expect that the algebraic expressions are equivalent. Thus, in the above illustration, you may reasonably conclude that $3x + 2x$ and $5x$ are equivalent and write $\forall x \; 3x + 2x = 5x$.

EXAMPLE 2. Are $x(x + 1)$ and $2x$ equivalent?

Using the same reasoning as in Example 1, you obtain the following.

Replacements for x	$x(x + 1)$	$2x$
0	$0(0 + 1) =$ $0 \cdot 1 = 0$	$2(0) = 0$
-1	$-1(-1 + 1) =$ $-1(0) = 0$	$2(-1) = -2$
$\frac{2}{3}$	$\frac{2}{3}(\frac{2}{3} + 1) =$ $\frac{2}{3} \cdot \frac{5}{3} = \frac{10}{9}$	$2(\frac{2}{3}) = \frac{4}{3}$
-1.2	$(-1.2)(-1.2 + 1) =$ $(-1.2)(-0.2) = 0.24$	$2(-1.2) = -2.4$

You could have stopped when x was replaced by -1. Since you found a real number for which $x(x + 1)$ and $2x$ do not name the same number, you can conclude that $x(x + 1)$ and $2x$ are *not equivalent*.

Exercises

A — Each of the following exercises contains two algebraic expressions that may or may not be equivalent. Following the form in Examples 1 and 2, use four replacements for the variable and then state whether or not you can reasonably conclude that the expressions are equivalent.

1. $3x + 5x$ and $8x$
2. $x(x + 2)$ and $3x$
3. x and $2x$
4. $6x - x$ and $5x$
5. $2(x + y)$ and $2x + 2y$
6. $-7m + (-6m)$ and $-13m$
7. $3x + 3y$ and $3(x + y)$
8. $x + x + x$ and $3x$
9. $|x + y|$ and $|x| + |y|$

B **10.** $|x \cdot y|$ and $|x| \cdot |y|$ **11.** $\dfrac{|x|}{y}$ and $\dfrac{|x|}{|y|}$

12. $|x - y|$ and $|x| - |y|$ **13.** $\dfrac{(a+b)(a-b)}{a-b}$ and $a + b$

14. $a^2 - b^2$ and $(a - b)^2$ **15.** $(a + b)^2$ and $a^2 + b^2$

16. $a(b + cd)$ and $ab + ac - ad$ **17.** x^2y and $x(xy)$

18. $a - b$ and $a + (-b)$ **19.** $\dfrac{a+b}{b}$ and $a + 1$

C ── Find the solution set for these sentences if the replacement set is the set of integers.

20. $3x + 5x = 8x$ **21.** $3x = x + x + x$

22. $x + 0 = x + 1$ **23.** $6x - x = 5x$

24. $x - 2\frac{1}{5} = 5\frac{4}{5}$ **25.** $3x = -15$

2–12   Simplifying Algebraic Expressions

In the preceding section, did you notice that of two equivalent expressions, one may be simpler in appearance than the other? The expressions $3(t^2 - 6n) - 5t^2 + 15n + 2t(t + \frac{5}{2}) + 5n$ and $5t + 2n$ are equivalent, but the second is much simpler than the first. The process of obtaining an equivalent expression that is simpler in appearance than a given expression is called **simplifying an algebraic expression.**

The formulas you use for the perimeters of polygons are expressions that have been simplified.

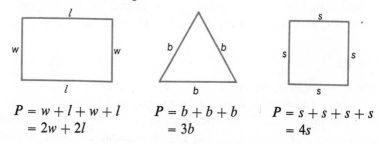

$$P = w + l + w + l \qquad P = b + b + b \qquad P = s + s + s + s$$
$$= 2w + 2l \qquad\qquad = 3b \qquad\qquad = 4s$$

To simplify algebraic expressions, use the postulates for the real numbers, usually the distributive postulate. Study the following.

a. $3a + 5a + 7b = (3 + 5)a + 7b$
$= 8a + 7b$

b. $3x^2y + 5x^2y + 7x = (3 + 5)x^2y + 7x$
$= 8x^2y + 7x$

c. $\frac{1}{2}ab^3 + \frac{1}{3}ab^3 + \frac{2}{5}a^2b = (\frac{1}{2} + \frac{1}{3})ab^3 + \frac{2}{5}a^2b$

$\qquad\qquad\qquad\qquad = \frac{5}{6}ab^3 + \frac{2}{5}a^2b$

d. $\frac{1}{2}mn + \frac{2}{5}m + \frac{1}{3}mn = \frac{1}{2}mn + \frac{1}{3}mn + \frac{2}{5}m$

$\qquad\qquad\qquad\qquad = (\frac{1}{2} + \frac{1}{3})mn + \frac{2}{5}m$

$\qquad\qquad\qquad\qquad = \frac{5}{6}mn + \frac{2}{5}m$

Notice that the distributive postulate is used only for terms that have the same variable or variables as factors. Thus, $3a + 5a + 7b$ can be simplified by using the distributive postulate on $3a + 5a$ because each of these terms has the same factor, a. And notice that the commutative postulate was used in **d** to transfer $\frac{2}{5}m$ and $\frac{1}{3}mn$ so the distributive postulate could be used.

If you know the numerical values of the variables in each of the simplified expressions in **a–d** above, the resulting expressions can be written as one numeral. For example, if a is 3 and b is 5, you can write $8a + 7b$ as $8(3) + 7(5)$, or $24 + 35$, or 59.

Study these examples to become more familiar with simplifying algebraic expressions.

EXAMPLE 1. Simplify $a + 3a$.

By the multiplicative identity postulate, $\forall a \quad 1 \cdot a = a \cdot 1 = a$.

Thus, to simplify $a + 3a$, you use the identity postulate and the distributive postulate.

$$a + 3a = 1a + 3a = (1 + 3)a = 4a$$

EXAMPLE 2. Simplify $8x - 3x$.

To use the distributive postulate, think $8x - 3x$ is $8x + (-3x)$.

$$8x - 3x = 8x + (-3x) = [8 + (-3)]x = 5x$$

EXAMPLE 3. Combine $-a$ and $3a$.

To simplify this expression, you use the fact that $-a = (-1)a$ is true and the distributive postulate.

$$-a + 3a = (-1)a + 3a = (-1 + 3)a = 2a$$

EXAMPLE 4. Combine $6ab$ and $7ba$.

Terms such as $6ab$ and $7ba$ have the same factors and the order of the factors in each term may be interchanged by applying the commutative postulate of multiplication: $ba = ab$.

$6ab + 7ba = 6ab + 7ab$	Commutative postulate.
$\quad = (6 + 7)ab$	Distributive postulate.
$\quad = 13ab$	Closure postulate.

EXAMPLE 5. Simplify $3(a + 2) + 2a - 6$.

$$
\begin{aligned}
3(a + 2) + 2a - 6 &= (3a + 6) + 2a - 6 && \text{Distributive postulate.} \\
&= 3a + (6 + 2a) - 6 && \text{Associative postulate.} \\
&= 3a + (2a + 6) - 6 && \text{Commutative postulate.} \\
&= (3a + 2a) + (6 - 6) && \text{Associative postulate.} \\
&= 5a + 0 && \text{Closure and additive inverse} \\
& && \qquad \text{postulates.} \\
&= 5a && \text{Additive identity postulate.}
\end{aligned}
$$

You know that a simpler expression for $3a + 7b + 6a$ is $9a + 7b$. You can say that $3a + 7b + 6a = 9a + 7b$ is true for all replacements of a and b. When you simplify an algebraic expression, the original expression and the simplified expression will always have the same value when the variables are replaced by numbers.

EXAMPLE 6. Replace a by 8 and b by 4 to show that $3a + 7b + 6a = 9a + 7b$ is true.

$$
\begin{aligned}
3a + 7b + 6a &= 3 \cdot 8 + 7 \cdot 4 + 6 \cdot 8 \\
&= 24 + 28 + 48 \\
&= 100
\end{aligned}
$$

$$
\begin{aligned}
9a + 7b &= 9 \cdot 8 + 7 \cdot 4 \\
&= 72 + 28 \\
&= 100
\end{aligned}
$$

You can see that both expressions name the same number.

Exercises

A ——— Simplify each of the following.

1. $3x + 5x$

2. $7m + 6m$

3. $3a + 7b + 2a$

4. $6ab + 7ab$

5. $7x + 2x + 3y + 5y$

6. $8xy + 3xy + x + 3x$

7. $10mn + 3mn + 6y$

8. $12x + 3y + x + 2y$

9. $4ab + 7ba$

10. $3(a + b) + 4(a + b)$

11. $5xy + 7xy + 8x + x$

12. $2\frac{1}{2}mn - mn + 3\frac{1}{3}nm$

13. $10r - 2r + 3r + 5r - 6s + 6s$

14. $15xy - 2xy - 7y + 4$

15. $10x + (3r - r) + (x - 3x)$

16. $19m + m - 3n + 7n + 2n$

17. $4xy - xy + 3yx + 4yx$

18. $7(x - y) + 6(x - y)$

19. $4\frac{1}{2}(x-y) + 7\frac{1}{3}(x-y) + 2\frac{1}{4}(x-y)$

20. $42xy + 75xy + 7x^2y + 8xy^2$

B **21.** The area of rectangular region I is ab. The area of region II is _?_. The area of region III is _?_. Find the combined area of regions I, II, and III.

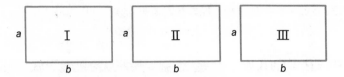

The area of region IV is _?_; of region V is _?_.

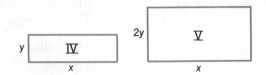

The combined area of all five rectangular regions is _?_.

—— If x is replaced by 9 and y by 6, does the expression in Column I have the same value as the expression in Column II? Answer *Yes* or *No*. Be prepared to give a reason.

COLUMN I	COLUMN II
22. $3x + 4y - 5x + 2y$	$8x + 6y$
23. $3x^2 + 7xy - x^2y$	$2x^2y + 7xy^2$
24. $4x^2y + 5x^2y + y^2$	$9x^2y^3$
25. $3xy + 7yx + 2x^2$	$10x^2y^2 + 2x^2$
26. $12x + 3y + 2x + y$	$14x + 4$
27. $3(x - y) + 7(x - y)$	$10(x - y)$
28. $8(x + y) + 3(x + y)$	$11(x + y)$
29. $2xy + 3y + 7yx + 2y$	$9xy + 6y$
30. $2x + 5x + x + 7y + 4$	$7x + 7y + 4$
31. $4xy + 9yx + 2xy$	$15\frac{1}{2}xy$

32. Are the expressions in Exercises 22–31 equivalent if x and y can be replaced by any numbers?

C —— Write the solution set for each of the following. The replacement set is the set of real numbers.

33. $3a + 10a = 13a$

34. $3x - 4 = 8$

35. $\frac{x}{3} - 1 = 7$

36. $\frac{3x}{2} + 4 = 10$

37. $5x + 2(3x + 7) = 59$

38. $\frac{1}{2}(4x + 1) = 5 + x$

Write each of the following in its simplest form.

39. $3 \cdot 5a - 7 \cdot 3b - 3 \cdot 2a + 2 \cdot 9b$

40. $\frac{5}{8}c - \frac{1}{4}d - \frac{3}{7}c + \frac{3}{5}d$

41. $7x - 3y + 2z - x + 4y + 6z$

42. $2c - 1\frac{1}{2}d + 1\frac{1}{4}c - 2\frac{3}{4}d$

43. $5x - y + 3 \cdot 5z - 1\frac{1}{6}z + 2\frac{1}{2}x + 3\frac{1}{4}y$

CHAPTER REVIEW

1. Know the meaning of and be able to use each of the following words or phrases. The number shown after each word or phrase indicates where it is introduced, in case you need to review.

integers (*52*)
rational numbers (*53*)
irrational numbers (*53*)
real numbers (*53*)
unit square (*53*)
unit circle (*54*)
opposites (*56*)
negative of (*56*)
absolute value (*57*)
vector (*59*)
closure postulates for real
   numbers (*63, 75*)
commutative postulates for
   real numbers (*63, 75*)

associative postulates for real
   numbers (*63, 75*)
identity postulates (*63, 75*)
inverse postulates (*64, 75*)
theorem (*67*)
subtraction of real
   numbers (*72*)
distributive postulate (*75*)
division of real
   numbers (*82*)
deviation from the mean (*85*)
equivalent expressions (*87*)
simplifying an algebraic
   expression (*88*)

2. If R is the set of real numbers, Q is the set of rational numbers, I is the set of integers, P is the set of positive integers, Ne is the set of negative integers, N is the set of natural numbers, and W is the set of whole numbers, replace ● with $\subseteq$ or $\nsubseteq$ to make each of the following sentences true.

a. I ● Q **b.** P ● Q **c.** P ● N

d. R ● Q **e.** P ● I **f.** Ne ● I

g. W ● I **h.** P ● W **i.** W ● R

3. Using the same sets as in Exercise 2, replace ● with $\in$ or $\notin$ to make each of the following sentences true.

a. $\sqrt{2}$ ● Q **b.** $-\frac{2}{3}$ ● R **c.** $-\frac{5}{8}$ ● I

d. 6 ● N **e.** 0 ● N **f.** $\frac{7}{6}$ ● W

g. $\sqrt{36}$ ● I **h.** $\sqrt{10}$ ● R **i.** $|4|$ ● P

4. If x is replaced by -3, what is the value of each of the following?

a. $|x|$ **b.** $|-x|$ **c.** $-x$ **d.** x

5. Draw a number line and a single vector to show the result of each of the following, starting from zero.

   a. A gain of 3 and a loss of 5.
   b. A gain of 2 and a gain of 6.
   c. A loss of 6 and a gain of 9.
   d. A loss of 3 and a loss of 4.

6. Give an equation that illustrates each of the following postulates for addition of real numbers.

   a. Inverse postulate. **b.** Commutative postulate.
   c. Associative postulate. **d.** Identity postulate.

7. Name each sum with a single numeral.

   a. $8 + 6$ **b.** $9 + (-2)$ **c.** $(-12) + (-10)$
   d. $-8.96 + 5.24$ **e.** $(-\frac{2}{3}) + (-\frac{5}{6})$ **f.** $-76 + 76$

8. Add -3 to the sum of each of the following.

   a. $-7 + 5$ **b.** $(-13) + (-2)$ **c.** $8 + 19$

9. What number would replace n to make each sentence true?

   a. $7 + n = 13$ **b.** $7 + n = 3$
   c. $-7 + n = 3$ **d.** $-7 + n = -3$

10. Name each difference with a single numeral.

   a. $18 - 6$ **b.** $-9 - (-9)$ **c.** $-8 - (|-13|)$
   d. $5\frac{3}{4} - (-7\frac{1}{2})$ **e.** $-38 - 47$ **f.** $123 - (-154)$

11. Give an equation to illustrate each of the following postulates for multiplication of real numbers.

   a. Inverse postulate. **b.** Commutative postulate.
   c. Associative postulate. **d.** Identity postulate.

12. Find the products of the following numbers.

   a. -7 and -4 **b.** -8 and 5 **c.** 7 and 6
   d. $-\frac{5}{8}$ and 0 **e.** $-\frac{7}{8}$ and $-\frac{8}{7}$ **f.** $\frac{2}{3}$ and 1

13. Multiply each product by -10.

   a. $(-13)(-6)$ **b.** $(-11)(5)$ **c.** $(18)(3)$

14. What number should replace n to make each sentence true?

a. $-6n = -24$ **b.** $-9n = 45$

c. $4n = -28$ **d.** $6n = 72$

15. Divide as indicated.

a. $\frac{-10}{5}$ **b.** $\frac{-9}{-3}$ **c.** $\frac{18}{-6}$ **d.** $\frac{26}{13}$ **e.** $\frac{-3.9}{-1.3}$

16. Let $x = -3$, $y = -15$, and $z = 5$. What is the value of each of the following?

a. $x + y + z$ **b.** $\frac{x}{y}$ **c.** yz **d.** $x - z$ **e.** $\frac{x+y}{z}$

17. Simplify each of the following.

a. $3x + 7x$ **b.** $5x - 9x$ **c.** $4x - 2y + 3x - 7y$

d. $-8(3x + y)$ **e.** $-3xy + 2 - 7xy$ **f.** $-5(x + y) - 6(2x - y)$

—— What postulates for the real numbers should be given as reasons for each of the following?

18. $(-15) + (19) = (-15) + (15 + 4)$

a. $\qquad = (-15 + 15) + 4 \qquad \underline{\ ?\ }$

b. $\qquad = \qquad 0 \quad + 4 \qquad \underline{\ ?\ }$

c. $\qquad = 4 \qquad\qquad\qquad \underline{\ ?\ }$

19. $n + (-9) = 2$

a. $[n + (-9)] + 9 = 2 + 9 \qquad \underline{\ ?\ }$

b. $n + [(-9) + 9] = 2 + 9 \qquad \underline{\ ?\ }$

c. $n + \qquad 0 \quad = 2 + 9, \qquad \underline{\ ?\ }$

$\qquad$ or $n = 11$

20. You know that $5 \cdot 6 = 30$ is true. If the sum of $5 \cdot 6$ and $5 \cdot (-6)$ is 0, then $5(-6)$ is equal to $\underline{\ ?\ }$. Why?

CHAPTER TEST

—— Name each of the following with a single numeral.

1. $-8 + 5$ **2.** $-9 + 12$

3. $-6\frac{1}{2} + (-3\frac{1}{2})$ **4.** $-7 - (+5)$

5. $-8\frac{1}{2} - (-6\frac{1}{4})$ **6.** $(-5) \cdot (-6)$

7. $(+8) \cdot (3\frac{1}{2})$ **8.** $\frac{-30 - 2}{-7}$

9. $(-1)^2(-2)(-3)$ **10.** $(-5)(-8)(-2)[6 + (-6)]$

Write *True* or *False* to describe each of the following sentences.

11. $8(-3 + 5) = -24 + 40$ **12.** $(15 - 6) - 3 = 15 - (6 - 3)$

13. $+9 + (-9) = 0 \cdot |-6|$ **14.** $-|-2| < \frac{1}{2}$

15. $(-2 \cdot -7) - (-5) = 9$ **16.** $-16(\frac{3}{4}) = \frac{1}{2}(18) + 3$

17. $\frac{2}{5} \cdot 2\frac{1}{2} = 5\frac{1}{3} \cdot \frac{3}{16}$ **18.** $(+3 + -1) - (-|+4|) = 4$

19. $\frac{2 + (-2)}{15} = 0$ **20.** $\frac{|+6|}{-11} < 0$

Where do you stop on the number line if you start at zero and make successive moves as indicated in each of the following?

21. $+6, -4, -7, +5$

22. $-8, +7, -2, -6, +5, -9, 0, +6$

23. $-8, -2, +6, -4$

24. $-7\frac{1}{2}, +6, +3\frac{1}{2}, -\frac{1}{2}, +2$

Simplify each of the following expressions.

25. $7k + 4k + 3k$

26. $7mn + 4nm + 3m^2n$

27. $3km + 2m + m$

28. $10m + 2m - 3m + 6n + 4m - 4n$

29. $\frac{2m}{3km} - \frac{1}{k} + \frac{n^2}{2k}$

30. $3km + 4k^2m - k^2m + 5km + 4m - 2k$

If $k = 1$, $m = -2$, and $n = \frac{1}{2}$, evaluate the following expressions.

31. $8m^2 + 2k - n$

32. $5k - 8m + 3m + n^3$

33. Mr. Kearney bought 5 shares of stock at $25\frac{1}{2}$ each. The stock went up $1\frac{1}{4}$, up $\frac{3}{8}$, down $\frac{1}{2}$, and up $1 before he sold it. What total profit did he make?

34. Suppose you walk to the top of a hill that is 150 feet above sea level. Walking on a winding path down the other side of the hill, you go down 40 feet, up 10 feet, down 15, and up 2. How much farther is it down to sea level?

35. In a series of plays, a football team made two advances of 7 yards, a loss of 5, a gain of 12, and 2 losses of 3. Express the total change in its position as one number.

—— Which postulate or postulates justify the following true sentences? The replacement set is the set of real numbers.

36. $\frac{1}{x}(x + y) = 1 + \frac{y}{x}$

37. $ab + ac = a(c + b)$

38. $\left(s \cdot \frac{1}{s}\right)t = t$

39. $a[(b + c)]\frac{1}{d} = [a(b + c)]\frac{1}{d}$

40. $b(a - a) = b \cdot 0$

41. $-x(1 - y) = -x + xy$

ENRICHMENT

Equivalent Infinite Sets

A finite set can be counted, with the counting coming to an end. The set of names of days of the week is an example of a finite set.

Some infinite sets can also be counted, but the counting does not come to an end. If an infinite set can be put in one-to-one correspondence with the natural numbers, it is countably infinite, or **countable.** The following sets are countable and they are equivalent.

Natural numbers	$\{1, 2, 3, 4, 5, \cdots, n, \cdots\}$
Even whole numbers	$\{0, 2, 4, 6, 8, 10, \cdots, 2n, \cdots\}$
Multiples of 10	$\{0, 10, 20, 30, 40, 50, \cdots, 10n, \cdots\}$

Are all infinite sets countable? No, the real numbers are not countable, and the points on a line are not countable. Can they be put in one-to-one correspondence? Yes. As you know from the beginning of this chapter, the set of real numbers and the points on a line are equivalent; they can be put in one-to-one correspondence.

Now look at some other examples of infinite sets. Do you think there are as many points on a line segment one inch long as there are on a line segment two inches long? It would seem that the number of points is different, but look at the following construction.

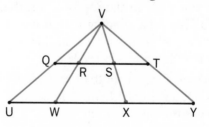

Segment QT is one inch long, and segment UY is two inches long. A one-to-one correspondence can be established between the points of the two line segments. Some of the correspondences are as follows.

$$Q \longleftrightarrow U \qquad S \longleftrightarrow X$$
$$R \longleftrightarrow W \qquad T \longleftrightarrow Y$$

Describe the procedure by which the four correspondences were made. Can all the points on $\overline{QT}$ be matched with all the points on $\overline{UY}$ by the same procedure? Then do $\overline{QT}$ and $\overline{UY}$ contain the same number of points?

Suppose you consider a line segment AB and the same line segment without the endpoints, designated by $(\overline{AB})$. Can you establish a one-to-one correspondence between $\overline{AB}$ and $(\overline{AB})$?

Just in thinking about setting up the correspondence, it would seem that you would make a correspondence between the points of both segments and have A and B left over. But a similar case would be setting up a one-to-one correspondence between the whole numbers and the natural numbers; that is, the whole numbers are the natural numbers plus zero, and the sets are still equivalent; zero is not left over. So how can you show that $\overline{AB}$ and $(\overline{AB})$ are equivalent? One way to do it is to construct a countable subset of each of the uncountable sets and to form a correspondence between those. Follow the procedure below. (*Note:* $\overline{M_1B}$) may be interpreted as a line segment with M_1 as one endpoint, but no endpoint on the other end.)

① Let M_1 be the midpoint of $\overline{AB}$.
Let M_2 be the midpoint of $\overline{M_1B}$.
Let M_3 be the midpoint of $\overline{M_2B}$.
.
.
.

② Let M_1 be the midpoint of $(\overline{AB})$.
Let M_2 be the midpoint of $\overline{M_1B}$.
Let M_3 be the midpoint of $\overline{M_2B}$.
.
.
.

③ Let Q be the set of points on $(\overline{AB})$ other than the set $\{M_1, M_2, M_3, \cdots\}$. Then $(\overline{AB})$ is Q $\cup$ $\{M_1, M_2, M_3, \cdots\}$ and $\overline{AB}$ is Q $\cup$ $\{A, B, M_1, M_2, M_3, \cdots\}$.

(*Continued on next page.*)

④ Therefore, Q can be put in one-to-one correspondence with itself and $\{M_1, M_2, M_3, \cdots\}$ can be put in one-to-one correspondence with $\{A, B, M_1, M_2, M_3, \cdots\}$.

$$Q \cup \{M_1, M_2, M_3, M_4, \cdots\}$$
$$\updownarrow \quad \updownarrow \quad \updownarrow \quad \updownarrow \quad \updownarrow$$
$$Q \cup \{A, \quad B, \quad M_1, M_2, \cdots\}$$

Thus, the two sets are equivalent and $\overline{AB}$ and $(\overline{AB})$ have the same number of points.

Exercises

1. Are there as many points on a line segment one unit long as there are on the entire number line extending from 0 to the right indefinitely? You need to show a one-to-one correspondence between the segment and the number line. Can you explain this correspondence by studying the figure below?

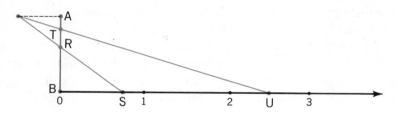

2. Think back to the problem about the one-to-one correspondence between the segment with endpoints (closed segment) and the segment without endpoints (open segment). Does it matter in Exercise 1 that the endpoint of the segment of 1 unit does not have a corresponding point on the number line by that construction?

3. What relationship exists between the points of any two lines or line segments?

4. For the figure shown at the right, let P be the set of points on rectangle $ABCD$. Let Q be the set of points on triangle ABC. Then classify each of the following as true or false. Explain.

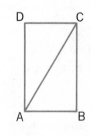

a. $P \subset Q$

b. $P = Q$

c. P is equivalent to Q.

d. $Q \subset P$

5. Perhaps you can see how these ideas can be extended beyond straight lines. Can you think of a way to show that there are as many points on the large square shown as on the smaller one? You may want to use three-dimensional space. Think of the squares as pieces of cardboard that you are holding parallel to one another.

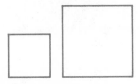

THE GROWTH OF MATHEMATICS

Mathematics Between the Tigris and the Euphrates

The Sumerians, the first people and culture to develop writing, flourished around 3500 B.C. in a region now known as Iraq, situated between the Tigris and the Euphrates rivers. In addition to writing, they developed a versatile system of numeration with 60 as its base.

Although various other peoples occupied this region through the years, there was a good deal of continuity in the growth of mathematics. Over the years, the peoples of the land added new refinements to their numeration system and progressed in the development of algebra. It was the Babylonians, the great astronomers, who attained the highest level of civilization in this one region.

Mathematics was still practical, with little consideration given to theory. Since much of the computation was done by the tedious process of trial and error, the Babylonians kept records of their results and became great compilers of tables. Of the thousands of Babylonian clay tablets available today, nearly two hundred are mathematical tables of all kinds: multiplication tables, tables of squares and square roots, cubes and cube roots, reciprocals, exponents, and so on.

Another one hundred tablets are problem texts. On them are explicit procedures for solving problems, followed by many more problems arranged in order of difficulty, indicating that they were probably used for teaching. The problems were of many different types, illustrating that they could solve many algebraic equations, including such equations as $x^2 + x = 6$, which you will learn to solve later in the book. But with all their advancement of algebra, they still did not state solutions in general terms.

The Babylonians were not very skilled in geometry. They used 3 as the value for π. Their formulas for the area of a quadrilateral and for the volume of the frustum of a cone and a pyramid were incorrect. Their main contributions were in the number system and algebra.

CHAPTER 3

SENTENCES AND PROBLEM SOLVING

Many problems can be solved with the aid of mathematics, although not all of these problems are mathematical ones. A mathematical sentence, that is, an equation or an inequality, is often used as a mathematical model for solving problems. The solution of the mathematical sentence is the solution to the problem when the sentence is a faithful model of the problem.

● In the upper left photograph a child is taking a test. The blocks must be placed in the holes in the board. The hole is similar to a mathematical sentence. When the correct one from the set of blocks is chosen, the block fits and the problem is solved. In solving a sentence, when the correct number from the replacement set is chosen, the sentence is true and the problem is solved.

● The lever in the lower right photograph can be described by the formula $lw = LW$. It does not describe the physical properties of the lever, but for solving problems about levers, it is a satisfactory model.

● When equations are complicated, it is helpful to find simpler, equivalent sentences. Experimenting with a balance scale can suggest the principles for obtaining sentences that are equivalent to a given sentence. If the scale is already in balance, for example, what happens when you add equal weights to the two sides?

● The upper right photograph shows the tracks made by subatomic particles in the field of a powerful magnet. Physicists identify the type of particle from two conditions: the length of the path and how the magnet affects the path. Each condition is needed for identification. Many problems involve more than one condition.

3–1 Equivalent Sentences

Recall that $3a + 2a$ and $5a$ are equivalent expressions if they represent the same number for all numbers that may replace a. **Equivalent sentences** has a slightly different meaning from *equivalent expressions*. Can you guess what *equivalent sentences* means?

In the table below, the sentence in column B is equivalent to the corresponding sentence in column A. Check each sentence in B to see if it has the same solution set as the sentence in that row in column A. Recall that the *solution set* is the set of numbers from the replacement set that make the sentence true. In this case the replacement set is the set of integers.

	A	Solution set	B	Solution set
a.	$3x = -9$	$\{-3\}$	$15x = -45$	?
b.	$15 + 2x = 5x$	$\{5\}$	$15 = 3x$	?
c.	$5\frac{1}{2} = n - 9$	$\emptyset$	$11 = 2n - 18$	?
d.	$x + 2 > 5$	$\{4, 5, 6, 7, \cdots\}$	$2x + 4 > 10$	?
e.	$8 - y = 3$	$\{5\}$	$-y = 3 - 8$	?
f.	$2x + 3x = 10$	$\{2\}$	$5x = 10$	?

Now you should be able to understand the definition of equivalent sentences.

Definition   Two sentences are <u>equivalent</u> if and only if they have the same solution set.

One way to find an equivalent sentence is by replacing an expression by an equivalent expression. Suppose, however, you have the equation $x + 7 = 15$. Then, this method will not help. You know, however, that $8 + 7 = 15$, so the solution set of $x + 7 = 15$ is $\{8\}$ when the replacement set is the set of integers. Therefore, $x + 7 = 15$ and $x = 8$ are equivalent sentences.

Using the simple example above, you can discover a procedure for finding the solution set of certain equations.

$$x + 7 = 15$$

Add -7 to $x + 7$ and -7 to 15. $x + 7 + (-7) = 15 + (-7)$
Find equivalent expressions. $x + 0 = 8$
$$x = 8$$

By adding -7 to $x + 7$ and -7 to 15, you get the equation $x = 8$, whose solution set, obviously, is $\{8\}$. Do you think that you will always get an equivalent equation if you add the same number to both sides of any equation? Well, you will! This property is so important and so useful that it is stated as a postulate.

Postulate 3–1 (Addition Postulate for Equations) If the same number is added to both sides of an equation, the result is an equivalent equation.

If $a = b$ is true, then $a + c = b + c$ is true.

Now try these

—— For each exercise, answer these questions: What is added to the left side of equation **a** to get the left side of equation **b**? What is added to the right side of **a** to get the right side of **b**? Is equation **b** equivalent to equation **a**?

Be able to give an explanation for each answer.

1. a. $x - 4 = 15$
   b. $x - 4 + 4 = 15 + 4$
2. a. $x - 8 = 6$
   b. $x - 8 + 3 = 6 + 2$
3. a. $4x + 12 = 6$
   b. $4x + 12 + (-12) = 6$
4. a. $\frac{3}{4}x - 17 = 24$
   b. $\frac{3}{4}x = 17 + 24$
5. a. $18 + 3x = 6 + 7x$
   b. $18 + 3x + (-3x) = 6 + 7x + (-3x)$

—— What must be added to the expression in **a** to get the expression in **b**?

6. a. $x + 7$ **7. a.** $3x - 9$
   b. x **b.** $3x$
8. a. $8 - 7x$ **9. a.** $3t + 0.2$
   b. $-7x$ **b.** $3t$

Answers: **1.** 4, 4, yes.   **2.** 3, 2, no.   **3.** -12, 0, no.   **4.** 17, 17, yes.   **5.** $-3x$, $-3x$, yes.   **6.** -7 **7.** 9   **8.** -8 **9.** -0.2

1. What are equivalent expressions? Give an example.
2. What are equivalent equations? Give an example.
3. State the addition postulate for equations in your own words.

Exercises

A ── Is sentence **a** equivalent to sentence **b**?

1. a. $x + 4 = 9$
   b. $x + 4 - (-4) = 9 + (-4)$

2. a. $y - 9 = 3$
   b. $y - 9 + 9 = 3$

3. a. $2n + 9 = 11$
   b. $2n = 11 + (-9)$

4. a. $t = 6$
   b. $t + 6 = 12$

5. a. $3x - 8 = 2x + 5$
   b. $3x - 8 + 7 = 2x + 5 + (-5)$

6. a. $9 = 11 - 4m$
   b. $20 = -4m$

7. a. $17 - 6x = 22$
   b. $17 = 22 + 6x$

8. a. $17 - 6x = 22$
   b. $-6x = 39$

9. a. $2(3x + 8) - 2x = 23$
   b. $4x + 16 = 23$

10. a. $5n - 3(7 - 2n) = n + 2$
   b. $12n = 23$

── For the following exercises, use the addition postulate for equations to write an equivalent equation with only the variable on one side. Use braces to show the solution set after you have checked the solution in the original equation. The replacement set is the set of real numbers.

Example. Solve $x + 9 = 12\frac{1}{2}$ where the replacement set for x is the set of real numbers.

Add -9 to both sides. $x + 9 + (-9) = 12\frac{1}{2} + (-9)$
Find equivalent expressions. $x = 3\frac{1}{2}$

To check, replace x in the original equation with $3\frac{1}{2}$.

$$\text{Check}\quad 3\frac{1}{2} + 9 = 12\frac{1}{2}$$
$$12\frac{1}{2} = 12\frac{1}{2}$$

Solution set: $\{3\frac{1}{2}\}$

11. $x + 7 = 13$

12. $8 + n = 5$

13. $m + 3\frac{1}{2} = 7$

14. $t + 11.2 = 3.7$

15. $14 = y - 6$

16. $t - 4 = 9$

17. $8\frac{1}{2} = x + 13\frac{1}{8}$

18. $x - 6\frac{1}{4} = 12\frac{1}{2}$

19. $3 - y = 17$

20. $5.4 - n = -0.6$

B —— Solve each equation below. The replacement set is the set of integers.

Example. $3x - 9 = 2x + 12$

Add $-2x$. $3x + (-2x) - 9 = 2x + (-2x) + 12$
$$x - 9 = 12$$

Add 9. $x - 9 + 9 = 12 + 9$
$$x = 21$$

Check $3(21) - 9 = 2(21) + 12$
$$63 - 9 = 42 + 12$$
$$54 = 54$$

Solution set: $\{21\}$

21. $3x + 5 = 2x - 6$ **22.** $4 - 7n = 1 - 6n$

23. $\frac{1}{2}y - \frac{3}{4} = \frac{1}{4} - \frac{1}{2}y$ **24.** $4m + 9 = 9 + 5m$

25. $3n + 4 = 2n + 8$ **26.** $5m + 12 = 7 + 6m$

27. $8m - 9 = 7m + 5$ **28.** $m = 2m - 9$

29. $4m - 15 = 5m - 9$ **30.** $5x - 5\frac{1}{2} = 4x + 5\frac{1}{2}$

C **31.** Prove that if $a + c = b + c$ is true, then $a = b$ is true. How is this different from the addition postulate for equations?

3–2 The Multiplication Postulate for Equations

You may use a similar pattern of thinking for multiplication and addition when you want to find an equivalent sentence to help in finding a solution to an equation. Start with an equation such as $\frac{3}{4}x = 15$ and multiply both sides by $\frac{4}{3}$. You get the new equation $\frac{4}{3}(\frac{3}{4}x) = \frac{4}{3}(15)$, or $x = 20$. If 20 replaces x, will both equations be true? Is the solution set of $\frac{3}{4}x = 15$ and of $x = 20$ the same? Are the equations equivalent?

The idea illustrated by this example can be stated as a postulate.

Postulate 3–2 (Multiplication Postulate for Equations)
If both sides of an equation are multiplied by any nonzero number, the result is an equivalent equation.

If $a = b$ is true and $c \neq 0$, then $ac = bc$ is true.

The multiplication postulate for equations can be used to solve an equation such as $-8w = 80$. Since the product of any number and its multiplicative inverse is 1, it is necessary to multiply $-8w$ by $-\frac{1}{8}$ to give a product of $1 \cdot w$. If you multiply $-8w$ by $-\frac{1}{8}$, by what number must you multiply 80? The sentence obtained when both sides of the equation $-8w = 80$ are multiplied by $-\frac{1}{8}$ is $w = -10$. Show that $w = -10$ is equivalent to $-8w = 80$.

EXAMPLE. Solve $-4a = 20$. The replacement set is the set of integers.

$$\text{Multiply both sides by } -\tfrac{1}{4}. \qquad -\tfrac{1}{4}(-4a) = -\tfrac{1}{4}(20)$$
$$a = -5$$
$$Check \qquad -4(-5) = 20$$
$$Solution \ set: \ \{-5\}$$

Now try these

—— In each exercise, answer these questions: By what is the left side of equation **a** multiplied to get the left side of **b**? By what is the right side of **a** multiplied to get the right side of **b**? Is equation **b** equivalent to equation **a**?

1. a. $\frac{1}{3}x = 9$
b. $3(\frac{1}{3}x) = 3(9)$

2. a. $\frac{5}{2}y = 10$
b. $\frac{2}{5}(\frac{5}{2}y) = \frac{2}{5}(10)$

3. a. $\frac{x}{2} = \frac{5}{2}$
b. $x = 3(\frac{5}{2})$

4. a. $0.05x = 3$
b. $20(0.05x) = 20(3)$

—— By what must you multiply expression **a** to get expression **b**?

5. a. $3x$
b. $1(x)$

6. a. $-2x$
b. $1(x)$

7. a. $0.02n$
b. n

8. a. $\frac{2}{3}n$
b. $1(n)$

Answers: **1.** 3, 3, yes. **2.** $\frac{2}{5}$, $\frac{2}{5}$, yes. **3.** 2, 3, no. **4.** 20, 20, yes. **5.** $\frac{1}{3}$
6. $-\frac{1}{2}$ **7.** 50 **8.** $\frac{3}{2}$

Exercises

A —— Use the multiplication postulate for equations to find the solution set of each. The replacement set is the set of real numbers. Check.

1. $2x = 8$

2. $\frac{1}{4}x = 7$

3. $\frac{2}{3}n = 12$

4. $\frac{1}{2}y = -4$

5. $3x = 19$

6. $\frac{2}{3}m = -8$

7. $-2x = 12$

8. $-\frac{3}{4}y = 27$

9. $-5y = -8$

10. $10 = -\frac{3}{4}n$

11. $\frac{2}{3} = 5t$

12. $-9 = \frac{5}{4}v$

_____ Use the addition or the multiplication postulate to find the solution set of each. The replacement set is the set of real numbers. Check.

13. $n + 3\frac{1}{2} = 9\frac{3}{4}$ **14.** $n - \frac{1}{2} = 4$ **15.** $3\frac{1}{4} = x + 2\frac{1}{2}$

16. $-9a = 4$ **17.** $\frac{x}{1.4} = 4.5$ **18.** $-6x = 0.48$

19. $n + 7\frac{1}{2} = 9\frac{2}{3}$ **20.** $\frac{x}{2} = 2\frac{1}{2}$ **21.** $\frac{n}{2.4} = 0.06$

22. $-13\frac{1}{2}a = 27$ **23.** $2.3 = 4.9 + t$ **24.** $4 = \frac{8}{3}v$

_____ Recall that the formula $\vec{d} = \vec{v}t$ gives the distance $\vec{d}$ traveled in a given direction (positive or negative) if the velocity $\vec{v}$ and the time t are known. Write an equation for each exercise and solve.

25. $\vec{v} = +10$ miles per hour; $t = 5$ hours; find $\vec{d}$.

26. $\vec{v} = -10$ miles per hour; $t = 7$ hours; find $\vec{d}$.

27. $\vec{d} = 120$ meters; $\vec{v} = 30$ meters per second; find t.

28. $\vec{d} = 352$ feet; $t = 4$ seconds; find $\vec{v}$.

29. $\vec{d} = -\frac{2}{3}$ kilometer; $t = 240$ seconds; find $\vec{v}$.

30. $\vec{d} = -2.5$ kilometers; $\vec{v} = -40$ kilometers per hour; find t.

31. $\vec{d} = -0.06$ meter; $\vec{v} = -1.2$ meters per second; find t.

32. $\vec{d} = -55.4$ centimeters; $t = 5.2$ seconds; find $\vec{v}$.

B _____ Write *True* or *False* to describe each of the following sentences.

33. $\forall x \ \ x + 2 = 3$ **34.** $\forall x \ \ x = x + 1$

35. $\forall x \ \ 3x + 2x = 5x$ **36.** $\forall x \ \ \frac{x}{2} = \frac{1}{2}x$

_____ Find the solution set of each equation if the replacement set is the set of whole numbers. Remember that the solution set is empty if no whole number gives a true sentence.

37. $\frac{1}{4}x = 20$ **38.** $\frac{1}{3}t = 2$ **39.** $\frac{1}{2}x = -4$

40. $\frac{2}{3}x = 1$ **41.** $\frac{3}{4}n = 16$ **42.** $2.5y = 6.25$

3–3   Using Two Postulates to Solve Equations

Sometimes it is necessary to find several equivalent equations before you find one that has the variable alone on one side. For example, to solve an equation such as $3x + 8 = 23$, you must use both postulates for equations. The postulates for equations and the other postulates about real numbers that you have studied in earlier chapters enable you to give reasons for each step in finding a chain of equivalent equations. Look at the way the equation $3x + 8 = 23$ can be solved.

$$3x + 8 = 23$$

Add -8 to both sides, using the addition postulate for equations.

$$3x + 8 + (-8) = 23 + (-8)$$

Use additive inverse postulate and addition of real numbers.

$$3x = 15$$

Multiply both sides by $\frac{1}{3}$, using multiplication postulate for equations.

$$\tfrac{1}{3}(3x) = \tfrac{1}{3}(15)$$

Use multiplicative inverse postulate and multiplication of real numbers.

$$x = 5$$

When 5 replaces x in $3x + 8 = 23$, the true equation $3(5) + 8 = 23$ results. Hence, the solution set is $\{5\}$.

The number that makes the equation true is the **solution** of the equation, or the **root** of the equation. You may also say that 5 *satisfies* the equation.

Look again at the chain of five equivalent equations above. The goal is the last equation, the one whose solution set is obvious.

A different order of steps for solving equations is quite permissible as shown below.

$$3x + 8 = 23$$

Multiply both sides by $\frac{1}{3}$.
$$\tfrac{1}{3}(3x + 8) = \tfrac{1}{3}(23)$$

Apply distributive postulate.
$$x + \tfrac{8}{3} = \tfrac{23}{3}$$

Add $-\frac{8}{3}$ to both sides.
$$x + \tfrac{8}{3} + (-\tfrac{8}{3}) = \tfrac{23}{3} + (-\tfrac{8}{3})$$

Find equivalent expressions.
$$x = \tfrac{15}{3}, \text{ or } 5$$

Check $\quad 3(5) + 8 = 23$

Solution set: $\{5\}$

Which method of finding a chain of equivalent equations do you prefer?

EXAMPLE. Solve $\frac{3}{5}n - 7 = 14$.

		Check
	$\frac{3}{5}n - 7 = 14$	$\frac{3}{5}(35) - 7 = 14$
Add $+7$.	$\frac{3}{5}n = 21$	$21 - 7 = 14$
Multiply by $+\frac{5}{3}$.	$n = 35$	$14 = 14$

Solution set: $\{35\}$

Now try these

— Solve for x.

1. $2x + 4 = 8$

2. $3x - 1 = 8$

3. $5 - x = 9$

4. $\frac{x}{4} - 2 = -1$

Answers: **1.** $\{2\}$ **2.** $\{3\}$ **3.** $\{-4\}$ **4.** $\{4\}$

Checkpoint

1. Does the order in which the addition and multiplication postulates for equations are applied affect the solution of an equation?

2. What steps other than applying the addition and multiplication postulates for equations may occur in solving an equation such as $5x + 9 = 29$?

Exercises

A — Find the solution sets of the following equations. The replacement set is the set of rational numbers. When you use an equation postulate in finding the solution set, indicate which one. Check your results.

1. $5n + 3 = 33$

2. $5n - 3 = 17$

3. $2n + 3 = 7$

4. $5x - 9 = -19$

5. $3t + 17 = 5$

6. $4a + 17 = 53$

7. $2n + 5 = 17$

8. $3n - 4 = 17$

9. $3n - 17 = 4$

10. $3n + 17 = 4$

11. $2a + 15 = 3$

12. $6a + 1 = 37$

13. $8a - 7 = 41$

14. $2b + 3 = 21$

15. $4v + 27 = 3$

16. $3a + 5 = 32$

17. $9a - 1 = 80$

18. $5 - 2y = 15$

19. $7 = 6x + 19$

20. $8 = 5t + 33$

21. $4 = 30 - 6m$

22. $3b - 5 = 32$

23. $6x + 37 = 17$

24. $\frac{2}{3}t + 5 = 23$

25. $9a - 8 = 73$

26. $\frac{y}{2} + 11 = 5$

27. $15 - \frac{5}{4}v = 23$

28. $8n + 22 = 70$

29. $1.2t + 3.4 = -1.0$

30. $-0.6n + 11 = 17$

31. $2.1 = 4.3 - 1.1w$

32. $0.8n + 7.0 = 2.2$

33. $0 = 0.6n - 3.6$

34. $\frac{7}{10}n + 6 = 41$

35. $\frac{5}{6}n + 34 = 9$

36. $\frac{6}{8}n + 12 = 84$

37. $\frac{9}{10}x - 17 = 19$

38. $\frac{16}{15}x + 78 = 14$

39. $\frac{3}{4}x - 3 = 18$

40. $\frac{7}{8}t - 8 = 34$

41. $\frac{2}{3}t - 13 = 57$

42. $\frac{5}{12}t - 12 = 48$

43. $28 = \frac{17}{32}n - 23$

44. $6 = 26 + \frac{2}{5}n$

45. $15 = \frac{3}{10}n - 15$

46. $18 - \frac{9}{32}x = 27$

47. $53 + \frac{3}{5}x = 26$

48. $49 + \frac{3}{5}x = 16$

Solve and check the following equations. The replacement
set is the set of real numbers.

49. $32,845 + 49x = 41,284$ **50.** $-271 + 33t = -485$

51. $\frac{2}{3} = \frac{3}{4}y - \frac{5}{6}$ **52.** $-\frac{4}{5} = \frac{7}{12} - \frac{w}{3}$

53. $0.6x + 0.06 = 0.006$ **54.** $0.12 - 0.35x = 0.049$

55. $2\pi + 7x = 5\pi$ **56.** $9 + 4x = 5\pi$

3–4   Sets and Existence

You have learned several ways to describe a set. Explain why
the following are all descriptions for the same set.

a. The set of even whole numbers less than twenty.

b. {the even whole numbers less than twenty}

c. $\{0, 2, 4, 6, 8, 10, 12, 14, 16, 18\}$

d. $\{0, 2, 4, \cdots, 16, 18\}$

There is another method of describing a set that is frequently
convenient. A variable may be used together with a rule. For example, the set described above in **a–d** could also be given as follows.

e. The set of all whole numbers that replace n so that n is even and
less than 20.

The description in **e** has a simple abbreviation, as shown in **f**.

f. $\{n : n$ **is an even whole number less than 20**$\}$

The colon is read as "such that," so **f** may be read "The set of all
numbers n such that n is an even whole number less than 20."

The set description in **f** is an example of **set-builder notation.**
Usually equations and other mathematical sentences are used with
set-builder notation, rather than word descriptions. For example,
an even number is a whole-number multiple of 2, so either of the
following descriptions would also name the set described in **a–f**.

g. $\{n : n < 20, n = 2a, a \in W\}$

h. $\{2n : n < 10, n \in W\}$

Frequently it is desirable to write statements containing variables
that are not open sentences. One way that you have previously used
involves ∀, "for all." Thus, the sentences ∀x $x + x = 2x$ and
∀x $x + 3 = 5$ are not open. Notice that ∀x $x + x = 2x$ is a true

sentence and $\forall x \ \ x + 3 = 5$ is false. There is another method that is also useful. The symbol $\exists$ means "there exists." Thus, the sentence $\exists x \ \ x + 3 = 5$, read "There exists an x such that $x + 3 = 5$ is true," is a true sentence. Is $\exists a \ \ a = a + 1$ true or false?

A sentence such as $\exists x \ \ x + x = 2x$ is a true sentence. Why? Do you think that whenever $\exists$ replaces $\forall$ in a true sentence the result is a true sentence?

Notice that for both $\forall$ and $\exists$ it is often necessary to supply some indication of the replacement set for the variable. For example, $\exists x \in R \ \ 2x + 4 = 5$ is a true sentence, but $\exists x \in W \ \ 2x + 4 = 5$ is false. When no replacement set for the variable is indicated, you should assume that the replacement set is the set of real numbers.

The symbols $\forall$ and $\exists$ may both occur in the same sentence. For example, $\forall x \in R \ \ \exists y \in R \ \ x + y = 0$ is the statement of one of the postulates for the real numbers. Which one is it? Notice that order is important. The sentence $\exists y \in R \ \ \forall x \in R \ \ x + y = 0$ is false because it means "There exists a real number y such that for every real number x, the sum of x and y is zero."

Checkpoint

1. Describe the way you would use set-builder notation to denote the set of odd whole numbers between 0 and 20.

2. Describe two ways in which a sentence that is not open may contain a variable.

Exercises

A —— Use the roster method to denote each set below. Check.

1. $\{x : x - 2\frac{1}{2} = 6\}$ **2.** $\{b : -2\frac{1}{3}b = 7\}$

3. $\{x : x + 5 = 5\}$ **4.** $\{y : y - 8\frac{4}{5} = 6\frac{2}{3}\}$

5. $\{y : y - 8 = -10\}$ **6.** $\{x : 0.7x = 0.014\}$

7. $\{t : \frac{t}{0.6} = 8\}$ **8.** $\{n : n - 3\frac{1}{4} = 2\frac{1}{3}\}$

9. $\{x : 3x - 5 = -11\}$ **10.** $\{x : 12 = 4 - \frac{x}{3}\}$

—— Write *True* or *False* to describe each sentence.

11. $\forall x \in R \ \ x + 3 = 7$ **12.** $\exists x \in R \ \ x + 3 = 7$

13. $\forall x \in R \ \ x = x - 1$ **14.** $\exists x \in R \ \ x = x - 1$

15. $\forall x \in R$ $5x - 2x = 3x$ **16.** $\exists x \in R$ $5x - 2x = 3x$

17. $\exists x \in R$ $x + 5 = 0$ **18.** $\exists x \in R$ $3x = 0$

19. $\exists x \in N$ $x + 5 = 0$ **20.** $\exists x \in N$ $3x = 0$

B **21.** Set-builder notation is a precise way to describe sets, but often the description is harder to read than necessary. For example, the following is a correct description of the set $\{5\}$.

$$\{x : \tfrac{3}{5}x + 9 = 12, x \in R\}$$

What is the easiest name for this set?

$$\{a : a = a + 1, a \in Q\}$$

—— Use set-builder notation to denote the following sets.

22. $\{3, 6, 9, 12, 15, 18\}$ **23.** $\{\cdots, -4, -3, -2, -1, 0\}$

24. $\{7\}$ **25.** $\emptyset$

C —— Write *True* or *False* to describe each sentence.

26. $\forall x \in R$ $\exists y \in R$ $xy = 1$ **27.** $\exists x \in R$ $\forall y \in R$ $xy = 1$

28. $\forall x \in R$ $\exists y \in R$ $x + y = x$ **29.** $\exists x \in R$ $\forall y \in R$ $x + y = x$

3–5 Solving Equations

By now you should be able to solve fairly complicated equations. All you need to do is simplify each side of the equation and use the postulates for equations.

Your goal is to get the terms containing the variable on one side of the equation. You may choose to do it on the left or on the right.

EXAMPLE 1. Solve $x + (3x - 9) + x + (3x - 9) = 62$.

$$x + (3x - 9) + x + (3x - 9) = 62$$

Simplify the left side. $8x - 18 = 62$

Add 18 to both sides. $8x = 80$

Multiply both sides by $\tfrac{1}{8}$. $x = 10$

     Check $10 + (30 - 9) + 10 + (30 - 9) = 62$

                $10 + 21 + 10 + 21 = 62$

                         $62 = 62$

Solution set: $\{10\}$

EXAMPLE 2. Solve $4x - 5x + 7 = 17 + 9x$.

$$4x - 5x + 7 = 17 + 9x$$
$$-x + 7 = 17 + 9x \quad \text{Why?}$$
$$7 = 17 + 10x \quad \text{Why?}$$

Add -17.
$$-10 = 10x$$

Multiply by $\frac{1}{10}$.
$$-1 = x$$

$$\textit{Check} \quad 4(-1) - 5(-1) + 7 = 17 + 9(-1)$$
$$-4 + 5 + 7 = 17 - 9$$
$$8 = 8$$

Solution set: $\{-1\}$

EXAMPLE 3. Solve $4x - 3(x - 2) = 41$.

You will find it easier to use the distributive postulate first. Then simplify the left side.

$$4x - 3(x - 2) = 41$$
$$4x - 3x + 6 = 41 \quad \text{Why?}$$
$$x + 6 = 41 \quad \text{Why?}$$
$$x = 35$$

Check to see that $\{35\}$ is the solution set.

Now try these

—— First use the distributive postulate on the left side of the equation. Then solve.

1. $3a + 5a = 8$ **2.** $6a - 2a + 3 = 15$ **3.** $7b + 3b - 2b = 16$
4. $2(x + 3) = 0$ **5.** $5(a + 7) = 25$ **6.** $2x + 0.25x + 0.5x = 0$
7. $8(2 - 6x) = 2$ **8.** $8(m - 9) = 35$ **9.** $-2(-3 - 4x) = -10$

Answers: **1.** $\{1\}$ **2.** $\{3\}$ **3.** $\{2\}$ **4.** $\{-3\}$ **5.** $\{-2\}$ **6.** $\{0\}$ **7.** $\{\frac{7}{24}\}$ **8.** $\{13\frac{3}{8}\}$
9. $\{-2\}$

Exercises

A —— Find the solution set of each of the following equations. The replacement is the set of real numbers.

1. $7x - 3x = -9$ **2.** $2n - 5n = 12$
3. $-3n - 4n = -21$ **4.** $2(x - 3) = -10$
5. $2(x - 5) = -8$ **6.** $2(x - 5) = 3$
7. $3(2x + 1) = 1$ **8.** $4(5x + 7) = 13$
9. $2(3n - 5) = -15$ **10.** $-7b + 4(2b - 3) = 16$

11. $-3x + 6(x - 4) = 9$ **12.** $15a = 26a + 33$

13. $-5a - 19 = 13a + 17$ **14.** $63a + 13 = 15a - 11$

15. $9a = 44a - 70$ **16.** $12a = 19a - 15 - 20$

—— List the members in these sets. The replacement set is R.

17. $\{x : 8x - 13x = 2x + 56\}$ **18.** $\{n : -6n + 13 = -5n + 12\}$

19. $\{n : 5n - 20 = -32 - 7n\}$ **20.** $\{n : -16 - 3n = 5n + 16\}$

21. $\{t : 11 - 2t - 16 = 8t\}$ **22.** $\{n : 14n = 14n - 5n + 6\}$

23. $\{n : 26n - 9n = 46 + 26n\}$ **24.** $\{c : 5c - 13 = 6c - 18\}$

25. $\{c : 4c + 12 = 7c + 3\}$ **26.** $\{x : 5 - 3x = 5x + 21\}$

27. $\{a : 3a - 5 = 4a + 23\}$ **28.** $\{a : 11a - 5 = 4a - 13\}$

29. $\{r : -5r + 2 = -9r - 16\}$ **30.** $\{s : -6s = -7 + 2s - 13\}$

31. $\{r : 8r - 7 - 3r = -5r + 3\}$

32. $\{u : 5u - 3u + 9 = 2(6u - 5u) - 1\}$

B —— Solve the following equations where the replacement set is the set of real numbers.

33. $7x - (x - 4) = 25$ **34.** $-5y - (2 - y) = 18$

35. $2(x - 3) + 3(x - 2) = 8$ **36.** $2(2n + 1) - 3(n - 5) = 0$

37. $\frac{1}{2}n + \frac{3}{4}n - n = 2.5$ **38.** $1.5x - 0.2x + 1.2x = 0.25$

39. $1.3 + 0.4n - 0.03n = 3.52$ **40.** $c + 5 + 0.05c = 11.3$

3–6 Conditional Equations and Identities

In the last chapter you learned to write equivalent algebraic expressions. You learned, for example, that $3x - 7x + 9x - 4$ is equivalent to $5x - 4$. The two expressions name the same number for all replacements for x, which may be indicated by the following true sentence.

$$\forall x \in R \quad 3x - 7x + 9x - 4 = 5x - 4$$

Such an equation is an **identity**. For any real number that replaces x, the value of the left side is identical to the value of the right side.

> **Definition** An <u>identity</u> is an open equation that is true for every replacement of the variable for which the equation has meaning.

The sentence $\frac{3}{x} = \frac{1}{x}(3)$ has no meaning when x is replaced by 0, but it is true for every other replacement. Thus, $\frac{3}{x} = \frac{1}{x}(3)$ is an identity.

Look at the example below to see what happens when you use the addition and multiplication postulates on an identity.

EXAMPLE. Solve the equation $3x - 7x + 9x - 4 = 5x - 4$.

$$3x - 7x + 9x - 4 = 5x - 4$$

Use equivalent expressions. $\qquad 5x - 4 = 5x - 4$

Add $-5x + 4$ to each side. $\quad 5x - 4 + (-5x + 4) = 5x - 4 + (-5x + 4)$

Use equivalent expressions. $\qquad\qquad 0 \cdot x = 0 \cdot x$

Is the last equation equivalent to the first? What replacements for x make $0 \cdot x = 0 \cdot x$ true? Then, do all real numbers satisfy $3x - 7x + 9x - 4 = 5x - 4$?

When you solve an equation and find an equivalent equation that is true for all values of x, the original equation is an identity. In the example, you could go one step further to obtain $0 = 0$, which is obviously a true statement. If you obtain a true statement such as $0 = 0$ or $-4 = -4$ in solving an equation, the equation is an identity. You can think of $-4 = -4$ as $0 \cdot x - 4 = -4$ also.

Why is the solution set of most identities the set of real numbers? When is the solution set of an identity not the set of real numbers?

The main work of this chapter so far has been with sentences such as $2x - 3 = 11$, which are true only for certain real numbers. The equation $2x - 3 = 11$ is true under the condition that x is replaced by 7. Thus, $2x - 3 = 11$ is a **conditional equation.**

> **Definition**   A conditional equation is an open equation that is not an identity.

Why must the solution set of a conditional equation whose replacement set is the set of real numbers be a proper subset of the set of real numbers?

Checkpoint

1. What is an identity?

2. What is a conditional equation? What is the characteristic of the solution set for a conditional equation?

Exercises

A —— Which are identities and which are conditional equations?

1. $2x + 3 = 3x + 8$ **2.** $10x - 4 = 7x - 7$

3. $3(x - 1) = x - 3 + 2x$ **4.** $5x = 3x$

5. $x + 2 = 2 + x$ **6.** $3x - 5 = x - (9 + 2x)$

7. $4x + 2 + 3x = 2x + 3 + 5x$ **8.** $8y + 6 = 4(3y + 1\frac{1}{2})$

9. $3t + (7 - 4t) = (3t + 7) - 4t$ **10.** $\frac{5 + 3}{x} = \frac{1}{x}(6 + 2)$

B —— Write *True* or *False* for each sentence.

11. $\forall x \in R \quad x + 2 = x$ **12.** $\forall x \in R \quad 7x - 2x = 5x$

13. $\forall x \in R \quad 2x > x$ **14.** $\forall x \in R \quad 4x - 15 + 2x = 8x - 10$

15. $\exists x \in R \quad 2x < x$ **16.** $\exists x \in R \quad x + 7 > x$

17. $\exists x \in R \quad x + 7 < x$ **18.** $\forall x \in R \quad |x| + |x| > x$

—— Write *All* if the sentence is true for every real number, *Some but not all* if it is true for some real numbers but not for all of them, and *None* if it is true for no real number.

19. $4(x - 5) = -20 + 4x$ **20.** $8(y + 2) - 2(y - 4) = 6$

21. $x + x < x$ **22.** $-x < x$

23. $|x| < x$ **24.** $|x + 2| < |x| + 2$

—— The following exercise shows what happens when you use the postulates with an equation whose solution set is empty.

25. Supply reasons for each step in rewriting the equation.

$$3(x + 1) = 3(x - 3\tfrac{2}{3})$$
$$3x + 3 = 3x - 11$$
$$0 \cdot x = -14, \text{ or } 0 = -14$$

26. Is each equation in Exercise 25 equivalent to the first? Will any number make $0 \cdot x = -14$ true?

C **27.** Think of a number and double it. Add 4 to the result. Divide by 2 and then subtract 2. You have the number you started with.

Number you started with.	x
Double it.	$2x$
Add 4.	$2x + 4$
Divide by 2.	$\dfrac{2x + 4}{2}$
Subtract 2.	$\dfrac{2x + 4}{2} - 2$

Show that $\frac{2x + 4}{2} - 2 = x$ is an identity.

28. Think of a number. Multiply it by 4 and then add 8. Divide the result by 2 and then subtract twice the original number. Your result is 4. Explain why.

29. What is the graph of an identity?

3–7 Solving and Graphing Inequalities

Is {4} the solution set of the equation $2x + 3 = 11$ if the replacement set for x is the set of integers? Then what do you think is the solution set of the inequality $2x + 3 > 11$? of the inequality $2x + 3 < 11$?

The following table shows the number that results from $2x + 3$ when x is replaced by integers. Cover the values for $2x + 3$ in the table, and find them yourself. Then check your results.

When x is	-1	0	1	2	3	4	5	6	7	8
Then $2x + 3$ is	1	3	5	7	9	11	13	15	17	19

Note the following.

① The number 4 makes $2x + 3$ equal to 11.

② Numbers less than 4 make $2x + 3$ less than 11.

③ Numbers greater than 4 make $2x + 3$ greater than 11.

The solution sets and graphs of $2x + 3 < 11$, $2x + 3 = 11$, and $2x + 3 > 11$ are shown below for x, when x is an integer.

Sentence	Solution set	Graph
$2x + 3 < 11$	$\{\cdots, -1, 0, 1, 2, 3\}$	-6 -5 -4 -3 -2 -1 0 1 2 3 4 5 6
$2x + 3 = 11$	$\{4\}$	-6 -5 -4 -3 -2 -1 0 1 2 3 4 5 6
$2x + 3 > 11$	$\{5, 6, 7, 8, \cdots\}$	-6 -5 -4 -3 -2 -1 0 1 2 3 4 5 6

The graph of each inequality is the set of points extending without bound on one side of the point for 4. Which sentence has a graph that extends to the left? Which sentence has a graph that extends to the right?

The **comparison postulate** insures that the kind of reasoning indicated may be used with many different kinds of inequalities.

> **Postulate 3–3** (Comparison Postulate) For any two real numbers a and b, one and only one of the following is true.
>
> $$a < b \qquad a = b \qquad a > b$$

EXAMPLE 1. Solve and graph each sentence if x is an integer.

  a. $-2x < -2$ **b.** $-2x = -2$ **c.** $-2x > -2$

By the comparison postulate, any number you choose for x will make one and only one of the sentences true.

First, find the solution set for $-2x = -2$.

$$-2x = -2$$
$$x = 1$$

Solution set: $\{1\}$

Then see if numbers less than 1 satisfy $-2x < -2$ or $-2x > -2$. Cover the values for $-2x$ in the table and find them first yourself. Then check your results against the table. (The numbers less than 1 and the product numbers that are less than -2 are shown in color.)

When x is	-3	-2	-1	0	1	2	3	4	5
Then $-2x$ is	6	4	2	0	-2	-4	-6	-8	-10

① Numbers *greater than* 1 make $-2x < -2$ true.   The solution set for $-2x < -2$ is $\{2, 3, 4, 5, \cdots\}$.

② Numbers *less than* 1 make $-2x > -2$ true.   The solution set of $-2x > -2$ is $\{\cdots, -3, -2, -1, 0\}$.

Sentence	Solution set	Graph
$-2x < -2$	$\{2, 3, 4, 5, \cdots\}$	← • • • • • • • • • ● ● ● ● ● → $-6\,-5\,-4\,-3\,-2\,-1\ 0\ 1\ 2\ 3\ 4\ 5\ 6$
$-2x = -2$	$\{1\}$	← • • • • • • • ● • • • • • → $-6\,-5\,-4\,-3\,-2\,-1\ 0\ 1\ 2\ 3\ 4\ 5\ 6$
$-2x > -2$	$\{\cdots, -3, -2, -1, 0\}$	← ● ● ● ● ● ● ● • • • • • • → $-6\,-5\,-4\,-3\,-2\,-1\ 0\ 1\ 2\ 3\ 4\ 5\ 6$

If the replacement set were the set of real numbers, how would the graphs of the solution sets differ from the graphs above?

EXAMPLE 2. Solve $3 - 2x > 9$ and graph the solution set. The replacement set for x is the set of real numbers.

① Solve the equation $3 - 2x = 9$.

$$\begin{aligned} 3 - 2x &= 9 \\ -2x &= 6 \qquad \text{Why?} \\ x &= -3 \qquad \text{Why?} \end{aligned}$$

Check $\quad 3 - 2(-3) = 9$
$3 + 6 = 9$
$9 = 9$

Solution set: $\{-3\}$

② Place your pencil point on the number line at -3. All numbers on one side of -3 make $3 - 2x > 9$ true.

Try -2. Does -2 make $3 - 2x > 9$ true? Does -1 make it true? Does 0? 1? 2?

Try -4. Does -4 make $3 - 2x > 9$ true? Does -5? Does -6? $-3\frac{1}{2}$? -3.01? -3.00001? Any number whose coordinate is to the left of -3 makes $3 - 2x > 9$ true.

③ The solution set of $3 - 2x > 9$ is $\{x : x < -3\}$.

④ The graph of $3 - 2x < 9$ is a **half-line,** the portion of a line on one side of a particular point, not including the point.

$$\xleftarrow{\quad\bullet\ \bullet\ \bullet\ \circ\ \bullet\ \bullet\ \bullet\ \bullet\ \bullet\ \bullet\ \bullet\ \bullet\ \bullet\quad}\rightarrow$$
$$\text{-6 -5 -4 -3 -2 -1 0 1 2 3 4 5 6}$$
$$\{x : x < -3\}$$

Checkpoint

1. Explain what an inequality is.

2. Explain a method for solving an inequality.

3. Describe the graph of an inequality when the replacement set is the set of integers; when the replacement set is the set of real numbers.

Exercises

A **1.** What is the solution set of $3x + 7 = 16$ if the replacement set is the set of real numbers? Which graph at the right is the graph of the solution set of $3x + 7 < 16$? of $3x + 7 > 16$?

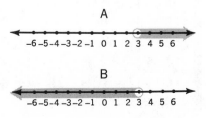

A

$$\xleftarrow{\quad\bullet\ \bullet\ \bullet\ \bullet\ \bullet\ \bullet\ \bullet\ \bullet\ \circ\ \bullet\ \bullet\ \bullet\quad}\rightarrow$$
$$\text{-6 -5 -4 -3 -2 -1 0 1 2 3 4 5 6}$$

B

$$\xleftarrow{\quad\bullet\ \bullet\ \bullet\ \bullet\ \bullet\ \bullet\ \bullet\ \bullet\ \circ\ \bullet\ \bullet\ \bullet\quad}\rightarrow$$
$$\text{-6 -5 -4 -3 -2 -1 0 1 2 3 4 5 6}$$

Find the solution set of each equation. Then write the letter for the correct graph of each inequality after the inequality. The set of real numbers is the replacement set in each case.

2. $7x = 14$

$7x > 14$

$7x < 14$

A

-6 -5 -4 -3 -2 -1 0 1 2 3 4 5 6

B

-6 -5 -4 -3 -2 -1 0 1 2 3 4 5 6

3. $-4x = 8$

$-4x > 8$

$-4x < 8$

A

-6 -5 -4 -3 -2 -1 0 1 2 3 4 5 6

B

-6 -5 -4 -3 -2 -1 0 1 2 3 4 5 6

4. $8 - 5x = -7$

$8 - 5x > -7$

$8 - 5x < -7$

A

-6 -5 -4 -3 -2 -1 0 1 2 3 4 5 6

B

-6 -5 -4 -3 -2 -1 0 1 2 3 4 5 6

5. $17 - 4x = 7 - 9x$

$17 - 4x > 7 - 9x$

$17 - 4x < 7 - 9x$

A

-6 -5 -4 -3 -2 -1 0 1 2 3 4 5 6

B

-6 -5 -4 -3 -2 -1 0 1 2 3 4 5 6

Solve and graph each inequality if the replacement set is the set of integers.

6. $x + 7 > 16$

7. $2x < 8$

8. $-4x > 12$

9. $2x + 2\frac{1}{2} > 10\frac{1}{2}$

10. $-6x < 0$

11. $16 < 3x + 4$

12. $7y < 20 - 3y$

13. $2t + 3 > 4t - 7$

14. $5 + 2x < 17$

15. $3x + 9 > -2$

16. $-3x - 4x > -21$

17. $5 - 6x < 17$

18. $4(5x + 7) < 13$

19. $-3x + 6(x - 4) > 9$

20. $2(x + 2) - 3(x - 1) < 0$ **21.** $4x + 12 > 7x + 3$

22. a. Solve $2x - 7 > 15$ by the method used in Section 3–7.

b. Now look at another way to solve the inequality.

$$2x - 7 > 15$$

Add $+7$. $2x - 7 + 7 > 15 + 7$

$$2x > 22$$

Multiply by $\frac{1}{2}$. $\frac{1}{2} \cdot 2x > \frac{1}{2} \cdot 22$

$$x > 11$$

Is $\{x : x > 11\}$ the result you obtained in **a**?

c. In **b**, two postulates for inequalities are illustrated.

> **Postulate 3–4**   Adding any nonzero number to both sides of an inequality produces an equivalent inequality.
>
> **Postulate 3–5**   Multiplying both sides of an inequality by the same positive number produces an equivalent inequality.

Use the postulates to solve $3x + 9 < 19 + x$.

d. Find the solution set for $-x > 3$, using the same method as in Exercises 1–21.   Does multiplying both sides by -1 give an equivalent inequality?   Explain your answer.

e. In **d**, you should have seen that multiplying both sides by a negative number, -1, did not produce an equivalent inequality. But reversing the inequality sign *and* multiplying by -1 would produce an equivalent inequality.

$$-x > 3$$

Multiply by -1 and re- $(-1)(-x) < (-1)(3)$
verse the inequality sign.

$$x < -3$$

Solution set: $\{x : x < -3\}$

This illustrates another postulate for inequalities.

> **Postulate 3–6**   Multiplying both sides of an inequality by a negative number produces an equivalent inequality if and only if the inequality sign is reversed.

Solve, using the inequality postulates.

23. $5x > 45$ **24.** $-5x > 45$ **25.** $x + 9 < 16$

26. $x - 15 > -22$ **27.** $-9x < 36$ **28.** $-9x < -36$

29. $2x + 5 > 10$ **30.** $2x - 5 > 10$ **31.** $-2x + 5 > 10$

32. $-2x - 5 > 10$ **33.** $-2x + 5 < 10$ **34.** $-2x - 5 < 10$

B **35.** $12x + 3 < 3x - 9$ **36.** $-4x + 2 < x + 9$

37. $3(x + 2) < -x + 4$ **38.** $-3(x - 2) < 19$

39. $-7(-3x + 4) < 0$ **40.** $3(x + 2) > -2(x + 1)$

41. I am thinking of a certain set of numbers. If you multiply any one of them by 3, the result is greater than 12. Of what set of numbers am I thinking? (*Hint:* Let x represent any of the numbers in the set. Write an inequality.)

42. If 7 is added to 4 times any number in a certain set, the result is always less than 19. What is the set of numbers?

3–8   Intersection and Union of Sets

The following examples illustrate the meaning of the intersection of two sets.

EXAMPLE 1. The drawing represents two roads. How do you describe the part of the road that is a part of M–13 *and also* a part of M–18? The part of the road in common is the **intersection** of the two roads.

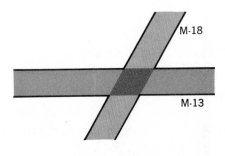

EXAMPLE 2. Set A consists of the even numbers less than 12 and set P consists of the prime numbers less than 12. What number is in A *and also* in P? The set {2} is the intersection of the two sets.

The diagram at the right is a *Venn diagram*. The points inside

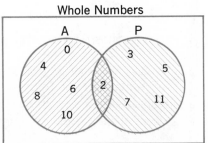

the rectangular region represent the whole numbers (nonnegative integers). One circular region represents set A; the other represents P. The crosshatched region represents the intersection of A and P.

EXAMPLE 3. The drawing represents two geometric figures. Set A is a circle and set B is a parabola. Which are the points that are in A *and also* in B? The set of points that are in A and B is the intersection of the sets A *and* B. The intersection is {*P, Q*}.

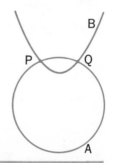

Definition   The <u>intersection</u> of sets A and B is a set that contains elements that are both in A *and* in B. The symbol A ∩ B means the intersection of A and B and is read "A intersect B."

The two lines at the right are parallel and have no points in common. Their intersection is the null set, ø or { }. Sets that have no elements in common are **disjoint sets.**

Look again at the drawing in Example 1. Think of both roads together — the road that is M–18 *or* M–13. Now you are thinking of the **union** of the two roads.

In Example 2, think of the set containing all the numbers in either of sets A *or* P. You are thinking of the set {0, 2, 3, 4, 5, 6, 7, 8, 10, 11}. Call this set C. Set C is the *union* of set A and set P. What part of the Venn diagram represents the union of sets A and P?

The set that contains all the points shown in Example 3 is the set that is the *union* of sets A and B. The union includes all the points that are on the circle and all the points that are on the parabola.

Definition   The <u>union</u> of two sets A and B is a set C that contains all elements in either of the sets A *or* B. Elements that are common to both A and B need to be listed only once in set C. The symbol A ∪ B means the union of A and B and is read "A union B."

It may help you to remember the symbol $\cup$ by thinking of it as the first letter of the word *union*.

The operations of union and intersection can be applied to sets defined by sentences.

EXAMPLE 4. If the replacement set for x is $\{0, 2, 4, 6, 8, 10, 12, 14\}$ and $A = \{x : x > 6\}$ and $B = \{x : x < 12\}$, what is $A \cap B$? $A \cup B$?

$$A \cap B = \{x : x > 6\} \cap \{x : x < 12\}$$
$$= \{8, 10, 12, 14\} \cap \{0, 2, 4, 6, 8, 10\}$$
$$= \{8, 10\}$$
$$A \cup B = \{8, 10, 12, 14\} \cup \{0, 2, 4, 6, 8, 10\}$$
$$= \{0, 2, 4, 6, 8, 10, 12, 14\}$$

The number line can be used to show the graphs of $A \cap B$ and $A \cup B$. A is the graph of set A and B is the graph of set B. The points that occur in the same position on A *and also* on B are the graph of $A \cap B$. If you put the graphs over one another, the graph of the intersection is the set of overlapping points. How many points are in the graph of $A \cap B$?

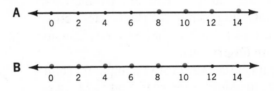

The points on A *or* on B are the graph of $A \cup B$. How many points are in the graph of $A \cup B$?

Suppose the replacement set is the set of real numbers. Use the number line to describe the graphs of the following sets.

EXAMPLE 5. If $A = \{x : x > 3\}$ and $B = \{x : x < 6\}$, graph $A \cap B$ and $A \cup B$.

The graph of set A is all the points to the right of the point for 3. The graph is a half-line.

The graph of set B is all the points to the left of the point for 6.

$A \cap B$ is the set of points that are common to both. The graph is an **open interval** (a line segment with the endpoints missing).

$A \cup B$ is the set of points that are graphs of A *or* B. It is the entire line.

Now try these

—— If A = {2, 3, 5, 7}, B = {1, 5, 7, 8}, and C = {3, 6, 9, 12}, what sets are named below?

1. A ∩ B   **2.** A ∪ B   **3.** A ∩ C
4. B ∩ C   **5.** A ∪ C   **6.** B ∪ C

Answers: **1.** {5, 7}   **2.** {1, 2, 3, 5, 7, 8}   **3.** {3}   **4.** ∅   **5.** {2, 3, 5, 6, 7, 9, 12}
      6. {1, 3, 5, 6, 7, 8, 9, 12}

Checkpoint

1. What is the meaning of *intersection of two sets*?

2. What is the meaning of *union of two sets*?

3. Is the word *and* used to define intersection or union? For which is the word *or* used?

4. How do you graph the union of two sets? the intersection of two sets?

Exercises

A   **1.** If E = {2, 4, 6, 8, ···} and P = {x : x is a prime number}, find E ∩ P and E ∪ P.

—— Use the diagram below to complete each sentence so that it is true. (Recall that $\overline{AC}$ is read "line segment *AC*.")

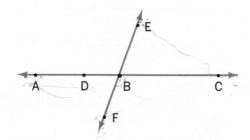

2. $\overline{AC}$ ∩ $\overline{FE}$ = _?_   **3.** $\overline{AC}$ ∪ $\overline{FE}$ = _?_
4. $\overline{BE}$ ∪ $\overline{BF}$ = _?_   **5.** $\overline{AB}$ ∪ $\overline{BC}$ = _?_
6. $\overline{EC}$ ∩ F = _?_   **7.** $\overline{AB}$ ∩ $\overline{BC}$ = _?_
8. $\overline{BC}$ ∩ $\overline{AD}$ = _?_   **9.** $\overline{AC}$ ∩ $\overline{AD}$ = _?_

For each of the sentences in column I, select its appropriate graph in column II. The replacement set is the set of real numbers.

I	II
10. $\{x : 3x = 15\}$ $\cup \{x : x > 5\}$	**a.** $-4\ -3\ -2\ -1\ 0\ 1\ 2\ 3\ 4\ 5\ 6\ 7$
11. $\{x : x < 6\} \cup \{x = 6\}$	**b.** $-6\ -5\ -4\ -3\ -2\ -1\ 0\ 1\ 2\ 3\ 4\ 5$
12. $\{t : t > 4\}$ $\cap \{t : t < -8\}$	**c.** $-6\ -5\ -4\ -3\ -2\ -1\ 0\ 1\ 2\ 3\ 4\ 5$
13. $\{t : -3 < t\}$ $\cap \{t : t < 6\}$	**d.** $-1\ 0\ 1\ 2\ 3\ 4\ 5\ 6\ 7\ 8\ 9\ 10$
14. $\{y : y \geq 2\} \cap \{y = 2\}$	**e.** $-2\ -1\ 0\ 1\ 2\ 3\ 4\ 5\ 6\ 7\ 8\ 9$
15. $\{b : -3 < b\}$ $\cap \{b : b \leq -1\}$	**f.** $-3\ -2\ -1\ 0\ 1\ 2\ 3\ 4\ 5\ 6\ 7\ 8$

Use $\cup$ and $\cap$ to write names for the sets that are graphed below, as in Exercises 10–15.

	Graph	Replacement set
16.	$-6\ -5\ -4\ -3\ -2\ -1\ 0\ 1\ 2\ 3\ 4\ 5\ 6$	Real numbers.
17.	$-6\ -5\ -4\ -3\ -2\ -1\ 0\ 1\ 2\ 3\ 4\ 5\ 6$	Real numbers.
18.	$-6\ -5\ -4\ -3\ -2\ -1\ 0\ 1\ 2\ 3\ 4\ 5\ 6$	Real numbers.
19.	$-6\ -5\ -4\ -3\ -2\ -1\ 0\ 1\ 2\ 3\ 4\ 5\ 6$	Integers.
20.	$-6\ -5\ -4\ -3\ -2\ -1\ 0\ 1\ 2\ 3\ 4\ 5\ 6$	Real numbers.

Graph the following sets. Show the graph in red or use heavier black marks. In each case the replacement set is the set of real numbers. Name each graph.

21. $\{x : x > 2\} \cap \{x : x < 5\}$

22. $\{x : x = 4\} \cup \{x : x < 3\}$

23. $\{x : x > -2\} \cup \{x : x = 2\}$

24. $\{x : x < -1\} \cup \{x : x = -1\}$

25. $\{x : x + 5 = 6\} \cap \{x : x + 3 = -8\}$

26. $\{x : 3x + 1 > 4\} \cup \{x : 2x + 3 < 15\}$

B —— Subsets of points in the plane are named as follows. (Recall that $\overleftrightarrow{AB}$ is read "line AB"; $\overrightarrow{OB}$ is read "ray OB" and means point O and all the points of the line on the same side as B.)

I = The set of points above $\overleftrightarrow{AB}$ and to the right of $\overleftrightarrow{CD}$.

II = The set of points above $\overleftrightarrow{AB}$ and to the left of $\overleftrightarrow{CD}$.

III = The set of points below $\overleftrightarrow{AB}$ and to the left of $\overleftrightarrow{CD}$.

IV = The set of points below $\overleftrightarrow{AB}$ and to the right of $\overleftrightarrow{CD}$.

P = The set of points above $\overleftrightarrow{AB}$.

N = The set of points to the right of $\overleftrightarrow{CD}$.

Write *T* or *F* for each sentence.

27. $\overrightarrow{OB} \subseteq I$

28. $I \cap II = \emptyset$

29. $O = (\overleftrightarrow{AB} \cap \overleftrightarrow{CD})$

30. $O \in \overline{AB}$

31. $D \in \overline{AB}$

32. $P \cap N = I$

33. $(I \cup \overrightarrow{OB}) \cup IV = N$

—— Write *True* or *False* for each sentence, using the geometric figure at the right. Think of all the points on lines AD and EB as U, the replacement set.

34. $C = \overline{AC} \cap \overline{CD}$

35. $\overline{EB} = \overline{EC} \cup \overline{CB}$

36. $G \in U$

37. $G \in (\overline{BC} \cup \overline{CD})$

38. $\overline{CD} \subseteq (\overline{AC} \cap \overline{AD})$

39. $\overline{EC} \cup \overline{CD} = \triangle ECD$

40. $(\overline{AC} \cup \overline{CB}) \cup \overline{AB} = \triangle ABC$

41. $\overline{AB} \cap \overline{ED} = \emptyset$

42. $F \notin \triangle ABC$

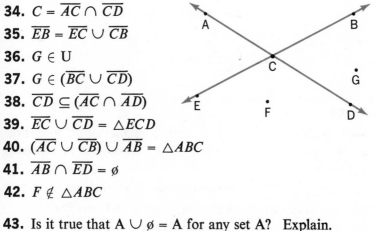

43. Is it true that $A \cup \emptyset = A$ for any set A? Explain.

44. Is it true that $A \cap \emptyset = \emptyset$ for any set A? Explain.

3–9 Translating Words into Algebraic Expressions

To solve verbal problems, you need to make certain that you can translate word expressions into algebraic symbols. An unknown number in a verbal problem may be represented by a variable. The algebraic expression involving the variable, numbers, and operations stated in a verbal expression is a mathematical model of the verbal expression. For example, a mathematical model of "Twice an unknown number subtracted from 7" would be $7 - 2n$. Notice that you must read the verbal expression carefully to make sure that the operations are performed in the correct order. Numbers in the algebraic expression will not always occur in the order that they occur in the verbal expression.

Now try these

—— Which of the algebraic expressions conveys the same information as the given verbal expression?

1. The sum of an unknown number and 3.

   a. $n + 3$ **b.** $n - 3$ **c.** $3n$ **d.** $\frac{n}{3}$

2. Eight less than six times some unknown number.

   a. $8 - 6n$ **b.** $6n - 8$ **c.** $(6 - 8)n$ **d.** $(8 - 6)n$

3. Five times the difference when a number is decreased by six.

   a. $5n - 6$ **b.** $6 - 5n$ **c.** $(5 - 6)n$ **d.** $5(n - 6)$

4. The quotient when some number is divided by 8.

   a. $\frac{n}{8}$ **b.** $\frac{8}{n}$ **c.** $8n$ **d.** $8 \div n$

Answers: **1.** a   **2.** b   **3.** d   **4.** a

Exercises

A —— Use algebraic symbols to write a mathematical model of each word expression in Exercises 1–10. Choose n to represent the unknown number.

   1. The sum of five times an unknown number and seven.

   2. The sum of twice a certain number and twenty-seven.

   3. Twice the sum of a certain number and twenty-seven.

   4. The quotient formed when some number is divided by five.

5. Five less than the quotient produced when some number is divided by nine.

6. Some number is divided by thirteen and the quotient increased by eleven.

7. The sum of seventeen and the quotient formed when a certain number is divided by eight.

8. Some number decreased by nine.

9. Twice the sum of some number and six.

10. Five times the difference formed by twelve minus some number.

11. One number is five more than seven times a second number. If you let *n* represent the second number, how may you represent the first number using *n*?

12. One number is three times a second number. To avoid fractions, let *n* represent the second number. Write the first number using *n*. Write the sum of the two numbers. Write the difference formed by subtracting the second number from the first.

13. The length of the rectangle shown here is 4 times its width, *w*. How will you represent its length using *w*? Write an expression for its perimeter in terms of *w*.

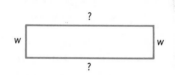

14. The first of two numbers is 57 more than the second. If *n* is the second number, what is the first in terms of *n*?

15. Each of the two equal sides in the triangle shown at the right is twice the third side, *b*. Write an expression for the perimeter in terms of *b*.

16. Express the sum of 3 times a certain number *n* and 8 times the same number.

17. The reading on Ted's bike odometer shows a mileage 6 times as much as that on Mike's odometer. Which of the two readings would you represent by *n*? Write an expression for the sum of the two odometer readings.

18. Sue is 8 years older than her sister Alice. Write an expression for their total ages.

19. If the difference between two whole numbers is 12 and the smaller number is *n*, what is the larger in terms of *n*?

20. If the difference between two whole numbers is 12 and the larger number is *n*, what is the smaller in terms of *n*?

21. If one addend in a sum of 36 is n, what is the other addend in terms of n?

22. If the length of a rectangle is 3 inches more than the width and the width is w, what is the perimeter?

23. How far will an airplane travel if it goes n mph for 5 hours? $2n$ mph for 6 hours?

24. To travel 500 miles at an average speed of 50 mph will take how many hours? at r mph?

25. If a is an integer, what is the next consecutive integer? (*Hint:* 24 and 25 are consecutive integers, but 32 and 34 are not.)

26. If x is an odd integer, what is the next consecutive odd integer? (*Hint:* The pairs (1, 3), (3, 5), (5, 7), (7, 9), $\cdots$, are pairs of consecutive odd integers.)

27. If y is an even integer, what is the next even integer after y?

—— Write an equation for each of the following statements.

28. The sum of n and $n + 57$ is 191.

29. The sum of $3n$ and $8n$ is 216.

30. The sum of $6n$ and n is 189.

31. The sum of n and $n + 8$ is 24.

32. Decreasing three times a number by 6 gives 9.

33. Eight less than 6 times some number is 10.

34. The sum of 15 and the quotient of a certain number divided by 4 is 17.

35. The difference between $4n$ and n is 29.

3–10　Conditions in Problems

Suppose that you know only one thing about the rectangle pictured at the right.

1. The length is three units more than twice the width.

From this one condition, there are an infinite number of possible dimensions for the rectangle. Which pairs of measures in the set shown below are possible dimensions for this one condition?

$$\{1 \text{ by } 5, \ 4 \text{ by } 11, \ 7 \text{ by } 17, \ \tfrac{1}{2} \text{ by } 4, \ 20 \text{ by } 40\}$$

Suppose you found out a second condition about the rectangle.

2. *The perimeter is 30 units.*

If condition 2 is satisfied, which of the pairs of numbers in the following set could be the dimensions?

$$\{1 \text{ by } 5, 7 \text{ by } 8, 3 \text{ by } 9, 4 \text{ by } 11, 9 \text{ by } 21\}$$

Are there any pairs of numbers that satisfy both conditions? What is the intersection of the two sets shown above? Do the dimensions 4 by 11 satisfy both conditions of the problem? Will any other dimensions satisfy both conditions?

Consider another example. Suppose your friend is thinking about a pair of numbers and he tells you one thing about the numbers.

1. **One number is five times the other.**

Which of the pairs of numbers in the following set could he be thinking of?

$$\{(1, 5), (2, 10), (-5, -25), (-5, 25), (10, 25)\}$$

Give some other pairs of numbers that he could be thinking of.

Which of the possible second conditions below would pick out a single pair from those that are possible when using condition 1 only?

a. The sum of the numbers is even.

b. One number is $\frac{1}{5}$ of the other.

c. One number is prime.

d. The sum of the numbers is -30.

Do you see that conditions **a–c** do not contain enough information to tell you the unique pair? Condition **d** picks out the pair when combined with condition 1. What numbers is your friend thinking of?

Exercises

A —— In each exercise below, a question is asked. Then one condition is stated as I. Which conditions in II are sufficient when combined with the information in I to answer the question?

1. What are the dimensions of the rectangle?

I. The length is 3 times the width.

II. a. The length and width are integers.

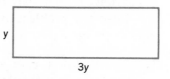

b. The length is 12.

c. The width is $\frac{1}{3}$ the length.

d. The perimeter is greater than 30.

e. The length and width are prime numbers.

2. Of what two numbers am I thinking?

I. Two numbers are consecutive integers.

II. **a.** Both are even.   **b.** Both are odd.

    c. Both are prime.   **d.** Both are composite.

        e. Their sum is 20.

3. How many dollars does Neal have?

I. He has twice as many as Jody.

II. **a.** Together they have 30 dollars.

  b. Jody has an even number of dollars.

  c. Neal has a prime number of dollars.

  d. Twice Jody's plus Neal's makes 40 dollars.

  e. Jody has 10 dollars.

B   **4.** Of what two numbers am I thinking?

I. Two numbers are consecutive integers.

II. **a.** Their product is odd.

  b. Their sum is odd.

  c. Both are prime.

  d. Both are composite.

  e. The square of one is equal to the other.

3–11   Solving Problems

The problems in the following examples each contain two conditions. As you know, one condition is often not enough to answer the question asked in the problem. One way to solve a problem is to use one condition to write an algebraic expression for each quantity. Then you can use the second condition to write an equation.

EXAMPLE 1. Kevin is thinking of two numbers. **The larger is five more than twice the smaller** (condition 1). *Their sum is forty-seven* (condition 2). What are the numbers?

Read the problem and ask, "What are the unknowns (the two numbers) that satisfy the conditions?"

① Use condition 1 to write   Let x equal the smaller number;
the algebraic expressions. $2x + 5$ equals the larger number.

② Use condition 2 to write $x + (2x + 5) = 47$
the equation.

③ Solve for the variable and find the unknowns of the problem.

$$x + 2x + 5 = 47$$
$$3x = 42$$
$$x = 14 \text{ (smaller number)}$$
$$2x + 5 = 2(14) + 5$$
$$= 33 \text{ (larger number)}$$

④ Now check to see that the numbers satisfy the two conditions of the problem.

Is 5 more than twice 14 equal to 33? Is the sum of 14 and 33 equal to 47?

Now you try to work the same problem but use condition 2 in step ① and condition 1 in step ②. Do you get the same answer? You should.

EXAMPLE 2. The length of a rectangle is 6 inches more than its width (condition 1). *The perimeter is 56 inches* (condition 2). What are the dimensions?

① Unknowns are length and width. Let w equal the width; then the length equals $w + 6$.

② $w + (w + 6) + w + (w + 6) = 56$
③ $\qquad\qquad 4w + 12 = 56$
$$4w = 44$$
$$w = 11$$
Solution set: $\{11\}$

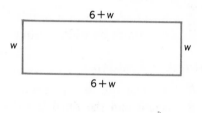

If w is 11, then $w + 6$ is 17.

④ The width is 11 inches and the length is 17 inches. Is the length 6 inches more than the width? Is the perimeter 56 inches?

Exercises

A —— One condition in each problem is given in color. It will be easier to use this condition to write algebraic expressions for the unknowns (step ①). In some problems the second condition is in italics. It may be used to write an equation (step ②). Solve the following problems.

1. The length of a rectangle is 20 feet more than its width and *the perimeter is 240 feet.* What are the dimensions of the rectangle?

2. Gene Buckolls paid *$3612 for two cars.* One cost $1246 more than the other. Find the cost of each.

3. Ellen has three times as many records as Sue. *Together they have 32 records.* How many has each?

4. The *sum* of the angles of a triangle *is 180°*. Angle A is twice as large as angle C, and angle B is 20° more than angle C. How many degrees are there in each angle?

5. Judy weighs 12 pounds more than twice the weight of her brother. What is the weight of each if *their combined weight totals 180 pounds?*

6. The height of the flagpole is 12 feet more than the height of Jackson High School. *Twice the sum of the height of the school and the height of the flagpole is 140 feet.* Find the height of each.

7. Bill earns $4.50 per week on his paper route. This is $1.00 less than twice Earl's earnings per week. How much does Earl earn per week?

8. On a recent trip, Mr. Ridley traveled 300 miles more by plane than by train. The distance traveled by plane was three times the distance traveled by train. How many miles did he travel in all?

9. The length of a tennis court for singles is 3 feet shorter than three times its width. Find the length if the perimeter is 210 feet.

Number Problems

A **1.** The sum of three numbers is 72. The first is three times the second and the third is twice the result of subtracting 6 from the second. What are the numbers?

2. A man spent $58 for a watch, a chain, and a wallet. He paid $2 more for the chain than for the wallet and twice as much for the watch as for the chain. How much did he pay for each?

3. a is 2 more than b. The sum of 25 times a and 50 times b is 500. Find a and b.

4. The first of two numbers is three times the second. If 15 is added to each, the first result is twice the second result. What are the two numbers?

5. Find the two consecutive integers whose sum is 147.

6. There are three consecutive integers with a sum of 279. What are the integers?

7. There are three consecutive integers such that if the sum of the first two is decreased by the third, the result will be 68. What are the integers?

8. Find the three consecutive integers such that if three times the smallest is decreased by the sum of the other two, the difference between them will be 46.

9. Are there **two consecutive integers** such that twice the smaller plus the larger is 12? (*Hint:* If you do not get an integer when you solve the equation you write, you will know the answer is *No.*)

10. Are there **three consecutive integers** whose sum is 94? If so, find them.

11. What are the **two consecutive integers** whose sum is −25?

12. What are the **two consecutive integers** such that four times the smaller is three times the larger?

B **13.** Are there **two consecutive odd integers** whose sum is 212? If so, find them.

14. If twice the smaller of **two consecutive odd integers** is decreased by the larger, the difference is 53. What are the integers?

15. There are **three consecutive even integers** such that twice the smallest plus three times the largest will give the middle integer increased by 82. What are the 3 integers?

Age Problems

Example. **Larry's father is three times as old as Larry** (condition 1). *In 14 years, his father will be only twice as old as Larry will be at that time* (condition 2). What is the age of each now?

① The unknowns are the age of Larry now and the age of his father now.

> Let Larry's age now be n;
> then his father's age now is $3n$.

② To write the equation, you must state that his father's age 14 years from now equals twice Larry's age 14 years from now.

> Larry's age 14 years from now equals $n + 14$,
> and his father's age 14 years from now is $3n + 14$.

Hence, $3n + 14 = 2(n + 14)$ is a mathematical model of the problem.

③

$$3n + 14 = 2(n + 14)$$

Use the distributive postulate. $3n + 14 = 2n + 28$

Add $-2n$ to each side. $n + 14 = 28$

Add -14 to each side. $n = 14$

Solution set: $\{14\}$

If n is 14, then $3n$ is 42, so Larry is now 14 and his father is now 42.

④ Do these results check with the conditions of the problem?

B **1.** Tom's present age is twice Sue's age; 10 years ago Tom was three times as old as Sue was. Find the age of each now.

2. Andy's present age exceeds Bob's age by 25 years. In 15 years Andy will be twice as old as Bob. Find their present ages.

3. Skip is now three times as old as his brother Paul. In 5 years Skip will be twice as old as Paul will be. What will be their ages in 5 years?

4. Mary is now twice as old as Jane. Seven years ago the sum of their ages was 16. What are their ages now?

5. A man is now 40 years old and his son is 14 years old. A number of years from now the father will be twice as old as his son. What is this number of years? (*Hint:* In step ①, express the age of each x years from now.)

6. Mae is now 17 years old and her aunt is 50. In how many years will Mae be one half as old as her aunt?

7. A father's age is 32 years and his daughter's age is 2 years. He is now sixteen times as old as his daughter. In how many years will he be only four times as old?

C **8.** Jane's father is two years older than her mother. Jane's age is one third her father's age. When Jane was born, the sum of her parents' ages was 42. How old are Jane's parents now?

Lever Problems

Example. Leonard wants to move a 150-pound rock. He inserts the end of a board under the rock and then places a log under the board 3 feet from the rock. How much force (weight) must be used on the other end of the board to move the rock if the distance from the log to the other end is 10 feet?

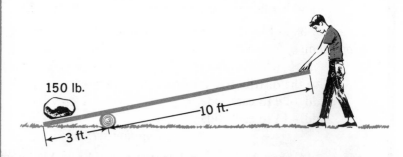

150 lb.

10 ft.

3 ft.

The board acts as a lever. To solve this kind of problem, you use a **formula,** an equation that expresses a known relationship between two or more quantities. In this case you use a formula that expresses the law of the lever.

If W represents the first weight, w represents the second, D represents the distance from the fulcrum (point at which a lever is supported) to the first weight, and d represents the distance from the fulcrum to the second weight, then the formula is

$$WD = wd.$$

In this formula, the weight of the lever is ignored.

① Decide which weights and distances will be represented by which variables in the formula.

(Weight of rock)(Distance to log)
$$= \text{(weight exerted)(distance to log)}$$

② Replace the variables in the formula with numbers where possible.

$$150(3) = w \cdot 10$$

③ Solve the equation that results.

$$150(3) = w \cdot 10$$
$$450 = 10w$$
$$w = 45$$

Solution set: $\{45\}$

Leonard must exert 45 pounds on the log.

A — In Exercises 1–5 the board is 13 feet long and is being used to lift a rock, as in the example above.

1. If the fulcrum is 3 feet from the rock, how much weight is needed to raise a rock weighing 300 pounds? 500 pounds?

2. How much weight is needed to raise a 150-pound rock if the fulcrum is 4 feet from the rock? (The fulcrum will then be 9 feet from the other end.)

3. How much weight is needed to raise 150 pounds if the fulcrum is 7 feet from the rock?

4. How much weight is needed to raise 150 pounds if the fulcrum is 1 foot from the rock?

5. If Leonard weighs 135 pounds, what is the heaviest rock he can lift if the fulcrum is 3 feet from the rock?

6. Two boys sit on opposite sides of the fulcrum of a balanced seesaw (a lever). One boy weighs 120 pounds and sits 6 feet from the fulcrum. The heavier boy sits only 5 feet from the fulcrum. What is the weight of the heavier boy?

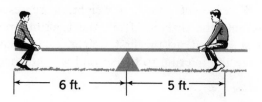

7. If a rock weighing 340 pounds is placed on a lever 2 feet to the left of a fulcrum, how far to the right must a 170-pound man put all of his weight to move the rock?

8. Two boys sit at opposite ends of a balanced seesaw. One boy weighs 20 pounds less than the other and sits 6 feet from the fulcrum. The heavier boy sits only 5 feet from the fulcrum. What is the weight of each boy?

9. Sandy weighs 92 pounds and, in order to balance a seesaw, must sit 1.5 feet farther from the fulcrum than her sister Amy, who weighs 112 pounds. How far (to the nearest tenth of a foot) from the fulcrum must each girl sit?

10. Bud and Bob balance Neal as shown in the figure. Bud weighs 96 pounds and sits 1 foot farther from the fulcrum than Bob, who weighs 88 pounds. Neal weighs 150 pounds and balances Bud and Bob by sitting 8 feet from the fulcrum. How far from the fulcrum do Bud and Bob sit?

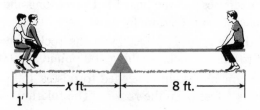

11. Lucy Buran and her younger sister sit on opposite sides of a balanced seesaw. Lucy weighs 30 pounds more than her sister. If Lucy sits 3 feet from the fulcrum and her sister sits 4 feet from the fulcrum, find the weight of each girl.

Time-Rate-Distance Problems

Example. Two cars 400 miles apart travel toward each other. One car travels at a rate of 48 miles per hour and the other car at 32 miles per hour. In how many hours will they meet?

① Do you recognize that each car will travel the same number of hours? Then, let t equal the number of hours until the cars meet.

Then $48t$ is the distance the faster car travels in t hours and $32t$ is the distance the slower car travels in t hours.

② Do you also recognize the other condition in the problem? The distance traveled by one car plus the distance traveled by the other car is the total distance, or 400 miles.

Then $48t + 32t = 400$ is a mathematical model of the problem.

③
$$48t + 32t = 400$$
$$80t = 400$$
$$t = 5$$

Solution set: $\{5\}$

The two cars will meet in 5 hours.

④ Does the solution, 5 hours, check with the conditions of the problem?

A —— In each of the following problems, you will be asked to find the rate or the time. For step ①, represent the unknown rate or time and the expressions for the distances. For step ②, write an equation involving the distance traveled. Be sure to check each rate or time with the original condition of the problem.

1. A freight train traveling at an average rate of 30 miles per hour is followed two hours later from the same station by a passenger train traveling at an average rate of 50 miles per hour. How many hours after the passenger train leaves will it pass the freight train?

① Let t be the number of hours the passenger train travels;
then $t + 2$ is the number of hours the freight train travels;
and $50t$ is the distance traveled by the passenger train (in t hours at 50 mph),
and _?_ is the distance traveled by the freight train (in $t + 2$ hours at 30 mph).

② Recognize that the distance traveled by the passenger train equals the distance traveled by the freight train at the point the trains pass.

$$50t = 30(t + 2)$$

Solve this equation and check.

2. Frank and Bob start from home in their cars and travel in opposite directions. Frank's rate of speed is twice Bob's. In 4 hours they are 150 miles apart. Find the rate of speed at which each travels.

① Let *r* be Bob's rate. Then _?_ is Frank's rate, and 4*r* is the distance Bob traveled.

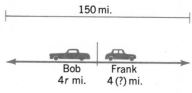

② 4*r* + _?_ = 150

Complete the solution of the problem.

3. Two automobiles start at the same time at the same place and travel in opposite directions. One travels at the rate of 45 miles per hour and the other at the rate of 40 miles per hour. In how many hours will they be 255 miles apart?

4. Two boys on bicycles start from the same place at the same time. One rides at the rate of 8 miles an hour and the other at 5 miles an hour. They go in the same direction. In how many hours will they be 15 miles apart?

B **5.** If, in Exercise 4, the boy riding faster starts 1 hour later than the other, in how many hours will he overtake the other boy?

6. One car traveling 40 miles an hour left a certain place 4 hours later than another car traveling in the same direction at the rate of 30 miles an hour. In how many hours will the faster car overtake the other?

7. A plane leaves a certain airport at 10 o'clock, flying due north. Another plane starts from the same airport at 12 o'clock, flying due south. At 2 o'clock they are 1200 miles apart. Find the rate of speed of each, if the rate of the first is one half that of the second.

8. Mildred left camp 4 hours after Margaret did. They traveled in opposite directions. Mildred drove at 30 miles an hour, Margaret at 45 miles an hour. How many hours after Mildred left were the two girls 630 miles apart?

140   CHAPTER 3

40 mph.

9. A cyclist had been traveling 15 miles an hour for 8 hours when he was overtaken by a motorist who left the same starting point 5 hours after the cyclist. Find the speed of the motorist.

10. Two drivers 240 miles apart start toward each other at the same time. The faster one travels 50 miles an hour and the slower one travels 35 miles an hour. If the faster is delayed 2 hours on the trip, how long will it be before they meet?   *4 hour.*

11. Ann starts from a certain place, traveling at 4 mph. Five hours later Fred starts from the same place and travels in the same direction at 6 mph. In how many hours will Fred overtake Ann?   *10 hr.*

12. An airplane is 75 miles directly behind a ship sailing a straight course. The rate of the plane is 120 mph and that of the ship is 20 mph. How long will it take the plane to overtake the ship?

13. At 2 P.M. a train traveling at 50 miles an hour started from Westville toward Easton. At 3 P.M. a train traveling at 40 miles an hour started from Easton toward Westville. Westville is 410 miles from Easton. At what time will the engines of the two trains pass one another? (The trains are on parallel tracks.)

14. A freight train left Kansas City for St. Louis at the rate of 12 miles an hour at the same time that a passenger train running 45 miles an hour left St. Louis for Kansas City on a parallel track. If the distance between the two cities is 285 miles, how long will it be before they pass one another?

3–12 Solving Equations for a Variable

If you were asked to solve the equation $x + a = b$ for x, you might say, "I can't solve for x until I know a number for a and a number for b." You cannot get a *numerical* solution to the equation, but you can find x in terms of a and b. The solution in terms of a and b will make the equation $x + a = b$ true when it replaces x.

Compare the solution of a specific numerical equation, shown on the left, with the solution of the general equation on the right.

EXAMPLE 1. Solve $x + 7 = 12$.

Add -7 to each side. $x = 5$

      Check $5 + 7 = 12$

             $12 = 12$

    Solution set: {5}

Solve $x + a = b$ for x.

Add $-a$ to each side. $x = b - a$

    Check $(b - a) + a = b$

                $b = b$

    Solution set: {$b - a$}

EXAMPLE 2.

Solve $38 = 16 + 2w$.

Add -16 to each side. $\quad 22 = 2w$

Multiply by $\frac{1}{2}$. $\qquad 11 = w$

$$\begin{aligned} \textit{Check} \quad 38 &= 16 + 2(11) \\ 38 &= 16 + 22 \\ 38 &= 38 \end{aligned}$$

Solution set: $\{11\}$

Solve $p = 2 + 2w$ for w.

Add -2 to each side. $\quad p - 2 = 2w$

Multiply by $\frac{1}{2}$. $\qquad \frac{p-2}{2} = w$

$$\begin{aligned} \textit{Check} \quad p &= 2 + 2\left(\tfrac{p-2}{2}\right) \\ p &= 2 + p - 2 \\ p &= p \end{aligned}$$

Solution set: $\left\{\frac{p-2}{2}\right\}$

EXAMPLE 3. Solve $-12 = -3t$.

Multiply by $-\frac{1}{3}$. $\qquad 4 = t$

$$\begin{aligned} \textit{Check} \quad -12 &= -3(4) \\ -12 &= -12 \end{aligned}$$

Solution set: $\{4\}$

Solve $d = rt$ for t.

Multiply by $\frac{1}{r}$. $\quad \frac{d}{r} = t$

$$\begin{aligned} \textit{Check} \quad d &= r\left(\tfrac{d}{r}\right) \\ d &= d \end{aligned}$$

Solution set: $\left\{\frac{d}{r}\right\}$

Exercises

A ══ Solve the equation in column **a**. Ask yourself, "What process did I use?" Then use the same process to solve the equation in column **b** for x in terms of the other variables or numbers. Check your solutions.

	a	**b**
1.	$x + 5 = 7$	$x + a = c$
2.	$x - 9 = 2\frac{1}{2}$	$x - a = b$
3.	$3x = 27$	$ax = b$
4.	$\frac{x}{6} = 24$	$\frac{x}{a} = b$
5.	$5x + 4 = 10$	$ax + b = c$
6.	$\frac{3x}{5} = 2$	$\frac{ax}{b} = c$
7.	$x + 6 = 8 + \frac{1}{4}$	$x + a = b + c$
8.	$5x + 4 = 10$	$5x + a = b$
9.	$-2x = 16$	$-ax = b$
10.	$3(x + 4) = 8$	$3(x + a) = b$
11.	$-x + 4 = -5$	$-x + a = b$
12.	$-2x + 6 = 0$	$-2x + a = b$

Solve each equation for the variable indicated.

13. Formula for the circumference of a circle; solve for d.

$$C = \pi d$$

14. Formula for the area of a parallelogram region; solve for b.

$$A = bh$$

15. Formula for a lever; solve for W.

$$WD = wd$$

16. Formula for the area of a triangular region; solve for h.

$$A = \tfrac{1}{2}bh$$

17. Formula for the perimeter of a rectangle; solve for w.

$$p = 2l + 2w$$

18. Formula for the perimeter of a triangle; solve for b.

$$p = a + b + c$$

Solve each equation and check the results obtained.

19. $3x + 5 + 4x = 2x + 35$ **20.** $-8x - 3 + 6x = 4 + 15x$

21. $6x - 2x = 5x + 8$ **22.** $7y + 21 + y = 2y - 11 + 2$

23. $2w - 5 = w + 8$ **24.** $3t + 6 = t - 2$

25. $3c + 4 = 9c - 4$ **26.** $3 + 3v = 8 + 4v$

27. $3x - 2 + x = x - 5x$ **28.** $6 - 11h = 6h + 16$

29. $4x + 12 = 13x - 15$ **30.** $7n - 4 = 9 - 8n$

B Solve each equation for n.

31. $2n + a = b$ **32.** $2n + 5a = 8a$

33. $6a + 2b = 2n$ **34.** $2n - a = b$

35. $3a + n = 5b$ **36.** $2n - b = 5a$

37. $n + a = b + c$ **38.** $\frac{n}{a} = b + c$

39. $2a + 2n = b + c$ **40.** $-n = -4b$

41. $-n + a = b$ **42.** $an = b + c$

43. $-n - a = -b$ **44.** $an + ac = b$

C Solve each equation for the variable indicated.

45. $a(b + n) = c$ for b.   **46.** $\frac{n}{a} = b + n$ for a.

47. $(a + b)n = c$ for a.   **48.** $b(n - a) = c$ for n.

49. $A = \tfrac{1}{2}h(b + b')$ for b and also for h.

3–13　Compound Mathematical Sentences

The truth or falsity of a sentence is called the **truth value.** The following are **compound sentences** using the connective *and.* Note the truth values of the two sentences (called **components**) that make up the compound sentences and of each compound sentence. The first sentence is labeled *p* and the second *q.*

p　　　　　　*q*	*p*	*q*	*p and q*
$2 + 3 = 5$ *and* $3 > 2$	True	True	True
$2 + 3 = 5$ *and* $2 > 3$	True	False	False
$2 + 3 \neq 5$ *and* $3 > 2$	False	True	False
$2 + 3 \neq 5$ *and* $2 > 3$	False	False	False

The examples illustrate the following.

> **The compound sentence *p and q* is true if and only if *p* is true and also *q* is true.**

Compound sentences using *or* are shown below. Study the examples, which tell when the sentence *p or q* is true.

p　　　　　　*q*	*p*	*q*	*p or q*
$2 + 3 = 5$ *or* $3 > 2$	True	True	True
$2 + 3 = 5$ *or* $3 < 2$	True	False	True
$2 + 3 \neq 5$ *or* $2 < 3$	False	True	True
$2 + 3 \neq 5$ *or* $2 > 3$	False	False	False

You probably have no trouble accepting the truth values of the last three sentences above. In those, the meaning of *or* is the same as in ordinary language, "one or the other, but not both." In the sentence $2 + 3 = 5$ *or* $3 > 2$, however, *or* is not used as it is in ordinary language. When *or* is used in mathematics, it means "either one or the other or both," unless it is otherwise stated. In fact, most legal documents use *and/or* to signify the meaning of *or* as it is used in mathematics. The examples above illustrate the following.

> **The compound sentence *p or q* is true if and only if *p* or *q* or both are true, that is, if and only if either component sentence is true or if both components are true.**

EXAMPLE 1. If the replacement set is the set of nonnegative integers, what is the solution set of $x \leq 6$? What is the graph of $x \leq 6$?

You may think of the sentence $x \leq 6$ as the compound sentence

$$x < 6 \text{ or } x = 6.$$

The solution set for $x < 6$ is $\{0, 1, 2, 3, 4, 5\}$. Why?
The solution set for $x = 6$ is $\{6\}$.   Why?   Hence,
the solution set for $x \leq 6$ is $\{0, 1, 2, 3, 4, 5, 6\}$.
The graph is seven points, as shown below.

EXAMPLE 2. If the replacement set is the set of integers, what is the solution set of $-6 < x < 2$?

You may think of the sentence $-6 < x < 2$ as the compound sentence

$$-6 < x \text{ and } x < 2.$$

The solution set for $-6 < x$ is $\{-5, -4, -3, -2, -1, 0, 1, 2, 3, \cdots\}$.
The solution set for $x < 2$ is $\{\cdots, -6, -5, -4, -3, -2, -1, 0, 1\}$.
Hence, the solution set for $-6 < x < 2$ is $\{-5, -4, -3, -2, -1, 0, 1\}$.
Explain how each solution set was obtained.

If the compound sentence uses,	then the solution set is
or	$\cup$ of solution sets of components.
and	$\cap$ of solution sets of components.

Now try these

—— In each of the following, determine the truth values of the components and of the compound sentence. Copy each exercise and replace each ? with either a T for True or an F for False.

1. $4 < 6$ *and* $3 < 8$

a. T   b. ?

c. ?

2. $-3 < 4$ *and* $0 > -1$

a. ?   b. T

c. ?

3. $-5 > -7$ *or* $6 > -2$

a. ?   b. ?

c. T

4. $3 > 2$ *or* $-5 < -6$

a. ?   b. ?

c. ?

5.

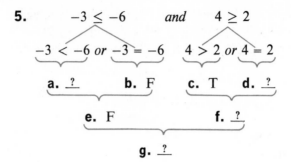

Answers: **1. b.** T **c.** T **2. a.** T **c.** T **3. a.** T **b.** T **4. a.** T **b.** F **c.** T
5. a. F **d.** F **f.** T **g.** F

Checkpoint

1. In a compound sentence with components p and q, when is *p and q* true?

2. When is *p or q* true?

3. Given the solution sets of two component sentences, what is the solution set of the compound sentence whose connective is *and*? the solution set of the compound sentence whose connective is *or*?

Exercises

A —— Use the roster method to show the solution sets of the following compound sentences. The replacement set is the set of integers. Graph each solution set.

1. $9 < x$ *and* $x < 12$

2. $0 < x$ *and* $x < 5$

3. $x = 9$ *or* $x + 3 = 10$

4. $2x - 3 = 15$ *or* $9x = 4x + 2$

5. $-2 < x$ *or* $x > -10$

6. $-10 < 2x$ *or* $-20 < 2x$

7. $12 \leq x$ *and* $x \leq 15$

8. $-10 \leq x$ *and* $x > -15$

—— Show that the compound sentence in **b** is equivalent to the compound sentence in **a**.

	a	**b**
9.	$2x - 3 > x - 9$ *and* $3x < 15$	$x > -6$ *and* $x < 5$
10.	$-2x > 14$ *and* $9x > 45$	$x < -7$ *and* $x > 5$
11.	$8 - x > 4$ *or* $3x - 9 = 16$	$-x > -4$ *or* $x = 8\frac{1}{3}$
12.	$3x - 7 = 4(x - 2)$ *or* $9x - 3 < 32$	$x = 1$ *or* $x < 3\frac{8}{9}$

—— For each of the following, first find a simpler compound sentence that is equivalent to the given one. Then solve the compound sentence and graph the solution set. The replacement set is the set of real numbers.

Example 1. $2x - 7 < 9$ *and* $3x - 7 > x - 9$

First find simpler equivalents to the component sentences.

$$2x - 7 < 9 \qquad\qquad 3x - 7 > x - 9$$
$$2x < 16 \qquad\qquad 3x > x - 2$$
$$x < 8 \qquad\qquad 2x > -2$$
$$x > -1$$

The solution set is $\{x : x < 8\} \cap \{x : x > -1\}$. The graph is shown below.

Example 2. $2x - 7 < 9$ *or* $3x - 7 > x - 9$

$$2x - 7 < 9 \qquad\qquad 3x - 7 > x - 9$$
$$x < 8 \qquad\qquad x > -1$$

The solution set is $\{x : x < 8\} \cup \{x : x > -1\}$, and all real numbers are in the solution set.

13. $3x - 7 < 28$ *and* $9x - 4 > x + 4$

14. $3x - 7 < 28$ *or* $9x - 4 > x + 4$

15. $6a - 9 = 17a + 13$ *or* $3(a - 4) = 2(3a - 9)$

16. $3x - 9 > -3$ *and* $9x < 0$

—— Graph each compound sentence, using the set of integers as the replacement set.

17. $12 < x < 15$ **18.** $0 < x < 5$

19. $-10 < x < -5$ **20.** $10 < 2x < 20$

21. $5 < (x + 2) < 15$ **22.** $0 \le (x - 5) \le 12$

23. The weight of each boy on the football team is more than 130 pounds and less than 205 pounds. If x represents the weight of any boy, then $\underline{\ ?\ } < x < \underline{\ ?\ }$ is true.

24. Write a compound sentence whose solution set is the set of numbers between 10 and 20.

25. Stocks are sold only in integral numbers of dollars and eighths of a dollar. The sentence $51\frac{1}{8} < x < 52\frac{3}{4}$ indicates that a stock sold on a particular day above $51\frac{1}{8}$ and below $52\frac{3}{4}$. What is the solution set for this sentence?

26. Twice the age of any student in the algebra class is more than 26, but is less than 34. If x represents the age of any pupil, then $\underline{\ ?\ } < 2x < \underline{\ ?\ }$ is true. Solve the inequality.

27. Billy Fitzgerald has a certain number of arrowheads. If he doubles this number and adds 4, the result is greater than 56 and is less than 60. How many arrowheads has Billy?

28. Adding the product of 417 and x to 57 gives a number that is less than $57x$ added to 2577. Find x.

B **29.** Two sides of a triangle are 3 and 7. What can you say about the length of the third side?

30. Mr. Edgar Mitchell has a cattle farm. When asked how many cows he had, he said: "Four times the number minus 167 is greater than the number plus 16; and five times the number plus 100 is less than 226 added to three times the number." How many cows has he?

3–14   Equations Involving Absolute Value

You know that if $|x|$ names 6, then x can be replaced by -6 or by 6. Then, solving $|x| = 6$ is equivalent to solving the compound sentence $x = -6$ or $x = 6$. The solution set is $\{-6, 6\}$.

The following examples show how you can use your knowledge of compound sentences to solve equations involving absolute value.

EXAMPLE 1. Solve $|x + 6| = 14$.

If $x + 6$ is 14 or if it is -14, $|x + 6|$ will be 14. Hence, the sentence $|x + 6| = 14$ is equivalent to the compound sentence $x + 6 = 14$ or $x + 6 = -14$.

$$x + 6 = 14 \ or \ x + 6 = -14$$
$$x = \ \ 8 \ or \ x = -20$$

$Check$ $\quad |8 + 6| = 14 \qquad\qquad |-20 + 6| = 14$
$\qquad\qquad\quad |14| = 14 \qquad\qquad\qquad |-14| = 14$
$\qquad\qquad\quad\ \ 14 = 14 \qquad\qquad\qquad\quad 14 = 14$

$Solution \ set:$ $\{8, -20\}$

EXAMPLE 2. Solve $|2k + k| - 12 = 5$.

$$|2k + k| - 12 = 5$$
$$|3k| = 17$$

$$3k = 17 \ or \ -3k = 17$$
$$k = \tfrac{17}{3} \ or \quad k = -\tfrac{17}{3}$$

Check $|2(\tfrac{17}{3}) + \tfrac{17}{3}| - 12 = 5$ $|2(-\tfrac{17}{3}) + (-\tfrac{17}{3})| - 12 = 5$

            $|\tfrac{34}{3} + \tfrac{17}{3}| - 12 = 5$ $|(-\tfrac{34}{3}) + (-\tfrac{17}{3})| - 12 = 5$

               $|\tfrac{51}{3}| - 12 = 5$ $|-\tfrac{51}{3}| - 12 = 5$

                 $17 - 12 = 5$ $17 - 12 = 5$

                      $5 = 5$ $5 = 5$

Solution set: $\{\tfrac{17}{3}, -\tfrac{17}{3}\}$

Exercises

A — Solve each of the following equations. Check before writing the solution set.

1. $|a + 3| = 2$ **2.** $|\tfrac{1}{2}k| = 6$

3. $|5y| = 10$ **4.** $|-2v| = 2$

5. $|3k - 6| = 2$ **6.** $|2y + 6| = 0$

7. $12 = |3 - x|$ **8.** $|\tfrac{5}{6} + y| = \tfrac{2}{3}$

9. $|\tfrac{1}{5}(2 - k)| = 3$ **10.** $|y + y + y| = \tfrac{1}{3}$

11. $|t + 1| = 9$ **12.** $|7x - 5| = \tfrac{1}{2}$

13. $|\tfrac{1}{4}(5t - 2)| = 6$ **14.** $|3d - 2| = \tfrac{1}{2}$

15. $|4k + 6 + 2k| = 5$ **16.** $|15| = |w + 2|$

17. $|\tfrac{2}{3}y| = \tfrac{1}{12}$ **18.** $|n| + 6 = 2$

19. $|3m + 6| = 4$ **20.** $|-3m| = 14$

21. $6 - 2 = |x| + 3$ **22.** $|\tfrac{1}{2}w + \tfrac{1}{2}w| = 1$

23. $|2w + w| - 2 = 8$ **24.** $|6r + 2| + 6 = 9$

B — Find a simple name for each set.

Example 1. $A = \{x : 2(x + 2) - 3(x + 5) = -(x + 11)\}$

$$2(x + 2) - 3(x + 5) = -(x + 11)$$
$$2x + 4 - 3x - 15 = -x - 11$$
$$2x - 3x + 4 - 15 = -x - 11$$
$$-x - 11 = -x - 11$$

The equation is true for all replacements for x. Hence, A is the same as the set of real numbers. R is the simple name for the set.

Example 2. $B = \{y : 5(y - 3) + 2(y + 2) = 3y + 2 + 2(2y - 5)\}$
Solving the sentence gives the following.

$$7y - 11 = 7y - 8$$
$$-11 = -8$$

The equation is true for no values of y. Hence, set B is the same as ø. ø is the simple name.

25. $A = \{x : x - 1 = -x - (x + 2) + 3x\}$

26. $E = \{t : 4(2t - 3) - 6(t - 2) = 2(t + 4)\}$

27. $F = \{f : -1 + 5f = 5(f - \frac{1}{5})\}$

28. $G = \left\{g : \frac{g - 1}{4} = 2g + 5\right\}$

29. $H = \{a : 5 \cdot |a + 2| = 25\}$

30. $I = \left\{k : \frac{(\frac{2}{3})(k)}{\frac{1}{3}} = \frac{1}{12}\right\}$

31. $J = \{n : n - 1 = n - (n - 1) + n\}$

32. $K = \{c : (\frac{1}{3})(c + 2) - 3(12c - \frac{1}{3}) = -3(c + 4) - \frac{1}{2}(3c + 6)\}$

33. $L = \{d : 3(2d - 5) = 5(4 - d)\}$

34. $A = \{b : 3(b - 2) + 3(b - 3) = b\}$

35. $Z = \{y : \frac{1}{4}y + 12 = -(y + 2) + \frac{1}{4}\}$

36. $A = \{x : |x| = -3\}$

37. $C = \left\{y : y + 2 = \frac{2y + 16}{-10}\right\}$

38. $B = \left\{t : \frac{(3t - 5)}{6}(\frac{2}{3}) = 3t + 1\right\}$

39. $Y = \{y : 3(y - 2) + 6 = 2y\}$

40. $S = \left\{t : (\frac{2}{3})(t - 2) = t + 2 - \left(5 - \frac{t}{3}\right)\right\}$

41. $T = \left\{k : 3k + 1 = -k\left(\frac{1}{k} - 3\right)\right\}$

42. $A = \left\{u : \left|\frac{2 + 3u}{4}\right| = 5\right\}$

43. $B = \{m : |m + 2m| = \frac{1}{2}\}$

44. $D = \{d : 2|d + 1| = 6\}$

More Challenging Problems

1. George rode out of town on the bus at an average speed of 20 miles per hour and walked back at an average speed of 3 miles per hour. How far did he go out of town if the entire trip took eight hours and if two hours of this was spent visiting his friend Tom?

2. A ship can go downstream from town *A* to town *B* at 20 miles per hour in five hours less time than it takes to go upstream from *B* to *A* at 15 miles per hour. How far apart are the towns?

3. At what two times between 7 o'clock and 8 o'clock will the minute hand and the hour hand of a clock be exactly 15 minute spaces apart?

4. A man bought two airplanes but found them unsatisfactory for his purpose. He sold them for $6000 each, making 20% on one and losing 20% on the other. Did he make money or lose money and how much?

5. An Australian farmer divided his sheep among his three sons. Alfred got 20% more than John, and Alfred got 25% more than Charles. John's share was 3600. How many sheep did Charles get?

6. Mr. Teal has a 99-year lease on a piece of property. When asked how much of the lease had expired, he said: "Two thirds of the time past is equal to four fifths of the time to come." How much of the lease had expired?

CHAPTER REVIEW

1. Know the meaning and be able to use each of the following words or phrases. The number shown after each word or phrase indicates where it is introduced, in case you need to review.

equivalent sentences (*102*)
addition postulate for
   equations (*103*)
multiplication postulate
   for equations (*105*)
solution, or root, of an
   equation (*108*)
set-builder notation (*110*)
identity (*114*)
conditional equation (*115*)

comparison postulate (*118*)
half-line (*119*)
intersection (*123*)
disjoint sets (*123*)
union (*123*)
open interval (*124*)
formula (*136*)
compound sentence (*144*)
truth value (*144*)
components (*144*)

—— If the replacement set is U = $\{-3, -1, 0, 1, 3\}$, what is the solution set of each sentence?

2. $2x + 3 = x$

3. $4 + 3x > 10$

4. $2y + 7 = 7 + 2y$

5. $2x = 6$ *and* $19 + x = 16$

6. $2x = 10 - x$

7. $x > x - 1$

8. $a = 4 + a$

9. $8(3 + x) = 5x + 15x$ *or* $6x = 9x$

10. Is the equation $4(x - 3) - 2x = -12 + 2x$ a conditional equation or an identity? How do you know?

11. Write *Yes* if the sentence in column II is equivalent to the sentence in column I; otherwise, write *No*.

I	II
a. $6a + 2 - 2a = a - 1$	$3a + 2 = -1$
b. $7x = 14$	$6x + x = -x + 14 + x$
c. $9y + 6 = 18y$	$-9y + 4 = 0$
d. $3x - 2 = 18x - 17$	$0 = 15x - 15$
e. $\frac{3}{4}x = 17$	$\frac{4}{3} \cdot (\frac{3}{4}x) = 17 \cdot \frac{4}{3}$
f. $3(n - 9) = 6 + 3n$	$3n - 9 = 6 + 3n$
g. $-\frac{7}{6}x = 1$	$x = -\frac{6}{7}$
h. $an = b + c$	$n = \frac{b}{a} + c$

—— Find the solution set of each sentence if the replacement set is the set of real numbers.

12. $3n = 2$ **13.** $|-2n| = 3$

14. $\frac{n}{2} + \frac{3}{4} = 6$ **15.** $6 + 2x > 8$

16. $-4x > 20$ **17.** $9x + 2 > -7$ *or* $x + 9 < 0$

18. $|-n + 7| = -2$ **19.** $3y - 2y < 12$ *and* $-2y < 4$

—— Write *True* if the sentence is true and *False* if it is false.

20. $\forall x \quad 4x + 2x = 6x$ **21.** $\forall x \quad x + 2 > x$

22. $\exists x \quad x > x + 2$ **23.** $\forall x \quad 3x - 9 = x + 6$

24. $\exists x \quad 2x + 5 = 17$ **25.** $\exists x \quad 5(x + 2) < 3(x - 9)$

—— For each inequality, give the solution set and graph it on a number line. The replacement set is R.

26. $x + 4 < 8$ **27.** $2x - 2 > 7$

28. $\frac{1}{2}x - 3 > 1$ **29.** $-4x \leq 8$

30. $2(x - 5) - 2(x + 3) \leq 14$ **31.** $12 - 9x < -8x$

—— Use the roster method to list the members of these sets if the replacement set is the set of integers.

32. $\{x : x + 15 = 29\}$ **33.** $\{x : x + 2 > 14\}$

34. $\left\{n : 2\frac{2}{5} - \frac{n}{10} = \frac{7n}{10}\right\}$ **35.** $\{y : y + \frac{1}{2} = 5\}$

36. Describe the solution set of a compound sentence whose connective word is *and*.

37. Describe the solution set of a compound sentence whose connective word is *or*.

— Find the solution set of these compound sentences and graph it. The replacement set is the set of integers.

38. $-3 > x$ *and* $x < 4$

39. $2x - 7 < x + 2$ *and* $x > -1$

40. $-3 < x$ *or* $x > 4$

41. $5x + 4 \geq 9$ *or* $3x - 2 < -8$

— Show that the compound sentence in column II is equivalent to the compound sentence in column I.

I	II
42. $x + 2 < 11$ *and* $x - 17 < -5$	$9 > x$ *and* $x < 12$
43. $12 \geq x$ *and* $x \leq 15$	$x - 6 \leq 6$ *and* $x - 8 \leq 7$
44. $x = 1$ *or* $x < 6$	$3x - 4 = 7$ *or* $\frac{1}{2}x < 3$
45. $-2 < x$ *and* $x > -10$	$5x - 3 > -13$ *and* $x + 3 > -7$
46. $x < -7$ *or* $x > 5$	$-2x > 14$ *or* $9x > 45$

— Solve the equation in **a.** Then use the same process to solve the equation in **b** for the same variable as in **a.**

a	**b**
47. $4n = 19$	$bn = a$
48. $3n + 7 = 42$	$3n + b = c$
49. $\frac{2b}{3} = 5$	$\frac{ab}{c} = f$

— Each sentence below expresses one condition of a problem. Use one variable to write algebraic expressions for the unknowns (given in parentheses) that use the condition.

Example. The sum of two numbers is 42. (the two numbers)

$$\text{Let} \qquad x = \text{one number}$$
$$42 - x = \text{the other number}$$

50. Two cars are 500 miles apart. (distance each traveled)

51. The length of a rectangle is twice the width. (length and width)

52. The greater of two numbers is 10 less than twice the smaller. (two numbers)

53. Paul's 25 coins are dimes and quarters. (number of coins of each)

— Solve the following problems.

54. After an airplane has been flying west from Chicago at 150 miles per hour for 5 hours, it is passed by another airplane that left Chicago 2 hours after the first airplane left. At what speed is the second airplane traveling?

55. Are there three consecutive integers such that twice the first added to the second gives 7 more than 4 times the third? If there are, find them.

CHAPTER TEST

—— Find the solution set of these sentences if the replacement set is the set of real numbers.

1. $5y - 6 = 2y + 9$ **2.** $2(7 - x) = 5(x + 3) - 6$

3. $2(x - 6) + 3(7 - x) = 5$ **4.** $|-9k| < 33$

5. $2x + 3 > 7$ **6.** $9 - 3x < 15$

7. $3x + 2 > 11$ *and* $5x < 35$ **8.** $-15 < 3x < 12$

—— Write *True* or *False* for each statement.

9. $\forall x \quad 8 - x = 8 + (-x)$ **10.** $\forall a \quad \frac{1}{a} \cdot a = 1, a \neq 0$

11. $\exists x \quad -19\frac{1}{6} + x = 0$ **12.** $\{x : 2x - 5 = 13\} = \{9\}$

13. The equation $2x - 19 = 5x + 27$ is equivalent to the equation $3x = 46$.

14. $\{n : na + b = c\} = \{n : n = \frac{c}{a} - b\}$

15. The solution of $2x - 1 = 8 - 7x$ is -1.

16. $\{x : 3 < x < 9\} = \{x : 3 < x \text{ or } x < 9\}$

17. $\{x : x \geq 7\} = \{x : x > 7 \text{ or } x = 7\}$

—— Solve for the variable indicated.

18. $A = bh$, for h.   **19.** $P = 2l + 2w$, for w.   **20.** $V = dr$, for d.

21. The sum of two numbers is 57. One number is 13 more than the other. What are the numbers?

22. Are there three consecutive even integers whose sum is 42? If so, find the numbers.

23. A car traveling 50 mph leaves A for B at 8 A.M. Another car leaves A at 10 A.M. heading for B traveling 60 mph. At what time will the second car catch the first?

24. The difference between two numbers is 6. If three times the larger is subtracted from 52, the result is the same as if 56 is subtracted from seven times the smaller. Find the numbers.

25. Alfred is now twice as old as his sister. Eight years ago the sum of their ages was 11. What are their ages now?

CUMULATIVE REVIEW

Give the letter of the response that best completes the sentence or answers the question.

1. Which of the following sets is not well-defined?

a. The set of odd numbers. **b.** The set of children.

c. The set of 1923 cars. **d.** The set of electrical engineers.

2. Which set is equivalent to $\{3, 4, 5, 4\}$?

a. $\{3, 4, 5\}$ **b.** $\{3, 4, 5, 3\}$

c. $\{0, 2, 4, 6, 8\}$ **d.** $\{3, 4, 5, \cdots\}$

3. Which replacements for a, b, c, and d make $\frac{a}{b} = \frac{c}{d}$ true?

a. $a = 2, b = 3, c = 4, d = 5$

b. $a = 7, b = 6, c = 2, d = 9$

c. $a = 13, b = 16, c = 65, d = 80$

d. $a = 15, b = 45, c = 30, d = 21$

4. Which of the following sentences is false?

a. $|-6| > 0$ **b.** $-(2) = -2$ **c.** $(-1)(-2) = -(2)$ **d.** $-(-\frac{1}{2}) = \frac{1}{2}$

5. A simplified form of $\dfrac{-2+7}{-\frac{1}{2}}$ would be

a. $\dfrac{5}{-\frac{1}{2}}$. **b.** $-2\frac{1}{2}$. **c.** $4\frac{1}{2}$. **d.** -10.

6. Which of the following illustrates the distributive postulate for fractional numbers?

a. $\frac{1}{2} + 0 = \frac{1}{2}$ **b.** $\frac{3}{4}(12 + 1\frac{1}{3}) = (\frac{3}{4} \cdot 12) + (\frac{3}{4} \cdot 1\frac{1}{3})$

c. $\frac{5}{6} \times \frac{3}{5} = \frac{3}{5} \times \frac{5}{6}$ **d.** $\frac{3}{2} \times \frac{2}{3} = 1$

7. Which group of three measurements may be the lengths of the sides of a right triangle?

a. $x = 15, y = 8, z = 55$ **b.** $x = 20, y = 30, z = 15$

c. $x = 5, y = 7, z = \sqrt{74}$ **d.** $x = \sqrt{7}, y = \sqrt{12}, z = 21$

8. Which is a true sentence?

a. $|-7| = |0 + 11 - 4|$ **b.** $-6 < [-4 + (-3)]$

c. $[(+4) \cdot (+5)] > [(-4) \cdot (-5)]$ **d.** $(-6 - 2) = 6 + 2$

9. What is another name for $12xy + 3y - x + 2y$?

a. $16xy$ **b.** $12xy + 5y - x$ **c.** $9xy + 2y$ **d.** $12xy - x$

10. For which is $+19$ the correct difference?

    a. $(-11) - (8)$ **b.** $-11 - (-8)$

    c. $11 - (+8)$ **d.** $11 - (-8)$

11. If a is -3, b is -8, and c is -6, the value of $\frac{ab}{2c}$ is

    a. $12.$ **b.** $-12.$ **c.** $2.$ **d.** $-2.$

12. When three negative numbers are multiplied, the product is

    a. larger than any of the numbers.

    b. the product of the absolute values of the numbers.

    c. the negative of the product of the absolute values of the numbers.

    d. a positive number.

13. Which sentence is true if n is replaced by -6?

    a. $3n = 18$ **b.** $-3(n) = -18$

    c. $3n = -18$ **d.** $-4n = -24$

14. If the replacement set is the set of real numbers, which of the following is not true?

    a. $\forall x \quad x = x$ **b.** $\forall x \quad x \cdot 1 = x$

    c. $\forall x \quad x \cdot x = 2x$ **d.** $\forall x \quad x + 0 = x$

15. If the replacement set is the set of real numbers, what is the solution set for $-3(x + 4) = 18$?

    a. $\{-2\}$ **b.** $\{-10\}$ **c.** $\{-4\frac{2}{3}\}$ **d.** $\{7\}$

16. If $A = \{a, b, c, d\}$ and $B = \{b, c\}$, then $A \cap B$ is

    a. $\{a, b, c, d\}.$ **b.** $\emptyset.$

    c. $\{b, c\}.$ **d.** $\{a, d\}.$

17. Solving $\frac{3x + y}{a} = 3z$ for y gives

    a. $y = 3za - 3x.$ **b.** $y = 3z - \frac{3x}{a}.$

    c. $y = \frac{3z}{a} - 3x.$ **d.** $y = 9xza.$

18. The set of ? is dense.

    a. Integers.   **b.** Whole numbers.

    c. Natural numbers.   **d.** Real numbers.

19. Fred has $2.25 in dimes and nickels. If he has twice as many dimes as nickels, how many of each coin does he have?

a. 20 dimes and 10 nickels

b. 18 dimes and 9 nickels

c. 16 dimes and 8 nickels

d. 14 dimes and 7 nickels

20. What rational number is equal to $\frac{11}{15}$?

a. $\frac{2}{3}$ **b.** $\frac{4}{5}$ **c.** $\frac{22}{30}$ **d.** $\frac{30}{45}$

ENRICHMENT

Linear Transformations.

Look at the number line, x, shown in black at the right. Cover everything in the diagram except the black line. Now there is nothing to indicate where the point for 0 should be or where the point for 1 should be. You only know that 1 should be to the right of 0.

In other words, the name, or **coordinate**, of a point on a number line depends upon where 0 is placed and the distance between 0 and 1.

Uncover the diagram and look at the gray number line, x'. The distance between 0 and 1 is the same as it is on x. But 0 on x' is in the position that corresponds to -2 on x. And 2 on x' is in the position that corresponds to 0 on x. What point on x' corresponds with -1 on x? with 3 on x? with 6 on x? In general, how do the x' coordinates compare to the x coordinates? The number line is shifted two units to the left. This can be expressed as a linear equation.

$$x' = x + 2$$

If the number lines are kept in corresponding positions, then the points will be shifted. The points corresponding to A and B will be A' and B', respectively, which are two units to the right of the original points. This relocation can be shown by the diagram at the right.

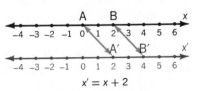

Any system of relocating points is called a **transformation of coordinates.** The two transformations above are the same; $x' = x + 2$

has just been represented in two different ways. In the rest of this section, the number lines will remain in corresponding positions and the points will be shifted.

A transformation of coordinates on the number line in such a way that the new coordinate x' can be found from the original by an equation of the form $x' = x + a$, for any real number a, is a **translation.** It shifts all coordinates to the left or to the right $|a|$ units.

Another transformation of basic importance is one such as $x' = 2x$. Here each point with coordinate x is relocated with a coordinate equal to twice the original coordinate. Thus, the point originally labeled 0 is still 0; 1 is now 2;

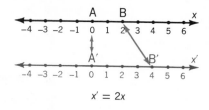

$$x' = 2x$$

2 is now 4; and so forth. This is the **stretching transformation.**

What do transformations do to measures of lengths? The first transformation, $x' = x + 2$, is a translation. Point A is labeled 0, and A after the translation, A', is labeled 2. Point B is labeled 2, and B' is labeled 4. Then the length of $\overline{AB}$, symbolized $|\overline{AB}|$, is $|2 - 0|$ or $|0 - 2|$, or 2; $|\overline{A'B'}|$ is $|4 - 2|$, or 2. The measure of the length of the segment was not changed by translation.

The second transformation is $x' = 2x$, stretching. Again, let A be 0 and B be 2. Then A' is 0 and B' is 4. Now $|\overline{AB}|$ is $|2 - 0|$, or 2, but $|\overline{A'B'}|$ is $|4 - 0|$, or 4. The measure of the length is double.

One of the most important transformations used in mathematics is the **linear transformation,** defined by $x' = ax + b \, (a \neq 0)$. The number lines illustrate the linear transformation $x' = 2x + 4$.

This transformation is frequently shown by two successive transformations, and the end result is called the **product** of the two transformations. Suppose the coordinates of A and B are transformed by $x' = x + 2$ and then by $x'' = 2x'$. The end result is shown by the third line, which is the same as the line for $x' = 2x + 4$.

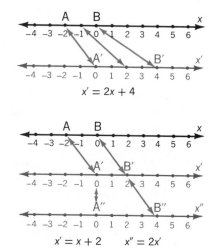

$$x' = 2x + 4$$

$$x' = x + 2 \qquad x'' = 2x'$$

Algebraic results are the same; $x + 2$ can be substituted for x' in $x'' = 2x'$ and the transformation is $x'' = 2(x + 2)$, or $x'' = 2x + 4$.

Exercises

1. Let A be -1 and B be 2. Draw number lines to illustrate the following transformations. The new points will be A' and B'.

   a. $x' = \frac{1}{2}x$ **b.** $x' = x + 3$ **c.** $x' = 3x + 2$

2. Show by drawing number lines that the following two transformations are equivalent.

   a. $x' = x + 1$ followed by $x'' = 3x'$.   **b.** $x'' = 3x + 3$

3. For each of the following, determine a translation and a stretching whose product is the linear transformation.

   a. $x'' = 2x + 4$ **b.** $x'' = \frac{1}{3}x + 3$ **c.** $x'' = x + 5$

4. Pick a particular case and show that a linear transformation $x' = ax + b$, $a \neq 0$, $b \neq 0$, multiplies the measure of the length of a segment by $|a|$.

5. Determine the linear transformation that relabels $X(1)$ as $X'(5)$ and $Y(2)$ as $Y'(7)$.

6. Show that if a translation leaves the coordinate of any point unchanged, it leaves them all unchanged. (*Hint:* Show a is 0.)

7. Show that if a stretching leaves the coordinate of any point, except 0, unchanged, then it leaves all the points unchanged.

THE GROWTH OF MATHEMATICS

Egyptian Algebra

Much of Egyptian arithmetic and algebra is known from the Rhind Papyrus of about 1700 B.C. It is a collection of 85 problems with answers (but little explanation), copied by the scribe Ahmes from an older manuscript, and called "directions for knowing all dark things."

The first part of the work deals with fractions because they presented such problems to the Egyptians. They could only work with fractions with numerators of 1. The next part deals with the fundamental operations of arithmetic. Then simple algebraic problems are treated. One problem is to find a number such that "the sum of it and one seventh of it shall together equal 19." The answer is $16\frac{5}{8}$, but it was given in an interesting form: $16 + \frac{1}{2} + \frac{1}{8}$. Symbols were used for an unknown and to show addition, subtraction, and equality. But the Egyptians did not attain in algebra what they did in geometry.

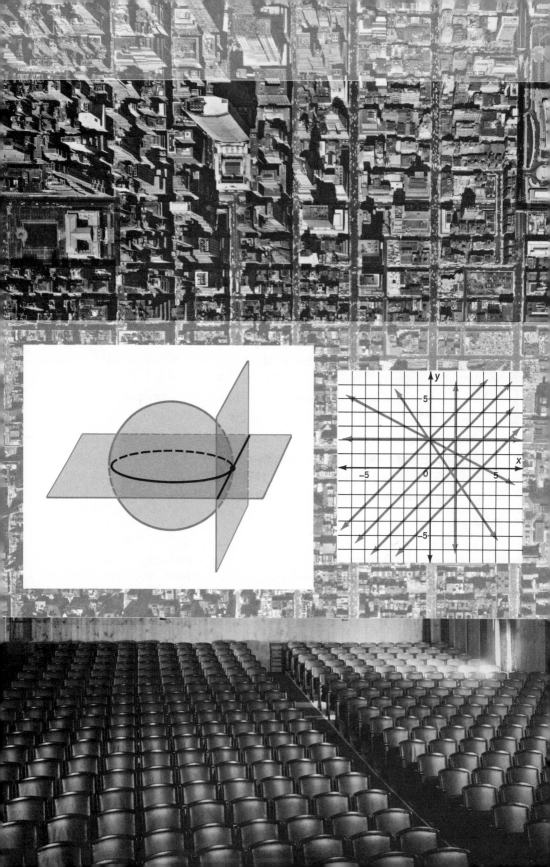

CHAPTER 4
GRAPHING RELATIONS

Many ideas of geometry are included in this chapter. You may be reviewing some terms you already know or you may be learning them for the first time.

● The figures in the center left diagram illustrate many geometric figures. The vertical plane and the sphere intersect in a point. What is the intersection of the horizontal plane and the sphere? of the two planes? How does the model of a plane differ from a geometric plane? How does the intersection of the two planes differ from a line?

● Look at the diagram at the center right. Several of the lines have a point in common. Several of the lines are parallel; they will never intersect. Yet they have something in common. What is it? What kind of lines are the ones labeled x and y? Can you tell which of the lines is defined by $y = -\frac{1}{2}x + 2$ just by looking at the equation?

● Suppose a UN delegate in New York City wanted to walk from the corner of 46th Street and First Avenue to the Public Library at 42nd Street and Fifth Avenue. How many different ways are there for him to reach the Library? If he wanted to tell someone else how to get to the Library, what would be the simplest directions he could give? Do you reach the same spot by taking a zigzag path as you would if you went in a straight path?

● Usually, seats in a theater are located by two numbers — row and seat. If you bought a theater ticket with only a row number on it, would you know exactly where to sit? Would it be enough just to have a seat number? What would tell you *exactly* where to sit? Would it make any difference if (3, 11) meant "row 3, seat 11" or "seat 3, row 11"? What would be the set of chairs with the same seat number as row number? Are any two seat numbers or row numbers the same?

4–1   Points, Lines, and Planes

From your previous study of geometry, can you tell what each of the following is: Point, line, line segment, ray, half-line, plane, half-plane, parallel lines, and perpendicular lines?

In geometry, *point*, *line*, and *plane* are **undefined terms.** They are the basic concepts needed to define the other terms. Although not formally defined, they can be described to clarify their meaning.

A **point** shows position. If you thought of a dot on a table becoming smaller and smaller until it vanished, the spot where it vanished should make you think of a point. It has no length, no width, no thickness. Points are *represented* by dots and named by capital letters.

A•

B•

C•

A **line** is an infinite set of points. If you thought first of two points and then of all the points on the straight path between them and of all the points extending without bound in either direction, you would be thinking of a line. A line has no width or thickness. A line is named by any two points on it or by one lower-case letter. The line shown in A below is named $\overleftrightarrow{MN}$. Give names for the lines shown in B and C. The points on a line are *collinear* points.

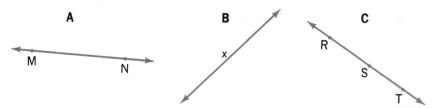

A line segment is a part of a line. In A above, points M and N and all the points between them make up a line segment. A segment, too, is an infinite set of points because there is an infinite number of points between any two points. Recall that a segment is named by a bar over the two letters, $\overline{MN}$, rather than the arrow. Points M and N are the **endpoints** of the segment.

Think of $\overline{MN}$ extended to the right to become $\overline{MX}$, as shown below. Now think of the segment extending to the right without bound, so far that for any boundary you could think of in that direction, the line would pass through it. You are thinking of a **ray.**

The ray at the bottom of the previous page is made up of point M and all the points on the N-side of M. The ray is named $\overrightarrow{MN}$. Point N and all the points on the M-side of N is ray NM, or $\overrightarrow{NM}$.

Another way to describe a line is to say that it is the union of two collinear rays such as $\overrightarrow{MN}$ and $\overrightarrow{NM}$. When you see the word *line*, it always means "straight line."

The union of two *noncollinear* rays with a common endpoint forms an **angle** such as angle MNX. The point where the two rays meet is called the **vertex.**

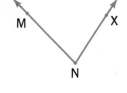

Think of ray MN. Now think of the same set of points without point M. You are thinking of a half-line. A **half-line** is a ray without the endpoint of the ray. The half-line shown below would be named $\overset{\circ}{\overrightarrow{MN}}$. The circle indicates that point M is the boundary of the half-line but not part of it.

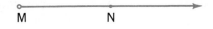

Why is the union of $\overset{\circ}{\overrightarrow{MN}}$ and $\overset{\circ}{\overrightarrow{MX}}$ not $\overleftrightarrow{XN}$, shown below?

A **plane** is an infinite set of points extending without bound in all directions. Any perfectly flat surface you can think of *represents* a *part* of a plane. Can you think of anything that would truly represent a plane? A plane has no thickness and no edges anywhere. A plane, Z, can be represented as shown at the right.

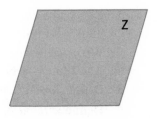

Think of line *l* contained in plane *Z*. Plane *Z* is separated into three sets: the set of points on the *A*-side of *l*, the set of points on the *B*-side of *l*, and the set of points that is *l*. The sets of points on either side of *l* are called **half-planes.**

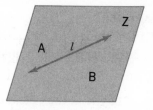

> **Definition**   A half-plane is the set of points of a plane that is on one side of a line.

The line is the **boundary,** or edge, of each half-plane, but its points do not belong to either half-plane. A half-plane can be shown with a dotted line for the boundary.

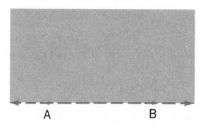

A **polygon** is a simple closed path formed by the union of three or more line segments. A polygon separates a plane into three sets of points: the points of the polygon, the points in the **interior** of the polygon, and the points in the **exterior** of the polygon.

Two lines in a plane that have no points in common are **parallel lines.** Two lines that intersect (have one point in common) forming right angles (angles of 90°) are **perpendicular lines.**

Checkpoint

1. Can you *define* a point? Can you give an example that helps you think of a point?

2. What is the relationship between a point and a line? a ray and a half-line? a plane and a half-plane?

3. Define *parallel lines; perpendicular lines.*

4. Define *without bound.*

Exercises

A   **1.** Name three pairs of parallel lines and three pairs of perpendicular lines in the drawing at the right.

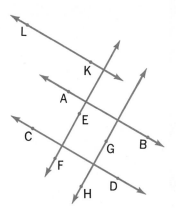

2. Two segments are parallel if they are parts of parallel lines. How would you define *perpendicular segments*? *perpendicular rays*?

3. Name four pairs of perpendicular segments in rectangle *ABCD*. Name two pairs of parallel segments.

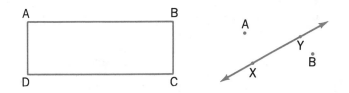

4. Think of any two points in the plane on the *A*-side of $\overleftrightarrow{XY}$. Does any segment with the two points as endpoints contain a point of $\overleftrightarrow{XY}$? Think of a point on the *A*-side and a point on the *B*-side. Does the segment with the two points as endpoints contain a point of $\overleftrightarrow{XY}$?

5. Draw a separate diagram to show the points on the

  a. *D*-side of $\overleftrightarrow{AB}$.

  b. *C*-side of $\overleftrightarrow{AB}$.

  c. *A*-side of $\overleftrightarrow{DC}$.

  d. *Y*-side of $\overleftrightarrow{CD}$.

  e. *D*-side of $\overleftrightarrow{AB}$ and also on the *B*-side of $\overleftrightarrow{DC}$.

  f. *C*-side of $\overleftrightarrow{AB}$ and also on the *A*-side of $\overleftrightarrow{CD}$.

  g. *M*-side of $\overleftrightarrow{CD}$ and also on the *Y*-side of $\overleftrightarrow{CD}$.

6. The drawing represents two perpendicular lines, $\overleftrightarrow{YY'}$ and $\overleftrightarrow{XX'}$, and all the points in a plane. The four **quadrants** bounded by the lines are named I, II, III, and IV. Which quadrant contains

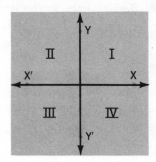

a. X-side of $\overleftrightarrow{YY'} \cap Y$-side of $\overleftrightarrow{XX'}$?

b. Y'-side of $\overleftrightarrow{XX'} \cap X$-side of $\overleftrightarrow{YY'}$?

c. X'-side of $\overleftrightarrow{YY'} \cap Y'$-side of $\overleftrightarrow{XX'}$?

d. X'-side of $\overleftrightarrow{YY'} \cap Y$-side of $\overleftrightarrow{XX'}$?

7. Use the drawing for Exercise 6. Which points are

a. on neither side of $\overleftrightarrow{YY'}$? on neither side of $\overleftrightarrow{XX'}$?

b. not in I, II, III, or IV?

c. on neither side of either line?

d. the union of I, II, III, IV, $\overleftrightarrow{YY'}$, and $\overleftrightarrow{XX'}$?

8. Consider any three points A, M, and X not on one line. Make a separate drawing to represent the points for each of the following.

a. A-side of $\overleftrightarrow{MX}$

b. A-side of $\overleftrightarrow{MX} \cap X$-side of $\overleftrightarrow{AM}$

c. (A-side of $\overleftrightarrow{MX} \cap X$-side of $\overleftrightarrow{AM}$) $\cap M$-side of $\overleftrightarrow{AX}$

d. {Points from **c**} $\cup \overline{AM} \cup \overline{AX} \cup \overline{MX}$

9. In the drawing at the right, $\overleftrightarrow{XY}$ is parallel to $\overleftrightarrow{MB}$. Complete sentences **a–h**.

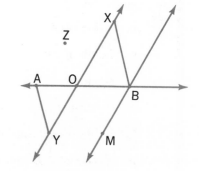

a. $\overrightarrow{OA} \cup \overrightarrow{OB} = \underline{\ ?\ }$

b. $\overrightarrow{OA} \cap \overrightarrow{OB} = \underline{\ ?\ }$

c. $(\overline{AO} \cup \overline{OY}) \cup \overline{AY} = \underline{\ ?\ }$

d. $\overleftrightarrow{XY} \cap \overleftrightarrow{MB} = \underline{\ ?\ }$

e. $\overline{OX} \cap \overline{BX} = \underline{\ ?\ }$

f. $\overline{OX} \cap \overline{AY} = \underline{\ ?\ }$

g. (Y-side of $\overleftrightarrow{AB}$) $\cap$ (A-side of $\overleftrightarrow{XY}$) $\cap$ (O-side of $\overleftrightarrow{AY}$) = _?_

h. Point _?_ is on the A-side of $\overleftrightarrow{XY}$ and the X-side of $\overleftrightarrow{AB}$.

10. Use the drawing for Exercise 9. Replace the ● with ⊆ (is contained in) or ⊄ (is not contained in) to make true sentences.

a. $\overline{XB}$ ● O-side of $\overline{AY}$

b. $\overleftrightarrow{MB}$ ● B-side of $\overleftrightarrow{XY}$

c. $\triangle AOY$ ● A-side of $\overleftrightarrow{XY}$

d. Interior of $\triangle AOY$ ● A-side of $\overline{XY}$

e. X ● A-side of $\overleftrightarrow{XY}$

f. Z ● (A-side of $\overleftrightarrow{XY}$ ∩ X-side of $\overleftrightarrow{AB}$)

4–2   Associating Points with Numbers

You know that there is a one-to-one correspondence between points on a line and the real numbers. This can be represented in many ways. Begin by choosing *any* point to match 0. Then choose a unit vector, $\vec{u}$, place its initial point at zero, and match its terminal point with a point on the line, as shown above. Call this point 1. How do you locate the point for 2? for 10? for 100? −1? −7?

To locate the point that matches $\frac{1}{3}$, separate the unit vector into three vectors of equal length. The point at the end of the first vector matches $\frac{1}{3}$.

The point at the end of the second vector matches $\frac{2}{3}$; the point at the end of the third vector matches $\frac{3}{3}$, or 1. How do you locate the point that matches $7\frac{1}{3}$? $-1\frac{3}{4}$? $2\frac{5}{7}$? In the same way, you can match all rational numbers with points on the line. But some points, infinitely many, are left over. The remaining points are matched with other real numbers, the irrational numbers, such as $\sqrt{2}$, π, $\sqrt[3]{3}$, and $-\sqrt{7}$.

Is there a relationship between the real numbers and points in a plane that is similar to the relationship between the real numbers and points on a line? In the following example, numbers are associated with *finite* sets of points not on a line.

Think of the diagram below as a classroom. The dots represent seats lined up in 5 rows, with 7 seats in a row. If the teacher asked the students in row number 3 to stand, seven people would stand up. By asking all students sitting in seat number 2, five people would stand. But by specifying *row 3, seat 2*, only one person would stand. One **ordered pair** of numbers is needed to locate each person.

Which labeled dot is named by

a. row 2, seat 3? **b.** row 5, seat 1?
c. row 1, seat 7?

Give the row number and seat number for

d. *B.* **e.** *D.* **f.** *E.*
g. *G.* **h.** *H.*

The pair of numbers (3, 5) is ordered: 3 is the number for the row and is first, and 5 is the number for the seat and is second. Which dot matches (3, 5)? (5, 1)? (1, 1)? (2, 3)?

The example of the classroom suggests a way to establish a one-to-one correspondence between points of the plane and ordered pairs of numbers.

Begin with a plane. Choose any line in the plane, such as $\overleftrightarrow{XX'}$, and associate real numbers with points on the line, as in Figure 1.

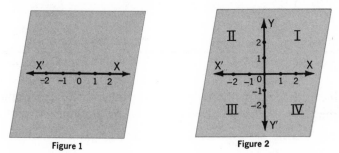

Figure 1   Figure 2

Now think of a line, $\overleftrightarrow{YY'}$, perpendicular to $\overleftrightarrow{XX'}$ at 0. Use the same unit as on $\overleftrightarrow{XX'}$ and associate numbers with each point on this line, as in Figure 2 at the bottom of page 168.

Now you can associate a pair of real numbers with any point in the plane by referring to $\overleftrightarrow{XX'}$ and $\overleftrightarrow{YY'}$. These lines are called **axes**: $\overleftrightarrow{XX'}$ is the horizontal axis, or x axis, and $\overleftrightarrow{YY'}$ is the vertical axis, or y axis. The point of intersection is the **origin**. The axes separate the plane into *quadrants*, as you saw in Exercise 6 on page 166.

The diagram below shows points for four ordered pairs of numbers. The point A for the pair (+6, +8) is located by vectors. Think of a +6 horizontal vector beginning at 0, and a +8 vector perpendicular to it at its terminal point. Then A is 6 units *to the right* and 8 units *up*.

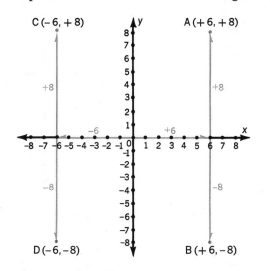

B, (+6, −8): +6 vector from 0 and −8 vector perpendicular to it (6 units *to the right* and 8 units *down*).

C, (−6, +8): −6 vector from 0 and +8 vector perpendicular to it (6 units *to the left* and 8 units *up*).

D, (−6, −8): −6 vector from 0 and −8 vector perpendicular to it (6 units *to the left* and 8 units *down*).

In the ordered pair that names a point in a plane, the x number, the **abscissa,** is always first and the y number, the **ordinate,** second. The two numbers are the **coordinates** of the point. They may be called *rectangular coordinates* because of the way the point is located. The point is the graph of the number pair. A plane with number pairs associated with the points is called a **coordinate plane.**

1. What is a rectangular-coordinate plane? How is a point located in this system?

2. What is the abscissa of an ordered pair? the ordinate?

Exercises

A **1.** One coordinate of each point shown on the diagram is given. What is the other coordinate?

$A(4, ?)$ $B(?, 6)$
$C(-4, ?)$ $D(?, 6)$
$E(-6, ?)$ $F(?, -8)$
$G(?, -7.5)$ $H(4, ?)$
$I(?, -4)$ $J(?, 0)$
$K(?, 4)$ $L(?, -10)$

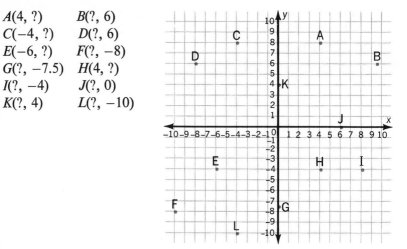

2. Name the abscissa and ordinate for each point graphed in Figure 1 below.

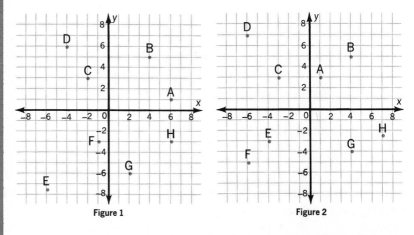

Figure 1   Figure 2

3. Write the coordinates for each point graphed in Figure 2 above.

4. Make your own coordinate plane on graph paper, and graph the following points.

$A(-2\frac{1}{4}, 6)$ $B(-1, -4)$ $C(0, 5)$ $D(-3, 0)$
$E(6, 6)$ $F(3, 7.5)$ $G(-3, -7)$ $H(5, -5)$
$I(-5, 5)$ $J(0, 0)$ $K(8, -2)$ $L(-5, -3\frac{1}{2})$

5. Draw axes on graph paper and graph these points: $A(3, 1)$, $B(-1, 1)$, $C(-2, -2)$, $D(2, -2)$. Connect A to B, B to C, C to D, and D to A by line segments. What is the name of the geometric figure you obtain?

6. Draw axes and graph these points: $(-6, 3)$, $(-4, 3)$, $(-1\frac{1}{2}, 3)$, $(0, 3)$, $(2.6, 3)$, $(4, 3)$. What do you observe about the ordinates of all six points? If you graphed *all* points with the ordinate of 3, your graph would be a _?_ parallel to the _?_ axis.

7. Use the same axes as in Exercise 6, and locate these points: $(-6, -4)$, $(-4\frac{3}{4}, -4)$, $(-1, -4)$, $(0, -4)$, $(3\frac{1}{3}, -4)$, $(5, -4)$. What is true about the ordinates of these six points? If you graphed *all* points with the ordinate -4, your graph would be a _?_ parallel to the _?_ axis.

8. From your answers to Exercises 6 and 7, what statement can you make about the graph of all points with the same ordinate?

9. Draw axes on graph paper and graph these points: $(4, 5)$, $(4, 3)$, $(4, \frac{1}{2})$, $(4, 0)$, $(4, -1)$, $(4, -4\frac{2}{3})$, $(4, -6)$. What pattern do you see in the coordinates for these six points? If you graph *all* the points with 4 as their abscissa, the graph will be a _?_ parallel to the _?_ axis.

10. Using the same axes as in Exercise 9, graph these points: $(-2, -5.75)$, $(-2, -4)$, $(-2, -1)$, $(-2, 0)$, $(-2, 2)$, $(-2, 3\frac{1}{2})$, $(-2, 6)$. What is alike for the coordinates of these points? What will be the graph of *all* points with the abscissa -2?

11. From your answers to Exercises 9 and 10, what statement can you make about the graph of all points with the same abscissa?

12. The figure at the right shows the four quadrants into which the coordinate plane is separated. Both the abscissa and ordinate of any point in the first quadrant are positive. Describe the abscissa and ordinate of any point in each of the other three quadrants.

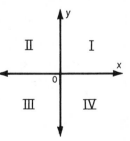

B **13.** Referring to the figure below, complete the following sentences with I, II, III, or IV.

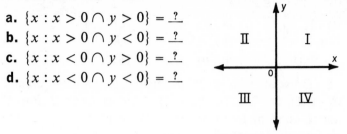

a. $\{x : x > 0 \cap y > 0\}$ = _?_
b. $\{x : x > 0 \cap y < 0\}$ = _?_
c. $\{x : x < 0 \cap y > 0\}$ = _?_
d. $\{x : x < 0 \cap y < 0\}$ = _?_

14. If the x axis in the figure for Exercise 13 is $\overleftrightarrow{XX'}$ and the y axis is $\overleftrightarrow{YY'}$, complete the following to make true sentences.

a. $\overleftrightarrow{YY'} \cap \overleftrightarrow{XX'}$ = _?_
b. $\overleftrightarrow{YY'} \cap I$ = _?_
c. $I \cap II$ = _?_
d. $I \cup II \cup III \cup IV \cup \overleftrightarrow{XX'} \cup \overleftrightarrow{YY'}$ = _?_

15. The following groups of coordinates each represent three vertices of a rectangle. Graph the points in each group. Then locate the fourth vertex and give its coordinates.

a. $(-3, -3), (-7, -5), (-7, -3)$
b. $(-7, 3), (-4, 3), (-7, 5)$
c. $(6, 8), (7, 2), (7, 8)$
d. $(0, 3\frac{1}{2}), (6, -4), (6, 3\frac{1}{2})$
e. $(-6, 1), (-1, 5), (-6, 5)$
f. $(-5, -1), (-8, -4), (-6, -6)$

16. The following groups of coordinates each represent three vertices of a parallelogram. Graph the points in each group. Then locate two points, each of which could be the fourth vertex. Give the coordinates of both points.

a. $(-3, -3), (-7, -5), (-7, -3)$
b. $(-7, 3), (-4, 3), (-7, 5)$
c. $(6, 8), (7, 2), (7, 8)$
d. $(3, 4), (2, 7), (3, 7)$
e. $(-6, 1), (-1, 5), (-6, 5)$
f. $(-6, 8), (-8, 5), (-1, 6)$

17. The following pairs of coordinates locate the endpoints of the hypotenuse of a right triangle. There is only one point below the hypotenuse that could be the third vertex if the triangle is to be a right triangle. Give the coordinates of that point.

  a. (0, 6) and (5, 0)   **b.** (−5, 0) and (0, −3)
  c. (4, 4) and (1, −2)   **d.** (−2, 7) and (2, −2)

C **18.** Points in a plane can also be located by a distance on a ray and an angle measure in degrees.

Designate a horizontal ray pointing to the right as the **zero ray.** This ray can be rotated in a circle, sweeping over 360°. Thus, $\frac{1}{360}$ of a rotation is equivalent to 1°. Assign a ray that has made $\frac{1}{36}$ of a rotation as the 10° ray; a ray that has made $\frac{1}{18}$ of a rotation as the 20° ray, and so on. The zero ray is assigned to 0°. Assign units to the zero ray as you would a number line. The endpoint of the zero ray, the **pole,** is 0. Then with the pole as the center, draw a circle with a radius of 1 unit, a circle with a radius of 2 units, and so on. This model represents the **polar-coordinate plane.**

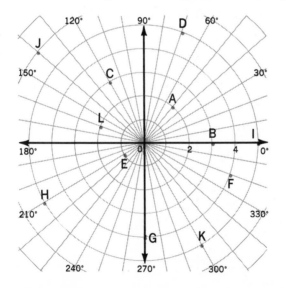

To locate a point, move along the zero ray, or **polar axis,** a certain number of units and then move along in a circle to the ray for the correct degree measure. As with the rectangular-coordinate plane, points are named by ordered pairs. The point for (2, 50°) is point *A* in the diagram. What is the name for point *B*? It is at the point for 3 on the zero ray, so it would be (3, 0°).

Give the ordered pairs for points *C–L*.

4–3 Graphing Relations

A space vehicle is moving through space at 7 miles per second. The total distance it travels can be found by multiplying by 7 the number of seconds it is moving.

This is an example of a **relation.** In mathematics, a relation, such as that between the d miles that a space vehicle travels in t seconds at 7 miles per second, can be expressed in several ways, any one of which is correct.

① A sentence: The distance traveled in miles is 7 times the number of seconds.

② An equation: $d = 7t$.

③ Ordered pairs of numbers in a table.

t	0	1	2	3	4	5	6 $\cdots$
d	0	7	14	21	28	35	42 $\cdots$

④ Ordered pairs of numbers in set form.

$\{(0, 0), (1, 7), (2, 14), (3, 21), (4, 28), (5, 35), (6, 42), \cdots\}$

⑤ Ordered pairs of numbers, (t, d), graphed as points in a plane.

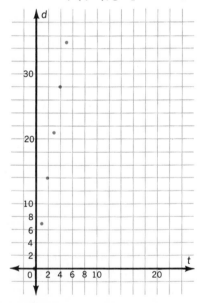

Here is another relation. A railroad divided its line into zones and charged one fare to any station in a zone. For $0.50 you could ride to station 1, 2, or 3. For $0.75 you could ride to station 4 or 5. For $1.10 you could ride to station 6, 7, or 8.

This relation cannot be expressed using an equation. You could use the graph, but graphs are often not compact. In this book, a relation is a set of ordered pairs as in the table or in set notation.

$$\{(0, 0), (1, 7), (2, 14), (3, 21), (4, 28), (5, 35), (6, 42), \cdots\}$$

Definition A relation is a set of ordered pairs.

The **domain** of a relation is the set of first numbers of the ordered pairs. The **range** is the set of second numbers in the pairs.

In the space-vehicle example, the domain is $\{0, 1, 2, 3, 4, \cdots\}$ and the range is $\{0, 7, 14, 21, 28, \cdots\}$. The problem is such that the domain could also be defined as the set of nonnegative real numbers.

In the train-fare example, if the domain is $\{\$0.50, \$0.75, \$1.10\}$, what is the range?

The graph of a relation is the set of points whose coordinates are the ordered pairs of the relation.

To graph a relation defined by an equation, plot the points whose coordinates are the pairs of numbers that make the equation true.

EXAMPLE. Graph the relation defined by $y = 3x - 2$ if the replacement set for x, or domain, is $\{0, 1, 2, 3, 4, 5\}$. Give the range.

① Determine the ordered pairs of the relation.

When x is	0	1	2	3	4	5
y is	−2	1	4	7	10	13

Notice that the range is $\{-2, 1, 4, 7, 10, 13\}$.

② Set up coordinate axes and locate a point for each pair. The six points that form the graph are shown at the right.

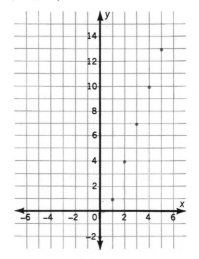

Since the domain in the above example was a finite set of whole numbers, the graph consisted of a finite set of points. If the domain were given as the set of nonnegative real numbers, as it was for $d = 7t$, then there would be infinitely many points and the graph would be a line, as will be shown in a later section.

1. What is a relation? Give some examples of how it may be defined.

2. A relation has a domain and a range. Explain these terms.

Exercises

A — Give the domain and range of each relation defined below. Draw the graph of each.

1. {(1, 2), (2, 2), (3, 1), (4, 3), (5, 3), (6, 6)}

2. {(1, 1), (3, 3), (6, 6)}

3. {(1, 1), (3, 3), (4, 4), (5, 3), (6, 1), (6, 7), (7, 5)}

4. The equation $y = 3x + 4$ defines a relation between x and y. Complete the table showing the number pairs that satisfy the relation $y = 3x + 4$, if the domain is {−1, 0, 1, 2, 3, 4, 7}.

When x is	−1	0	1	2	3	4	7
y is	1	4	?	?	?	?	?

5. The perimeter of a regular hexagon is related to the length of one side. The relation is defined by $p = 6s$. Complete the table below for $p = 6s$. Then graph the relation.

When s is	0	1	2	3	4	5	6
p is	0	6	?	?	?	?	?

6. The ordered pairs listed below define a relation between the two sets {0, 2, 3, 4, 5} and {1, 2, 3, 4}.

{(0, 1), (2, 1), (3, 2), (4, 2), (4, 3), (5, 4)}.

Graph the relation.

7. The graph at the right defines a relation. Define this relation by listing the ordered pairs that are the coordinates of the points.

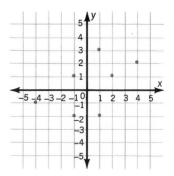

8. The relation in Exercise 7 cannot be defined easily by a simple sentence, but it can be defined easily by a table. Construct such a table for this relation.

9. Draw the graph of the relation defined by $y = 2x + 1$ where x is $\{-1, -2, -3, -4, -5\}$.

—— Make a table showing the ordered pairs of each relation. Then graph the relation. The domain given for the variable is to be represented on the horizontal axis.

Equation	Domain
10. $\{(x, y) : y = 2x\}$	$x \in \{0, 2, 4, 6\}$
11. $\{(x, y) : y = 2x + 3\}$	$x \in \{0, 2, 4, 6\}$
12. $\{(x, y) : y = x^2\}$	$x \in \{-3, -2, -1, 0, 1, 2, 3\}$
13. $\{(x, y) : y = -x^2\}$	$x \in \{-3, -2, -1, 0, 1, 2, 3\}$
14. $\{(x, y) : xy = 24\}$	$x \in \{1, 2, 3, 4, 6, 8, 12, 24\}$
15. $\{(x, y) : x + y = 10\}$	$x \in \{-5, -3, -1, 1, 3, 5\}$

16. Which relations in Exercises 10–15 have graphs that lie along a line? What do the equations for these relations have in common?

B **17.** A relation defined by the equation $y = |2x + 5|$ has the domain $\{-1, -2, -3, -4, -5\}$. What is its range?

—— Give the domain and range of each of the graphed relations.

18.

19.

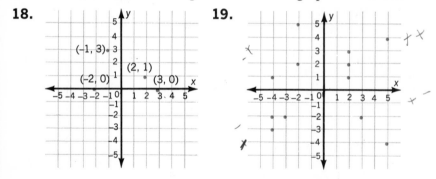

C —— Give the domain and range of each of the graphed relations.

20.

21.

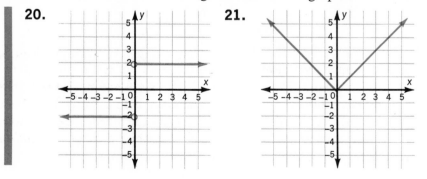

4–4 Graphing Linear Functions

A relation is a set of ordered pairs.

a. {($0.50, 1), ($0.50, 2), ($0.50, 3), ($0.75, 4), ($0.75, 5), ($1.10, 6), ($1.10, 7), ($1.10, 8)}

b. {(0, 0), (1, 7), (2, 14), (3, 21), (4, 28), (5, 35), (6, 42)}

The first elements of the ordered pairs of some relations, such as **b**, are always different. Such relations are called **functions.**

> **Definition**   A <u>function</u> is a set of ordered pairs of which no two first elements are the same.

If a function is expressed as an equation, the variables can be classified as dependent or independent. The **independent variable** is the variable whose replacement set is the domain of the function. The value of the **dependent variable** is found by choosing values from the replacement set for the independent variable and solving the equation; that is, the value of one variable *depends* on the value chosen for the other variable.

Below are the graphs of three relations.

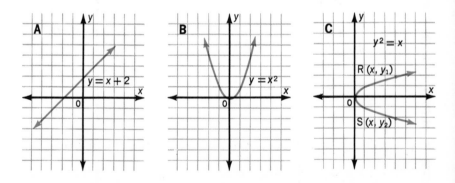

If you examine the ordered pair for any point on the graph in A, the first member will always be different from the first member in any other ordered pair. The same is true in B. So A and B are the graphs of functions. But in C, the ordered pairs for points R and S have the same first member, that is, the same value for the independent variable, x. In fact, except for (0, 0), there is an infinite number of pairs of ordered pairs with the same first member. Explain why.

It is easy to see from a graph whether or not the relation is a function. Think of a vertical line moving from left to right. If the line in every position intersects the graph in only one point, the relation graphed is a function.

A function of special importance is the **linear function.** It is *linear* because its graph is a line. The function graphed in A is a linear function. It will be defined in algebraic terms in a later section.

EXAMPLE 1. Graph $y = x + 4$ if the domain is the real numbers.

① Make a table of some pairs of numbers that satisfy $y = x + 4$. Choose any numbers for x and find the corresponding numbers for y.

When x is	−5	−4	−3	−2	−1	0	1	2	3	4	5
y is	−1	0	1	2	3	4	5	6	7	8	9

The table shows only eleven of the infinite set of ordered pairs that make $y = x + 4$ true.

② On coordinate axes, locate a point for each ordered pair in the table.

The points are shown at the right.

③ The eleven points lie in a line. If you were to locate a point for every ordered pair that satisfies the equation, all the points would form a line. *The line is the graph of $y = x + 4$.*

Use a straightedge and draw the part of the line that includes the set of points represented in the table. The complete graph of $y = x + 4$ continues indefinitely in both directions. The arrows show that the graph is a line.

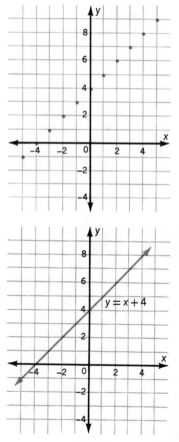

If you know that an equation defines a linear function, you actually need to plot only two points (with a third point as a check).

EXAMPLE 2. $x + y = 10$ defines a linear function if the domain for x is the set of real numbers. Graph the function $\{(x, y) : x + y = 10\}$.

① Find two ordered pairs that satisfy the equation. (It is wise to choose values so that the corresponding points are not too close together.)

$$\{(0, 10), (5, 5)\}$$

② Plot, or locate, the points.

③ Draw the line containing the two points.

④ Check another pair of numbers to verify that you have the correct line for the linear function. For example, $(2, 8)$ makes $x + y = 10$ true, and the point is on the graph.

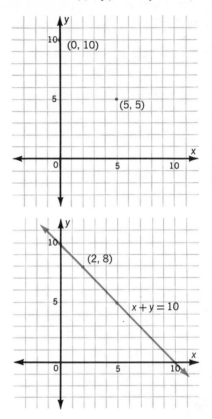

Checkpoint

1. How is a function a special relation?
2. What is a linear function?

Exercises

A ── In Exercises 1–10, tell which ordered pair satisfies the equation.

1. $y - x = 6$; $(-2, 8), (2, 8)$ **2.** $x - 3y = 12$; $(3, 5), (6, -2)$
3. $2y + 6x = 0$; $(0, 0), (6, 2)$ **4.** $4x - 5y = 1$; $(0, 0), (-1, -1)$
5. $\frac{y}{5} = 2x$; $(1, -10), (-2, -20)$ **6.** $\frac{y}{4} = x$; $(12, -3), (-1, -4)$

7. $2(x - 3) = 4(y - 2)$; $(0, -\frac{1}{2})$, $(-1, 0)$

8. $1\frac{1}{2}x + y = 2$; $(0, 2)$, $(2, 1)$

9. $5x - 3y - 30 = 0$; $(6, 0)$, $(-3, 15)$

10. $3y = 7x$; $(0, 1)$, $(0, 0)$

11. $y = 2x - 6$ defines a function. Complete the following table.

When x is	−4	−2	0	2	4	6	10
y is	−14	?	?	?	?	?	?

Draw the graph for the function if the domain is the set of real numbers, using the ordered pairs in the table.

12. Why does $y = 2x - 6$ in Exercise 11 define a linear function?

13. Does $y = x - 3$ define a linear function? Explain.

—— Make a table containing several pairs of numbers for the function defined in each of the following sets. The domain is the set of real numbers. Draw the graph of each function and tell if it is a linear function.

14. $\{(x, y) : y = x + 2\}$ **15.** $\{(x, y) : y = 3x - 2\}$

16. $\{(x, y) : y = 5x + 6\}$ **17.** $\{(x, y) : y = 4x\}$

18. $\{(x, y) : y = 4x - 5\}$ **19.** $\{(x, y) : y = \frac{1}{2}x + 3\}$

20. $\left\{(x, y) : y = \frac{6 - 2x}{3}\right\}$ **21.** $\left\{(x, y) : y = \frac{-2x + 1}{5}\right\}$

B —— Draw the graph of each equation. The replacement set is the set of real numbers.

Example. Graph $\{(x, y) : y = 5\}$.

① Think $y = (0 \cdot x) + 5$.

When x is	−5	−3	0	4
y is	5	5	5	5

② Graph the points.

③ The graph is a line parallel to the x axis, crossing the y axis at $(0, 5)$.

22. $y = (0 \cdot x) - 4$ **23.** $y = (0 \cdot x) + 7$ **24.** $x = 3$

25. $x = 6\frac{1}{2}$ **26.** $y = -9$ **27.** $x = -8$

28. Which equations in Exercises 22–27 define a relation? a function? Equations of the form $y = b$, where b is a constant number, define the **constant function.**

4–5 Equations for Linear Functions

You know from the previous section that the following equations define linear functions if x is in the set of real numbers.

a. $y = x + 4$ b. $y = -x + 10$ c. $y = 2x - 6$

From these examples, the following definition is stated.

> **Definition**   A <u>linear function</u> is a function defined by the equation $y = mx + b$, where m and b are constants ($m \neq 0$) and the domain for x is the set of real numbers.

What is m in sentences **a** and **b** above? What is b in sentence **a**? in sentence **c**?

To see if an equation defines a linear function, write an equivalent equation in the form $y = mx + b$.

EXAMPLE 1. Write an equivalent equation for $2x - 3y = 12$ in the form $y = mx + b$. Then graph the equation.

① For convenience, make y have a positive coefficient by multiplying both sides of the equation by -1.
$$-1(2x - 3y) = -1(12)$$
$$-2x + 3y = -12$$

② Add $2x$.
$$-2x + 3y + 2x = -12 + 2x$$
$$3y = -12 + 2x$$

③ Multiply by $\frac{1}{3}$.
$$\tfrac{1}{3}(3y) = \tfrac{1}{3}(-12 + 2x)$$
$$y = -4 + \tfrac{2}{3}x,$$
$$\text{or } y = \tfrac{2}{3}x - 4$$

Then $2x - 3y = 12$ is equivalent to $y = \frac{2}{3}x - 4$, which is in the form $y = mx + b$, and it is a linear function.

If x is 0, then y is $0 - 4$, or -4.

The table shows some other ordered pairs.

x	0	3	-3	6	-6
y	-4	-2	-6	0	-8

Locate the points on the coordinate plane. The graph is a line, as shown at the right.

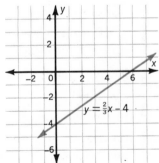

EXAMPLE 2. Express $2x + 5y = -8$ in the form $y = mx + b$ and graph the equation.

$$2x + 5y = -8$$

① Add $-2x$.
$$2x + 5y - 2x = -8 - 2x$$
$$5y = -8 - 2x$$

② Divide by 5.
$$y = \frac{-8 - 2x}{5}$$
$$y = -\tfrac{8}{5} - \tfrac{2}{5}x, \text{ or } -\tfrac{2}{5}x - \tfrac{8}{5}$$

③ Find some ordered pairs of the function. Try to choose integers for x such that the corresponding values for y will be integers. When x is -9, y is $-\tfrac{2}{5}(-9) - \tfrac{8}{5}$, or $\tfrac{18}{5} - \tfrac{8}{5}$, or 2. Check to see that the other ordered pairs in the table are correct.

x	-9	-4	1	6
y	2	0	-2	-4

④ Use the ordered pairs to draw the graph.

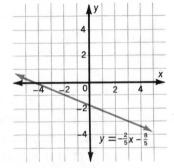

$$y = -\tfrac{2}{5}x - \tfrac{8}{5}$$

Now try these

—— Write the following equations in $y = mx + b$ form.

1. $2x + y = 1$ **2.** $x + 6y = 9$

3. $4x - \tfrac{1}{2}y = 3$ **4.** $-\tfrac{1}{5}x + \tfrac{1}{3}y = -2$

5. Which of the following are linear functions?

  a. $3x(2y) = -8$ **b.** $15 - \tfrac{3}{4}y = 3x$

  c. $-x + 4 = 7y$ **d.** $y = 1.6 - 2x^2$

Answers: **1.** $y = -2x + 1$ **2.** $y = -\tfrac{1}{6}x + 1\tfrac{1}{2}$ **3.** $y = 8x - 6$ **4.** $y = \tfrac{3}{5}x - 6$
    5. b and c

Checkpoint

  1. Define *linear function*.

  2. How do you know if an equation defines a linear function?

Exercises

A —— Write each equation in $y = mx + b$ form.

1. $2x + y = 3$ **2.** $3x + y = 4$

3. $2x + 3y = 7$ **4.** $x + 2y = 5$

5. $2x - y = 3$ **6.** $3x - y = 4$

7. $5x - y = -6$ **8.** $3x - 2y = 4$

9. $2x - 3y = -7$ **10.** $5x - 7y = 12$

11. $3x + 4y = -5$ **12.** $4x - 3y = 5$

—— Find three ordered pairs that satisfy each of the following linear functions. The replacement set is the set of real numbers. Graph each function.

13. $2x + y = 3$ **14.** $3x + y = 4$

15. $2x + 3y = 7$ **16.** $3x + 2y = 5$

17. $2x - y = 3$ **18.** $3x - 2y = 0$

19. $2x - 3y = -7$ **20.** $5x - 7y = 12$

21. $3x + 4y = -5$ **22.** $4x - 3y = 5$

—— Draw the graphs for the following sets of number pairs. The replacement set is the set of real numbers. Represent the variable that is first in each pair on the horizontal axis.

23. $\{(x, y) : x + y = 5\}$ **24.** $\{(x, y) : 3x + 2y = -1\}$

25. $\{(x, y) : \frac{x}{2} + y = 3\}$ **26.** $\{(x, y) : 3(x + 2) = 2(y + 1)\}$

27. $\{(a, b) : a = b + 1\}$ **28.** $\{(s, t) : -2s + t = 3\}$

—— Find the coordinates of the point at which the graph of each equation crosses the x axis (y will be 0) and the coordinates of the point at which the graph crosses the y axis (x will be 0).

29. $y = 2x - 6$ **30.** $9y - 26 = 2x$

31. $2x + 3y = 6$ **32.** $3x + y = 4$

33. $y = -2x$ **34.** $3(2x - 4) = 2(y - 5)$

35. $x - y = 10$ **36.** $3\left(\frac{x}{2}\right) + y = 3$

37. $12x - 5 = 5y$ **38.** $\frac{x}{6} = 3x + 4$

B   **39.** What is the graph of the equation $x = 0$? of $x = 1$? $x = -2$? If b is any constant, does $x = b$ define a linear function?

40. What is the graph of the equation $y = 0$? What is the graph of $y = -3\frac{1}{2}$? $y = 5$? If b is any constant, does $y = b$ define a function? Does $y = b$ define a linear function?

41. Complete this table showing seven ordered pairs that satisfy $y = x^2 + 2$. Then graph the ordered pairs.

x	-5	-3	-1	0	1	3	5
y	27	11	$?$	$?$	$?$	$?$	$?$

Does $y = x^2 + 2$ define a linear function? Sketch a smooth curve containing the seven points you plotted.

42. Complete the table showing six number pairs that satisfy $xy = 6$. Then plot the six points.

x	12	6	3	2	1	$\frac{1}{2}$
y	$\frac{1}{2}$	1	$?$	$?$	$?$	$?$

Do the points lie in a line? Does $xy = 6$ define a function? a linear function? Sketch a smooth curve containing the six points.

4–6 Slope of a Line

If you choose any two points on a line, the segment between the two points slants in a particular direction. Segments of the same line all slant in the same direction. To get from one point on the line to another, you could move along the line. You could also move between the two points, first in a horizontal direction and then in a vertical direction, as shown by the graphs below.

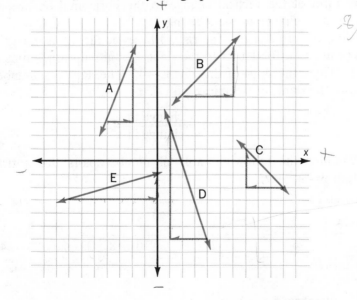

Consider the equation $y = 4x + 2$. The graph of the equation is shown at the right below.

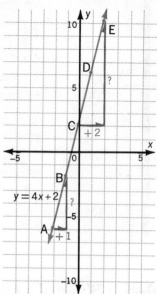

Start at point A and draw a +1 vector horizontally. What vertical vector then brings you to B? Start at B and draw a +1 vector horizontally. What vector then brings you to C? If you start at any point and draw a +1 vector horizontally, what vertical vector brings you to a point of the line?

All along the line, as x changes by +1, y changes by _?_. The ratio of the number for which the vertical vector is a model, +4, to the number for which the horizontal vector is a model, +1, is _?_. This can be abbreviated as

$$\frac{\text{vertical vector}}{\text{horizontal vector}} = \frac{+4}{+1}.$$

If you start at point C and draw a +2 vector horizontally, what vertical vector brings you to a point on the line? If you start at any point on the line and draw a +2 vector horizontally, what vertical vector brings you to a point of the line?

As x changes by +2, y changes by _?_. The ratio of the number for which the vertical vector is a model, +8, to the number for which the horizontal vector is a model, +2, is _?_. This could also be expressed as the ratio of the vertical change to the horizontal change, or the ratio of the y change to the x change.

You can see that the line rises 4 times as fast as it moves to the right (4 units up for 1 unit to the right; 8 units up for 2 units to the right). Then, the **slope** of this line is +4. The slope is a number that indicates the slant, or steepness, of a line.

$$\text{Slope} = \frac{\text{change in } y}{\text{change in } x}$$

Examine the following table of number pairs that satisfy the equation $y = 4x + 2$.

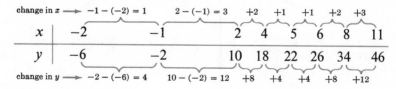

From the table it can be seen that the ratio of the change in y to the change in x is always the same, $+4$.

$$\frac{\text{change in } y}{\text{change in } x} = \frac{+4}{+1}, \text{ or } \frac{+8}{+2}, \text{ or } \frac{+12}{+3}$$

If you are given the coordinates of two points, (x_1, y_1) and (x_2, y_2), you can find the change by subtracting the coordinates, rather than by graphing. The slope of a line is $\frac{y_2 - y_1}{x_2 - x_1}$, as shown in the table.

Shown below are the graphs of the lines that you saw at the beginning of the section. The equation for A is $y = 2\frac{1}{2}x + 13$; the slope is $\frac{+5}{+2}$, or $2\frac{1}{2}$. The equation for C is $y = -x + 8$; the slope is $\frac{+3}{-3}$, or -1. The equation for B is $y = x + 3$; for D, $y = -3x + 6$; for E, $y = \frac{2}{7}x - 1$. What are the slopes for B, D, and E?

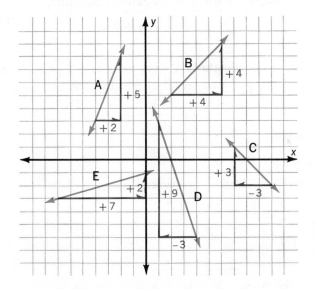

Do you see a pattern between the numbers for the slopes and the equations of the lines? The slope of the line is the coefficient of x for a linear equation with y alone on one side. In other words, **the slope of $y = mx + b$ is m.**

If you compare the slopes and the lines, you will see that the lines with positive slopes slant up to the right. How would you describe the lines with negative slopes?

Another characteristic of a graph can be read from its equation. The point at which a line crosses the y axis is called the **y intercept.**

If you extended each of lines A–E on the previous page so they crossed the y axis, you could give the coordinates of the y intercept. You can do this by simply laying a straightedge along the line and seeing where it crosses the y axis.

	Equation	Slope	y intercept
A	$y = \frac{5}{2}x + 13$	$\frac{5}{2}$	(0, 13)
B	$y = x + 3$	1	?
C	$y = -x + 8$	-1	(0, 8)
D	$y = -\frac{3}{2}x + 6$	$-\frac{3}{2}$	?
E	$y = \frac{2}{7}x - 1$	$\frac{2}{7}$	?

What are the y intercepts for B, D, and E?

The y coordinate of the ordered pair for the y intercept is what constant in the equation for the line?

In general **the y intercept for $y = mx + b$ is (0, b).** To understand this further, use 0 for x in the general equation.

$$y = (m \cdot 0) + b$$
$$y = b$$

Since the x coordinate is always zero at the point where a line crosses the y axis, you can see algebraically that the y coordinate is always b.

Now try these

— Complete the table.

Equation	Slope	y intercept
1. $y = 2x + 5$	?	?
2. $y = 6x - 7$	?	?
3. $y = \frac{2}{3}x + \frac{1}{2}$	?	?
4. $5x + y = 6$	?	?

Answers: **1.** 2, (0, 5) **2.** 6, (0, −7) **3.** $\frac{2}{3}$, (0, $\frac{1}{2}$) **4.** −5, (0, 6)

Checkpoint

1. What is meant by the *slope of a line*? When is the slope positive? negative?

2. How could you tell the slope of a line if you were given its graph? its equation?

3. What is the y intercept of a line?

Exercises

A —— What is the slope of the graph for each equation below?

1. $y = 2x$ **2.** $y = \frac{3}{4}x + 7$ **3.** $y = -2x + 9$

4. $y = -\frac{1}{3}x$ **5.** $y = 5x$ **6.** $y = -\frac{3}{5}x - 2$

7. $y = 3x - 4$ **8.** $y = -1\frac{1}{4}x - \frac{1}{2}$ **9.** $y = x + 5$ -5^{x}

10. $y = 4x + 1$ **11.** $y = -9x$ **12.** $y = \frac{2}{3}x - 3$

—— Change each equation to $y = mx + b$ form, and then give the slope and the y intercept of the graph for the equation.

13. $2x - 5y = 8$ **14.** $y - 5x = 10$ **15.** $3y - x = 7$

16. $y - \frac{1}{2}x = 8$ **17.** $4x - 2y = 12$ **18.** $8 + y = 6x$

19. $y - 2x = -4$ **20.** $8 + 4x = 3y$ **21.** $3x - 4y = -7$

22. $5 - 2y = 5x$ **23.** $y - x = 0$ **24.** $x - y = 0$

25. Graph the points with the coordinates $(-3, -14)$, $(-1, -8)$, $(1, -2)$, $(3, 4)$, and $(5, 10)$. Draw a line through the five points. As x changes by $+2$, y changes by $\underline{?}$. What is the slope of the line? The equation of the line is $y = \underline{?} \, x - 5$.

26. What is the equation of a line that has a slope of 3 and that crosses the y axis at $(0, 5)$?

27. What is the slope of each of the lines graphed below?

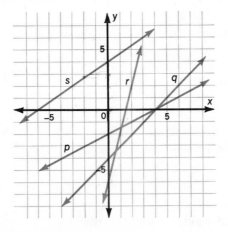

28. Refer to the figure for Exercise 27 to complete the following.

   a. The equation for line p is $y = \underline{?} \, x - 2$.

   b. The equation for line q is $y = \underline{?} \, x - 4$.

   c. The equation for line r is $y = \underline{?} \, x - 6$.

   d. The equation for line s is $y = \underline{?} \, x - \underline{?}$.

B —— In each of the following exercises, you are given the equation for a function and its domain. Draw the graph of each function. Then describe the graph and state the range for each function.

29. $y = 4x$; $\{0, 1, 2, 3, 4\}$

30. $y = x - 8$; $\{4, 7, 9\}$

31. $y = 2x + 4$; {real numbers 2 through 8}

32. $y = -6$; {real numbers -4 through $+4$}

33. At a supermarket, chewing gum sells at 3 packages for 10¢ or 5¢ each if not bought in threes.

a. Complete the table below showing the cost in cents of x packages of gum if x is 10 or less.

When x is	0	1	2	3	4	5	6	7	8	9	10
Cost is	0	5	10	10	?	?	?	?	?	?	?

b. Plot the eleven points taken from the completed table.

c. What is the domain?

d. What is the range?

34. The cost of first-class mail is 6¢ per ounce or fraction of an ounce. Thus, the cost of mailing a letter weighing $2\frac{1}{4}$ ounces is 3×6¢, or 18¢.

a. Complete the table that shows the cost in cents of mailing a letter weighing w ounces.

When w is	0	$\frac{1}{2}$	$\frac{3}{4}$	1	$1\frac{1}{2}$	$1\frac{7}{8}$	2	$2\frac{1}{8}$	3	$3\frac{1}{2}$	4	5
Cost is	0	6	6	6	?	?	?	?	?	?	?	?

b. If your letter weighs 5 ounces or less, then the cost will be any one of the numbers ? .

c. Part of the graph is shown at the right. Complete the graph for w that are equal to 0 through 4.

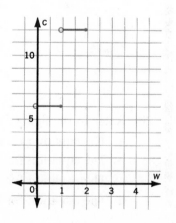

35. Canned cherries sell at 3 cans for 49¢ or 17¢ for each can. Make a table that shows the cost of n cans if n is 10 or less. Graph the points.

4–7   Graphing by Slopes

You have graphed linear functions by choosing several ordered pairs of numbers. You can also draw the graph if you know only the slope of the line and the coordinates for one point.

EXAMPLE 1. Draw the graph of a line that has a slope of 3 and passes through the point $(0, -5)$.

Locate $(0, -5)$. Since the slope is 3, or $\frac{3}{1}$, y changes by 3 as x changes by 1. From $(0, -5)$, move 1 unit to the right and then 3 units up. This locates a second point and you can draw the line through two points.

Could you also have correctly located a second point by moving 2 units to the right and then 6 units up? Why?

Locate one or two more points to check your work.

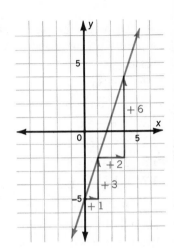

EXAMPLE 2. Use a point and the slope to graph $y = -\frac{3}{4}x + 2$.

Find the coordinates of one point on the line. The simplest one is found when x is 0. The point is $(0, 2)$. Locate that point.

From the equation, the slope is $-\frac{3}{4}$. You can interpret the $-\frac{3}{4}$ as meaning y changes by -3 as x changes by $+4$, $\frac{-3}{+4}$, or y changes by $+3$ as x changes by -4, $\frac{+3}{-4}$. Locate a point and draw the graph. You can see from the graph that both points are on the line and either one would give the correct line.

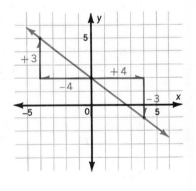

Notice that one of the changes is negative and the other positive. The minus sign in front of the fraction for the slope could not mean that both changes were negative, because that would give a positive slope; that is, $\frac{-3}{-4}$ is $+\frac{3}{4}$, which is not the slope of this line.

Exercises

A ——— In each of the following exercises, you are given the coordinates of a point and the slope of a line. Use them to draw a line.

1. $(0, 5)$; 4

2. $(0, 0)$; $-\frac{1}{2}$

3. $(-3, -2)$; 3

4. $(0, -3)$; -6

5. $(3, 4)$; $\frac{2}{3}$

6. $(-5, 7)$; $-\frac{3}{5}$

——— Draw the graph for each of the following equations by using a point and the slope. Be sure each equation is in the $y = mx + b$ form.

7. $y = 3x - 2$

8. $y = -6x$

9. $y = 5x - 6$

10. $-2x + y = 4$

11. $y = -\frac{2}{3}x - 6$

12. $3x = y + 6$

13. $y - 3x = 1$

14. $4y = 5x + 12$

15. $2x - y = 3$

16. $-5y + 2x = -10$

17. $-\frac{7}{8}x = -y + 5$

18. $2x = 9 + 3y$

19. From your results in Exercises 7–18, which way does a line slant if its slope is positive? if its slope is negative? Can you draw a line whose slope is zero?

B **20.** Draw the graphs of the following three equations on the same set of axes.

    a. $y = \frac{1}{2}x$ **b.** $y = 2x$ **c.** $y = 3x$

If you have graphed the lines correctly, they should intersect in one common point. What is that point?

——— Graph the following to find the point that is common to each of the groups of three equations.

21. $y = 2$
$y = -x + 5$
$y = \frac{1}{3}x + 1$

22. $y = -2x + 1$
$y = -\frac{2}{5}x + 2\frac{3}{5}$
$y = \frac{1}{2}x + 3\frac{1}{2}$

23. $x - y = 0$
$x + 4y = -5$
$3x + y = -4$

24. $y = 1\frac{1}{2}x - 8$
$2x + \frac{1}{2}y = 7$
$3x + 4y = 4$

25. $x + y = 1$
$y = x + 1$
$x = 0$

26. $y = 2x - 3$
$x - 6 = -y$
$4y - x = 9$

27. $y = -\frac{3}{2}x + 4$
$y = -2$
$y = x - 6$

28. $2x + y = -10$
$3y + 10 = -x$
$y = \frac{1}{2}x$

192   CHAPTER 4

4–8 Writing Equations for Lines

Given the slope of a line, m, and the coordinates of the y intercept, $(0, b)$, you can write the equation of the line in the form $y = mx + b$. Now you will learn some other methods for writing equations.

Equations from a Point and the Slope

Suppose you are given the coordinates $(6, 3)$ and the slope 2, and you are asked to determine the equation of a line through the given point and having the given slope.

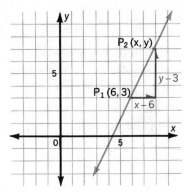

① Let (x, y) be the coordinates of any other point on the line containing $(6, 3)$. Then the change in y is $y - 3$ and the change in x is $x - 6$. The slope of the line may be expressed as $\frac{y - 3}{x - 6}$.

But the slope is given as 2.

$$\frac{y - 3}{x - 6} = 2$$
$$(x - 6) \cdot \frac{y - 3}{x - 6} = 2(x - 6)$$
$$y - 3 = 2x - 12$$
$$y = 2x - 9$$

This is the equation of the line.

② Check to see that $(6, 3)$ is a point on the line.

$$3 = 2(6) - 9, \text{ or } 12 - 9, \text{ or } 3$$

Suppose you are given the **point** (x_1, y_1) and the **slope** m. Then using the method above, the following is true.

$$\frac{y - y_1}{x - x_1} = m$$

Multiply both sides of the equation by $(x - x_1)$.

$$(x - x_1)\left(\frac{y - y_1}{x - x_1}\right) = m(x - x_1)$$
$$y - y_1 = m(x - x_1)$$

This is the **point-slope form** of the equation of a line and can be used to find the equation of a line, given any point and slope.

Equations from Two Points

Suppose you are given the coordinates for two points, (3, 2) and (4, 5), and you are asked to determine the equation of the line passing through these two points.

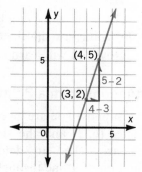

① Find the slope of the line through the points.

$$m = \frac{5-2}{4-3} = \frac{3}{1}, \text{ or } 3$$

Then in $y = mx + b$ form, you can write $y = 3x + b$. You must still determine b.

② If (3, 2) and (4, 5) are on the line for the desired equation, then they must satisfy the equation. Substitute the coordinates of either of the points in the equation to find b. Use (3, 2).

$$y = 3x + b$$
$$2 = 3(3) + b$$
$$2 = 9 + b$$
$$-7 = b$$

Then the equation is $y = 3x - 7$.

③ Use the coordinates of the second point (4, 5) to check.

$$y = 3x - 7$$
$$5 = 3(4) - 7$$
$$5 = 12 - 7, \text{ or } 5$$

If the two points were given as (x_1, y_1) and (x_2, y_2), you could follow the same method to find the equation of a line.

① Find the slope.

$$m = \frac{y_2 - y_1}{x_2 - x_1}$$

Then using $y = mx + b$, you get

$$y = x\left(\frac{y_2 - y_1}{x_2 - x_1}\right) + b.$$

② Substitute the coordinates of one of the points, say (x_1, y_1), in the equation and get b.

$$y_1 = x_1\left(\frac{y_2 - y_1}{x_2 - x_1}\right) + b$$

$$y_1 - x_1\left(\frac{y_2 - y_1}{x_2 - x_1}\right) = b$$

③ Substitute the value for b in the equation from step ① and simplify.

$$y = x\left(\frac{y_2 - y_1}{x_2 - x_1}\right) + y_1 - x_1\left(\frac{y_2 - y_1}{x_2 - x_1}\right)$$

$$y - y_1 = x\left(\frac{y_2 - y_1}{x_2 - x_1}\right) - x_1\left(\frac{y_2 - y_1}{x_2 - x_1}\right), \text{ or } (x - x_1)\left(\frac{y_2 - y_1}{x_2 - x_1}\right)$$

$$\frac{y - y_1}{x - x_1} = \frac{y_2 - y_1}{x_2 - x_1}$$

This is the **two-point form** of the equation of a line and can be used to find the equation of a line through any two given points.

Now try these

— Write an equation of a line, using the information given.

1. The slope is -2; a point is $(-3, 1)$.

2. One point is $(0, 1)$; another point is $(2, -4)$.

3. $m = \frac{3}{4}$, $(x, y) = (2, 0)$

Answers: **1.** $y = -2x - 5$ **2.** $y = -\frac{5}{2}x + 1$ **3.** $y = \frac{3}{4}x - 1\frac{1}{2}$

Checkpoint

How do you find the equation of a line, using the point-slope form? using the two-point form?

Exercises

A — Given the following points and slopes, find the equations by the point-slope method. Write the equations in $y = mx + b$ form.

1. $(2, 3)$; $m = 2$ **2.** $(0, 4)$; $m = 3$

3. $(4, 5)$; $m = -3$ **4.** $(0, 0)$; $m = 1$

5. $(-2, 1)$; $m = 1$ **6.** $(0, 0)$; $m = -1$

7. $(-1, 1)$; $m = \frac{1}{2}$ **8.** $(\frac{1}{2}, 3)$; $m = -\frac{2}{3}$

9. $(-3, 4)$; $m = -\frac{1}{3}$ **10.** $(\frac{1}{4}, \frac{1}{5})$; $m = -1$

— Find the equation of the line passing through the given points.

11. $(1, 1)$, $(2, 3)$ **12.** $(0, 0)$, $(-3, 4)$

13. $(0, 1)$, $(-1, 1)$ **14.** $(0, 0)$, $(-1, -2)$

15. $(3, 4)$, $(-2, 5)$ **16.** $(5, -1)$, $(3, -2)$

17. $(-3, -4)$, $(-5, -6)$ **18.** $(2, 3)$, $(-1, 5)$

19. $(4, -3)$, $(6, 0)$ **20.** $(1, 0)$, $(0, 0)$

B —— In each of the following exercises, use the given slope and one point to write an equation of a line. Then determine whether the other point lies on that line.

21. 6, (2, 3); (6, 9) **22.** $\frac{1}{2}$, (4, 2); (−2, −1)

23. $-\frac{3}{5}$, (−5, 7); (0, 4) **24.** −4, (2, 6); (−1, 13)

25. 2, (−1, −2); (2, 4) **26.** −3, (−2, 2); (1, 6)

—— Tell whether or not the three points in each of the following exercises are collinear.

27. (−5, 11), (0, 8), (5, 5)

28. (0, 1), (4, −2), (6, −4)

29. (6, 3), (3, 2), (0, 0)

30. (4, 1), (−1, 7), (3, 3)

4–9 Direct Variation

Consider the simple relationship between the total cost and the number of six-cent stamps you buy. If c represents the total cost and n the number of stamps, the relation can be shown in the following ways.

① A sentence: The total cost of n 6-cent stamps is $6n$.

② An equation: $c = 6n$.

③ A table of ordered pairs.

n	0	1	2	3	4
c	0	6	12	18	24

④ A graph, as shown at the right.

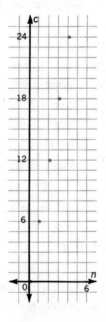

For any x and y, if y is always equal to the product of x and a constant k, $y = kx$, then y is said to *vary directly* as x. The number that k represents is called the *constant of variation*. Examine the following diagram to see the effect the constant has on the graphs.

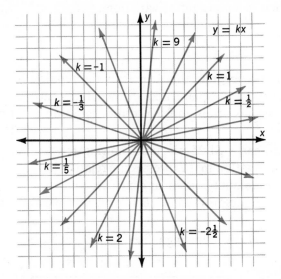

In the postage-stamp example, c is said to vary directly as n; that is, c is always 6 times as large as n.

No matter which way is chosen to show the relation, the important idea is that the first number, c, is always a multiple of a constant and the second number n. This illustrates **direct variation,** a "times-as-much" relation.

> When $y = kx$ is true, where k is a constant number, there is a __direct variation__ between x and y.

Any equation of the form $y = mx + b$, $m \neq 0$, is a linear equation. The equation $y = mx$, $b = 0$, shows *direct variation* between x and y.

You can contrast direct variation with an example such as the cost of repairing a television set. The repairman charges $10 for a house call and $6 per hour. Then the total cost, c, is 6 times the number of hours, h, plus $10, that is, $c = 6h + 10$. If h is one hour, then c is 16; if h is 2, then c is 22; if h is 3, then c is 28. The relation in this example is not one of direct variation because it is not a simple case of multiplication only. Special attention is given to relations that are direct variations because they have such wide applications.

1. Explain *direct variation*.
2. What is a constant of variation?

Exercises

A   **1.** Write a formula that expresses the relation between the perimeter, P, of a square and the length, s, of a side. Is this an example of direct variation? Explain.

2. John earns $1.25 an hour mowing lawns. Write an equation that expresses the relation between the amount earned in cents, A, and the number of hours worked, n. Is this an example of direct variation? Explain.

3. Look at the following table.

x	0	1	2	3	4	5	6
y	0	$2\frac{1}{2}$	5	$7\frac{1}{2}$	10	$12\frac{1}{2}$	15

a. Does each number for y equal a constant times the corresponding number for x? Does y vary directly as x? Explain.

b. Write an equation that shows the relation between x and y. ($y = \underline{?}$)

c. When x is 4, y is 10. When x is 8, y is $\underline{?}$. If you double the value of x, is the corresponding value of y doubled? If you choose any value of x and double it, the corresponding value of y is $\underline{?}$.

d. When x is 2, y is $\underline{?}$. When x is 6, y is $\underline{?}$. If you triple any value of x, the corresponding value of y is $\underline{?}$.

4. Which of the following are examples of direct variation?

a. $x = 4y$ **b.** $x + y = 6$ **c.** $y = 6x$

d. $x - y = 4$ **e.** $\frac{x}{4} = y$ **f.** $y = \frac{x}{6}$

g. $x = -5y$ **h.** $x + 5y = 10$ **i.** $x - 8y = 0$

j. $xy = 10$ **k.** $xy + 4 = y$ **l.** $y = \frac{1}{4}x$

m. $\frac{x}{y} = 7$ **n.** $y = \frac{18}{x}$ **o.** $y - 5x = 9$

5. The equation $y = \frac{1}{2}x$ shows that y varies directly as x.

    a. When x is 4, y is _?_. When x is 8, y is _?_. If you double any value of x, the corresponding value of y is _?_.

    b. When x is 1, y is _?_. When x is 3, y is _?_. If you triple any value of x, the corresponding value of y is _?_.

    c. When x is 10, y is _?_. When x is 5, y is _?_. If you multiply any value of x by $\frac{1}{2}$, the corresponding value of y is _?_.

    d. Is the graph of the equation a line if $x \in R$?

6. $C = \pi d$ expresses the relation between the circumference of a circle and the length of a diameter.

    a. Does C vary directly as d? Explain.

    b. When d is 10″, C is 10π″. When d is 20″, C is _?_. If you take one circle and draw another circle whose diameter is twice that of the first, its circumference is _?_ the circumference of the first circle.

7. If y varies directly as x, and you choose a number for x and double it, is the corresponding number for y doubled? If you choose a number for x and triple it, the corresponding number for y is _?_. If one number for x is multiplied by n, the corresponding number for y is multiplied by _?_.

8. The equation $y = -5x$ shows that y varies directly as x.

    a. Make a table showing at least six number pairs that satisfy the equation.

    b. Pick a number for x and double it. Is the corresponding number for y doubled?

    c. As x increases, y _?_ (increases or decreases).

    d. If one number for x is halved, the corresponding number for y is _?_.

    e. If any number for x is multiplied by n, the corresponding number for y is _?_.

9. If y equals a positive number times x, then

    a. as x increases, y _?_ (increases or decreases).

    b. as x decreases, y _?_ (increases or decreases).

    c. when any number for x is doubled, the corresponding number for y is _?_.

    d. when any number for x is multiplied by n, the corresponding number for y is multiplied by _?_.

10. If y equals a negative number times x, then

   a. as x increases, y _?_ (increases or decreases).

   b. as x decreases, y _?_ (increases or decreases).

   c. when any number for x is doubled, the corresponding number for y is _?_.

   d. when any number for x is multiplied by n, the corresponding number for y is _?_.

11. If y varies directly as x, which statements.are always true?

   a. If x increases, y increases.

   b. If a value of x is multiplied by n, the corresponding value of y is multiplied by n.

   c. The graph of the relation between x and y is a line.

B —— Tell which of the following exercises illustrate direct variation. Give an example to verify your answer.

12. The perimeter of an equilateral triangle varies with respect to one side.

13. The amount of interest at a fixed rate earned on a given sum of money varies with respect to time.

14. The length of a rectangle of a fixed perimeter varies with respect to the width.

15. A steel bar's length varies with respect to its temperature.

4–10 Direct Variation and Proportions

You know that $y = kx$ expresses direct variation between x and y. In chemistry and in other areas of science, it is often easier to express direct variation by using a **proportion.**

Consider (x_1, y_1) and (x_2, y_2). If $\frac{y_1}{x_1} = 5$ and $\frac{y_2}{x_2} = 5$ are true, then $\frac{y_1}{x_1} = \frac{y_2}{x_2}$ is true because each term in the equation is equal to 5. The equation $\frac{y_1}{x_1} = \frac{y_2}{x_2}$ is a proportion.

> **Definition** A <u>proportion</u> is an equation that shows that the ratio of two numbers is equal to the ratio of two other numbers.

Think of $y = kx$ expressed as the equivalent equation $\frac{y}{x} = k$. The ratio of y to x is always a constant k. If k is 5, then any given value of y divided by the corresponding value of x is 5. Then you would know that any two number pairs that satisfy the equation $\frac{x}{y} = 5$ would have the same ratio; (1, 5) and (2, 10) are two such pairs, since $\frac{5}{1}$ and $\frac{10}{2}$ are both names for 5.

EXAMPLE 1. A recipe uses 3 cups of sugar for each 24 cookies. How much sugar is needed for 66 cookies?

You can summarize the information as follows to set up the proportion.

24 cookies   66 cookies

3 cups of sugar x cups of sugar

Since the problem shows direct variation, you can write the following proportion.

$$\frac{24}{3} = \frac{66}{x}$$

Then solve the proportion for x.

$$\frac{24}{3}, \text{ or } \frac{8}{1} = \frac{66}{x}$$
$$\frac{8}{1} \cdot x = \frac{66}{x} \cdot x$$
$$8x = 66$$
$$x = \frac{66}{8}, \text{ or } 8\tfrac{1}{4}$$

Thus, $8\tfrac{1}{4}$ cups of sugar are needed for 66 cookies.

Often, you will see the term *directly proportional* refer to direct variation when it is expressed as a proportion.

Checking to see that two ratios are equal, or that a proportion is true, is done in the same way as for two rational numbers, $\frac{a}{b}$ and $\frac{c}{d}$.

If $\frac{a}{b} = \frac{c}{d}$ is true, then $ad = bc$ is true.

$$\frac{a}{b} = \frac{c}{d}$$
$$bd\left(\frac{a}{b}\right) = bd\left(\frac{c}{d}\right)$$
$$da = bc$$
$$ad = bc$$

The definition for equality of two ratios can be used to solve a proportion such as the one in Example 1, or it may be used to check the result.

Solve Example 1 again.

$$\frac{24}{3} = \frac{66}{x}$$

$$24x = 3 \cdot 66, \text{ or } 198$$

$$x = \frac{198}{24}, \text{ or } 8\frac{1}{4}$$

Check

$$\frac{24}{3} = \frac{66}{8\frac{1}{4}}$$

$$24 \cdot 8\frac{1}{4} = 3 \cdot 66$$

$$198 = 198$$

EXAMPLE 2. Solve the proportion $\frac{x}{13} = \frac{25}{65}$ for x.

$$\frac{x}{13} = \frac{25}{65}$$

$$65x = 13 \cdot 25$$

$$65x = 325$$

$$x = \frac{325}{65}, \text{ or } 5$$

Check

$$\frac{5}{13} = \frac{25}{65}$$

$$325 = 325$$

Now try these

—— Solve the following proportions.

1. $\frac{x}{2} = \frac{9}{18}$

2. $\frac{2}{3} = \frac{x}{27}$

3. $\frac{5}{x} = \frac{20}{48}$

4. $\frac{9}{11} = \frac{16}{x}$

—— Write the proportion you would use to solve these problems. You need not solve them at this time.

5. If you can travel for 120 miles and use 6 gallons of gasoline, how far can you travel at the same rate of gas consumption and use 15 gallons of gasoline?

6. If 36 grams of salt will dissolve in 100 grams of water at a given temperature, how many grams of salt will dissolve in 250 grams of water at the same temperature?

Answers: **1.** 1 **2.** 18 **3.** 12 **4.** $19\frac{5}{9}$ **5.** $\frac{6}{120} = \frac{15}{x}$ **6.** $\frac{36}{100} = \frac{x}{250}$

Checkpoint

1. What is a *proportion*?

2. How do you solve a proportion?

Exercises

A — Solve for x.

1. $\frac{7}{8} = \frac{x}{40}$ **2.** $\frac{9}{2} = \frac{63}{x}$ **3.** $\frac{11}{x} = \frac{132}{24}$

4. $\frac{x}{13} = \frac{10}{65}$ **5.** $\frac{7}{x} = \frac{1}{9}$ **6.** $\frac{5}{13} = \frac{x}{65}$

7. $\frac{21}{5} = \frac{x}{2.5}$ **8.** $\frac{29}{7} = \frac{x}{1.75}$ **9.** $\frac{17}{2} = \frac{8.5}{x}$

— Solve for n.

Example. $\frac{2 + n}{n} = \frac{15}{9}$

$$\begin{array}{cc} & Check \\ 9(2 + n) = 15n & \frac{2 + 3}{3} = \frac{15}{9} \\ 18 + 9n = 15n & \\ 18 = 6n & \frac{5}{3} = \frac{15}{9} \\ 3 = n & 45 = 45 \end{array}$$

10. $\frac{12 - n}{n} = \frac{5}{7}$ **11.** $\frac{n}{16 - n} = \frac{5}{3}$ **12.** $\frac{n + 4}{5} = \frac{2n}{6}$

13. $\frac{3n}{8} = \frac{6n}{16}$ **14.** $\frac{3 + n}{n} = \frac{4}{3}$ **15.** $\frac{n}{3 - n} = \frac{a}{b}$

16. If an automobile goes 110 miles in 3 hours, how far will it go in 5 hours at the same rate? $\left(\frac{110}{x} = \frac{3}{5} \right)$

17. If 90 feet of wire weighs 18 pounds, what will 110 feet of the same kind of wire weigh?

18. A recipe for a 2-pound cake uses $1\frac{1}{2}$ cups of butter. How many cups of butter are needed for a 5-pound cake?

19. If 40 pounds of fertilizer are used for 5000 square feet of lawn, how much is needed for the Clarks' lawn, which is rectangular in shape and measures 80 feet by 150 feet?

20. If $1\frac{1}{2}$ inches on a map represents 60 miles, what distance does $2\frac{7}{8}$ inches on the map represent?

B **21.** Separate 72 into two parts that are in the ratio 4 to 5.

METHOD I: Let the smaller part be x. The other will be $72 - x$.

$$\frac{x}{72 - x} = \frac{4}{5}$$

METHOD II: Let the smaller part be $4x$. The other will be $5x$.

$$4x + 5x = 72$$

Use either method to find the two parts.

22. Separate 99 into two parts that are in the ratio 4 : 7.

23. Henry and his younger brother decided to divide a profit of $12 in the ratio 5 : 3. How should it be divided?

24. If a man reaches the moon, he will weigh much less there than on earth. The ratio of the weight of an object on the moon to the weight of an object on earth is 0.16 to 1.

  a. James Explorer weighs 150 pounds. How much would he weigh on the moon?

  b. How much would a 10-ton rocket weigh on the moon?

  c. A 100-pound sack of flour on the moon would weigh how much on earth?

C **25.** The heights of two columns of water are directly proportional to the pressures exerted by the columns. Since the pressure exerted by a column of water one foot high is 0.433 pound per square inch, this proportion can be written as follows.

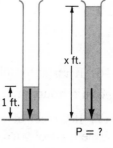

$$\frac{1}{\substack{\text{height of any}\\ \text{column of water}\\ \text{in feet}}} = \frac{0.433}{\substack{\text{pressure of the}\\ \text{column in lb.}\\ \text{per sq. in.}}},$$

or $\dfrac{1}{x} = \dfrac{0.433}{P}$

What then is the pressure exerted by a column of water 20 feet high?

26. What is the water pressure (in pounds per square inch) on the bottom of a tank in which the water is 30 feet deep?

27. For a liquid contained in a closed pipe or container, the forces on any two areas are directly proportional to the areas. For example, for a bottle such as the one pictured at the right, this law may be expressed as follows.

$$\frac{\text{force at small end}}{\text{force at large end}} = \frac{\text{area of small end}}{\text{area of large end}}$$

If the force at the small end is 50 pounds and its area is 12 square inches, what will be the force at the large end if its area is 108 square inches?

28. The principle in Exercise 27 governs the operation of hydraulic brakes. If a driver presses with a force of 10 pounds on a brake pedal with a hydraulic fluid line that has an area of 3 square inches, how much force will be applied on the piston at the brake if the piston has an area of 16 square inches?

4–11   Graphing Inequalities

You graphed a simple inequality such as $x > 3$ on a number line like that below, and you graph $x + y > 3$ on a plane.

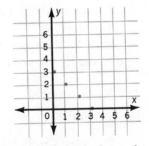

To graph $x + y > 3$, you begin with the graph of $x + y = 3$. Suppose the replacement set for x and y is $\{0, 1, 2, 3, 4, 5, 6\}$. Four pairs of numbers make $x + y = 3$ true. These pairs are graphed at the right.

In relation to the graph of $x + y = 3$, where are the points whose coordinates satisfy $x + y > 3$?

For the inequality $x + y > 3$, if x is 2, y can be 2, 3, 4, 5, or 6. Where are the points for (2, 2), (2, 3), (2, 4), (2, 5), and (2, 6)?

Where are the points whose ordered pairs would have 1 as the x coordinate and still satisfy the inequality?

Since the replacement set is finite, you can list all the ordered pairs that satisfy the inequality. Complete the following table.

When x is	y can be
0	4, 5, 6
1	3, _?_, _?_, _?_
2	2, 3, 4, 5, 6
3	1, _?_, _?_, _?_, _?_, _?_
4	0, _?_, _?_, _?_, _?_, _?_, _?_
5	0, _?_, _?_, _?_, _?_, _?_, _?_
6	0, _?_, _?_, _?_, _?_, _?_, _?_

The graph of the ordered pairs of numbers will be the set of points *above* and to the right of the points for $x + y = 3$, as in Figure 1.

Examine the points on the other side of the graph of $x + y = 3$. List the ordered pairs. Do the coordinates satisfy $x + y < 3$?

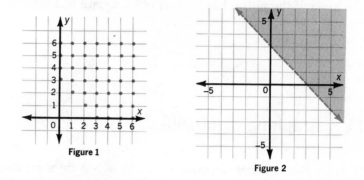

Figure 1

Figure 2

What is the graph of $x + y = 3$ if the replacement set is the set of real numbers? It is the dashed line shown in red on the graph in Figure 2. Then the graph of $x + y > 3$ would be the half-plane on the right side of the line for $x + y = 3$. The half-plane is shown by the shading above the red dashed line.

To graph an inequality whose replacement set is the set of real numbers, first graph the corresponding equation. Then points on one side of the line have coordinates that satisfy the inequality.

EXAMPLE. Graph $3x - 4y < 12$.

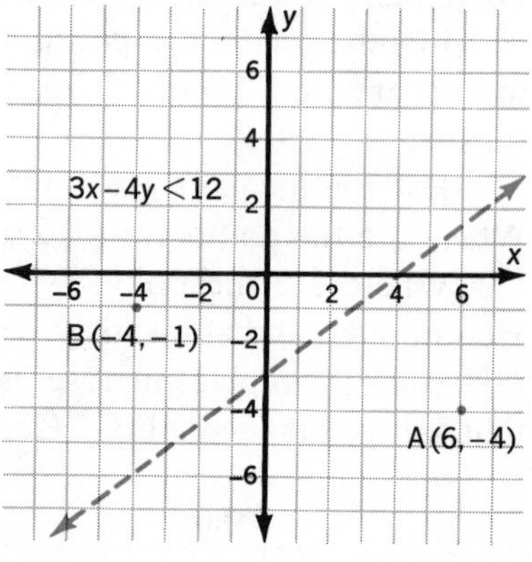

① Graph the equation

$$3x - 4y = 12.$$

Use a dashed line to represent the graph as shown at the right.

② Points on one side of the line have coordinates that satisfy $3x - 4y < 12$. Choose a point on one side of the line and see if its coordinates satisfy the inequality. Do the coordinates of A satisfy $3x - 4y < 12$?

$$3(6) - 4(-4) \overset{?}{<} 12$$
$$18 + 16 \overset{?}{<} 12$$
$$34 \nless 12$$

A is not on the graph of $3x - 4y < 12$.

Do the coordinates of B satisfy the inequality?

$$3(-4) - 4(-1) \overset{?}{<} 12$$
$$-12 + 4 \overset{?}{<} 12$$
$$-8 < 12$$

Then B is on the graph of $3x - 4y < 12$.

③ All points on the B side of the
line have coordinates that satisfy the inequality. Shade this
side of the line, as shown at
the right. The half-plane that
is the graph of $3x - 4y < 12$
extends indefinitely upward to
the left. Why does it not include the dashed line?

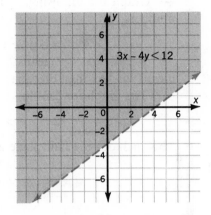

The inequality $3x - 4y < 12$
is a **linear inequality** because
the boundary of its graph is a
line.

The relation defined by $3x - 4y < 12$ is not a function. Why?

Exercises

A —— The replacement set is $\{0, 1, 2, 3, 4, 5, 6, 7, 8\}$. Graph the
equation in **a**. Then, on the same axes, graph the inequalities in
b and **c**.

	a	**b**	**c**
1.	$y = x + 8$	$y > x + 8$	$y < x + 8$
2.	$x - y = 6$	$x - y > 6$	$x - y < 6$
3.	$2x - 3y = 6$	$2x - 3y > 6$	$2x - 3y < 6$
4.	$3x + 4y = 12$	$3x + 4y > 12$	$3x + 4y < 12$
5.	$x = 8$	$x > 8$	$x < 8$
6.	$y = 7$	$y > 7$	$y < 7$

—— Let the replacement set be the set of real numbers. Graph
the following as you did Exercises 1–6.

7.	$2x - y = -4$	$2x - y > -4$	$2x - y < -4$
8.	$x = -3\frac{1}{2}$	$x > -3\frac{1}{2}$	$x < -3\frac{1}{2}$
9.	$\frac{1}{2}x + y = 4$	$\frac{1}{2}x + y > 4$	$\frac{1}{2}x + y < 4$
10.	$3x - 2 = 5y$	$3x - 2 > 5y$	$3x - 2 < 5y$

—— Graph each inequality. The replacement set is the set of real numbers.

11. $x + y > 10$ **12.** $x - y > 10$ **13.** $y - x > 10$

14. $2x + y > 5$ **15.** $x - 2y < 4$ **16.** $2x - y > -4$

17. $3x - 2y < -6$ **18.** $y > -5$ **19.** $x > 0$

—— Graph the following. The replacement set is the set of real numbers.

Example. Graph $2x + y \geq 6$.

Recall that $\geq$ means "is greater than or equal to" and $\leq$ means "is less than or equal to."

The graph for $2x + y \geq 6$ is the union of the graphs for

$$2x + y > 6 \text{ and } 2x + y = 6.$$

This includes the half-plane and the line.

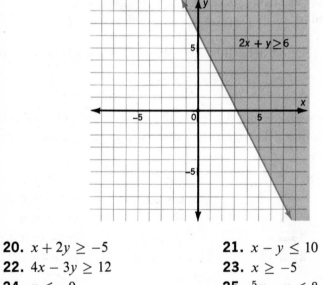

20. $x + 2y \geq -5$ **21.** $x - y \leq 10$

22. $4x - 3y \geq 12$ **23.** $x \geq -5$

24. $y \leq -9$ **25.** $\frac{5}{4}x - y \leq 8$

26. $x \geq 0$ **27.** $y \leq 0$

B —— The replacement set for the following is the set of real numbers. Graph each set.

28. $\{(x, y) : x + 3y \geq 2\} \cup \{(x, y) : x > 0\}$

29. $\{(x, y) : -2x - y \leq 4\} \cap \{(x, y) : x = y\}$

30. $\{(x, y) : 5x - 4y \geq 2\} \cap \{(x, y) : y \geq 0\}$

31. $\{(x, y) : 3x + y \leq 7\} \cup \{(x, y) : x - y = 3\}$

To graph an equation such as $y = |x|$, find several pairs of numbers that satisfy the equation and locate the points. Recall that x may be positive, negative, or zero, but y will always be nonnegative, by definition of absolute value. The replacement set is the set of real numbers. Complete the table of pairs of numbers that satisfy $y = |x|$.

When x is	−5	−4	−3	−2	−1	0	1	2	3	4	5
y is	5	?	?	2	?	0	1	2	3	?	?

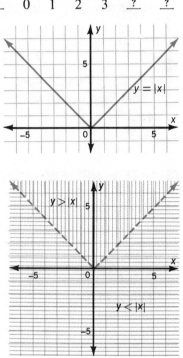

Locate a point for each pair of numbers. All points whose coordinates satisfy the equation will form a V-shaped figure, that is, two rays with their initial point at the origin.

The relation defined by $y = |x|$ is a function. Explain why this is so. Why is it not a linear function? How does the graph of $y = |x|$ compare with the graph of $y = x$?

To graph $y > |x|$, check the coordinates of points inside (or above) the V. Try $(0, 4)$. Is $4 > |0|$ true? Try $(2, 5)$. Is $5 > |2|$ true? Try $(−4, 5)$. Is $5 > |−4|$ true?

Check by substitution to see that points outside the V satisfy $y < |x|$. The graphs are shown at the right.

Neither of the relations defined by $y > |x|$ and $y < |x|$ is a function. Can you explain why?

Exercises

A —— Graph these equations if the domain is the set of real numbers. If the equation defines a function, write the word *Function*.

1. $y = |x| - 4$ **2.** $y = |2x| - 5$

3. $y = |-3x| + 7$ **4.** $y = |5x|$

5. $y = -|x|$ **6.** $y = -|2x|$

(*Hint:* In Exercises 5 and 6, every value of y will be negative except when $x = 0$.)

7. $x = |y|$

8. $x = |2y| - 4$

9. $x = |-2y|$

10. $x = |-4y| + 3$

11. $x = -|3y|$

12. $x = -|2y| - 6$

13. $x + |y| = 4$

14. $x - |y| = 6$

15. $y + |x| = 10$

16. $|x| - y = 8$

B ━━ Graph the following equations. The replacement set is the set of real numbers.

17. $|x| + |y| = 10$ (*Hint:* Neither x nor y can be greater than 10 or less than -10. Why?)

x	-10	$+10$	-8	$+8$	-6	$+6$	-4	$\cdots$
y	0	0	± 2	± 2	?	?	?	$\cdots$

Continue the table for a few more values of x and draw the graph. What kind of figure do you obtain?

18. $|y| = |x| + 5$ **19.** $|x| = |y|$

CHAPTER REVIEW

1. Know the meaning of and be able to use each of the following words, phrases, or equations. The number shown after each word, phrase, or equation indicates where it is introduced, in case you need to review.

undefined term (*162*)

point (*162*)

line (*162*)

line segment (*162*)

endpoints (*162*)

ray (*162*)

angle (*163*)

half-line (*163*)

plane (*163*)

half-plane (*164*)

boundary (*164*)

polygon (*164*)

interior (*164*)

exterior (*164*)

parallel lines (*164*)

perpendicular lines (*164*)

quadrant (*166*)

ordered pair (*168*)

axes (*169*)

origin (*169*)

abscissa (*169*)

ordinate (*169*)

coordinates (*169*)

coordinate plane (*169*)

rectangular-coordinate plane (*169*)

polar-coordinate plane (*173*)

polar axis (*173*)

relation (*174*)

domain (*175*)

range (*175*)

function (*178*)

independent variable (*178*) ✕

dependent variable (*178*) ⤳

linear function (*179*)

$y = mx + b$ (182)
slope (186)
y intercept (187)
$y - y_1 = m(x - x_1)$ (193)

$\dfrac{y - y_1}{x - x_1} = \dfrac{y_2 - y_1}{x_2 - x_1}$ (195)
direct variation (197)
proportion (200)

2. Consider the figure at the right. Which of the following names the part of the plane containing point A?

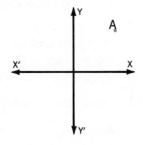

a. X' side of $\overleftrightarrow{YY'} \cap Y'$ side of $\overleftrightarrow{XX'}$

b. Y' side of $\overleftrightarrow{XX'} \cap X$ side of $\overleftrightarrow{YY'}$

c. X side of $\overleftrightarrow{YY'} \cap Y$ side of $\overleftrightarrow{XX'}$

d. X' side of $\overleftrightarrow{YY'} \cap Y$ side of $\overleftrightarrow{XX'}$

3. Draw coordinate axes on graph paper. Then draw a line connecting $(-6, -1)$, $(-3, 2)$, and $(0, 5)$ and a line connecting $(-3, -6)$, $(0, -3)$, and $(3, 0)$. What appears to be the relationship between the two lines?

4. It costs $3.00 to print the first 100 copies of a handbill and $2.00 for each 100 additional copies. This relation may be expressed by the equation $c = 3 + 2x$, where x represents the number of 100's of copies after the first 100. Express the relation as a table. The domain of x is $\{0, 1, 2, 3, 4, 5, 6, 7, 8\}$. Express the relation as a graph, using the ordered pairs in the table. Why is the graph a set of discrete points?

5. For each equation, give three ordered pairs that satisfy it. Draw the graph for each equation if the domain is the set of real numbers.

a. $3x - 2y = 5$ **b.** $-2x - 7y = 4$ **c.** $5x + y = 7$

6. Consider the equation $2x - 5y = 8$.

a. Is this a linear function? Explain.

b. Write the equation in the form $y = mx + b$.

c. What is the slope of the line that is the graph of the function?

d. What is the y intercept of the line?

e. Graph the line for $2x - 5y = 8$ if the replacement set is the set of real numbers.

7. A point on line l has coordinates $(0, -3)$. The slope of the line is $-\frac{3}{2}$. Write the equation of the line. Draw line l.

8. Two points on line m are $(-3, 4)$ and $(-4, -3)$. Write the equation of the line that contains these two points. Draw line m.

9. Which of the following equations are examples of direct variation? Why?

    a. $xy = -3$ **b.** $\frac{x}{y} = 5$ **c.** $\frac{x}{y} = \frac{x'}{y'}$ **d.** $x = -\frac{2}{3}y$ **e.** $x - y = 0$

10. Which of the following is an example of direct variation? Why?

    a. At 50 miles per hour, a driver may drive $50n$ miles in n hours.

    b. On a business trip, Mr. Jacobs drove 15 miles in the city in heavy traffic and then drove at 50 miles per hour on the highway for h hours. The distance he drives in all is represented by the equation $d = 15 + 50h$.

11. Solve the following proportions for x.

    a. $\frac{4}{x} = \frac{-2.5}{10}$ **b.** $\frac{x}{16} = \frac{2}{3}$ **c.** $\frac{9}{25} = \frac{x}{75}$

12. Alice receives a commission of 8% on the total amount she sells in a week. Find her commission, x, on \$525 by writing a proportion and solving for x. (*Hint:* Remember 8% may be written as $\frac{8}{100}$.)

13. A punch recipe calls for 1 cup of lemon soda for each 3 cups of orange juice. If you use 10 cups of orange juice, how many cups of soda will you need? Solve by a proportion.

14. Graph each inequality. Let the replacement set be the set of real numbers.

    a. $3x - 2y < 12$ **b.** $2x - 5y \geq 9$

CHAPTER TEST

1. Write the coordinates for points A, B, C, D, E, and F.

2. If you graph all points such that $x < 0$, what kind of figure is the graph? Are all the points on one side of the x axis? on one side of the y axis? Does $x < 0$ define a relation that is a function or one that is not a function?

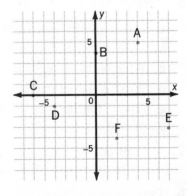

3. Which point in the figure is in the quadrant where $x < 0$ and $y < 0$?

4. Which labeled points are not in any of the four quadrants?

5. Without graphing, write *Yes* if the ordered pair is a member of the given set.   Otherwise write *No*.

    a. $\{(x, y) : 2x - y = 8\}$; $(4, 0)$

    b. $\{(x, y) : 2x + 3y = 11\}$; $(-1, 3)$

    c. $\{(x, y) : |x| + |y| = 4\}$; $(-1, 3)$

    d. $\{(x, y) : x > 3y - 9\}$; $(0, 3)$

    e. $\{(x, y) : 3x - 2y \le 16\}$; $(4, -2)$

    f. $\{(x, y) : y = 5\}$; $(7, 5)$

6. What is the slope of $\overleftrightarrow{AB}$? $\overleftrightarrow{CD}$? $\overleftrightarrow{XX'}$?

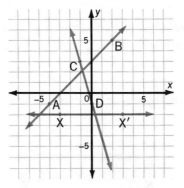

7. What is the slope of the graph of these equations?

    a. $y = 5x - 6$ **b.** $y = -\frac{2}{3}x - 9$

    c. $x + 3y = 8$ **d.** $2x - 6y = 11$

8. Which equations in Exercise 7 define a function?   a linear function?

9. Write the equation of the line passing through $(-5, 6)$ with a slope of 3; through $(2, 3)$ with a slope of $-\frac{1}{2}$.

—— Graph the following relations.   Write *Function* if the sentence defines a function.   Otherwise, write *Relation*.

10. $2x + y = 12$ **11.** $y > 3x + 5$

12. $y = |x| - 2$ **13.** $x + y \le 4$

—— Graph the following.

14. $\{(x, y) : x + y = 10\} \cup \{(x, y) : x - y = 4\}$

15. $\{(x, y) : y \ge 3x\} \cap \{(x, y) : -3 \le y \le 3\}$

—— Solve for x.

16. $\frac{x}{7} = \frac{15}{21}$ **17.** $\frac{14}{x} = \frac{25}{13}$ **18.** $\frac{x}{7} = \frac{7}{8}$ **19.** $\frac{6}{18} = \frac{14}{x}$

20. Write the equation of the line passing through $(-6, 2)$ and $(4, -\frac{1}{2})$; through $(3, 3)$ and $(-1, -5)$.

21. Which of the following are examples of direct variation?

a. The length of one side of a square and the perimeter.

b. The number of men working on a job and the number of weeks required to complete it.

c. The altitude of a parallelogram of constant area and the base.

d. Temperature and the length of a column of mercury in a thermometer.

e. Temperature in an oven and the amount of time needed for something to cook.

22. The ratio of the areas of two squares is 7 : 4. If the length of a side of the first square is 16 inches, what is the length of a side of the second square?

23. The scale on a map is given as 1 inch = 100 miles. How great a distance is represented by a line $2\frac{3}{8}$ inches long on the map?

ENRICHMENT

Vector and Force Problems

A force applied to a point can be thought of as a vector. A vector has magnitude, that is, a numerical value, and direction. A force has a numerical value, such as 10 pounds or 2 tons, and a direction in which it is acting, such as left, right, up, down, or at some acute angle.

Think of two unequal forces applied at one point, acting in opposite directions. An example of this would be a tug of war. One team pulls to the left with a force of 300 pounds; the other team pulls to the right with a force of 240 pounds. The forces can be represented by a vector diagram.

300 pounds   240 pounds

You know which team will win the tug of war — the team pulling with the greater force. How much greater is the force to the left? If you think of the 300-pound force as two forces, one of 240 pounds and one of 60 pounds, both acting in the same direction, then you can see that the 240-pound forces cancel each other out, and the **resultant force** is 60 pounds directed to the left.

What would be the result of two 4-pound forces acting at right angles to pull a rock? Represent the forces on coordinate axes with the rock at the origin. If you just think about it, you know that the rock would not move up because there is also a force pulling it to the right, and it would not move to the right because there is also a force pulling it up. Thus, it will move in some direction between the two.

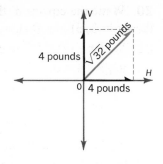

The problem can be solved mathematically by completing a vector rectangle. The diagonal of the rectangle is the resultant vector and can be found by the Pythagorean theorem to be $\sqrt{4^2 + 4^2}$, or $\sqrt{32}$, pounds.

Similarly, if you know the magnitude and direction of any vector, you can separate it into its horizontal and vertical components by placing the initial point of the vector at the origin and completing a vector rectangle. Each vector can be named by a pair of real numbers, those numbers being the coordinates of the endpoint of the vector, its initial point being the origin. Look at vectors $\vec{a}$, $\vec{b}$, and $\vec{c}$ in Figure 1 below. The name for $\vec{a}$ is (2, 0); for $\vec{b}$ is (−3, 0); and for $\vec{c}$ is (4, 3). This number pair then tells you both the length and direction of the vector.

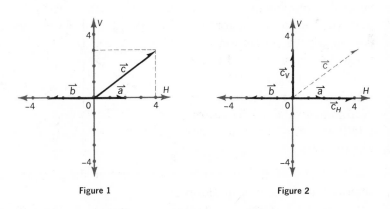

Figure 1   Figure 2

If you want the resultant of $\vec{a}$, $\vec{b}$, and $\vec{c}$, then $\vec{c}$ must be separated into its horizontal and vertical components, c_H and c_V, respectively. Look at Figure 2 above; $\vec{c_H}$ is (4, 0) and $\vec{c_V}$ is (0, 3). First, find the resultant of the horizontal forces: $-3 + 4 + 2 = +3$. Now you can find the resultant of two $+3$ vectors at right angles to each other by the Pythagorean theorem: $\sqrt{3^2 + 3^2} = \sqrt{18}$.

So the magnitude of the resultant of $\vec{a}$, $\vec{b}$, and $\vec{c}$ is "$\sqrt{18}$ directed as shown in the figure below."

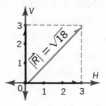

But it should be expressed in a way more precise than that. You can replace this geometric addition of vectors by real-number arithmetic. To add $\vec{a}$ (2, 0), $\vec{b}$ (−3, 0), and $\vec{c}$ (4, 3), add the coordinates in the following way.

$$(2, 0) \oplus (-3, 0) \oplus (4, 3) = (2 - 3 + 4, 0 + 0 + 3) = (3, 3)$$

Thus, $\vec{R}$ is (3, 3), which is the same as $\sqrt{18}$ in the previous diagram. Note that the sign $\oplus$ is used to alert you to the fact that you are defining a new type of addition.

Exercises

1. Copy the vector diagram at the right, substituting for each vector its horizontal and vertical components. Then find the resultant vector by combining the horizontal and vertical components and using the Pythagorean theorem.

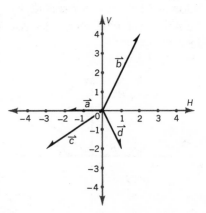

2. Find the resultant of the vectors in Exercise 1 by vector addition, $\oplus$. Do your two answers check?

——— For each of the following, draw a vector diagram and find the resultant by vector addition, $\oplus$.

3. $\vec{a}$ (4, 1), $\vec{b}$ (0, 2), $\vec{c}$ (−2, 4), $\vec{d}$ (−3, 0), $\vec{e}$ (−2, −2), $\vec{f}$ (0, −3), $\vec{g}$ (3, −2)

4. $\vec{a}$ (−4, 0), $\vec{b}$ (−3, −4), $\vec{c}$ (−2, −4), $\vec{d}$ (0, −4), $\vec{e}$ (−3, 3)

5. An engineer had a problem involving forces and he was using vectors to solve it. He had finished the problem and gone for coffee when the custodian accidentally threw away one page of the solution because it contained only one little ordered pair. The information that the engineer had left was $\vec{a}$ (2, 5), $\vec{b}$ (−3, −2), $\vec{c}$ (0, 4), $\vec{d}$ (3, −4), $\vec{R}$ (7, 7). ($\vec{R}$ is the resultant.)   What was $\vec{e}$, the vector that was thrown away?

6. Suppose in Exercise 5 that there had been two vectors on the paper that was thrown away.   The engineer knew that the vectors he had been working with were all named by pairs of integers.   And he remembered that the two lost vectors were both directed upward to the right, one having a magnitude of 5 pounds.   Can you determine the two vectors?

THE GROWTH OF MATHEMATICS

The Pythagoreans

Geometry and deductive thinking were introduced into Greece by Thales (640?–546 B.C.).   He traveled to Egypt as a trader and learned what he could from the priests there, returning to Miletus in Greece to study philosophy and mathematics.

A contemporary of Thales and, perhaps, a student of his was Pythagoras (569?–?500 B.C.).   Born on the island of Samos, he too studied in Egypt and Babylonia.   Eventually, he settled at Croton in southern Italy where he founded a secret brotherhood whose members were his students.   Pythagoras was fascinated by numbers and came to see numbers in everything, believing that numbers ruled the universe. He attributed special properties to each natural number; for example, the odd numbers were associated with masculinity, even numbers with femininity; 1 was identified with reason, 2 with opinion, and so on.

Because of the secretive and mystical nature of the Pythagoreans, they were suspected by the politicians of Croton.   Their buildings were attacked and destroyed, and Pythagoras was killed by a mob.   The school regrouped itself, but some members dispersed and began to tell and write of the society's discoveries, always crediting everything to Pythagoras.   Best known is the Pythagorean theorem.   Their discovery of the irrationality of $\sqrt{2}$ was disturbing as it could not be reconciled with the whole numbers, the basis of their entire philosophy.

They contributed greatly to geometric algebra and even gave the complete solution of the general quadratic equation with real roots. They developed a rather complete theory of proportion and did much great work in geometry, refining deduction and proof to a high degree.

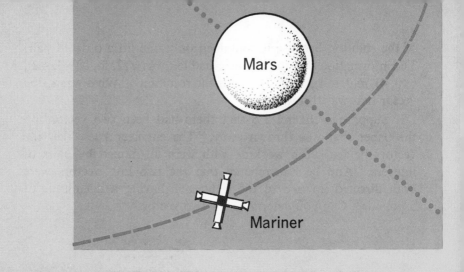

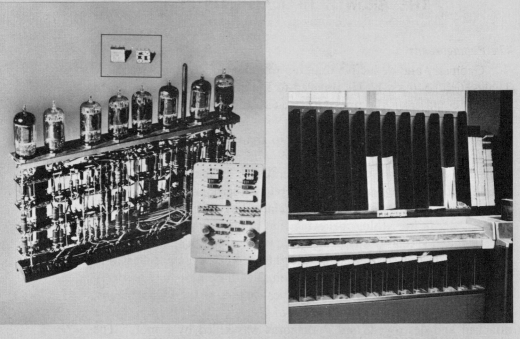

CHAPTER 5

SYSTEMS OF SENTENCES

You have been accustomed to solving problems by using a single equation or inequality. Many problems, however, must be described in terms of two or more equations or inequalities. Such systems of sentences can be solved through the use of graphs or by application of the postulates and theorems of algebra.

The photographs and diagrams suggest some ways to solve such systems.

● The diagram in the top corner shows the problem of hitting a moving planet with a moving space probe. Unless the probe is in the right part of its orbit when the planet arrives, the probe will miss. The point of intersection of the two paths is the point at which you must aim.

● The machine in the center right photograph sorts information on punched cards. You can use a card sorter to eliminate part of a problem so that the remaining part is easy to solve. A similar elimination process is used with systems of equations.

● The small crystal in the center left photograph is an integrated circuit that does the same work as the complicated electronic equipment also shown. Substitution of an integrated circuit can greatly simplify the construction of a television set or computer. In solving systems of equations, the substitution of the right expression can give the solution.

● In baseball, the rules state that the "fair ball" territory is between the rays from home plate through first and third base or on these rays. It is the region not shaded in the bottom photograph. As you will see in this chapter, this definition of "fair" territory is similar to the solution set of a system of two inequalities.

5–1 Graphing Systems of Sentences

Can you solve the following puzzle about a pair of numbers? Try it before reading the explanation.

"I am thinking of two numbers in a certain order. I will tell you two things about the numbers.

"① The sum of the two numbers is 7.

"② Multiply the first number by 3 and subtract 1, and you will get the second number.

"What are the numbers? Which is the first number and which is the second number?"

The two conditions of the puzzle can be expressed by two equations in two variables. Letting x represent the first number and y the second number, you get the following.

① $x + y = 7$
② $3x - 1 = y$

The answer to the puzzle is the pair of numbers that makes both sentences true. You can solve the puzzle by graphing. Look at the diagram and answer the questions below.

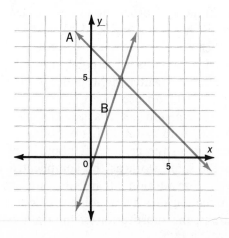

A is the graph of $x + y = 7$. Do the coordinates of every point on the line make $x + y = 7$ true? B is the graph of $3x - y = 1$. What can you say about the coordinates of every point on B?

How many points do the two lines have in common? Tell the coordinates. Now give the answer to the puzzle.

The two equations used to solve the puzzle together form what is called a **system of equations,** or a **system of sentences.** To solve a system of two equations, you find the ordered pair(s) of numbers (x, y) that make both equations true.

Solving a system of equations gives the same result as solving a compound sentence using the connective *and.* For example, the compound sentence

$$x + y = 7 \text{ and } 3x - 1 = y$$

has the same solution set as the system shown above. The solution set of the system or of the compound sentence can be described using the notation for set intersection.

$$\{(x, y) : x + y = 7 \text{ and } 3x - 1 = y\}$$
$$= \{(x, y) : x + y = 7\} \cap \{(x, y) : 3x - 1 = y\}$$

The solution set can be found by graphing, as you saw on page 220.

EXAMPLE. Solve the following system graphically.

$$\begin{cases} x + y = 10 \\ x - y = 2 \end{cases}$$

The two lines on the graph show all points that make either equation true. The point that makes *both* true is shown as a red dot. Its coordinates are $(6, 4)$. To show that $(6, 4)$ makes each equation true, substitute the values for x and y in both equations. Note that 6 is the replacement for x in (x, y) and that 4 is the replacement for y.

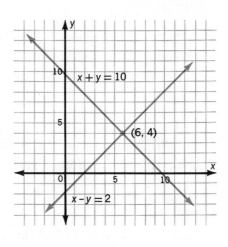

Check $\quad 6 + 4 = 10 \quad$ True.
$\qquad\quad 6 - 4 = 2 \qquad$ True.

Solution set: $\{(6, 4)\}$

The two lines are the graphs of

$$\{(x, y) : x + y = 10 \text{ or } x - y = 2\}.$$

The point of intersection is the graph of

$$\{(x, y) : x + y = 10 \text{ and } x - y = 2\}.$$

Explain.

Now try these

— At the right is the graph of the system $\begin{cases} 2x - y = 3 \\ 3x + y = 7 \end{cases}$. Use the graph for Exercises 1–3.

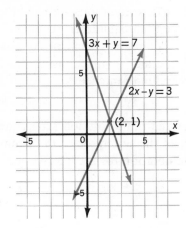

1. $\{(x, y) : 3x + y = 7\} \cap$
$\{(x, y) : 2x - y = 3\} = \{(\underline{?}, \underline{?})\}$

2. Give one ordered pair that makes each of the following sentences false.

    a. $2x - y = 3$ *and* $3x + y = 7$
    b. $2x - y = 3$ *or* $3x + y = 7$

3. What is the solution set of the system $\begin{cases} 2x - y = 3 \\ 3x + y = 7 \end{cases}$?

Answers: **1.** 2, 1   **2. a.** Any ordered pair except (2, 1). **b.** Any coordinates of points not on the lines. **3.** {(2, 1)}

Checkpoint

1. What is a system of sentences? How would you describe the solution set of a system of sentences?

2. What compound sentence has the same solution set as the system $\begin{cases} 2x + 3y = 5 \\ 4x + 7y = 10 \end{cases}$? as the system $\begin{cases} ax + by = c \\ dx + ey = f \end{cases}$?

3. Is the solution set of a system the intersection or the union of the solution sets of the sentences in the system?

4. How do you solve a system of sentences graphically?

Exercises

A — Draw a graph to find the solution set of each system or compound sentence.

1. $\begin{cases} x + y = 4 \\ 2x - y = 8 \end{cases}$ **2.** $\begin{cases} 4x - y = 1 \\ y = 2x - 3 \end{cases}$

3. $y = x - 1$ *and* $3x + y = 11$
4. $3x - y = 14$ *and* $2x + y = 6$
5. $x - y = 5$ *and* $x + 5y = 11$

Use your results from Exercises 1–5 to complete the following.

6. $\{(x, y) : x + y = 4\} \cap \{(x, y) : 2x - y = 8\} = \{(\underline{?}, \underline{?})\}$

7. $\{(x, y) : 4x - y = 1\} \cap \{(x, y) : y = 2x - 3\} = \{(\underline{?}, \underline{?})\}$

8. $\{(x, y) : y = x - 1\} \cap \{(x, y) : 3x + y = 11\} = \{(\underline{?}, \underline{?})\}$

9. $\{(x, y) : 3x - y = 14\} \cap \{(x, y) : 2x + y = 6\} = \{(\underline{?}, \underline{?})\}$

10. $\{(x, y) : x - y = 5\} \cap \{(x, y) : x + 5y = 11\} = \{(\underline{?}, \underline{?})\}$

B — Graph the following sets of points. If the graph is a finite set of points, give the coordinates of each point.

11. $\{(x, y) : x + y = 12\} \cup \{(x, y) : x - y = 3\}$

12. $\{(x, y) : x + y = 12\} \cap \{(x, y) : x - y = 3\}$

13. $\{(x, y) : x + y < 12\} \cap \{(x, y) : x - y < 3\}$

14. $\{(x, y) : x + y > 12\} \cap \{(x, y) : x - y > 3\}$

5–2 Equivalent Systems

Two systems of equations are graphed below. Study the systems and their graphs.

$$\begin{cases} x + y = 10 & 1 \\ x - y = 4 & 2 \end{cases} \qquad \begin{cases} x - 2y = 1 & 3 \\ x - 3y = -2 & 4 \end{cases}$$

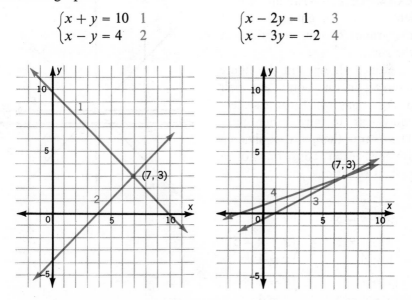

What is the solution set of each system? Because both systems have the same solution set, $\{(7, 3)\}$, the two systems are **equivalent systems** of equations.

> **Definition**   Two systems of equations or inequalities are equivalent if and only if they have the same solution set.

How is the use of the word *equivalent* in *equivalent systems* like its use in *equivalent sentences*? in *equivalent expressions*?

EXAMPLE 1. Show that the following two systems are equivalent.

$$\begin{cases} x = 2 & 1 \\ y = 5 & 2 \end{cases} \qquad \begin{cases} 2x + y = 9 & 3 \\ 3x - 2y = -4 & 4 \end{cases}$$

You can find the solution set of the first system by inspection It is $\{(2, 5)\}$. Now check in the second system.

$$\begin{cases} 2(2) + 5 = 4 + 5 = 9 \\ 3(2) - 2(5) = 6 - 10 = -4 \end{cases}$$

Since the two systems have the same solution set, they are equivalent. How can you use a graph to make sure that the solution set of the second system does not contain other points besides (2, 5)?

EXAMPLE 2. Write all equivalent systems of equations using the graphs of four equations at the right.

Since all lines in the figure intersect in one point, any pair of equations will form a system equivalent to any other pair. There are, then, six equivalent systems, each consisting of a pair of equations.

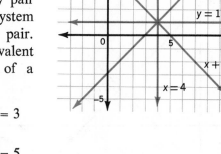

$$\begin{cases} x - y = 3 \\ x + y = 5 \end{cases} \qquad \begin{cases} x - y = 3 \\ y = 1 \end{cases}$$

$$\begin{cases} x - y = 3 \\ x = 4 \end{cases} \qquad \begin{cases} x + y = 5 \\ x = 4 \end{cases}$$

$$\begin{cases} y = 1 \\ x + y = 5 \end{cases} \qquad \begin{cases} y = 1 \\ x = 4 \end{cases}$$

Which system is easiest to solve by inspection?
Show that $\{(4, 1)\}$ is the solution set of each system.

1. What are equivalent systems of sentences?

2. Tell what kind of system is easiest to solve by inspection.

Exercises

A 1. Graph the set $\{(x, y) : x = 4\} \cup \{(x, y) : y = 3\}$. What is the solution set of the system $\begin{cases} x = 4 \\ y = 3 \end{cases}$?

2. What ordered pairs of numbers make $x = -2$ *and* $y = 3$ true?

3. What is the solution set of the system $\begin{cases} x = -3 \\ y = 8\frac{1}{4} \end{cases}$?

— Find the solution set $\{(x, y)\}$ for each compound sentence.

4. $x = 9$ *and* $y = 2$

5. $x = -2$ *and* $y = -4$

6. $x = -2\frac{1}{6}$ *and* $y = 0$

7. $x = -\frac{32}{5}$ *and* $y = \frac{12}{5}$

8. $x = 0$ *and* $y = -6$

9. $x = -8\frac{1}{6}$ *and* $y = 0$

— Four intersecting lines are shown in the figures below each exercise. Which lines are the graphs of the system shown?

10. $\begin{cases} x + y = 3 \\ 2x - y = 0 \end{cases}$

11. $\begin{cases} 2x + y = 8 \\ 5x - y = 6 \end{cases}$

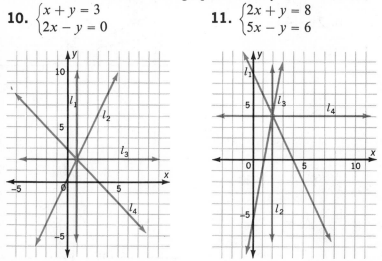

12. Write the system of equations whose graph is l_1 and l_2 in the figure for Exercise 10. What is its solution set?

13. In the graph for Exercise 11, what are the coordinates of the point in $l_2 \cap l_4$? Write the equations for the system of lines $\begin{cases} l_1 \\ l_2 \end{cases}$.

— Show that the system labeled **a** is equivalent to the system labeled **b**.

14. a. $\begin{cases} x + y = 5 \\ x - y = 1 \end{cases}$ **b.** $\begin{cases} x = 3 \\ y = 2 \end{cases}$

15. a. $\begin{cases} 2x + y = 8 \\ x - 2y = 9 \end{cases}$ **b.** $\begin{cases} x = 5 \\ y = -2 \end{cases}$

16. a. $\begin{cases} 2x - 3y = -14 \\ 4x + y = 0 \end{cases}$ **b.** $\begin{cases} x = -1 \\ y = 4 \end{cases}$

17. a. $\begin{cases} x + y = 3 \\ 2x - y = 4 \end{cases}$ **b.** $\begin{cases} x = \frac{7}{3} \\ y = \frac{2}{3} \end{cases}$

18. a. $\begin{cases} 2x - y = 3 \\ 2x + y = 9 \end{cases}$ **b.** $\begin{cases} 2x = 6 \\ y = 3 \end{cases}$

19. a. $\begin{cases} 2x - y = 4 \\ x + y = 6 \end{cases}$ **b.** $\begin{cases} 3x = 10 \\ 3y = 8 \end{cases}$

B — For Exercises 20 and 21, use the graph at the right to find the solution set of the system labeled **a**. Does the ordered pair in the solution set satisfy the equation labeled **b**? Write two other systems equivalent to **a**.

20. a. $\begin{cases} x - y = 5 \\ x + 5y = 11 \end{cases}$ 1
2
   b. $2x + 4y = 16$ 3

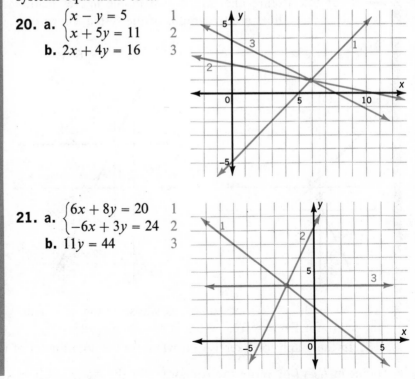

21. a. $\begin{cases} 6x + 8y = 20 \\ -6x + 3y = 24 \end{cases}$ 1
2
   b. $11y = 44$ 3

226   CHAPTER 5

22. Study Exercises 20 and 21. When you add the left sides of equations 1 and 2 and the right sides of equations 1 and 2, do you get an equation, 3, that is satisfied by the ordered pairs in the solution set of the system?

23. Graph the equation $x + y = 4$. What is the graph of $2x + 2y = 8$? of $5x + 5y = 20$? Is $\{(x, y) : x + y = 4\} \cap \{(x, y) : 2x + 2y = 8\}$ a set with no ordered pairs, one ordered pair, or an infinite number of ordered pairs? Explain.

5–3   Solving Systems of Equations by Addition

Graphic methods for solving systems help you understand the important meaning of the solution set of a system. Algebraic methods are needed as well, because a solution set such as $\{(2\frac{1}{3}, 3\frac{3}{5})\}$ is difficult to read from a graph, and one such as $\{(2\frac{1}{3}, \sqrt{3})\}$ cannot be read exactly at all. Also, algebraic methods are needed to program computers to solve systems.

The first algebraic method is called the addition method.

Below are three systems of equations. Is $\{(5, -5)\}$ the solution set of each system? Use substitution to find out.

$$\begin{cases} 3x + y = 10 \\ 2x + y = 5 \end{cases} \qquad \begin{cases} 3x - y = 20 \\ x - 2y = 15 \end{cases} \qquad \begin{cases} x + y = 0 \\ x - y = 10 \end{cases}$$

Now take the first pair of equations and add to get a third equation.

$$\begin{array}{r} 3x + y = 10 \quad 1 \\ + 2x + y = 5 \quad 2 \\ \hline 5x + 2y = 15 \quad 3 \end{array}$$

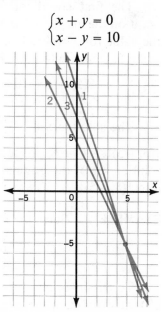

Does $(5, -5)$ satisfy equation 3? Since $(5, -5)$ does satisfy 3, the graph of the new equation passes through the point of intersection of the graphs of the original equations. Any ordered pair (x, y) that makes both 1 and 2 true will make 3 true, and the graphs of the three equations have a point in common.

> **In general, if you add two equations whose graphs intersect, you will get another equation whose graph passes through the point of intersection.**

In solving systems of equations by the addition method, you get an equation whose graph is a line parallel to one of the axes. This is done by eliminating one variable when you add.

EXAMPLE 1. Solve the following system. $\begin{cases} 3x + y = 10 & 1 \\ 2x + y = 5 & 2 \end{cases}$

Multiplying both sides of equation 2 by -1 and adding eliminates y and gives you an equation containing only x.

Multiply equation 2 by -1.
Add.

$$\begin{cases} 3x + y = 10 \\ -2x - y = -5 \\ \hline x = 5 \quad 3 \end{cases}$$

Now use equation 1 or 2 and equation 3 as a new, but equivalent, system.

$$\begin{cases} 3x + y = 10 & 1 \\ x = 5 & 3 \end{cases}$$

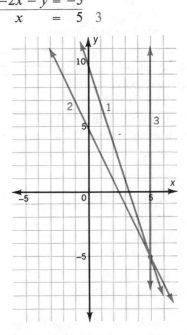

The first coordinate for every point on the graph of 3 is 5. Hence, the value for x where 1 and 3 intersect is 5. Substitute 5 into 1 to find y.

$$3(5) + y = 10$$
$$y = -5$$

The solution set of $\begin{cases} x = 5 \\ y = -5 \end{cases}$ is $\{(5, -5)\}$. Check to see that the solution set of the original system is also $\{(5, -5)\}$.

EXAMPLE 2. Solve the following system of equations.

$$\begin{cases} 2x + 3y = -1 & 1 \\ 5x - 2y = -12 & 2 \end{cases}$$

To eliminate one variable by addition, the sum of the coefficients of that variable in the two equations must be 0. For this to happen, the coefficients must be negatives of each other. The coefficients of y become negatives of each other if you multiply the sides of equation 1 by 2 and the sides of equation 2 by 3.

Multiply equation 1 by 2. $\qquad \begin{cases} 4x + 6y = -2 \\ 15x - 6y = -36 \end{cases}$
Multiply equation 2 by 3.
Add. $\qquad\qquad\qquad 19x \qquad = -38$
$$x = -2 \quad 3$$

Now solve either equivalent system. (Both are done for you here.)

$$\begin{cases} 2x + 3y = -1 & 1 \\ x = -2 & 3 \end{cases} \qquad \begin{cases} 5x - 2y = -12 & 2 \\ x = -2 & 3 \end{cases}$$

Substitute -2 for x in either equation 1 or equation 2.

$$2(-2) + 3y = -1 \qquad\qquad 5(-2) - 2y = -12$$
$$y = 1 \qquad\qquad\qquad\qquad y = 1$$

The solution set is $\{(-2, 1)\}$. Check by substituting -2 for x and 1 for y in both equation 1 and equation 2.

Here is a summary of the steps used in the addition method of solving a system of two linear equations in two variables.

① Make the coefficients of either x or y in both equations negatives of each other by using the multiplication postulate for equations.

② Add the sides to eliminate x or y, getting a third equation in y or x, respectively.

③ Choose the new equation and one of the original equations as an equivalent system.

④ Substitute the number for x or y in either original equation and solve for the other variable.

⑤ Check by substituting the number pair in both original equations.

Now try these

—— In each of the following, what have both sides of the equation in **a** been multiplied by to get the equation in **b**?

a	b
1. $3x - 2y = 6$	$6x - 4y = 12$
2. $-2x + y = -4$	$+8x - 4y = +16$
3. $3x - 2y = 5$	$6x - 4y = 10$
4. $5x - 7y = -2$	$15x - 21y = -6$

―― Add the two expressions.

5. $3x - 5y$
$\underline{6x + 5y}$

6. $4x - 3y$
$\underline{-4x - 6y}$

7. $9x - 8y - 5$
$\underline{7x + 8y - 3}$

―― What have both sides of each equation in **a** been multiplied by to get each respective equation in **b**?

<table>
<tr><td align="center">**a**</td><td align="center">**b**</td></tr>
<tr><td>**8.** $3x - 2y = -4$
$-5x + 3y = -1$</td><td>$15x - 10y = -20$
$-15x + 9y = -3$</td></tr>
<tr><td>**9.** $3x - 2y = -9$
$3x - 5y = -10$</td><td>$15x - 10y = -45$
$-6x + 10y = 20$</td></tr>
</table>

Answers: **1.** 2   **2.** -4 **3.** 2   **4.** 3   **5.** $9x$ **6.** $-9y$ **7.** $16x - 8$ **8.** 5; 3
9. 5; -2

Exercises

A ―― Solve the following systems of equations by addition.

1. $\begin{cases} 3x + y = 9 \\ 2x - y = 1 \end{cases}$

2. $\begin{cases} 3x + y = 10 \\ 2x + y = 7 \end{cases}$

3. $\begin{cases} 5r - s = -23 \\ 3r - s = -15 \end{cases}$

4. $\begin{cases} 2a + 3b = -5 \\ 5a + 3b = 1 \end{cases}$

5. $\begin{cases} 3x + 2y = -7 \\ 5x - 2y = -1 \end{cases}$

6. $\begin{cases} x + 3y = 14 \\ x - 2y = -1 \end{cases}$

7. $\begin{cases} 2m + 3n = 6 \\ 2m - 5n = 22 \end{cases}$

8. $\begin{cases} 2x + 3y = 8 \\ 3x + y = 5 \end{cases}$

9. $\begin{cases} 2x + y = 3 \\ 7x - 4y = 18 \end{cases}$

10. $\begin{cases} -4x - y = -16 \\ 5x - 3y = 3 \end{cases}$

―― Solve the following compound sentences.

11. $5x + y = 15$ *and* $3x + 2y = 9$

12. $7x - 5y = -2$ *and* $-8x - y = 9$

13. $4p - 2q = 20$ *and* $p + 5q = -17$

14. $2x + 5y = 18$ *and* $-5x + y = -18$

15. $2x + 2y = 8$ *and* $5x - 3y = 4$

16. $4a + 3b = -2$ *and* $8a - 2b = 12$

17. $2x - 5y = 7$ *and* $3x - 2y = -17$

18. $9c + 7d = 14$ *and* $-6c - d = -2$

19. $4x + 3y = 7$ *and* $4x + 4y = 12$

20. $5a + 9b = 6$ *and* $6a + 5b = 13$

—— List the members for each of the following sets.

21. $\{(x, y) : 2x + y = 8\} \cap \{(x, y) : 4x - y = -8\}$

22. $\{(x, y) : 2x + 3y = 9\} \cap \{(x, y) : 4x + 3y = 21\}$

23. $\{(a, b) : 4a + 3b = 0\} \cap \{(a, b) : -2a - b = 2\}$

24. $\{(x, y) : 5x + 3y = 2\} \cap \{(x, y) : 3x + 5y = -2\}$

25. $\{(m, n) : 5m + 9n = 61\} \cap \{(m, n) : 7m + 3n = 47\}$

26. $\{(x, y) : 7x - 2y = 55\} \cap \{(x, y) : -9x + 5y = -78\}$

27. $\{(a, b) : 2a + 3b = 0\} \cap \{(a, b) : 2b - 3a = 26\}$

28. $\{(x, y) : 5x - 6y = 1\} \cap \{(x, y) : 3x = 2y - 33\}$

29. $\{(r, s) : 11r = 3s + 2\} \cap \{(r, s) : 7r + 70 = 7s\}$

30. $\{(x, y) : 4x - 5y = 2\} \cap \{(x, y) : -8x - 3y = -30\}$

B —— Solve the following systems of equations by addition.

31. $\begin{cases} 9x - 2y = 2\frac{1}{2} \\ 5x - 6y = -3\frac{1}{2} \end{cases}$

32. $\begin{cases} 3x + 5y = 4\frac{1}{2} \\ -9x - 2y = -7 \end{cases}$

33. $\begin{cases} 8x + 6y = 10 \\ -4x + 3y = -1 \end{cases}$

34. $\begin{cases} 5x + 4y = -\frac{1}{3} \\ 7x + 2y = \frac{4}{3} \end{cases}$

35. $\begin{cases} 2x + 3y = 12.6 \\ -5x + 9y = -12.4 \end{cases}$

36. $\begin{cases} x + 3y = 17.3 \\ 2x - 7y = -36.9 \end{cases}$

37. $\begin{cases} -6x - 5y = -4.6 \\ 10x + 3y = 6.6 \end{cases}$

38. $\begin{cases} 2x + 7y = 52 \\ -3x + 5y = -16 \end{cases}$

—— Solve the following compound sentences.

39. $2x - 7y = 8$ *and* $4y - 9x = 19$

40. $4x - 6y = 8$ *and* $-9x - 6y = -96$

41. $2x - 3y = 8$ *and* $3x - 7y = 7$

42. $-2x - y = -7$ *and* $2x - y = 5$

43. $-3x - y = -10\frac{1}{2}$ *and* $6x - 2y = 7$

44. $2x - 3y = -14$ *and* $3x + 7y = 48$

45. $ax + 3y = 8a$ *and* $ax - y = 4a$

46. $7x + ay = 13a$ *and* $2x - ay = 5a$

C —— Solve the following systems of equations by addition.

47. $\begin{cases} 2x + 1.5y = -1 \\ 0.5x + 2y = 3 \end{cases}$

48. $\begin{cases} x - 2.3 = -5y \\ 2x - 2 = 3y \end{cases}$

49. $\begin{cases} 2a - 1.5b = 10 \\ 0.3a - 0.05b = 0.8 \end{cases}$

50. $\begin{cases} 2x - 3y = 0.1 \\ 3x - 3 = -5y \end{cases}$

51. $\begin{cases} 1.25s + 8.25t = 107.5 \\ 2.5s - t = 0.8 \end{cases}$

52. $\begin{cases} 10x + 5y = 3.5 \\ 3y - 0.6 = 3x \end{cases}$

53. $\begin{cases} 2.75m + n = 3.275 \\ 1.25m + 0.5n = 1.625 \end{cases}$ **54.** $\begin{cases} 3s - 0.7t = 26.3 \\ 0.7s + t = 7.3 \end{cases}$

—— List the members of each of the following sets.

55. $\{(x, y) : x - 1.6y = 0.38\} \cap \{(x, y) : 0.4x + 3y = 0.88\}$
56. $\{(a, b) : a - 2.33b = 0.67\} \cap \{(a, b) : a + 0.2b = 3.2\}$
57. $\{(x, y) : 2x - 0.2y = 4\} \cap \{(x, y) : 3x + y = 11.2\}$
58. $\{(a, b) : 6a + 0.3b = 1.2\} \cap \{(a, b) : 0.1 + 3a = 0.2b\}$
59. $\{(c, d) : 1.69d - 12 = 7c\} \cap \{(c, d) : 3c + 6d = 62.1\}$
60. $\{(x, y) : 1.7x + 1.3y = 6.8\} \cap \{(x, y) : 0.2x + 0.3y = -2.4\}$

5–4 Using Systems of Equations

Many verbal problems are easily solved using systems of equations. The procedure is similar to the method in Chapter 3, but now each condition is expressed with a single equation in two variables.

EXAMPLE 1. **The difference between two numbers is 6.** *Twice the larger is 5 more than 3 times the smaller.* Find the numbers.

① Let the larger number be x and the smaller number be y.

② Express each condition in an equation.

The difference is 6.	$x - y = 6$	1
Twice the larger is 5 more		
than 3 times the smaller.	$2x = 3y + 5$	2

③ Solve the systems of equations.

Multiply 1 by -3. $\qquad -3x + 3y = -18$
Rewrite 2. $\qquad\qquad\quad \underline{2x - 3y = 5}$
Add. $\qquad\qquad\qquad -x = -13$
$\qquad\qquad\qquad\qquad\quad x = 13 \quad 3$

Solve either the system of equations 1 and 3 or of 2 and 3.

$$13 - y = 6$$
$$-y = -7$$
$$y = 7$$

④ Check to see that 13 and 7 satisfy the two conditions of the problem.

$$13 - 7 = 6 \qquad 2(13) = 3(7) + 5, \text{ or } 26$$

EXAMPLE 2. At a high school play, **90 adult and student tickets were sold.** How many of each could have been sold?

① Let the number of student tickets be x and the number of adult tickets be y.

② Use the condition given to write an equation.

90 adult and student tickets were sold. $x + y = 90$

③ Since only one condition is given in the problem, the solution set is as follows.

$$\{(0, 90), (1, 89), (2, 88), \cdots, (88, 2), (89, 1), (90, 0)\}$$

The problem limits the domain to whole numbers. Why?

EXAMPLE 3. Suppose that the condition in Example 2 is true, and suppose further that you know that *student tickets cost 50 cents and adult tickets cost 80 cents, and the total receipts were $48.00.* How many of each kind were sold?

① Use the new condition to write an equation in x and y, where x and y have the same meaning as in Example 2.
The number of cents from the sale of x student tickets is 50x.
The number of cents from the sale of y adult tickets is 80y.
The total receipts are $48.00, or 4800 cents.

$$50x + 80y = 4800 \quad 2$$

② Combine this with the equation $x + y = 90$ to form a system.

$$\begin{cases} 50x + 80y = 4800 & 2 \\ x + y = 90 & 1 \end{cases}$$

③ Complete the solution of the system.

④ Check the solution set with the conditions of the problem. Do you find $\{(80, 10)\}$ to be the solution set?

Exercises

A —— Write two equations for each of the problems below and solve the resulting system by addition. Check your results.

1. The difference between two numbers is 4. Three times the larger is 2 more than five times the smaller. Find the numbers.

2. The sum of two numbers is 20. Twice one of them is three times the other. Find the numbers.

3. The width of a rectangle is 6 inches less than the length. The perimeter is 72 inches. Find the length and the width.

4. Find two numbers such that four times the first number minus five times the second number equals 100, and twice the first number plus the second number equals 8.

5. At a high school play, students paid 35 cents and adults paid 70 cents for admission. The total receipts for 100 tickets amounted to $48.30. How many of each kind were sold?

6. Six apples and one pear cost 37 cents. At the same price three apples and six pears cost 57 cents. Find the cost of each.

7. Nancy is paid $4.00 a week more than Helen. In 11 weeks Helen earns as much as Nancy does in 10 weeks. What is the weekly wage of each?

8. The sum of two numbers is 16. Twice their difference increased by 3 is 7. Find the numbers.

9. Five full-fare tickets and one half-fare ticket on the railroad cost $90.75, and four full-fare and two half-fare tickets cost $82.50. How much does a full-fare ticket cost? a half-fare ticket?

10. Phil's father is 25 years older than Phil. In 10 years he will be twice as old as Phil. What are their present ages? (*Hint:* Write one equation for their present ages and another for their ages 10 years from now.)

B **11.** Edith's present age is 2 less than twice her sister Jane's. In 5 years Edith's age will equal three times Jane's age now. What are their present ages?

12. Seven times the sum of two numbers is 28. If the second number is multiplied by 3 and added to the first number, the sum equals the second number. What are the two numbers?

13. The length of a rectangle is 3 inches more than twice the width. The perimeter is 45 inches. Find the length and the width.

C **14.** Find two numbers such that one is as much more than 30 as the other is less than 30, and eight times their difference is equal to the larger.

——————— **The Problem of the Twelve Coins** ———————

Of 12 coins, one is counterfeit and is either lighter or heavier than the other 11. Determine in three weighings on a platform balance which is the counterfeit coin, and tell if it is heavier or lighter than the other 11.

5–5 Solving Systems of Equations by Substitution

If the system at the right has an ordered pair of numbers in its solution set, call this pair (x, y). You can solve for x or for y in 1 and substitute in 2 to find the replacement for (x, y) that makes both equations true. This is solving systems of equations by **substitution**.

$$\begin{cases} 4x + y = 2 & 1 \\ 2x + 3y = -4 & 2 \end{cases}$$

① Solve for x or for y in either equation in terms of the other variable. Solve equation 1 for y.

$$4x + y = 2$$
$$y = 2 - 4x$$

② Replace the variable y in the other equation with the expression $2 - 4x$. This gives an equation in x.

$$2x + 3y = -4$$
$$2x + 3(2 - 4x) = -4$$
$$2x + 6 - 12x = -4$$
$$-10x = -10$$
$$x = 1 \qquad 3$$

③ Solve the system consisting of 1 and 3 or that consisting of 2 and 3

$$4(1) + y = 2 \qquad\qquad 2(1) + 3y = -4$$
$$4 + y = 2 \qquad\qquad 3y = -6$$
$$y = -2 \qquad\qquad y = -2$$

④ If the numbers obtained for the variables check in the original system, then they form the solution set. Is the solution set $\{(1, -2)\}$?

EXAMPLE. Solve the following system of equations by substitution.

$$\begin{cases} -x + 2y = 4 & 1 \\ 5x - 3y = 1 & 2 \end{cases}$$

① Solve equation 1 for x in terms of y.

$$-x = -2y + 4$$
$$x = 2y - 4$$

② Replace x in equation 2 with $2y - 4$ to find an equation for y.

$$5x - 3y = 1$$
$$5(2y - 4) - 3y = 1$$
$$10y - 20 - 3y = 1$$
$$7y = 21$$
$$y = 3 \qquad 3$$

③ Use equation 3 with 1 or 2.

$$-x + 2(3) = 4 \qquad\qquad 5x - 3(3) = 1$$
$$-x + 6 = 4 \qquad\qquad 5x - 9 = 1$$
$$x = 2 \qquad\qquad x = 2$$

④ Check to see if $\{(2, 3)\}$ is the solution set of the system.

Exercises

A —— Solve the following systems of equations by substitution.

1. $\begin{cases} x = y + 4 \\ 2x - 5y = 2 \end{cases}$

2. $\begin{cases} y = 3 - x \\ 5x + 3y = -1 \end{cases}$

3. $\begin{cases} x = 8y \\ x - 4y = 12 \end{cases}$

4. $\begin{cases} 5x - y = 1 \\ 3x + 2y = 13 \end{cases}$

5. $\begin{cases} 5a = b \\ a = 10b + 5 \end{cases}$

6. $\begin{cases} r = 5 - s \\ 2r + 7s = 0 \end{cases}$

7. $\begin{cases} c = d + 4 \\ 2c + 3d = -2 \end{cases}$

8. $\begin{cases} x + 3y = 5 \\ -3x + 2y = 18 \end{cases}$

9. $\begin{cases} c = d - 4 \\ 3c + d = 4 \end{cases}$

10. $\begin{cases} y = \frac{1}{4}x \\ 3x + 4y = 32 \end{cases}$

—— Use substitution to find the solution sets of the following compound sentences.

11. $3x + y = 7$ *and* $x - y = 1$

12. $4x - y = -7$ *and* $5x - 8y = -2$

13. $x + y = 3$ *and* $x - y = 1$

14. $2x + y = 5$ *and* $8x - y = 45$

15. $x = 3y$ *and* $2x - 5y = 4$

16. $5x - 3y = -1$ *and* $-x + 3y = -7$

17. $y = -2x$ *and* $x + 2y = 9$

18. $3x - y = -24$ *and* $7x - 9y = 14$

B —— List the elements for each set.

19. $\{(x, y) : y = 8 - x\} \cap \{(x, y) : 4x - 3y = -3\}$

20. $\{(x, y) : 3x + 2y = 16\} \cap \{(x, y) : 7x + y = 19\}$

21. $\{(x, y) : y + 2x = 41\} \cap \{(x, y) : 5y - 3x = 14\}$

22. $\{(x, y) : 2x + y = 11\} \cap \{(x, y) : x - y = 2\}$

23. $\{(x, y) : 4x - 2y = 3\} \cap \{(x, y) : 3x - y = 4\}$

24. $\{(x, y) : 5y - x = -9\} \cap \{(x, y) : 4y + 3x = -11\}$

25. $\{(x, y) : x - 5y = -2\} \cap \{(x, y) : 9x + 7y = 34\}$

26. $\{(a, b) : 4a + b = 8\} \cap \{(a, b) : 5a + 3b = 3\}$

27. $\{(u, v) : 2u - 3v = -12\} \cap \{(u, v) : 7u + v = 19\}$

28. $\{(s, t) : 4s + t = 8\} \cap \{(s, t) : s + 4t = 6\}$

5–6 Problem Solving Using Systems of Equations

In the decimal place-value numeration system, the ten digits are symbols for the whole numbers less than the base. The digits are the numerals 0, 1, 2, 3, 4, 5, 6, 7, 8, and 9. The place in which a digit occurs in a numeral determines the value it represents. The abacus and diagram below represent the important idea of place value in a decimal system by showing the value of 432.

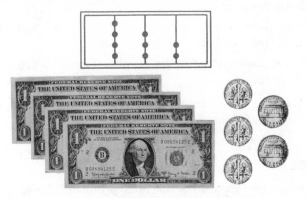

Since the digit 4 is in the second place to the left of the units place, it represents 4 hundreds; similarly, the digit 3 represents 3 tens; and the digit 2 represents 2 units, or 2 ones.

If you were told to write the numeral with 7 as the tens digit and 4 as the units digit, you would write 74. Or if you were told to write the numeral with 4 as the tens digit and 7 as the units digit, you would write 47. A numeral with 4 as the tens digit and 7 as the units digit names $4(10) + 7$, or 47.

You can use this idea of place value to solve many interesting problems.

EXAMPLE. The sum of the numbers named by the digits of a two-digit numeral is 15. The number named is 9 less than the number named when the digits are reversed. Find the number.

① Let t be the tens digit and u be the units digit.

② The number is $10t + u$ and the number formed when the digits are reversed is $10u + t$. Using the conditions of the problem gives the following system.

$$\begin{cases} t + u = 15 \\ 10t + u = 10u + t - 9 \end{cases}$$

③ Solve the system for t and u. The number should be 78.

Now try these

1. If 7 is the tens digit of a number and u is the units digit, which expression names the number?

    a. $7(10) + u$ **b.** $u(10) + 7$ **c.** $7u$

2. Write the expression for the number named when t is the tens digit and 4 is the units digit.

3. Write the expression for the number named when the digits in Exercise 2 are reversed.

4. If t is the tens digit of a number and u is the units digit, write the expression for the number.

5. Write the expression for the number formed when the digits in Exercise 4 are reversed.

Answers: **1. a** **2.** $t(10) + 4$, or $10t + 4$ **3.** $4(10) + t$, or $40 + t$ **4.** $t(10) + u$, or $10t + u$ **5.** $u(10) + t$, or $10u + t$

Exercises

A —— Write two equations for each problem. Solve the resulting system by addition or substitution, whichever you choose.

1. The sum of the numbers named by the two digits of a numeral is 9. The number named by the numeral is 27 more than the number named when the digits are reversed. Find the number.

2. Find the number named by two digits whose units digit names a number that is twice that named by the tens digit; the difference between the numbers named by the digits is 4.

3. The units digit of a two-digit numeral names a number 2 less than that named by the tens digit. The number named by the numeral is 2 more that 6 times the sum of the numbers named by the digits. Find the number.

4. A certain two-digit numeral represents a number that is 5 times the sum of the numbers named by its digits. The digits from left to right name consecutive integers. Find the number.

5. A certain two-digit numeral names a number 5 times the sum of the numbers named by its digits. If 9 were added to the number named by the numeral, the digits in the numeral would be reversed. Find the number.

6. One number exceeds another by 62. If 5 times the smaller is decreased by 2 times the larger, the difference is 155. What are the two numbers?

7. Two angles are supplementary (the sum of their measures is 180°). One of the angles measures 30° greater than 2 times the measure of the other. How many degrees do each of the two angles measure?

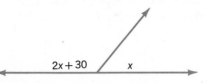

8. The perimeter of a rectangular playground is 480 meters. What are the length and width of the rectangle if twice the width is 30 meters more than the length?

B **9.** The sum of two amounts of money is $5000. If one amount is invested at 4% annual interest and the second at 7% annual interest, the total annual interest will be equal to the interest on $5000 at 6% for one year. What are the amounts invested? (*Hint:* If x and y represent the two amounts, you get the following.

$$\begin{cases} x + y = 5000 \\ 0.04x + 0.07y = 0.06(5000) \end{cases}$$

You can multiply the second equation by 100 and rewrite as

$$\begin{cases} x + y = 5000 \\ 4x + 7y = 30{,}000 \end{cases}$$

for ease in solving.)

10. The Smith Motor Company's total sales on new and used cars this year was $140,000. The total profit amounted to 10% of the sales. The profit on new cars was 8% and on used cars was 15%. What was the amount taken in on new-car sales? on used-car sales?

11. Mrs. Bunch is considering buying a television set or a stereo phonograph. The combined cost is $550. Two stereo phonographs cost $170 more than one television set. How much does each item cost?

12. Ken Cowing is now 6 years older than his youngest brother. In 8 years, 3 times Ken's age will equal 4 times his brother's age. What are their present ages?

13. Ken Levy's coin collection contains 7 more dimes than nickels. In all, the collection amounts to $3.25. How many of each coin does he have?

14. Barbara Rudolph wishes to mix 135 pounds of candy to sell for 80 cents a pound. How many pounds of candy at 60 cents and at $1.20 a pound must be used to make the desired mixture?

15. Tickets for 470 seats in an auditorium were sold for a play. The total sales was $346.50. How many tickets were sold to adults at 90 cents and how many to children at 40 cents?

5–7 Systems of Equations with Many and with No Solutions

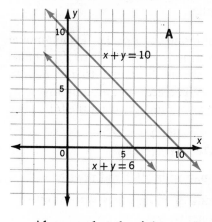

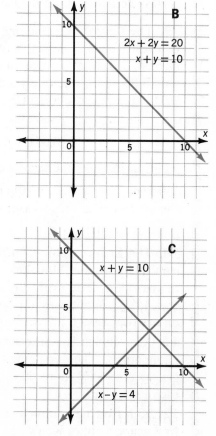

Above and at the right are the graphs of three systems of equations. Which has in its solution set one ordered pair? an infinite number of ordered pairs? no ordered pairs?

How do the slopes of the lines compare in each system? How do the y intercepts compare?

Systems of equations are classified by the number of pairs in their solution sets. The table on the next page is based on the graphs shown above. Use the following arbitrary system in considering the relations between constants.

$$\begin{cases} a_1x + b_1y + c_1 = 0 \\ a_2x + b_2y + c_2 = 0 \end{cases}$$

System	A	B	C
Number of solutions	None.	Infinite.	One.
Graphs	Parallel lines: slopes equal, intercepts different.	Same line.	Distinct, inter- secting lines.
Relations between constants	$\dfrac{a_1}{a_2} = \dfrac{b_1}{b_2} \neq \dfrac{c_1}{c_2}$ $\dfrac{1}{1} = \dfrac{1}{1} \neq \dfrac{-10}{-6}$	$\dfrac{a_1}{a_2} = \dfrac{b_1}{b_2} = \dfrac{c_1}{c_2}$ $\dfrac{2}{1} = \dfrac{2}{1} = \dfrac{-20}{-10}$	$\dfrac{a_1}{a_2} \neq \dfrac{b_1}{b_2} \neq \dfrac{c_1}{c_2}$ $\dfrac{1}{1} \neq \dfrac{-1}{1} \neq \dfrac{10}{4}$
Classification	Inconsistent.	Consistent and dependent.	Consistent and simultaneous, or independent.

Use the statements in the table to try to formulate definitions of *inconsistent, consistent, dependent,* and *simultaneous,* or *independent, systems of equations* before reading the definitions below.

Definition   A system of equations or inequalities whose solution set is ø is an <u>inconsistent</u> system.

Definition   A system is <u>consistent</u> if it has one or more ordered pairs in the solution set.

Definition   A consistent system of equations whose solution set has an infinite number of ordered pairs is a <u>dependent</u> <u>system.</u>

Definition   A consistent system of equations with one and only one ordered pair in the solution set is a <u>simultaneous,</u> or <u>independent, system.</u>

Note what happens in the examples on the following page when you use algebraic methods with inconsistent systems and with dependent systems.

EXAMPLE 1. Solve the following system by addition.

$$\begin{cases} x + y = 10 & 1 \\ x + y = 6 & 2 \end{cases}$$

If there is a solution, *then* the sum of the left sides and the sum of the right sides give an equation whose graph passes through the point of intersection of the system. Multiply 2 by −1 and add.

$$\begin{cases} x + y = 10 & 1 \\ -x - y = -6 \end{cases}$$
$$0 \cdot x + 0 \cdot y = 4$$
$$0 = 4 \quad 3$$

No pair will satisfy either of the following systems.

$$\begin{cases} x + y = 10 & 1 \\ 0 = 4 & 3 \end{cases} \qquad \begin{cases} x + y = 6 & 2 \\ 0 = 4 & 3 \end{cases}$$

Equation 3 is not true for any ordered pair (x, y). Hence, the system 1 *and* 2 is inconsistent, and the following is true.

$$\{(x, y) : x + y = 10\} \cap \{(x, y) : x + y = 6\} = \emptyset$$

When you use algebraic methods with a system and get an equation that is true for no value of x, the system is inconsistent.

EXAMPLE 2. Solve the following system by addition.

$$\begin{cases} 2x - 3y = 10 & 1 \\ 10x - 15y = 50 & 2 \end{cases}$$

Multiply equation 1 by −5.

$$\begin{cases} -10x + 15y = -50 \\ 10x - 15y = 50 & 2 \end{cases}$$

Add.

$$0 \cdot x + 0 \cdot y = 0$$
$$0 = 0 \quad 3$$

If 1 *and* 2 has a solution, then it is the same as the solution of 1 *and* 3 or of 2 *and* 3.

$$\begin{cases} 2x - 3y = 10 & 1 \\ 0 = 0 & 3 \end{cases} \qquad \begin{cases} 10x - 15y = 50 & 2 \\ 0 = 0 & 3 \end{cases}$$

There is an infinite number of pairs that will satisfy either system. There is also an infinite number of pairs that will satisfy the original system.

When you use algebraic methods with a system and get an equation that is an identity, the system is dependent.

Checkpoint

1. How many ordered pairs are in the solution set of an inconsistent system?   a dependent system?

2. Describe the graph of an inconsistent system; a dependent system.

3. What happens when you use algebraic methods to find the solution set of an inconsistent system?   a dependent system?   a simultaneous, or independent, system?

Exercises

A —— Find the slope and the y intercept of each equation below. Then use your results and write *Independent*, *Inconsistent*, or *Dependent* to classify each system.

1. $\begin{cases} 3x + y = 7 \\ 3x - y = 5 \end{cases}$

2. $\begin{cases} 3x + y = 7 \\ 3x + y = 5 \end{cases}$

3. $\begin{cases} 3x + y = 7 \\ 6x + 2y = 14 \end{cases}$

4. $\begin{cases} 3x + y = 7 \\ 6x + 2y = 10 \end{cases}$

5. $\begin{cases} x + y = 10 \\ x - y = 4 \end{cases}$

6. $\begin{cases} x + y = 10 \\ 4x + 4y = 4 \end{cases}$

7. $\begin{cases} 2x + y = 7 \\ 2x - y = 7 \end{cases}$

8. $\begin{cases} 6x + 8 = 2y \\ y = 3x + 4 \end{cases}$

9. $\begin{cases} x + y = 1 \\ y = -x \end{cases}$

10. $\begin{cases} 4x + 5y = 7 \\ 5x = 7 + 4y \end{cases}$

11. $\begin{cases} 2x - y = 2 \\ 4x - 2y = 0 \end{cases}$

12. $\begin{cases} 3x + 5y = 4 \\ 12 - 9x = 15y \end{cases}$

—— Solve the following systems.

13. $\begin{cases} 2x + 3y = 8 \\ x + y = 3 \end{cases}$

14. $\begin{cases} m + n = 14 \\ 28 - 2m = 2n \end{cases}$

15. $\begin{cases} x + y = 9 \\ x - y = 9 \end{cases}$

16. $\begin{cases} y = 2x - 8 \\ 2x - y = 10 \end{cases}$

17. $\begin{cases} y = -4x + 5 \\ 8x + 2y = 10 \end{cases}$

18. $\begin{cases} x = y + 5 \\ 2x - 2y = 7 \end{cases}$

19. $\begin{cases} 2\frac{1}{2}x - 4 = 3y \\ 6y + 8 = 5x \end{cases}$ **20.** $\begin{cases} y = 4x - 2 \\ x - 4y = 2 \end{cases}$

21. $\begin{cases} 4a + 3b = 2 \\ 2a + 3b = 4 \end{cases}$ **22.** $\begin{cases} 5u - 3v = 7 \\ 25u - 15v = 49 \end{cases}$

B —— Write *Independent, Inconsistent,* or *Dependent* to classify each system.

23. $\begin{cases} ax + by = c \\ ax + by = d, \ c \neq d \end{cases}$

24. $\begin{cases} ax + by = c \\ nax + nby = nc, \ n \neq 0 \end{cases}$

25. $\begin{cases} ax + by = c \\ ax - by = c, \ b \neq 0 \end{cases}$

26. $\begin{cases} ax + by = c \\ nax + nby = nd, \ c \neq d, \ n \neq 0 \end{cases}$

5–8 Systems of Inequalities

The solution set of the system of inequalities shown at the right is the set of ordered pairs that make both sentences true. Examine the graph of each inequality.

$\begin{cases} x + y > 10 & 1 \\ x - y > -4 & 2 \end{cases}$

① Any point in half-plane E has coordinates that make $x + y > 10$ true. Note that the graph of $x + y = 10$ is shown dashed to show that it is not included in the half-plane.

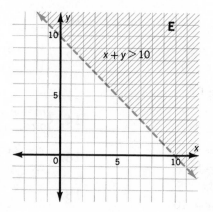

② Any point in half-plane F has coordinates that make $x - y > -4$ true.

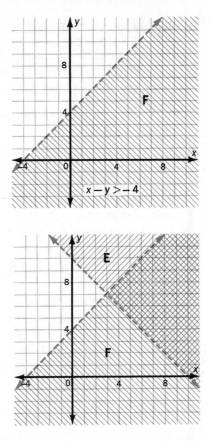

③ To show the points that are in both half-planes and whose coordinates are in both solution sets, draw both graphs on the same axes. The points in the intersection are indicated by the crosshatching.

The points with coordinates in the solution set may be graphed as shown in the diagrams. Since there is an infinite number of ordered pairs in the solution set, you could not possibly list them all. One way to indicate the solution set is by a graph.

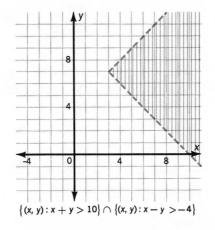

$\{(x, y) : x + y > 10\} \cap \{(x, y) : x - y > -4\}$

Exercises

A —— Graph each sentence in the system. Shade the graph of the solution set darker than the other points. Write the coordinates of at least three points in the solution set, unless it is empty.

Example. $\begin{cases} y \geq 2x - 4 \\ x + y \leq 5 \end{cases}$

The graph of $y \geq 2x - 4$ is the graph of $y = 2x - 4$ and all points on the left side of that line.

The graph of $x + y \leq 5$ is the graph of $x + y = 5$ and all points on the left side of that line.

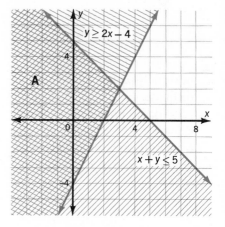

The graph of the solution set of the system is the set of points in both inequalities, which is shown by the crosshatching.

Three points in the solution set are (0, 0), (1, 2), and (2, 3).

1. $\begin{cases} x + y \leq 2 \\ x - y \leq 4 \end{cases}$

2. $\begin{cases} y > 3x \\ y \leq -3x \end{cases}$

3. $\begin{cases} x - y = 8 \\ x + y > 3 \end{cases}$

4. $\begin{cases} x + y > 10 \\ x + y < 4 \end{cases}$

5. $\begin{cases} y > 3x \\ y > 3x + 2 \end{cases}$

6. $\begin{cases} 2x + 3y \geq 6 \\ y \leq 4 \end{cases}$

B —— For the following compound sentences, shade only the points in the graph of the solution set. Do not shade the graphs of the parts unless these points are also in the graph of the compound sentence.

7. $x \geq 0$ *or* $2x - 3y \leq 6$

8. $x \geq 0$ *and* $2x - 3y \leq 6$

9. $x + y \leq 10$ *or* $x + y \geq -10$

10. $x + y \leq 10$ *and* $x + y \geq -10$

More Challenging Problems

—— Is there a pair of numbers that will satisfy each group of three equations? If so, find the number pair.

1. $\begin{cases} x - 5y = 27 \\ 2x + 3y = 2 \\ 5x + 8y = 3 \end{cases}$
$\qquad$
2. $\begin{cases} 9x + 4y = 0 \\ 5x - 2y = 6 \\ 3x + 14y = 2 \end{cases}$

—— Solve for x and y in terms of a, b, and c.

3. $\begin{cases} ax + by = c \\ bx - ay = 7c \end{cases}$
$\qquad$
4. $\begin{cases} ax + by + a^2 + b^2 = 0 \\ bx + ay + 2ab = 0 \end{cases}$

5. $\begin{cases} cy + (b + c)x = 2bc \\ by + (b - c)x = 2^2 - b^2 \end{cases}$

6. Lum is twice as old as Moe was when Lum was Moe's age. When Moe is as old as Lum now is, the sum of their ages will be 100. How old is each?

CHAPTER REVIEW

1. Know the meaning of and be able to use each of the following words or phrases. The number shown after each word or phrase indicates where it is introduced, in case you need to review.

system of sentences (*221*) $\qquad$ dependent system (*241*)
equivalent systems (*223*) $\qquad$ simultaneous, or
inconsistent system (*241*) $\qquad\quad$ independent, system (*241*)
consistent system (*241*)

2. How can you prove that (7, 2) is the solution set of the following system?

$$\begin{cases} x - y = 5 \\ -2x + 3y = -8 \end{cases}$$

3. Which of the following systems are equivalent to the system in Exercise 2? How do you know?

a. $\begin{cases} x = 7 \\ y = 2 \end{cases}$
$\qquad$
b. $\begin{cases} x + 2y = 11 \\ x + y = 9 \end{cases}$

c. $\begin{cases} x - y = 5 \\ (x - y) + (2x + 3y) = 5 - 8 \end{cases}$
$\qquad$
d. $\begin{cases} 2x + 3y = -8 \\ (x - y) + (2x + 3y) = -3 \end{cases}$

e. $\begin{cases} x - y - 5 = 0 \\ y = 2 \end{cases}$
$\qquad$
f. $\begin{cases} x - y = 5 \\ 2x + 3(x - 5) = -8 \end{cases}$

4. Complete: The solution set of the compound sentence

$$x - y = 5 \textit{ and } 2x + 3y = -8$$

is _?_.

5. Complete.

$$\{(x, y) : x - y = 5\} \cap \{(x, y) : 2x + 3y = -8\} = \underline{\ ?\ }$$

6. Is (7, 2) in the solution set of $x - y = 5 \textit{ or } 2x + 3y = -8$?

7. Find two systems equivalent to the following.

$$\begin{cases} x + y = -4 \\ 2x - 5y = 8 \end{cases}$$

8. Shown below is the graph of a system of two equations. What is the solution set of the system?

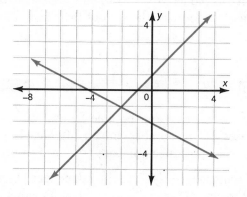

_____ Tell whether each of the following systems has one and only one, none, or an infinite number of ordered pairs in its solution set.

9. $\begin{cases} y = 2x - 6 \\ 2y = x + 5 \end{cases}$ **10.** $\begin{cases} 3x - y = 8 \\ 2y = 6x - 16 \end{cases}$

11. $\begin{cases} 2x + 3y = 7 \\ 6y - 13 = 4x \end{cases}$ **12.** $\begin{cases} 2x - 3y = 5 \\ 4x = 10 - 6y \end{cases}$

13. How would you describe the graphs in Exercises 9–12; that is, for which do you get distinct intersecting lines, for which do you get parallel lines, and for which do you get a single line?

14. Classify the systems in Exercises 9–12 as inconsistent, dependent, or simultaneous.

_____ Solve each system by graphing.

15. $\begin{cases} x + y = -5 \\ 3x - y = 9 \end{cases}$ **16.** $\begin{cases} 3x - 2y = 9 \\ 2x - 3y = 2 \end{cases}$ **17.** $\begin{cases} y \geq 5 \\ x + y < 10 \end{cases}$

Solve each by substitution.

18. $\begin{cases} y = -2x \\ 2x + 5y = 10 \end{cases}$ **19.** $\begin{cases} 4x + 5y = -1 \\ 3x - 2y = 5 \end{cases}$ **20.** $\begin{cases} 2a + 3b = 2 \\ a - 2b = 8 \end{cases}$

Solve each system by addition.

21. $\begin{cases} x - 2y = -13 \\ x + 2y = 3 \end{cases}$ **22.** $\begin{cases} 4x + 5y = 7 \\ 5x + 6y = 8 \end{cases}$ **23.** $\begin{cases} 2x - 3y = 11 \\ 4x = 6y + 15 \end{cases}$

24. Two girls went to the store for rice and sugar. One girl bought 3 pounds of sugar and 2 pounds of rice for 47 cents. The other girl bought 2 pounds of sugar and 2 pounds of rice for 39 cents. Find the price of a pound of sugar and of a pound of rice.

25. The sum of the numbers named by the digits in a two-digit numeral is 12. The number named by the numeral is 18 more than the number named when the digits are reversed. Find the number.

CHAPTER TEST

1. Which ordered pair (a, b) is in the solution set of the following system?

$$\begin{cases} 3a + b = 10 \\ b = 8 - 2a \end{cases}$$

a. $(4, -2)$ **b.** $(2, -4)$ **c.** $(-2, -4)$ **d.** $(2, 4)$

2. Which systems of equations are equivalent to the following system?

$$\begin{cases} 3x - 5y - 19 = 0 \\ 2x + y - 4 = 0 \end{cases}$$

a. $\begin{cases} 3x - 5y - 19 = 0 \\ (3x - 5y - 19) + (2x + y - 4) = 0 \end{cases}$ **b.** $\begin{cases} 2x + y - 4 = 0 \\ x - 4y - 23 = 0 \end{cases}$

c. $\begin{cases} 3x - 5y - 10 = 0 \\ 10x + 5y - 20 = 0 \end{cases}$ **d.** $\begin{cases} x = 3 \\ 2x + y - 4 = 0 \end{cases}$

e. $\begin{cases} x = 3 \\ y = 2 \end{cases}$

3. In Exercise 2, what is the solution set of $\begin{cases} 3x - 5y - 19 = 0 \\ 2x + y - 4 = 0 \end{cases}$?

4. Solve graphically. $\begin{cases} 2x - y = -8 \\ x + y = -1 \end{cases}$

5. Solve by substitution. $\begin{cases} y = 2x + 2 \\ 4x - y = 6 \end{cases}$

6. Solve by addition. $\begin{cases} 3a + 5b = -19 \\ 5a - 7b = 45 \end{cases}$

─── Solve by any method you wish.

7. $\begin{cases} p + 3q = 8 \\ 2p - 10q = -40 \end{cases}$

8. $\begin{cases} x + 3y = 6 \\ 5x + 7y = -2 \end{cases}$

9. Draw the graph of the system $\begin{cases} y \geq x + 5 \\ x + y \leq 8 \end{cases}$. Write the coordinates of three ordered pairs of numbers in the solution set.

10. The sum of two numbers is 56; their difference is 14. Find each number.

ENRICHMENT

A Computer Flow Chart for Linear Equations

Computers of all sizes and varying degrees of complexity are becoming everyday tools in many areas of life. Schools use computers to set up teaching schedules and examination schedules. Computers are used to play chess and checkers. They figure out such things as telephone bills and insurance premiums. And they are used in nearly all advanced science and space technology.

After the machines have been designed and built and before they can provide useful information, a set of instructions, a **program,** must be drawn up telling the machine, step by step, how to solve a given problem. Computers are constructed in such a way that they are able to do the basic processes of arithmetic: addition, multiplication, subtraction, division, finding roots, and finding absolute values. Computers can also compare different numbers by answering *Yes* or *No* to simple questions about relative magnitudes. For example, you may ask a computer if 5 is greater than 3; it will compute $5 - 3 = 2$, and answer *Yes*. It compares two numbers by subtracting.

The program given to a computer to enable it to solve a problem must be broken down into these simple operations. Each step of the program must involve only one operation and no steps can be omitted.

When the computer has been given a program, it operates on numbers that are stored in various numbered locations, such as [1], [17], and [n], in the machine until they are needed. And there are empty locations in which the machine may store any results it arrives at.

The final answer is printed on tape or on sheets of paper and the problem is solved, all in a matter of seconds.

The person who draws up the program, the programmer, usually sets it up in a diagram as shown below. It is called a **flow chart.** The arrows indicate the step-by-step process that the program follows.

Suppose you want to solve a linear equation in one unknown. Assume you have a computer that can handle such equations with up to ten terms, that is, $ax^r + bx^r + cx^r + dx^r + ex^r + fx^r + gx^r + hx^r + ix^r + jx^r$, $r = 0$ or 1. ($x^1 = x$; $x^0 = 1$; thus, $ax^0 = a$.) The terms ax^r through jx^r are assigned locations [1] through [10], respectively. All other locations in the computer begin empty.

To solve the equation, the computer is given the instructions in the flow chart below. It proceeds from box to box, following the appropriate path if the directions require a *Yes* or *No* answer. [N] stands for the number of the location. [11] is the location for constants, [12] for coefficients of the x term. Notice that the directions in one box read "Is [12] = 0?" This means "Is *the number in* [12] = 0?"

Flow Chart for Solving Linear Equation

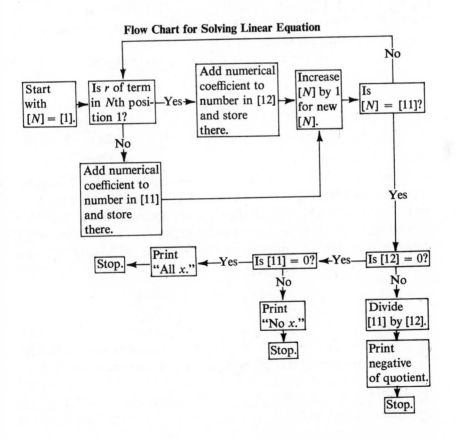

EXAMPLE. Solve $4x + 3 - 2x + 4x - 5 - 6x + 1 + x - 3x + 7 = 0$.

You can begin by making a simple table, showing the location of each term and putting each term in ax^r form.

Location	1	2	3	4	5	6	7	8	9	10	11	12
Term	$+4x^1$	$+3x^0$	$-2x^1$	$+4x^1$	$-5x^0$	$-6x^1$	$+1x^0$	$+1x^1$	$-3x^1$	$+7x^0$		

By following the chart, you reason as follows.

Start with $[N] = [1]$; the first term is $+4x^1$. Is $r = 1$? Yes. Add 4, the coefficient, to the number in [12] ([12] is empty until now) and store it there. Number in [12] is 4. Increase $[N]$ by 1; so $[N]$ is [2]. Is $[N] = [11]$? No. Go back to the second box. Is r of $+3x^0$ equal to 1? No. Add $+3$ to the number in [11]. Store $+3$ in [11]. Increase $[N]$ by 1. Is $[N] = [11]$? No, $[N]$ is now [3]. Go back to the second box. Is r of $-2x^1$ equal to 1? Yes. Add -2 to 4, which is in [12]. [12] is now 2. Increase $[N]$ by 1. Is $[N] = [11]$? No, $[N]$ is 4. Go back to the second box and continue through $[N] = [10]$.

After you do the term $+7x^0$ and add 1 to $[N]$, $[N]$ is [11]. Follow the *Yes* path. Is $[12] = 0$? No, [12] is -2; [11] should be $+6$. Divide $+6$ by -2. The quotient is -3. Print the negative of -3, or $+3$. Stop. The problem is solved; x is 3.

You can check the computer's work by using algebra.

$$4x + 3 - 2x + 4x - 5 - 6x + 1 + x - 3x + 7 = 0$$
$$(4x - 2x + 4x - 6x + x - 3x) + (3 - 5 + 1 + 7) = 0$$
$$-2x + 6 = 0$$
$$-2x = -6$$
$$x = 3$$

You may think that it is faster to solve such an equation by algebra instead of by following the flow chart, and for you it is. But the computer works so quickly that all the steps are accomplished in a number of seconds. Its use is so widespread because it is a great timesaving device and because it can perform the same operation over and over again in exactly the same way.

Exercises

1. Solve $2x + 1 - 4x + 5 - 3 + 3x - 2x + 4 - x + 1 = 0$. Begin by completing the following table as in the example.

Location	1	2	3	4	5	6	7	8	9	10	11	12
Term	$+2x^1$	$+1x^0$										

Then follow the flow chart on page 251. The path for the first term would be as shown below. Follow each step, filling in the blanks where necessary.

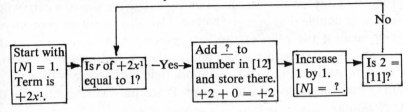

2. Solve $3x + 4 + 2x - 3 - x - 4 = 0$ by following the flow chart.

3. What did you do in Exercise 2 after the term 4? The rest of the terms should have been $0x^0$. So for $N = 7$, r was 0, and you added 0 to the number in [11]. For $N = 8$, r was 0, and again you added 0 to the number in [11]; and so on for $N = 9$ and $N = 10$. You performed four cycles that added nothing to the solution of the equation.

Place instructions in the program to eliminate excess cycles. You must do this by using questions that require *Yes* or *No* answers. The answers should be obtained by no more than the basic operations of arithmetic and comparing numbers.

4. Solve $3x + 5 - 8x + 4 - 9 + 5x = 0$, using the program with the additional instructions.

THE GROWTH OF MATHEMATICS

Greek Mathematics Through Diophantus

The Greeks are indebted to the Egyptians and the Orientals for the foundations of their mathematics. But whereas the Egyptians were very practical people, the Greeks were philosophical. In Greek society, manual and mechanical labor was done by slaves and was looked down upon by the leisure upper classes, who devoted their time to intellectual pursuits. Thus, mathematics changed greatly with the Greeks and became an abstract science.

One of Pythagoras' great contributions to mathematics was realizing that any postulational system had to begin with some assumptions. Then the rest of the system could be proven from the given assumptions.

After Pythagoras' death, Archytas (428–347 B.C.) was recognized as the head of the Pythagorean school in Tarentum. He advanced the theory of proportion and was one of the first to solve the ancient problem of duplicating the cube, that is, finding the side of a cube whose volume is double that of a given cube. He also advanced geometry by going against the rules of the Pythagoreans and applying it to mechanics: he supposedly worked out the theory of the pulley. When he was drowned in a shipwreck, the more rigid Pythagoreans thought it a fitting end for someone who had profaned pure mathematics by this application.

Philolaus, in the fifth century B.C., was another outstanding Pythagorean. He was the first to write a book on the Pythagorean teachings and revealed what had been kept secret for about a century.

Zeno of Elea (495–435 B.C.) greatly disturbed the philosophers of Athens by proposing four paradoxes involving infinitely small units of time or distance, the best known being the Achilles paradox: Achilles can run 10 times as fast as the tortoise he is going to race; if the tortoise is given a headstart of, say, 1000 yards, Achilles will never overtake him; for when Achilles has run 1000 yards, the tortoise is still 100 yards ahead of him; when Achilles has run that 100 yards, the tortoise is still 10 yards ahead of him; and so on. The fallacy in Zeno's reasoning was assuming that a finite distance can be divided into an infinite number of parts. But he had injected doubt into Greek thought, and the Greeks were ever suspicious of dealing with infinitely small quantities, or infinitesimals.

Plato (427?–347 B.C.), one of the greatest philosophers of antiquity, was not a mathematician in his own right, but he has been called "the maker of mathematicians" because he irritated so many into creating mathematics. His protegé was Eudoxus (408–355 B.C.), who developed the method of exhaustion for finding areas to avoid dealing with infinitesimals. [Think of a square inscribed in a circle (the four vertices touch the circle). Then think of an inscribed polygon with five sides, ten sides, twenty sides, and so on. The polygon more and more closely approximates the circle, and the area of the polygon is a good approximation for the area of the circle.] He also defined ratio sufficiently to allow mathematicians to work with irrational numbers as rigorously as they work with rational numbers.

Euclid (330?–?275 B.C.) is usually connected with geometry. But of the thirteen books of his *Elements*, a majority deal entirely or in part with number theory and algebra. Much of the work is probably not his own, but rather a compilation of the work of his predecessors, and as such he did mathematics a great service. The *Elements* was a standard text in geometry and logical thinking for almost two thousand years. A follower in the Euclidean tradition is Archimedes (287?–212 B.C.), who will be treated in a separate section.

After the death of Euclid, the Greeks were occupied with geometry, and arithmetic and algebra were neglected. One man did make a contribution during this time and that was Eratosthenes (275–194 B.C.) who devised the "sieve" for finding prime numbers.

Diophantus of Alexandria, who flourished around A.D. 250, wrote a treatise on algebra, using symbolism and abbreviations that were a major advance at the time. Although he solved linear, quadratic, and cubic equations and could solve equations simultaneously, he failed to recognize that an equation could have more than one solution and would not accept negative or irrational solutions. Thus, equations with positive integral solutions are called Diophantine equations. Although he did not seem to care about the general solutions of equations, Diophantus' real genius lay in the fact that he could reduce almost any problem to one of the few types of equations that he could solve.

Greek mathematics then declined, and when Alexandria fell to the Arabs in A.D. 641, the glorious age of learning was over. The following centuries in Europe were called the Dark Ages, and only because of the monks and a few learned men was Greek culture preserved at all.

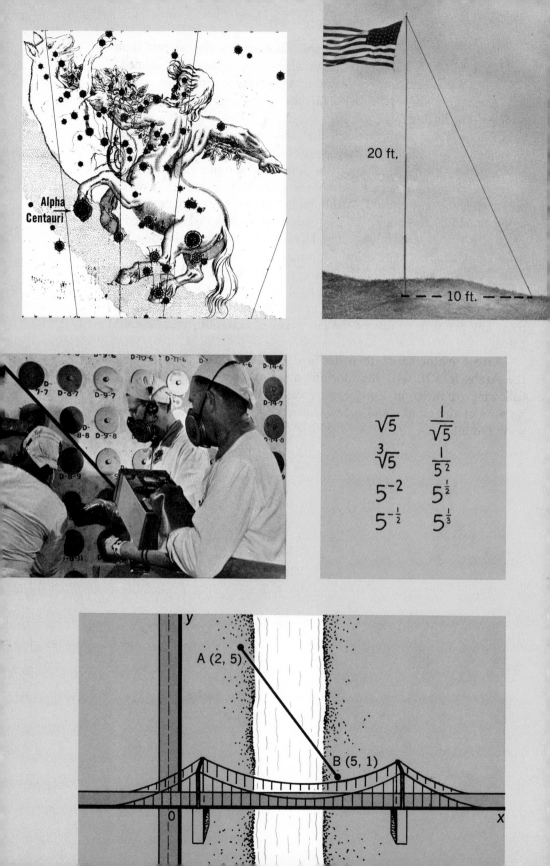

Alpha
Centauri

20 ft.

— — 10 ft. — —

$\sqrt{5}$ $\dfrac{1}{\sqrt{5}}$

$\sqrt[3]{5}$ $\dfrac{1}{5^2}$

5^{-2} $5^{\frac{1}{2}}$

$5^{-\frac{1}{2}}$ $5^{\frac{1}{3}}$

A (2, 5)

B (5, 1)

0

x

CHAPTER 6

EXPONENTS AND RADICALS

The use of exponents and radicals is an important method of representing numbers that has many applications, including the distance formula for the coordinate plane. The interrelationships between exponents and radicals are useful in many branches of mathematics as well.

● A radioactive substance, as shown in the center left photograph, loses mass at a constant rate. Suppose that the substance shown loses half its mass every hour. In four hours, a mass of m will be reduced to $m(\frac{1}{2})^4$, read "m times one-half to the fourth power." If $(\frac{1}{2})^4$ means $\frac{1}{2} \cdot \frac{1}{2} \cdot \frac{1}{2} \cdot \frac{1}{2}$, how much of the mass will be left at the end of four hours?

● Although Alpha Centauri (upper left photograph) is the nearest bright star to earth other than the sun, it is approximately 2.5×10^{13} miles away. This may not seem very far until you recall that 10^{13} means 10 used as a factor 13 times. Carrying out the multiplication gives 25,000,000,000,000. Why are exponents used in expressing such large numbers?

● By the Pythagorean theorem, the wire drawn in the upper right picture is $\sqrt{500}$ feet long. If you were buying wire, would you ask for $\sqrt{500}$ feet? What rational number could you give as an approximation for $\sqrt{500}$?

● In the lower drawing, points A and B are located with coordinates, using the bridge and the road as axes. How long is the cable across the river? Can you find the distance between any two points whose coordinates you know?

● In the center, can you match each expression in the left column with an expression in the right column? How are negative and fractional exponents defined?

6–1   Exponents and Multiplication

You know that 5^2 means $5 \cdot 5$ and 3^4 means $3 \cdot 3 \cdot 3 \cdot 3$. The ^{2} in 5^2 and the ^{4} in 3^4 are **exponents,** which show how many times the **base** (5 in 5^2 and 3 in 3^4) is taken as a factor. The expression 5^2 may be read as "five squared" or as "five to the second **power.**" The expression 3^4 is read as "three to the fourth power."

> **Definition**   If a is a positive integer, then x^a means
> $$\underbrace{x \cdot x \cdot x \cdot x \cdot \;\cdots\; \cdot x}_{a \text{ factors}}$$
> when a is greater than 1.   Also, $x^1 = x$ is true.

One way to find the product of such expressions as 3^5 and 3^2 is to name 3^5 as 243 and 3^2 as 9 and then multiply in the ordinary way to get 2187. Another way to find the product is to use exponents.

$$3^5 \cdot 3^2 = (3 \cdot 3 \cdot 3 \cdot 3 \cdot 3)(3 \cdot 3)$$
$$= 3 \cdot 3 \cdot 3 \cdot 3 \cdot 3 \cdot 3 \cdot 3 = 3^7$$

The product named in exponent form is 3^7 or in decimal form is 2187.

How is the definition of a **positive integral exponent** used in **a–d**?

a. $n^3 \cdot n^5 = (n \cdot n \cdot n)(n \cdot n \cdot n \cdot n \cdot n) = n^8$

b. $x^1 \cdot x^4 = x(x \cdot x \cdot x \cdot x) = x^5$

c. $n \cdot n^3 \cdot n^4 = n(n \cdot n \cdot n)(n \cdot n \cdot n \cdot n) = n^8$

d. $-x^5 \cdot x^3 = -1(x \cdot x \cdot x \cdot x \cdot x)(x \cdot x \cdot x) = -x^8$

In **d**, note that $-x^5$ means the negative of x^5, not the fifth power of $-x$, which would be represented by $(-x)^5$.

Do you see a pattern in finding products with exponents? Can you make a conclusion about a method for naming the product of two numbers in exponential form with the same base? When m and n are positive integers, you can name $a^m \cdot a^n$ as follows.

$$a^m \cdot a^n = (\underbrace{a \cdot a \cdot a \cdot a \cdot \;\cdots\; \cdot a}_{m \text{ factors}})(\underbrace{a \cdot a \cdot a \cdot a \cdot \;\cdots\; \cdot a}_{n \text{ factors}})$$
$$= \underbrace{a \cdot a \cdot a \cdot a \cdot \;\cdots\; \cdot a}_{m + n \text{ factors}}$$
$$= a^{m+n}$$

Thus, by the definition of a positive integral exponent, $a^m \cdot a^n = a^{m+n}$ is true. This proves the following theorem, stated first in words and then in symbols.

> **Theorem 6-1** To name the product of two numbers represented with exponents and the same base, add the exponents and use the same base.
>
> $$\forall a \in R \quad \forall m \in N \quad \forall n \in N \quad a^m \cdot a^n = a^{m+n}$$

You can now perform the operations in **a–d** on the previous page in a more efficient way.

a′. $n^3 \cdot n^5 = n^{3+5} = n^8$

b′. $x^1 \cdot x^4 = x^{1+4} = x^5$

c′. $n \cdot n^3 \cdot n^4 = n^{1+3+4} = n^8$ (Remember that n is n^1.)

d′. $-x^5 \cdot x^3 = -1(x^{5+3}) = -x^8$

Now try these

—— Use the definition of a positive integral exponent to name these products in exponential form.

1. $x^8 \cdot x^2$ **2.** $4^5 \cdot 4^3$ **3.** $9 \cdot 9^8$

4. $x^{17} \cdot x^3$ **5.** $x^{100} \cdot x^{100}$ **6.** $-a^6 \cdot a^3$

Answers: **1.** x^{10} **2.** 4^8 **3.** 9^9 **4.** x^{20} **5.** x^{200} **6.** $-a^9$

Exercises

A —— Name the following products using exponential form.

1. $(x \cdot x \cdot x \cdot x)(x \cdot x \cdot x)$ **2.** $(3 \cdot 3)(3 \cdot 3 \cdot 3 \cdot 3)$

3. $-1(m \cdot m \cdot m)(m)$ **4.** $x^4 \cdot x^5$ **5.** $x^2 \cdot x^4$

6. $m \cdot m^6$ **7.** $a^2 \times a^3$ **8.** $n^3 \times n^4$

9. $b \times b^2$ **10.** $a(a)$ **11.** $b^3 \times b$

12. $b^2 \times b^3$ **13.** $-b(-b)$ **14.** $b(-b)$

15. $-a^5(a^2)$ **16.** $x(-x^2)$ **17.** $-y^2(y^2)$

18. $-y^2(-y^2)$ **19.** $a(a^2)(a^3)$ **20.** $p^3 \times p^2$

21. $-x(-x^2)$ **22.** $3^6 \cdot 3^4$ **23.** $5(5^4)$

24. $2(2^3)(2^4)$ **25.** $3(3^2)(3^4)$ **26.** $5^2(-5^2)(5^3)$

—— Name the following products using exponential form.

Example. $(4 \times 10^5)(2 \times 10^8) = (4 \times 2) \times (10^5 \times 10^8)$
$$= 8 \times 10^{13}$$

27. $(2 \times 10^2)(3 \times 10^4)$　　　　**28.** $(7 \times 10)(9 \times 10^5)$

29. $(1.5 \times 10^3)(2 \times 10^6)$　　　　**30.** $(2.4 \times 10^7)(3.9 \times 10)$

31. $(2.8 \times 10^9)(a \times 10^2)$　　　　**32.** $(a \times 10^x)(b \times 10^y)$

B —— Find the products in exponential form. All exponents are considered to be positive integers.

33. $x^a \cdot x^2$ 　　　　**34.** $y^2 \cdot y^b$ 　　　　**35.** $x^a \cdot x^b$

36. $a^{x-2} \cdot a^5$ 　　**37.** $x^{3a} \cdot x^{2a}$ 　　**38.** $(x^{2a+7})(x^{2a-8})$

39. $3^x \cdot 3^2$ 　　　　**40.** $2^{4a} \cdot 2^{3a}$ 　　**41.** $(2^{2a+7})(2^{7a-6})$

C —— Find the products in exponential form. All exponents are considered to be positive integers.

42. $(x + 2)^2 \cdot (x + 2)^4$ 　　　　**43.** $(x + 2)^a \cdot (x + 2)^6$

44. $(x + 2)^{a+5} \cdot (x + 2)^{3a-2}$ 　　**45.** $(x + y)^{a+b} \cdot (x + y)^{a-b}$

46. $(2a - 3b)^{3a-2b} \cdot (2a - 3b)^{6a+10b}$ 　　**47.** $(3x + y)^{4a+1} \cdot (3x - y)^{2-4a}$

6–2　Exponents and Raising to a Power

Often you will need to raise products, quotients, and powers to a power. Explain each of the following.

a. $(2 \cdot 3)^4 = (2 \cdot 3)(2 \cdot 3)(2 \cdot 3)(2 \cdot 3)$
$$= (2 \cdot 2 \cdot 2 \cdot 2)(3 \cdot 3 \cdot 3 \cdot 3)$$
$$= (2^4)(3^4)$$

b. $(-x)^6 = (-x)(-x)(-x)(-x)(-x)(-x)$
$$= (-1)(-1)(-1)(-1)(-1)(-1)(x \cdot x \cdot x \cdot x \cdot x \cdot x)$$
$$= (-1)^6 x^6$$

c. $(xy)^3 = xy \cdot xy \cdot xy = (x \cdot x \cdot x)(y \cdot y \cdot y)$
$$= x^3 y^3$$

Can you find a pattern? Does it lead to the following theorem?

Theorem 6–2 The positive integral power of a product is the product of the powers of the factors.

$$\forall x \in R \quad \forall y \in R \quad \forall n \in N \quad (xy)^n = x^n y^n$$

The proofs of the theorems in this section will be left as exercises.

In **b** the expression $(-1)^6$ occurred. Do you know how to raise -1 to any positive integral power? What previous generalization tells you that $(-1)^n$ is equal to -1 when n is odd and to 1 when n is even? Then **b** could be rewritten as follows.

b'. $(-x)^6 = (-1)^6 x^6 = 1 \cdot x^6 = x^6$

Can you explain the following?

d. $(-5)^3 = (-1)^3(5)^3 = (-1)(5)^3$
$= -125$

e. $(-a)^4 = (-1)^4 a^4 = 1 \cdot a^4$
$= a^4$

f. $(-t)^7 = (-1)^7 t^7 = (-1)t^7$
$= -t^7$

> **Theorem 6–3** An even positive power of a negative number is positive and an odd integral power of a negative number is negative.

The rules for multiplication of numbers expressed as fractions provide another way to rewrite expressions involving exponents.

g. $\left(\dfrac{3}{4}\right)^3 = \dfrac{3}{4} \cdot \dfrac{3}{4} \cdot \dfrac{3}{4} = \dfrac{3 \cdot 3 \cdot 3}{4 \cdot 4 \cdot 4}$
$= \dfrac{3^3}{4^3}$

h. $\left(\dfrac{x}{y}\right)^4 = \dfrac{x}{y} \cdot \dfrac{x}{y} \cdot \dfrac{x}{y} \cdot \dfrac{x}{y} = \dfrac{x \cdot x \cdot x \cdot x}{y \cdot y \cdot y \cdot y}$
$= \dfrac{x^4}{y^4}$

> **Theorem 6–4** A positive integral power of a number expressed as a fraction is equal to the power of the numerator divided by the power of the denominator.
>
> $$\forall x \in R \quad \forall y \in R \ (y \neq 0) \quad \forall n \in N \quad \left(\frac{x}{y}\right)^n = \frac{x^n}{y^n}$$

Taking a positive integral power of a power can be viewed in two ways. You can go back to the basic definition of a positive integral exponent or you can use the theorem concerning powers of a product.

$$(x^2)^3 = x^2 \cdot x^2 \cdot x^2 \qquad\qquad (x^2)^3 = (x \cdot x)^3$$
$$= x^{2+2+2} \qquad\qquad\qquad\quad = x^3 \cdot x^3$$
$$= x^6 \qquad\qquad\qquad\qquad\quad = x^{3+3}$$
$$\qquad\qquad\qquad\qquad\qquad\qquad = x^6$$

Explain each of the following.

i. $(5^4)^2 = 5^4 \cdot 5^4 = 5^{4+4} = 5^8$

j. $(t^3)^6 = (t \cdot t \cdot t)^6 = t^6 \cdot t^6 \cdot t^6 = t^{6+6+6} = t^{18}$

k. $(r^a)^4 = r^a \cdot r^a \cdot r^a \cdot r^a = r^{a+a+a+a} = r^{4a}$, where a is a positive integer.

l. $(b^4)^c = (b \cdot b \cdot b \cdot b)^c = b^c \cdot b^c \cdot b^c \cdot b^c = b^{4c}$, where c is a positive integer.

> **Theorem 6–5** When a positive integral power is raised to a positive integral power, the base is raised to the product of the two powers.
>
> $$\forall x \in R \quad \forall m \in N \quad \forall n \in N \quad (x^m)^n = x^{mn}$$

The theorems of this section can be combined to give additional results.

m. $\left(\dfrac{x^5}{y^7}\right)^4 = \dfrac{(x^5)^4}{(y^7)^4} = \dfrac{x^{5 \cdot 4}}{y^{7 \cdot 4}} = \dfrac{x^{20}}{y^{28}}$

n. $(x^3 y^2)^5 = (x^3)^5 \cdot (y^2)^5 = x^{15} y^{10}$

Exercises

A —— Name each of the following in a simpler exponent form, so that each base is used only once and no power is raised to a power. The first example of each type is done for you. Variables in denominators may not represent 0.

1. $x^2(x^3) = x^5$
2. $3x(2x^2)$
3. $x^2(x^5)$

4. $(x^2 y^2)(xy)(x^3 y^2)$
5. $3x^2 y(y^2)$
6. $y^4(y)$

7. $3y^2(y^2)$
8. $2(2^4)$
9. $2x(2^3)(x^4)$

10. $(ab)^3 = a^3 b^3$
11. $(xy)^2$
12. $(2x)^2$

13. $(5x)^2$
14. $(2xy)^2$
15. $(xyz)^4$

16. $(-5)^2 = (-5)(-5) = 25$
17. $(-6)^2$
18. $(-3)^3$

19. $(-x)^4$
20. $(-x)^5$
21. $(-y)^2$

22. $(-4x)^2$
23. $(-3b)^3$
24. $(-ab)^3$

25. $\left(\dfrac{a}{b}\right)^3 = \dfrac{a^3}{b^3}$
26. $\left(\dfrac{x}{y}\right)^2$
27. $\left(\dfrac{1}{2}\right)^2$

28. $\left(\dfrac{2}{3}\right)^3$
29. $\left(\dfrac{1}{3}\right)^4$
30. $\left(\dfrac{c}{d}\right)^7$

31. $\left(\dfrac{x}{y}\right)^3$
32. $\left(\dfrac{2}{3}\right)^5$
33. $\left(\dfrac{ab}{c}\right)^5$

34. $(x^3)^2 = x^6$ **35.** $(x^2)^6$ **36.** $(x^4)^2$

37. $(y^5)^3$ **38.** $(a^3)^4$ **39.** $(x^3)^5$

40. $(x^7)^3$ **41.** $(x^5)^2$ **42.** $(x^3)^{12}$

43. $(x^2)^5$ **44.** $(y^3)^3$ **45.** $(a^5)^6$

46. $(b^4)^6$ **47.** $(a^2)^7$ **48.** $(y^4)^8$

49. $(3a^2b)^2 = 3^2a^4b^2 = 9a^4b^2$ **50.** $(6a^2)^3$

51. $(2x^5)^2$ **52.** $(-3b)^3$

53. $\dfrac{(2x^2)^3}{(3y)^2}$ **54.** $(3^2b^2)^3$

55. $(2x^3y^2)^3$ **56.** $(3^2a^2b^4)^2$

57. $(5x^2y^3)^2$ **58.** $(3x^2)^3$

59. $(4x^3y^2)^3$ **60.** $(2m^3n^2)^4$

61. $(10a^5b^2)^3$ **62.** $(7a^2b^3)^3$

63. $(x^2y)^4$ **64.** $(2a^2b)^3$

65. $(2^3x^2y^3)^4$ **66.** $(3a^3b^3)^4$

67. $(4a^4c^2d^3)^3$ **68.** $(16x^3y^2)^2$

69. $(3x^3y)^3$ **70.** $(2^3a^2b^4)^2$

71. $(2x^3y^2)^6$ **72.** $(a^2b)^3$

73. $(a^3b^2)^2$ **74.** $(-x^2y^3)^3$

75. $(-x^4y^3)^2$ **76.** $(-x^4y^2)^3$

77. $(2 \times 10^3)^2$ **78.** $(3 \times 10^5)^4$

79. $(1.1 \times 10^6)^3$ **80.** $(2.5 \times 10^{10})^2$

81. $\left(\dfrac{x^2}{y^3}\right)^2 = \dfrac{x^4}{y^6}$ **82.** $\left(\dfrac{x^2}{y^2}\right)^4$

83. $\left(\dfrac{b^2}{a}\right)^2$ **84.** $\left(\dfrac{c^2}{d}\right)^3$

85. $\left(\dfrac{a^2}{b^3}\right)^3$ **86.** $\left(\dfrac{a^3}{b}\right)^6$

87. $\left(\dfrac{x^3}{y^2}\right)^2$ **88.** $\left(\dfrac{c^3}{d^2}\right)^7$

89. $\left(\dfrac{a^4}{b^3}\right)^2$ **90.** $\left(\dfrac{2^2}{3^2}\right)^3$

B   **91.** $\left(\dfrac{5x^2y^3}{-3a^2b^3}\right)^2$ **92.** $(-2x^2)^2(2xy^2)^3$

93. $(-2a^3b^2)(3a^4b^6)$ **94.** $x \cdot x^2(x^3)^2$

95. $(-\tfrac{1}{3})^2(-\tfrac{1}{3})^3(-\tfrac{1}{3})^4$ **96.** $(-2)^2(-2)^3$

97. $(-3 \cdot 5x^2)^3 \cdot 2^4$ **98.** $\left(\dfrac{-3x^2}{4y^2}\right)^3$

In the following exercises, variables used as exponents represent positive integers. Variables in denominators may not represent 0. Rewrite each expression in a simpler form.

99. $(x^2)^n$ **100.** $(y^3)^n$ **101.** $(a^7)^x$

102. $(a^n)^m$ **103.** $(x^n)^n$ **104.** $(y^k)^c$

105. $(a^6)^m$ **106.** $(b^c)^9$ **107.** $(c^2)^w$

108. $(k^m)^t$ **109.** $\left(\dfrac{m}{n}\right)^k$ **110.** $\left(\dfrac{x^2}{y}\right)^c$

111. $\left(\dfrac{a^3}{b}\right)^d$ **112.** $\left(\dfrac{x^4}{y^a}\right)^b$ **113.** $\left(\dfrac{x^e}{y^z}\right)^5$

114. $\left(\dfrac{e^3}{f^2}\right)^x$ **115.** $\left(\dfrac{g^3}{h^4}\right)^m$ **116.** $\left(\dfrac{3m}{2n}\right)^c$

117. $\left(\dfrac{3x^n}{5y^m}\right)^c$ **118.** $\left(\dfrac{3x^3}{4y^2}\right)^m$ **119.** $\left(\dfrac{3a^mb^n}{2xy}\right)^k$

120. $\left(\dfrac{2ab}{4xy}\right)^d$ **121.** $\left(\dfrac{a^2b^2}{x^2y^3}\right)^b$ **122.** $\left((x^n)^n\right)^n$

C **123.** Prove Theorem 6–2.

124. Prove Theorem 6–3.

125. Prove Theorem 6–4.

126. Prove Theorem 6–5.

6–3   Exponents and Division

Does the number $\dfrac{2^5}{2^3}$ have a simpler name?   By definition,

$$\frac{2^5}{2^3} = \frac{2 \cdot 2 \cdot 2 \cdot 2 \cdot 2}{2 \cdot 2 \cdot 2} = 2 \cdot 2 = 4$$

is true.   Another way to say this is that $\dfrac{2^5}{2^3} = 2^2$ is true.   Can you use the same method to explain **a–c** below?

a. $\dfrac{3^6}{3^2} = \dfrac{3 \cdot 3 \cdot 3 \cdot 3 \cdot 3 \cdot 3}{3 \cdot 3} = 3^4$ **b.** $\dfrac{2^8}{2} = 2^7$ **c.** $\dfrac{4^{10}}{4^2} = 4^8$

The same principle applies to variables, provided that the variable is not equal to zero.   Explain each step in **d–f**.

d. $\dfrac{x^5}{x^3} = \dfrac{x \cdot x \cdot x \cdot x \cdot x}{x \cdot x \cdot x} = \dfrac{x \cdot x \cdot x}{x \cdot x \cdot x} \cdot x \cdot x = x^2, \ x \neq 0$

e. $\dfrac{x^6}{x^4} = x^2, \ x \neq 0$ **f.** $\dfrac{x^6}{x^5} = x, \ x \neq 0$

More complex expressions can be simplified in the same way. In **g–i**, none of the variables may represent 0.

g. $\dfrac{x^4y^3}{x^2y} = \dfrac{x \cdot x \cdot x \cdot x \cdot y \cdot y \cdot y}{x \cdot x \cdot y} = x \cdot x \cdot y \cdot y$

$\qquad = x^2y^2$

h. $\dfrac{a^3b^4c^2}{a^2b^2c} = \dfrac{a \cdot a \cdot a \cdot b \cdot b \cdot b \cdot b \cdot c \cdot c}{a \cdot a \cdot b \cdot b \cdot c} = a \cdot b \cdot b \cdot c$

$\qquad = ab^2c$

i. $\dfrac{-6a^5b^3c^2}{2a^3b^2c} = \dfrac{-3 \cdot 2 \cdot a \cdot a \cdot a \cdot a \cdot a \cdot b \cdot b \cdot b \cdot c \cdot c}{2 \cdot a \cdot a \cdot a \cdot b \cdot b \cdot c}$

$\qquad = -3 \cdot a \cdot a \cdot b \cdot c$

$\qquad = -3a^2bc$

You have probably noticed that there is a pattern in these examples. Can you put it in words?

It is easy to prove that a pattern exists. In the following, x cannot equal 0 and m is greater than n.

① Use definition of exponent.

$$\frac{x^m}{x^n} = \frac{\overbrace{x \cdot x \cdot x \cdot x \cdot \cdots \cdot x}^{m \text{ factors}}}{\underbrace{x \cdot x \cdot x \cdot x \cdot \cdots \cdot x}_{n \text{ factors}}}$$

② Divide numerator and denominator by x, repeated n times.

$$= \overbrace{x \cdot x \cdot x \cdot x \cdot \cdots \cdot x}^{(m - n) \text{ factors}}$$

③ Use definition of exponent.

$$= x^{m-n}$$

Theorem 6–6 To divide two numbers each with a positive integral exponent and with the same base, subtract the exponent of the denominator from the exponent of the numerator.

$$\forall x \in \mathbb{R} \ (x \neq 0) \quad \forall m, n \in \mathbb{N} \ (m > n) \quad \frac{x^m}{x^n} = x^{m-n}$$

Can you guess why the condition that m is greater than n is necessary? When n and m are the same, $m - n$ names 0; and when m is less than n, the expression $m - n$ names a negative number. So far, zero and negative exponents have not been defined. This will be done in the next section of this chapter.

Exercises

A ▬ Simplify each of the following exponential expressions. Variables in the denominators cannot represent 0.

1. $\dfrac{2^3}{2}$

2. $\dfrac{3^5}{3^2}$

3. $\dfrac{5^6}{5^3}$

4. $\dfrac{x^5}{x^3}$

5. $\dfrac{a^6}{a}$

6. $\dfrac{a^9}{a^7}$

7. $\dfrac{x^8}{x^7}$

8. $\dfrac{x^3y^2}{xy}$

9. $\dfrac{a^3y^3}{a^2y}$

10. $\dfrac{y^3}{y^2}$

11. $\dfrac{a^3b^5}{ab^2}$

12. $\dfrac{2x^7}{3x^4}$

13. $\dfrac{k^5m^3}{k^3m^2}$

14. $\dfrac{18x^3y^4}{2xy^2}$

15. $\dfrac{-15x^7y^5}{-3x^2y^4}$

16. $\dfrac{-36a^2b^2c^4}{4abc^3}$

17. $\dfrac{-27r^5s^8}{-3r^3s^6}$

18. $\dfrac{-2k^4m^3}{4k^2}$

19. $\dfrac{1.5 \times 10^4}{2.5 \times 10^2}$

20. $\dfrac{2.4 \times 10^7}{5.6 \times 10^4}$

21. $\dfrac{8.01 \times 10^{11}}{6.12 \times 10}$

B ▬ Perform the indicated operations to obtain an expression in a simple form. No variable in the denominator can be zero.

Example. $\dfrac{9xy(-4x^2y^3)}{-18x^2y^2} = \dfrac{-36x^3y^4}{-18x^2y^2} = 2xy^2$

22. $\dfrac{4ab(7a^2b^3)}{-14a^3b^3}$

23. $\dfrac{4ab^2(-5ab^3)}{10a^2b^2}$

24. $\dfrac{(-3ab^2)^2}{6ab}$

25. $\dfrac{(3ab^2)^2(-6a^3b)}{(3a^2b^2)^2}$

26. $\dfrac{(5ab)^2(-20a^3b)}{4a^2b^3}$

27. $\dfrac{(5a^2b)^2(-100b^3)}{(5^2b)^2}$

28. $\dfrac{(3.5 \times 10^2)^3}{1.5 \times 10^2}$

29. $\dfrac{(7.5 \times 10^3)^4}{(2.5 \times 10^2)^3}$

30. $\dfrac{(1.21 \times 10)^5}{(1.1 \times 10^2)^2}$

C ▬ Perform the indicated operations. Variables in exponents are all positive integers.

31. $\dfrac{a^xb^2y}{a^xby}$

32. $\dfrac{a^xb^4}{a^y}$

33. $\dfrac{a^tb^w}{a^vb^{25}}$

34. $\dfrac{x^{u-v}y^{w-z}}{x^{2v-u}y^w}$

35. $\dfrac{x^{3u-2v}y^3}{x^{2u+2v}y^2}$

36. $\dfrac{a^{3x}}{a^{2x}}$

37. $\dfrac{a^{2x}b^3yc^k}{abc}$

38. $\dfrac{ab^2c^4d^{2-k}}{ac^3d^k}$

39. $\dfrac{(x^{2a+1})^2}{x^{a-1}}$

40. $\dfrac{(y^{3a-9})^6}{y^{2a-4}}$

41. $\left[\dfrac{(x^{2a-4})^2}{x^{a+5}}\right]^3$

42. $\dfrac{(1.69 \times 10^3)^a}{(1.3 \times 10^a)^2}$

266   CHAPTER 6

6-4 Zero and Negative Integral Exponents

A positive integer as an exponent indicates the number of times the base is taken as a factor. You cannot apply the same meaning to cases such as a^0 or x^{-3}, for you cannot take a as a factor zero times or x as a factor negative three times. To use **zero and negative integral exponents,** you must give a new meaning to the idea of an exponent.

The definition of a zero exponent is chosen so that you can continue to use Theorem 6-6 $\left(\dfrac{a^m}{a^n} = a^{m-n}\right)$ when m and n are equal.

If $\dfrac{a^m}{a^n} = a^{m-n}$ is to be true, then when $m = n$	You know that	Then it is reasonable to define
$\dfrac{x^3}{x^3} = x^{3-3} = x^0,\ x \neq 0$	$\dfrac{x^3}{x^3} = 1,\ x \neq 0$	$x^0 = 1,\ x \neq 0$
$\dfrac{10^7}{10^7} = 10^{7-7} = 10^0$	$\dfrac{10^7}{10^7} = 1$	$10^0 = 1$
$\dfrac{a^m}{a^m} = a^{m-m} = a^0,\ a \neq 0$	$\dfrac{a^m}{a^m} = 1,\ a \neq 0$	$a^0 = 1,\ a \neq 0$

> **Definition** Any nonzero base with an exponent of zero is equal to 1.
>
> $$\forall a \in R\ (a \neq 0)\quad a^0 = 1$$

If a is 0, then a^0 is not defined. Is each of the following true?

a. $7^0 = 1$ **b.** $695^0 = 1$ **c.** $(-5\frac{1}{2})^0 = 1$

d. $(x^2y^3)^0 = 1,\ x \neq 0,\ y \neq 0$ **e.** $1^0 = 1$

The definition of a negative integral exponent is also chosen to be consistent with Theorem 6-6. In the table, x and a cannot be zero.

If $\dfrac{a^m}{a^n} = a^{m-n}$ is to be true, then when $m < n$	You know that	Then it is reasonable to define
$\dfrac{x^5}{x^8} = x^{5-8} = x^{-3}$	$\dfrac{x^5}{x^8} = \dfrac{x^5}{x^5 \cdot x^3} = \dfrac{1}{x^3}$	$x^{-3} = \dfrac{1}{x^3}$
$\dfrac{10^8}{10^{12}} = 10^{8-12} = 10^{-4}$	$\dfrac{10^8}{10^{12}} = \dfrac{10^8}{10^8 \cdot 10^4} = \dfrac{1}{10^4}$	$10^{-4} = \dfrac{1}{10^4}$
$\dfrac{a^5}{a^{5+m}} = a^{5-(5+m)} = a^{-m}$	$\dfrac{a^5}{a^{5+m}} = \dfrac{a^5}{a^5 \cdot a^m} = \dfrac{1}{a^m}$	$a^{-m} = \dfrac{1}{a^m}$

> **Definition** Any nonzero base raised to a negative power is the multiplicative inverse of the base raised to the corresponding positive power.
>
> $$\forall a \in R \ (a \neq 0) \quad \forall m \in I \quad a^{-m} = \frac{1}{a^m}$$

Explain why each of the following is true.

f. $x^{-5} = \frac{1}{x^5}$
g. $(\frac{1}{3})^{-2} = \frac{1}{(\frac{1}{3})^2} = 3^2$
h. $10^{-2} = \frac{1}{10^2} = \frac{1}{100}$

The use of zero and negative exponents gives you a new way to look at place value, one of the important characteristics of our numeration system. You know that a number such as 346.78 can be named as shown below.

$$346.78 = 3(100) + 4(10) + 6(1) + 7(\tfrac{1}{10}) + 8(\tfrac{1}{100})$$

You know that 10 and 100 are powers of ten and that each power is multiplied by one of the integers 0 through 9. Using the two new definitions concerning exponents in this section, you should recognize 1, $\frac{1}{10}$, and $\frac{1}{100}$ as powers of ten, also. Expressing a number as the sum of powers of ten multiplied by one of the integers 0 through 9 is known as representing the number in **expanded notation.**

$$346.78 = 3(10^2) + 4(10^1) + 6(10^0) + 7(10^{-1}) + 8(10^{-2})$$

The decimal point in a numeral indicates the units place and is placed just to the right of the units place.

Do you see the pattern? How do you determine the exponent of 10 for a digit 3 places to the right of the units place? 12 places to the left? n places to the right? n places to the left?

Exponents are also used in another way in representing numbers. In **scientific notation** a number is represented as a power of 10 multiplied by a number greater than or equal to 1 and less than 10. One advantage of scientific notation is that it is a compact way of representing numbers with a very large or very small absolute value. To indicate negative numbers in scientific notation, the multiplier should be a number less than or equal to -1 and greater than -10.

The following sentences indicate the usefulness of scientific notation. Explain each.

i. $24,000,000,000,000 = 2.4 \times 10^{13}$
j. $0.00000000368 = 3.68 \times 10^{-9}$
k. $346.78 = 3.4678 \times 10^2$
l. $-59,000,000 = -5.9 \times 10^7$

Now try these

—— Name without using exponents.

1. 3^0 **2.** $(-6\frac{1}{5})^0$ **3.** $(4)^{-2}$
4. $(-4)^{-1}$ **5.** $(-\frac{2}{3})^{-3}$ **6.** $(263)^0 \cdot (5)^{-2}$

—— Write in expanded notation.

7. 632.96   **8.** 0.00032   **9.** 3.00029

10. Rewrite Exercises 7 and 8 using scientific notation.

Answers: **1.** 1   **2.** 1   **3.** $\frac{1}{4^2} = \frac{1}{16}$ **4.** $\frac{1}{(-4)^1} = \frac{1}{-4} = -\frac{1}{4}$ **5.** $\frac{1}{(-\frac{2}{3})^3} = \frac{1}{-\frac{8}{27}} =$
$-\frac{27}{8}$ **6.** $1 \cdot \frac{1}{5^2} = \frac{1}{25}$ **7.** $6(10^2) + 3(10^1) + 2(10^0) + 9(10^{-1}) + 6(10^{-2})$
8. $3(10^{-4}) + 2(10^{-5})$ **9.** $3(10^0) + 0(10^{-1}) + 0(10^{-2}) + 0(10^{-3}) +$
$2(10^{-4}) + 9(10^{-5})$ **10.** 6.3296×10^2; 3.2×10^{-4}

Exercises

A —— Name without using exponents.

1. 5^{-2}	**2.** 10^{-2}	**3.** 2^{-3}	**4.** 8^0
5. 4^2	**6.** 3^{-2}	**7.** 10^0	**8.** 10^{-1}
9. 10^3	**10.** 10^{-4}	**11.** 6^0	**12.** $(-2)^3$
13. $(-2)^{-3}$	**14.** $(\frac{1}{2})^{-4}$	**15.** $(\frac{3}{4})^{-3}$	**16.** 157^0
17. $(\frac{1}{4})^{-2}$	**18.** $(-\frac{3}{4})^3$	**19.** $(-\frac{3}{4})^{-3}$	**20.** $(-4)^{-3}$
21. 10^{-3}	**22.** $(-\frac{1}{2})^{-2}$	**23.** $(-\frac{2}{3})^{-2}$	**24.** $(-\frac{1}{2})^{-5}$

—— Name each number as a multiple of a power of 10, that is, in scientific notation.

25. 600	**26.** 50	**27.** $\frac{3}{100}$	**28.** 7000
29. 9000	**30.** 20	**31.** $\frac{5}{1000}$	**32.** $\frac{3}{10}$
33. 3000	**34.** 40,000	**35.** $\frac{2}{100}$	**36.** $\frac{4}{10,000}$

—— Name each number in expanded form.

37. 5,000,000	**38.** 3600	**39.** 0.000027
40. 5,630,000	**41.** 342.968	**42.** 6829.6829
43. 349.6	**44.** 497.35	**45.** 4.732
46. 47.32	**47.** 473.2	**48.** 4732
49. 0.0043	**50.** 0.00057	**51.** 400.05
52. 0.000008	**53.** 50,000.04	**54.** 93,000,000

55. Name each of the numbers in Exercises 37–54 in scientific notation.

B **56.** Multiply each term of $(3 \times 10^3) + (2 \times 10^2) + (1 \times 10^1) +$ $(5 \times 10^0) + (8 \times 10^{-1}) + (9 \times 10^{-2})$ by 10. Use your results to explain why multiplying 3215.89 by 10 has the effect of moving each digit one place to the left with reference to the decimal point.

57. Repeat Exercise 56, but multiply by 10^2, or 100. Multiplying 3215.89 by 100 has the effect of doing what to each digit?

58. Repeat Exercise 56, but use 10^3, or 1000.

—— Find the number named by each of the following if x is -1 and y is 2.

59. $(x^2)(y^0)$ **60.** $(x^{-2})(y^3)$ **61.** $(x^{-3})(y)$ **62.** $3x^2y^{-4}$

63. y^{-5} **64.** $-2x^0y^{-2}$ **65.** $-3x^{-2}y^{-3}$ **66.** $-x^0y^{-6}$

67. $x^{-2} + y^{-2}$ **68.** $x^3 + y^{-3}$ **69.** $x^{-3} + y^{-3}$ **70.** $x^4 + y^{-4}$

C **71.** If $x > 0$, is x^{-9} positive, negative, or zero?

72. If $x < 0$, is x^9 positive, negative, or zero?

73. If $x < 0$, is x^{-8} positive, negative, or zero?

74. If $x < 0$, is x^{-9} positive, negative, or zero?

75. If $x > 0$ and m is an integer greater than zero, is x^m positive, negative, or zero?

76. If $x > 0$ and m is an integer less than zero, is x^m positive, negative, or zero?

77. If x is any nonzero real number and m is an even integer, is x^m positive, negative, or zero?

78. The definitions of zero and negative exponents were based upon Theorem 6–6. Prove that Theorems 6–1 and 6–5 are true for zero and negative exponents.

6–5   Roots of Numbers

Previously you have learned the following definition.

> **Definition**   A square root of a ($a \geq 0$) is a number b such that $b^2 = a$ is true.

The definition applies to nonnegative numbers only. If a is -25, could you find its square root? You could try -5, but $(-5)^2$ is 25.

According to the definition, −5 is a square root of 25, but not of −25. The number −25 has no real number as a square root.

One of the square roots of 25 is −5, as was seen in the last paragraph. You are already familiar with the other square root of 25, which is 5.

Every positive real number has two square roots.

For some numbers, for example, 2, the square roots are irrational. Can you tell which real number has just one square root?

The symbol $\sqrt{a}$ is used to denote the nonnegative square root of a ($a \geq 0$). The symbol $\sqrt{a}$ is a **radical** and $\sqrt{}$ is the **radical sign**. The number a is the **radicand**.

The sentence $5^3 = 125$ shows the operation of cubing 5. The inverse operation of cubing — taking the **cube root** of a number — is finding the solution of $125 = x^3$. Since $5^3 = 125$ is true, 5 is a cube root of 125. Is −5 a cube root also? The number $(-5)^3$ is equal to $(-5)(-5)(-5)$, or −125. Hence, 5 is the only real number whose cube is 125, and there is only one real number that makes $125 = x^3$ true.

Does −5 make the equation $-125 = x^3$ true? Does any other real number make the equation true? For negative numbers you can find a real number that is the cube root.

Definition The cube root of a is the number b such that $b^3 = a$ is true. The cube root of a may be written as the radical $\sqrt[3]{a}$.

In the radical sign for cube roots, the raised numeral 3 is the **index** of the radical. The index 2 for a square root is not usually written, so $\sqrt{a}$ means $\sqrt[2]{a}$.

Since, by convention, $\sqrt{a}$ denotes the nonnegative square root, the symbol $\sqrt{16}$ names only one number, 4. The other square root of 16 is $-\sqrt{16}$, or −4. Since there is only one real cube root, $\sqrt[3]{-8} = -2$ and $\sqrt[3]{125} = 5$. A radical always names just one number. This number is the **principal root**.

Definition The principal root of a number is the real root if there is only one. If there are two roots, the principal root is the positive one.

If you wish to name both square roots of 16, you may use the plus-or-minus sign. The two square roots of 16 may be written either as ± 4 or as $\pm\sqrt{16}$.

It is easy to extend the idea of roots and radicals to fourth roots, fifth roots, sixth roots, and so on.

$$\sqrt[4]{16} = 2 \quad \text{because} \quad 2^4 = 16$$
$$\sqrt[5]{32} = 2 \quad \text{because} \quad 2^5 = 32$$
$$\sqrt[10]{1024} = 2 \quad \text{because} \quad 2^{10} = 1024$$

Definition If $a^n = b$, where n is a positive integer, then a is the <u>nth root</u> of b.

Now try these

— Name the two square roots of each number below.

1. 81   **2.** 16   **3.** $\frac{25}{36}$

4. 10,000   **5.** $\frac{9}{100}$ **6.** $\frac{10{,}000}{144}$

— Name the real cube root of each number below.

7. 8   **8.** -1 **9.** 1000

10. -216 **11.** $-\frac{8}{27}$ **12.** $(-17)^3$

— Express each number without using the radical sign.

13. $-\sqrt{36}$ **14.** $\sqrt[3]{-27}$ **15.** $\sqrt[4]{3^4}$ **16.** $\sqrt[7]{-128}$

Answers: **1.** 9, -9 **2.** 4, -4 **3.** $\frac{5}{6}$, $-\frac{5}{6}$ **4.** 100, -100 **5.** $\frac{3}{10}$, $-\frac{3}{10}$ **6.** $\frac{100}{12}$, $-\frac{100}{12}$ **7.** 2   **8.** -1 **9.** 10   **10.** -6 **11.** $-\frac{2}{3}$ **12.** -17 **13.** -6 **14.** -3 **15.** 3   **16.** -2

Exercises

A — What number or numbers are named by each expression below? Name each number without using the radical sign.

1. $\sqrt{16}$ **2.** $-\sqrt{25}$ **3.** $\sqrt{49}$ **4.** $\pm\sqrt{144}$

5. $\pm\sqrt{100}$ **6.** $\pm\sqrt{81}$ **7.** $\sqrt{10{,}000}$ **8.** $\sqrt{5^2}$

9. $-\sqrt{4^2}$ **10.** $\pm\sqrt{8^2}$ **11.** $\pm\sqrt{100^2}$ **12.** $\sqrt{125^2}$

13. $\sqrt[3]{27}$ **14.** $\sqrt[3]{-64}$ **15.** $\sqrt[3]{125}$ **16.** $\sqrt[3]{-1000}$

17. $\sqrt[3]{\frac{1}{8}}$ **18.** $\sqrt[3]{-\frac{1}{64}}$ **19.** $\sqrt[3]{\frac{1}{125}}$ **20.** $\sqrt[3]{1{,}000{,}000}$

B —— What number or numbers are named by each expression below? Name each number without using the radical sign.

21. $(\sqrt{2})^2$ **22.** $(\sqrt[3]{2})^3$ **23.** $(\sqrt[4]{2})^4$ **24.** $(\sqrt[5]{2})^5$

25. $(\sqrt{a})^2$ **26.** $(-\sqrt{2})^2$ **27.** $(-\sqrt[3]{2})^3$ **28.** $(\sqrt[9]{7})^9$

29. $(\sqrt[n]{2})^n$ **30.** $(\sqrt[n]{a})^n$ **31.** $(4\sqrt{5})^2$ **32.** $(-2\sqrt{3})^2$

33. $(-2\sqrt[3]{3})^3$ **34.** $(5\sqrt{3})^{-2}$ **35.** $(8\sqrt{2})^0$ **36.** $5 \cdot (\sqrt{2})^0$

37. $(2\sqrt[3]{3})^{-3}$ **38.** $(3^0 \cdot \sqrt[4]{9})^4$ **39.** $(\sqrt[3]{-2})^3$ **40.** $(\sqrt[5]{-32})^3$

6–6   Rational Exponents

Study the table below to see if you can find a way to make a definition for exponents that are not integers, that is, **rational exponents.** The variables x and a represent nonnegative numbers.

If $x^a \cdot x^b = x^{a+b}$ and $(x^a)^b = x^{ab}$ are true for rational exponents, then	You know that	Then it is reasonable to define
$5^{\frac{1}{2}} \cdot 5^{\frac{1}{2}} = 5^{\frac{1}{2}+\frac{1}{2}} = 5^1 = 5$	$\sqrt{5} \cdot \sqrt{5} = 5$	$5^{\frac{1}{2}} = \sqrt{5}$
$2^{\frac{1}{3}} \cdot 2^{\frac{1}{3}} \cdot 2^{\frac{1}{3}} = 2^{\frac{1}{3}+\frac{1}{3}+\frac{1}{3}} = 2^1 = 2$	$\sqrt[3]{2} \cdot \sqrt[3]{2} \cdot \sqrt[3]{2} = 2$	$2^{\frac{1}{3}} = \sqrt[3]{2}$
$x^{\frac{1}{2}} \cdot x^{\frac{1}{2}} = x^{\frac{1}{2}+\frac{1}{2}} = x^1 = x$	$\sqrt{x} \cdot \sqrt{x} = x$	$x^{\frac{1}{2}} = \sqrt{x}$
$y^{\frac{1}{3}} \cdot y^{\frac{1}{3}} \cdot y^{\frac{1}{3}} = y^{\frac{1}{3}+\frac{1}{3}+\frac{1}{3}} = y^1 = y$	$\sqrt[3]{y} \cdot \sqrt[3]{y} \cdot \sqrt[3]{y} = y$	$y^{\frac{1}{3}} = \sqrt[3]{y}$
$(a^{\frac{1}{n}})^n = a^{\frac{1}{n} \cdot n} = a^{\frac{n}{n}} = a^1 = a$	$(\sqrt[n]{a})^n = a$	$a^{\frac{1}{n}} = \sqrt[n]{a}$

Why must x be nonnegative in the third row of the table? In the last row, if a were negative and n were even, then $\sqrt[n]{a}$ would not be a real number.

> **Definition** A number raised to the $\frac{1}{n}$th power can be expressed as a radical with the index n if the radical is defined.
>
> $$\forall x \in \mathrm{R} \ (x \geq 0) \ \ \forall n \in \mathrm{W} \ \ \ x^{\frac{1}{n}} = \sqrt[n]{x}$$
>
> $$\forall x \in \mathrm{R} \ \ \forall \text{ odd } n \ \ \ x^{\frac{1}{n}} = \sqrt[n]{x}$$

It is convenient to let $-x^{\frac{1}{n}}$ mean the same as $-(x^{\frac{1}{n}})$. Thus, $25^{\frac{1}{2}}$ means $\sqrt{25}$, but $-25^{\frac{1}{2}}$ means $-\sqrt{25}$. Of course, $(-25)^{\frac{1}{2}}$ is not a real number.

Negative fractional exponents may be interpreted in the same way as negative integral exponents. For example, the exponent $-\frac{1}{2}$ means 1 divided by the base with the positive exponent $\frac{1}{2}$.

$$16^{-\frac{1}{2}} = \frac{1}{16^{+\frac{1}{2}}} = \frac{1}{\sqrt{16}} = \frac{1}{4}$$

Now try these

—— Study each equation. Is the equation true or is it false? If it is false, change it to make it true.

1. $16^{\frac{1}{2}} = 4$ **2.** $8^{\frac{1}{3}} = 2$ **3.** $(-125)^{\frac{1}{3}} = -5$

4. $100^{\frac{1}{2}} = 50$ **5.** $27^{\frac{1}{3}} = 9$ **6.** $36^{-\frac{1}{2}} = \frac{1}{36^{\frac{1}{2}}} = \frac{1}{6}$

7. $49^{-\frac{1}{2}} = -7$ **8.** $\sqrt[n]{97} = 97^{\frac{1}{n}}$ **9.** $(81^5)^{\frac{1}{5}} = 81$

Answers: **1.** True.   **2.** True.   **3.** True.   **4.** False; $100^{\frac{1}{2}} = 10$.   **5.** False; $27^{\frac{1}{3}} = 3$.   **6.** True.   **7.** False; $49^{-\frac{1}{2}} = \frac{1}{7}$.   **8.** True.   **9.** True.

Exercises

A —— Rename each number without using exponents or radicals.

1. $9^{\frac{1}{2}}$ **2.** $125^{\frac{1}{3}}$ **3.** $16^{\frac{1}{4}}$ **4.** $(-27)^{\frac{1}{3}}$

5. $81^{\frac{1}{4}}$ **6.** $625^{\frac{1}{4}}$ **7.** $121^{\frac{1}{2}}$ **8.** $144^{\frac{1}{2}}$

9. $-36^{\frac{1}{2}}$ **10.** $-81^{\frac{1}{4}}$ **11.** $-(\frac{1}{4})^{\frac{1}{2}}$ **12.** $(\frac{1}{27})^{\frac{1}{3}}$

13. $-(\frac{1}{27})^{\frac{1}{3}}$ **14.** $(-\frac{1}{27})^{\frac{1}{3}}$ **15.** $\frac{1}{27}^{-\frac{1}{3}}$ **16.** $-(\frac{1}{27})^{-\frac{1}{3}}$

17. $(\frac{4}{9})^{\frac{1}{2}}$ **18.** $(-\frac{8}{125})^{\frac{1}{3}}$ **19.** $-(\frac{8}{125})^{\frac{1}{3}}$ **20.** $-25^{\frac{1}{2}}$

21. $-64^{\frac{1}{2}}$ **22.** 15^0 **23.** 9^{-2} **24.** 3^{-4}

—— Use a radical to name each of the following.

25. $7^{\frac{1}{2}}$ **26.** $(-8)^{\frac{1}{3}}$ **27.** $16^{\frac{1}{4}}$ **28.** $93^{\frac{1}{n}}$

—— Which triangles in Exercises 29–32 are right triangles? Do not trust the drawings. Instead, use the fact that only right triangles satisfy the Pythagorean theorem.

29.

30.

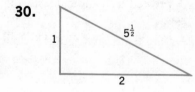

31.   **32.**

—— What number is named when a is 8, b is 9, and c is 1?

33. $a^{\frac{1}{3}} - b^{\frac{1}{2}}$ **34.** $(a+c)^{\frac{1}{2}}$ **35.** $-a^{\frac{1}{3}}$ **36.** $-b^{\frac{1}{2}}$

37. $a^{-\frac{1}{3}}$ **38.** $b^{-\frac{1}{2}}$ **39.** $(bc)^{-\frac{1}{2}}$ **40.** $c^{-\frac{1}{7}}$

41. Make a table of the squares of each integer from 1 through 15. The members of the set $\{1, 4, 9, \cdots\}$ are called perfect squares because each is the square of an integer. Keep trying until you can name all the perfect squares from 1 through 225.

—— For positive a, b, and c, if b is between a and c, then $\sqrt{b}$ is between $\sqrt{a}$ and $\sqrt{c}$. To approximate the irrational numbers named in the following sentences, replace x and y with consecutive integers to make true sentences.

42. $x < \sqrt{75} < y$ **43.** $x < \sqrt{42} < y$ **44.** $x < \sqrt{150} < y$

45. $x < \sqrt[3]{5} < y$ **46.** $x < \sqrt[5]{10} < y$ **47.** $x < \sqrt[4]{20} < y$

48. $x < \sqrt{200} < y$ **49.** $x < \sqrt[3]{-10} < y$ **50.** $x < \sqrt[3]{150} < y$

B **51.** The definition of rational exponents of the form $\frac{1}{n}$ is consistent with Theorems 6–5 and 6–6. Prove that it agrees with Theorems 6–1, 6–2, and 6–4 as well.

6–7   Approximations of Square Roots

The flagpole figure at the opening of the chapter is reproduced at the right. To install the guy wire whose length is x, you need to choose a rational number as an approximation for x. Imagine what a clerk in a hardware store would say if you asked for $\sqrt{500}$ feet of wire! The development that follows should help you find a way to give a rational approximation for $\sqrt{500}$.

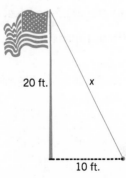

As an approximation for $\sqrt{2}$, you might choose any of the rational numbers shown as approximations. The squares of the approximations are shown for comparison.

Approximation	Check
$\sqrt{2} \approx 1$	$1^2 = 1$
$\sqrt{2} \approx 2$	$2^2 = 4$
$\sqrt{2} \approx 1.5$	$1.5^2 = 2.25$
$\sqrt{2} \approx 1.4$	$1.4^2 = 1.96$
$\sqrt{2} \approx 1.41$	$1.41^2 = 1.9881$

From the table, you can see that $\sqrt{2}$ is somewhere between 1.41 and 1.5, but closer to 1.41. The approximations in the table were obtained by guessing. There is a systematic way to locate approximations to a square root that, after the first guess, always gives you a better approximation.

To find a rational approximation for a square root of a number, you make a guess as to the square root, divide the given number by the guess, average the divisor and quotient, divide by this mean, average again, and so on until you get the precision you want. In this way the divisor and quotient get closer and closer. If the divisor and the quotient were the same, each would be the square root. Explain.

EXAMPLE. Find a rational approximation for $\sqrt{42}$.

① You know $\sqrt{42}$ is between 6 and 7, so let your first guess be 6.5.

Divide 42 by 6.5.

$$
\begin{array}{r}
6.4 \\
6.5\overline{)42.0\,0} \\
39\,0 \\
\hline
3\,0\,0 \\
2\,6\,0 \\
\end{array}
$$

② Average 6.5 and 6.4.

$\dfrac{6.5 + 6.4}{2} = 6.45$

First approximation: $\sqrt{42} \approx 6.45$

Divide 42 by 6.45.

$$
\begin{array}{r}
6.51 \\
6.45\overline{)42.00\,00} \\
38\,70 \\
\hline
3\,30\,0 \\
3\,22\,5 \\
\hline
7\,50 \\
6\,45 \\
\hline
\end{array}
$$

③ Average 6.45 and 6.51.

$$\frac{6.45 + 6.51}{2} = 6.48$$

Second approximation: $\sqrt{42} \approx 6.48$

Divide 42 by 6.48.

$$\begin{array}{r} 6.481 \\ 6.48\overline{)42.00\,000} \\ 38\,88 \\ \hline 3\,12\,0 \\ 2\,59\,2 \\ \hline 52\,80 \\ 51\,84 \\ \hline 960 \\ 648 \\ \hline \end{array}$$

④ Average 6.48 and 6.481.

$$\frac{6.48 + 6.481}{2} = 6.4805$$

Third approximation: $\sqrt{42} \approx 6.4805$

You can see that the divisor and dividend get closer and closer to the same number. You can continue this process as long as you wish and get a closer approximation for $\sqrt{42}$. But you can never find a rational number that is exactly $\sqrt{42}$ because $\sqrt{42}$ is irrational.

Now try these

1. $20^2 = \underline{\ ?\ }$ $30^2 = \underline{\ ?\ }$ Then is $20 < \sqrt{500} < 30$ true or false?

2. Divide 500 by 20. The divisor and the quotient tell you that $\sqrt{500}$ is between $\underline{\ ?\ }$ and $\underline{\ ?\ }$.

3. Average the divisor and quotient. Divide 500 by this number. Now you know that $\sqrt{500}$ is between $\underline{\ ?\ }$ and $\underline{\ ?\ }$.

4. To the nearest whole number, $\sqrt{500} \approx \underline{\ ?\ }$.

Answers: **1.** 400; 900; true. **2.** 20; 25 **3.** 22.2; 22.5 **4.** 22

Exercises

A — What two consecutive integers could x and y represent in each sentence to make the sentence true?

1. $x < \sqrt{67} < y$ **2.** $x < \sqrt{47} < y$ **3.** $x < \sqrt{26} < y$

4. $x < \sqrt{101} < y$ **5.** $x < \sqrt{123} < y$ **6.** $x < \sqrt{150} < y$

7. $x < \sqrt{136} < y$ **8.** $x < \sqrt{46} < y$ **9.** $x < \sqrt{56} < y$

10. $x < \sqrt{13} < y$ **11.** $x < \sqrt{260} < y$

12. $x < \sqrt{901} < y$ **13.** $x < \sqrt{1001} < y$

14. $x < \sqrt{100{,}001} < y$ **15.** $x < \sqrt{8101} < y$

16. If you choose any positive integer less than 100, how many digits are in the numeral for the integral part of its square root?

17. What is the smallest positive integer whose square root is an integer named by two digits?

18. Use the fact that 10^2 equals 100 and 100^2 equals 10,000 to answer the following questions. For any positive number less than 10,000, what is the maximum number of digits in the numeral for the integral part of its square root? What is the least positive number whose square root is named by three digits?

—— Which of the numbers below have square roots that are

    a. less than 10?

    b. greater than 10 but less than 100?

    c. greater than 100 but less than 1000?

19. 64 A	**20.** 86 A	**21.** 144 A	**22.** 492 A
23. 4900	**24.** 7638	**25.** 12,100 A	**26.** 16,419
27. 16,900	**28.** 23,842	**29.** 250,000 A	**30.** 756,208

—— Approximate each irrational number with a rational number to the nearest tenth.

31. $\sqrt{17}$	**32.** $\sqrt{12}$	**33.** $\sqrt{3}$	**34.** $\sqrt{130}$
35. $\sqrt{60}$	**36.** $90^{\frac{1}{2}}$	**37.** $450^{\frac{1}{2}}$	**38.** $800^{\frac{1}{2}}$

39. Find a rational approximation for $\sqrt{300}$ to the nearest hundredth. *17.32*

—— Find x to the nearest tenth.

40.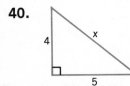

41.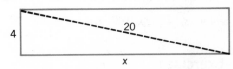

B **42.**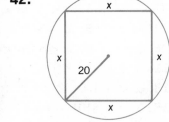

278   CHAPTER 6

6–8   Principal Square Roots with Variables

If x is a real number, you know that x^2 is never negative. There are two real numbers that are the square root of x^2, of which $\sqrt{x^2}$ is the principal root because it is nonnegative.

If $x = 3$,   then $\sqrt{x^2} = x$ because $\sqrt{9} = 3$.

If $x = -3$,   then $\sqrt{x^2} \neq x$ because $\sqrt{9} \neq -3$.

When the square root of the square of a variable is involved, you can use the absolute value symbol to indicate a square root that will apply for both positive and negative replacements of the variable.

If $x = 3$,   then $\sqrt{x^2} = |x|$ because $\sqrt{9} = |3|$.

If $x = -3$,   then $\sqrt{x^2} = |x|$ because $\sqrt{9} = |-3|$.

The examples below illustrate the way you can name square roots that involve variables.

a. $\sqrt{64a^2} = |8a|$, or $8|a|$

b. $(36b^2)^{\frac{1}{2}} = |6b|$, or $6|b|$

c. $\sqrt{49y^8} = |7y^4|$, or $7y^4$

d. $(81x^4y^6)^{\frac{1}{2}} = |9x^2y^3|$, or $9x^2|y^3|$

Why is it correct in **c** to rename $|7y^4|$ as $7y^4$? Does $7y^4$ always name a positive number? Explain **d**.

Now try these

—— Rename each number without using the radical sign. The replacement set for each variable is the set of real numbers.

1. $\sqrt{16x^2}$ **2.** $\sqrt{100x^2y^4}$ **3.** $\sqrt{0.36x^6}$ **4.** $\sqrt{400x^{12}y^4}$

Answers: **1.** $|4x|$, or $4|x|$ **2.** $|10xy^2|$, or $10y^2|x|$ **3.** $|0.6x^3|$, or $0.6|x^3|$

4. $|20x^6y^2|$, or $20x^6y^2$

Exercises

A. —— Rename each of the following numbers and expressions without using rational exponents or radical signs.

1. $\sqrt{4n^2}$ **2.** $(49b^2)^{\frac{1}{2}}$ **3.** $\sqrt{64x^4}$

4. $(36x^2)^{\frac{1}{2}}$ **5.** $\sqrt{100x^2}$ **6.** $(100y^2)^{\frac{1}{2}}$

7. $\sqrt{x^2y^2}$ **8.** $(x^2y^2z^4)^{\frac{1}{2}}$ **9.** $\sqrt{64a^2b^2}$

10. $\sqrt{\frac{4}{9}x^2}$ **11.** $\sqrt{\frac{1}{4}a^2}$ **12.** $\sqrt{\frac{1}{9}b^2}$

13. $(9a^4b^2)^{\frac{1}{2}}$ **14.** $(0.81y^2)^{\frac{1}{2}}$ **15.** $\sqrt{0.16t^4}$

16. $\sqrt{16x^{16}}$ **17.** $\sqrt{36x^{36}}$ **18.** $\sqrt{81a^4b^6}$

19. $(100x^8y^2)^{\frac{1}{2}}$ **20.** $(16a^8b^4)^{\frac{1}{2}}$ **21.** $\sqrt{100x^2y^6}$

22. $\sqrt{0.01a^2}$ **23.** $(169a^4b^2c^8)^{\frac{1}{2}}$ **24.** $(\frac{1}{25}r^2s^2)^{\frac{1}{2}}$

25. $\sqrt{121x^6y^{12}}$ **26.** $\sqrt{0.25a^6b^{10}}$ **27.** $(225r^{10})^{\frac{1}{2}}$

28. $(1.44a^6b^8)^{\frac{1}{2}}$ **29.** $(144a^{12})^{\frac{1}{2}}$ **30.** $(9a^2b^6)^{\frac{1}{2}}$

31. $(81m^{10})^{\frac{1}{2}}$ **32.** $(\frac{4}{25}x^8y^6)^{\frac{1}{2}}$ **33.** $\sqrt{\frac{1}{9}c^{20}}$

34. $\sqrt{225x^{10}y^{10}}$ **35.** $(400x^6y^4)^{\frac{1}{2}}$ **36.** $\sqrt{900x^2y^8}$

37. $(4900x^{20}y^{50})^{\frac{1}{2}}$ **38.** $\sqrt{36x^2y^{100}}$ **39.** $\sqrt{100x^2y^{12}}$

B **40.** $\sqrt{(x+y)^2}$ **41.** $\sqrt{(2y-3)(2y-3)}$

42. $\sqrt{x^2+2xy+y^2}$ **43.** $\sqrt{4y^2-12y+9}$

6–9 Simplifying Radicals

Give a reason why each of the following is true.

a. $\sqrt{36} = 6$ b. $\sqrt{4} \cdot \sqrt{9} = 2 \cdot 3 = 6$

c. $\sqrt{36} = \sqrt{4 \cdot 9}$ d. $\sqrt{4 \cdot 9} = \sqrt{4} \cdot \sqrt{9}$

Sentences **a–d** show that $\sqrt{4 \cdot 9}$ and $\sqrt{4} \cdot \sqrt{9}$ name the same number. It seems reasonable to ask if it is true in all cases that $\sqrt{ab}$ names the same number as $\sqrt{a} \cdot \sqrt{b}$ ($a, b \geq 0$). To prove that this is indeed true, you use the definition of square root. The numerical example in the left column below may help you with the general proof shown in the right column.

Show that $\sqrt{2 \cdot 3} = \sqrt{2} \cdot \sqrt{3}$. | Prove that $\sqrt{ab} = \sqrt{a} \cdot \sqrt{b}$.

The square of $\sqrt{2 \cdot 3}$ is $2 \cdot 3$. | The square of $\sqrt{ab}$ is ab.

$(\sqrt{2} \cdot \sqrt{3})^2 = (\sqrt{2} \cdot \sqrt{3})(\sqrt{2} \cdot \sqrt{3})$ | $(\sqrt{a} \cdot \sqrt{b})^2 = (\sqrt{a} \cdot \sqrt{b})(\sqrt{a} \cdot \sqrt{b})$

$\qquad = (\sqrt{2} \cdot \sqrt{2})(\sqrt{3} \cdot \sqrt{3})$ | $\qquad = (\sqrt{a} \cdot \sqrt{a})(\sqrt{b} \cdot \sqrt{b})$

$\qquad = 2 \cdot 3$ | $\qquad = ab$

Since $(\sqrt{2} \cdot \sqrt{3})^2$ is $2 \cdot 3$, | Since $(\sqrt{a} \cdot \sqrt{b})^2$ is ab,

$\qquad \sqrt{2} \cdot \sqrt{3}$ is $\sqrt{2 \cdot 3}$. | $\qquad \sqrt{a} \cdot \sqrt{b}$ is $\sqrt{ab}$.

This completes the proof of the following theorem.

Theorem 6–7 The square root of the product of two nonnegative numbers is the product of their square roots.

$$\forall a \in R \ (a \geq 0) \quad \forall b \in R \ (b \geq 0) \quad \sqrt{a \cdot b} = \sqrt{a} \cdot \sqrt{b}$$

Why is it necessary that a and b in Theorem 6–7 be nonnegative?

By an argument similar to the one for Theorem 6–7, a theorem for any root can be proved. It is stated below with the proof left as an exercise.

> **Theorem 6–8** The nth root of the product of two nonnegative numbers is the product of their nth roots.
>
> $$\forall a \in R\ (a \geq 0) \quad \forall b \in R\ (b \geq 0) \quad \sqrt[n]{a \cdot b} = \sqrt[n]{a} \cdot \sqrt[n]{b}$$

Theorem 6–7 is useful when one factor of the radicand is a perfect square. The radical is said to be *simplified* when it has no perfect square as a factor.

Explain how the theorems of this section are used in simplifying the radicals and powers in **e–j**. Note that in **e–h**, one factor of each radicand, or base, is a perfect square.

e. $\sqrt{50} = \sqrt{25 \cdot 2} = \sqrt{25} \cdot \sqrt{2} = 5\sqrt{2}$

f. $(48)^{\frac{1}{2}} = (16 \cdot 3)^{\frac{1}{2}} = (16)^{\frac{1}{2}}(3)^{\frac{1}{2}} = 4(3)^{\frac{1}{2}}$, or $4\sqrt{3}$

g. $\sqrt{50x^3} = \sqrt{25x^2 \cdot 2x} = \sqrt{25x^2} \cdot \sqrt{2x} = |5x|\sqrt{2x}$

h. $3\sqrt{8} = 3\sqrt{4 \cdot 2} = 3\sqrt{4} \cdot \sqrt{2} = 3 \cdot 2 \cdot \sqrt{2} = 6\sqrt{2}$

i. $\sqrt[3]{54} = \sqrt[3]{27} \cdot \sqrt[3]{2} = 3\sqrt[3]{2}$

j. $\sqrt[4]{32} = \sqrt[4]{16} \cdot \sqrt[4]{2} = 2\sqrt[4]{2}$

Now try these

—— Express each number below as the product of a perfect square and another number. In Exercises 10–15, choose the greatest perfect square possible as one of the factors.

1. $50 = \underline{\ ?\ } \cdot 2$ **2.** $27 = \underline{\ ?\ } \cdot 3$ **3.** $200 = \underline{\ ?\ } \cdot 2$

4. $24 = \underline{\ ?\ } \cdot 6$ **5.** $40 = \underline{\ ?\ } \cdot 10$ **6.** $4a^3 = 4a^2 \cdot \underline{\ ?\ }$

7. $8x^3y = 4x^2 \cdot \underline{\ ?\ }$ **8.** $20a^3b^2 = 4a^2b^2 \cdot \underline{\ ?\ }$ **9.** $27x^8y = \underline{\ ?\ } \cdot 3y$

10. $75 = \underline{\ ?\ } \cdot \underline{\ ?\ }$ **11.** $125 = \underline{\ ?\ } \ \underline{\ ?\ } \cdot$ **12.** $288 = \underline{\ ?\ } \cdot \underline{\ ?\ }$

13. $338 = \underline{\ ?\ } \cdot \underline{\ ?\ }$ **14.** $98 = \underline{\ ?\ } \cdot \underline{\ ?\ }$ **15.** $300 = \underline{\ ?\ } \cdot \underline{\ ?\ }$

—— Simplify these radicals.

16. $\sqrt{300}$ **17.** $\sqrt{32}$ **18.** $\sqrt{98}$ **19.** $\sqrt{20a^3b^2}$

Answers: **1.** 25   **2.** 9   **3.** 100   **4.** 4   **5.** 4   **6.** a **7.** $2xy$ **8.** $5a$ **9.** $9x^8$
10. $25 \cdot 3$ **11.** $25 \cdot 5$ **12.** $144 \cdot 2$ **13.** $169 \cdot 2$ **14.** $49 \cdot 2$
15. $100 \cdot 3$ **16.** $10\sqrt{3}$ **17.** $4\sqrt{2}$ **18.** $7\sqrt{2}$ **19.** $|2ab|\sqrt{5a}$

Exercises

A ── Simplify each of the following radicals or powers.

1. $\sqrt{8}$	**2.** $\sqrt{40}$	**3.** $\sqrt{20}$	**4.** $\sqrt{24}$
5. $12^{\frac{1}{2}}$	**6.** $63^{\frac{1}{2}}$	**7.** $\sqrt{75}$	**8.** $\sqrt{125}$
9. $\sqrt[3]{243}$	**10.** $5(96)^{\frac{1}{2}}$	**11.** $32^{\frac{1}{4}}$	**12.** $2(40)^{\frac{1}{2}}$
13. $242^{\frac{1}{2}}$	**14.** $\sqrt[5]{64}$	**15.** $\sqrt{196}$	**16.** $\sqrt[3]{-8}$
17. $4\sqrt{72}$	**18.** $(-27)^{\frac{1}{3}}$	**19.** $\sqrt{28}$	**20.** $3(18)^{\frac{1}{2}}$
21. $(36 + 49)^{\frac{1}{2}}$	**22.** $3\sqrt[3]{54}$	**23.** $54^{\frac{1}{3}}$	**24.** $\sqrt[6]{128}$
25. $(b^3)^{\frac{1}{2}}$	**26.** $\sqrt{b^5}$	**27.** $\sqrt{b^7}$	**28.** $(8a^2)^{\frac{1}{2}}$
29. $(8a^3)^{\frac{1}{3}}$	**30.** $\sqrt{27a^2}$	**31.** $(27b^3)^{\frac{1}{3}}$	**32.** $\sqrt{a^5}$
33. $\sqrt{a^4 b^3}$	**34.** $(36m^3)^{\frac{1}{2}}$	**35.** $(a^2 b^3)^{\frac{1}{2}}$	**36.** $\sqrt{a^3 b^2}$
37. $\sqrt{20a^2}$	**38.** $\sqrt{20a^3}$	**39.** $\sqrt{20a^3 b^2}$	**40.** $(a^4 b)^{\frac{1}{2}}$

── From the table on page 546, you can find the following approximations for $\sqrt{2}$, $\sqrt{3}$, and $\sqrt{5}$.

$$\sqrt{2} \approx 1.414 \qquad \sqrt{3} \approx 1.732 \qquad \sqrt{5} \approx 2.236$$

Use these three approximations to name the nonnegative square root of each number below to the nearest hundredth.

Example. 300

$$\sqrt{300} = \sqrt{100} \cdot \sqrt{3} = 10\sqrt{3} \approx 10(1.732) = 17.32$$

Hence, $\sqrt{300} \approx 17.32$.

41. 8	**42.** 12	**43.** 20	**44.** 45
45. 98	**46.** 50	**47.** 147	**48.** 320
49. 192	**50.** 216	**51.** 360	**52.** 200

B **53.** Prove Theorem 6–8.

6–10 Multiplication of Radical Expressions

You can use Theorem 6–7 and the symmetric property of equality to find the products of radicals with the same index. Is each of the following true?

a. $\sqrt{2} \cdot \sqrt{3} = \sqrt{2 \cdot 3} = \sqrt{6}$ b. $\sqrt{6} \cdot \sqrt{7} = \sqrt{6 \cdot 7} = \sqrt{42}$

c. $\sqrt[3]{2} \cdot \sqrt[3]{3} = \sqrt[3]{2 \cdot 3} = \sqrt[3]{6}$ d. $\sqrt[4]{5} \cdot \sqrt[4]{6} = \sqrt[4]{5 \cdot 6} = \sqrt[4]{30}$

> If the index of two or more radicals is the same, you may multiply the radicands and use the same index for the radical representing the product.

You can also use the distributive postulate to find another name for a radical expression involving multiplication and addition.

$$2(\sqrt{2} + \sqrt{3}) = 2\sqrt{2} + 2\sqrt{3}$$

Sometimes the new name will be much simpler than the old one.

$$
\begin{aligned}
2\sqrt{2}(3\sqrt{2} - 4\sqrt{3}) &= 2\sqrt{2}(3\sqrt{2}) + 2\sqrt{2}(-4\sqrt{3}) \\
&= 2 \cdot 3 \cdot \sqrt{2} \cdot \sqrt{2} + 2 \cdot (-4) \cdot \sqrt{2} \cdot \sqrt{3} \\
&= 6 \cdot 2 + (-8)\sqrt{6} \\
&= 12 - 8\sqrt{6}
\end{aligned}
$$

Generally, computation is less tedious if you first simplify the radical expression before applying the distributive postulate.

$$
\begin{aligned}
\sqrt{2}(3\sqrt{32} + 4\sqrt{45}) &= \sqrt{2}(3\sqrt{16} \cdot \sqrt{2} + 4\sqrt{9} \cdot \sqrt{5}) \\
&= \sqrt{2}(12\sqrt{2} + 12\sqrt{5}) \\
&= 2 \cdot 12 + 12\sqrt{10} \\
&= 24 + 12\sqrt{10}
\end{aligned}
$$

To simplify the indicated product of two binomial radical expressions, you apply the distributive postulate twice, as in the following examples. Notice that a and b must be nonnegative for the expressions to be defined.

EXAMPLE 1. Find the product of $(\sqrt{a} + 3)$ and $(\sqrt{b} + 2)$.

$$
\begin{aligned}
(\sqrt{a} + 3)(\sqrt{b} + 2) &= (\sqrt{a} + 3)(\sqrt{b}) + (\sqrt{a} + 3)(2) \\
&= \sqrt{ab} + 3\sqrt{b} + 2\sqrt{a} + 6
\end{aligned}
$$

EXAMPLE 2. $(\sqrt{a} + \sqrt{b})(\sqrt{a} - \sqrt{b})$

$$
\begin{aligned}
(\sqrt{a} + \sqrt{b})(\sqrt{a} - \sqrt{b}) &= (\sqrt{a} + \sqrt{b})(\sqrt{a}) + (\sqrt{a} + \sqrt{b})(-\sqrt{b}) \\
&= (\sqrt{a})(\sqrt{a}) + (\sqrt{b})(\sqrt{a}) + (\sqrt{a})(-\sqrt{b}) \\
&\qquad\qquad\qquad\qquad + (\sqrt{b})(-\sqrt{b}) \\
&= \sqrt{a^2} + \sqrt{ab} - \sqrt{ab} + (-\sqrt{b^2})
\end{aligned}
$$

Since $+\sqrt{ab}$ and $-\sqrt{ab}$ are additive inverses, their sum is 0.

$$
\begin{aligned}
\sqrt{a^2} + \sqrt{ab} - \sqrt{ab} + (-\sqrt{b^2}) &= \sqrt{a^2} + 0 + (-\sqrt{b^2}) \\
&= a + 0 + (-b) \\
&= a - b
\end{aligned}
$$

Exercises

A — Simplify each of the following indicated products. Exercises 13 and 19 are done for you.

1. $\sqrt{2} \cdot \sqrt{16}$ **2.** $\sqrt{3} \cdot \sqrt{7} \cdot \sqrt{2}$ **3.** $2\sqrt{3} \cdot 3\sqrt{6}$

4. $\sqrt[3]{3} \cdot \sqrt[3]{4}$ **5.** $\sqrt[3]{3} \cdot \sqrt[3]{9}$ **6.** $\sqrt[4]{18} \cdot \sqrt[4]{2}$

7. $\sqrt{27} \cdot \sqrt{2}$ **8.** $\sqrt[4]{4} \cdot \sqrt{3}$ **9.** $\sqrt{a} \cdot \sqrt{b} \cdot \sqrt{c}$

10. $2\sqrt{18} \cdot 5\sqrt{2}$ **11.** $\sqrt{2} \cdot 3\sqrt[3]{8}$ **12.** $2\sqrt{3} \cdot \sqrt{6}$

13. $\sqrt{7x} \cdot \sqrt{2x} = |x|\sqrt{14}$ **14.** $\sqrt{x^2 y} \cdot \sqrt{x}$

15. $\sqrt{15} \cdot \sqrt{5x}$ **16.** $\sqrt[4]{9x} \cdot \sqrt[4]{3x^2}$

17. $\sqrt[3]{9x} \cdot \sqrt[3]{3x^2}$ **18.** $\sqrt[3]{x^2} \cdot \sqrt[3]{xy}$

19. $3^{\frac{1}{2}} \cdot 4^{\frac{1}{2}} = 12^{\frac{1}{2}}$ **20.** $2^{\frac{1}{2}} \cdot 4^{\frac{1}{2}} \cdot 3^{\frac{1}{2}}$ **21.** $5(7^{\frac{1}{2}}) \cdot 3(5^{\frac{1}{2}})$

22. $5^{\frac{1}{3}} \cdot 2^{\frac{1}{3}}$ **23.** $5x^{\frac{1}{2}} \cdot 3x^{\frac{1}{2}}$ **24.** $2y^{\frac{1}{3}} \cdot 3y^{\frac{1}{3}}$

— Use the distributive postulate to rename each indicated product as an indicated sum.

25. $2(\sqrt{3} + \sqrt{6})$ **26.** $3(\sqrt{3} - 4\sqrt{3})$

27. $\sqrt{2}(\sqrt{3} + \sqrt{4})$ **28.** $2\sqrt{3}(3\sqrt{3} - 6\sqrt{9})$

29. $2(\sqrt{12} + \sqrt{72})$ **30.** $\sqrt{3}(5 + \sqrt{18})$

B — Simplify each of the following indicated products. The variables represent nonnegative real numbers.

31. $\sqrt{x} \cdot \sqrt{y} \cdot \sqrt{xy} \cdot \sqrt{x^2 y}$ **32.** $\sqrt[3]{x} \cdot \sqrt[3]{y^2} \cdot \sqrt[3]{xy}$

33. $(\sqrt{a} + 2)(\sqrt{a} - 6)$ **34.** $(\sqrt{a} + \sqrt{c})(\sqrt{a} - \sqrt{c})$

35. $(3\sqrt{x} + 6)(2\sqrt{x} - 3)$ **36.** $(5\sqrt{a} - 3\sqrt{b})(2\sqrt{a} - \sqrt{b})$

37. $(3\sqrt{x} - \sqrt{y})(3\sqrt{x} + \sqrt{y})$ **38.** $(2 - 5\sqrt{x})(2 + 5\sqrt{x})$

6–11   Rationalizing the Denominator

Theorem 6–4 stated that when n is a positive integer,

$$\left(\frac{x}{y}\right)^n = \frac{x^n}{y^n}$$

is true. Have you also shown that the equation is true when n is a rational number with 1 as the numerator? This result may be written using radicals.

When *n* is odd, it is not necessary to restrict *a* and *b* to non-negative values. You can prove Theorem 6–9 by showing that the *n*th power of $\frac{\sqrt[n]{a}}{\sqrt[n]{b}}$ is simply $\frac{a}{b}$.

Show in two ways that sentences **a–c** are true.

a. $\sqrt{\frac{9}{16}} = \frac{3}{4}$ 　　　b. $\sqrt[3]{\frac{8}{27}} = \frac{2}{3}$ 　　　c. $\sqrt[4]{\frac{16}{81}} = \frac{2}{3}$

In **d–f**, application of Theorem 6–9 may be used directly to give the simplest form of the radical.

d. $\sqrt{\frac{8}{16}} = \frac{\sqrt{8}}{\sqrt{16}} = \frac{\sqrt{4} \cdot \sqrt{2}}{\sqrt{16}} = \frac{2\sqrt{2}}{4} = \frac{\sqrt{2}}{2}$, or $\frac{1}{2}\sqrt{2}$

e. $\sqrt[3]{\frac{24}{27}} = \frac{\sqrt[3]{24}}{\sqrt[3]{27}} = \frac{\sqrt[3]{8} \cdot \sqrt[3]{3}}{\sqrt[3]{27}} = \frac{2\sqrt[3]{3}}{3}$, or $\frac{2}{3}\sqrt[3]{3}$

f. $\sqrt[4]{\frac{15}{81}} = \frac{\sqrt[4]{15}}{\sqrt[4]{81}} = \frac{\sqrt[4]{15}}{3}$, or $\frac{1}{3}\sqrt[4]{15}$

It is customary in mathematics to rename the number so that there is no radical in the denominator. If you have to compute an approximation of the number, it is easier to divide by a rational number than by an irrational number. Also, it is convenient to have a standard form for radicals.

The process of making the denominator a rational number is called **rationalizing the denominator.** You know that the numerator and denominator shown in a fraction may be multiplied by the same nonzero number without changing the value of the fraction. To rationalize the denominator, you choose the smallest multiple that makes the radicand of the denominator of the fraction a perfect square, cube, fourth power, or whatever power is equal to the index.

Explain the steps in each of **g–k.**

g. $\sqrt{\frac{9}{15}} = \frac{3}{\sqrt{15}} = \frac{3}{\sqrt{15}} \cdot \frac{\sqrt{15}}{\sqrt{15}} = \frac{3\sqrt{15}}{15} = \frac{\sqrt{15}}{5} = \frac{1}{5}\sqrt{15}$

h. $\sqrt[3]{\frac{1}{4}} = \frac{1}{\sqrt[3]{4}} = \frac{1}{\sqrt[3]{4}} \cdot \frac{\sqrt[3]{2}}{\sqrt[3]{2}} = \frac{1\sqrt[3]{2}}{\sqrt[3]{8}} = \frac{1\sqrt[3]{2}}{2} = \frac{1}{2}\sqrt[3]{2}$

Sometimes it is helpful to simplify the numerator before proceeding to rationalize the denominator.

i. $\sqrt{\frac{8}{15}} = \frac{\sqrt{4} \cdot \sqrt{2}}{\sqrt{15}} = \frac{2\sqrt{2}}{\sqrt{15}} = \frac{2\sqrt{2} \cdot \sqrt{15}}{\sqrt{15} \cdot \sqrt{15}} = \frac{2\sqrt{30}}{15} = \frac{2}{15}\sqrt{30}$

j. $\sqrt[3]{\frac{3}{4}} = \frac{\sqrt[3]{3}}{\sqrt[3]{4}} \cdot \frac{\sqrt[3]{2}}{\sqrt[3]{2}} = \frac{\sqrt[3]{6}}{\sqrt[3]{8}} = \frac{\sqrt[3]{6}}{2} = \frac{1}{2}\sqrt[3]{6}$

k. $\sqrt[4]{\frac{14}{5}} = \frac{\sqrt[4]{14}}{\sqrt[4]{5}} \cdot \frac{\sqrt[4]{125}}{\sqrt[4]{125}} = \frac{\sqrt[4]{1750}}{5} = \frac{1}{5}\sqrt[4]{1750}$

To simplify the products of radical expressions in fraction form, you first find the product of the numerators and the product of the denominators. Then simplify the resulting expression.

EXAMPLE 1. $\sqrt{\frac{2}{3}} \cdot \sqrt{\frac{3}{5}} = \frac{\sqrt{2} \cdot \sqrt{3}}{\sqrt{3} \cdot \sqrt{5}} = \frac{\sqrt{2} \cdot \sqrt{3}}{\sqrt{5} \cdot \sqrt{3}} = \frac{\sqrt{2}}{\sqrt{5}}$

$$= \frac{\sqrt{2} \cdot \sqrt{5}}{\sqrt{5} \cdot \sqrt{5}} = \frac{\sqrt{10}}{5}, \text{ or } \frac{1}{5}\sqrt{10}$$

EXAMPLE 2. $\sqrt[3]{\frac{1}{3}} \cdot \sqrt[3]{\frac{2}{3}} = \frac{\sqrt[3]{1} \cdot \sqrt[3]{2}}{\sqrt[3]{3} \cdot \sqrt[3]{3}} = \frac{\sqrt[3]{2}}{\sqrt[3]{9}} = \frac{\sqrt[3]{2}}{\sqrt[3]{9}} \cdot \frac{\sqrt[3]{3}}{\sqrt[3]{3}}$

$$= \frac{\sqrt[3]{6}}{\sqrt[3]{27}} = \frac{\sqrt[3]{6}}{3}, \text{ or } \frac{1}{3}\sqrt[3]{6}$$

Exercises

A — Simplify each of the following expressions.

1. $\sqrt{\frac{1}{2}}$

2. $(\frac{1}{8})^{\frac{1}{3}}$

3. $(\frac{3}{5})^{\frac{1}{2}}$

4. $\sqrt{\frac{4}{5}}$

5. $\frac{\sqrt[3]{4}}{\sqrt[3]{2}}$

6. $(\frac{9}{16})^{\frac{1}{3}}$

7. $\frac{3}{(2)^{\frac{1}{4}}}$

8. $\frac{2\sqrt{3}}{5\sqrt{7}}$

9. $\frac{\sqrt[3]{5}}{\sqrt[3]{9}}$

10. $\frac{3}{3\sqrt[3]{5}}$

11. $\sqrt{\frac{2}{3}}$

12. $(\frac{4.5}{8})^{\frac{1}{2}}$

13. $\frac{5(3)^{\frac{1}{2}}}{3(18)^{\frac{1}{2}}}$

14. $\sqrt[4]{\frac{2}{32}}$

15. $\frac{\sqrt[3]{3}}{\sqrt[3]{5}}$

16. $(\frac{3}{25})^{\frac{1}{3}}$

17. $\sqrt{\frac{5}{11}}$

18. $\sqrt{\frac{8}{9}}$

19. $\sqrt{\frac{2}{3}} \cdot \sqrt{\frac{3}{8}}$

20. $\sqrt{\frac{5}{6}} \cdot \sqrt{\frac{3}{2}}$

21. $\sqrt[3]{\frac{2}{3}} \cdot \sqrt[3]{\frac{4}{9}}$

22. $\sqrt[4]{\frac{2}{3}} \cdot \sqrt[4]{\frac{8}{9}}$

23. $\sqrt[3]{\frac{3}{7}} \cdot \sqrt[3]{\frac{2}{3}}$

24. $\sqrt[3]{\frac{9}{2}} \cdot \sqrt[3]{\frac{3}{4}}$

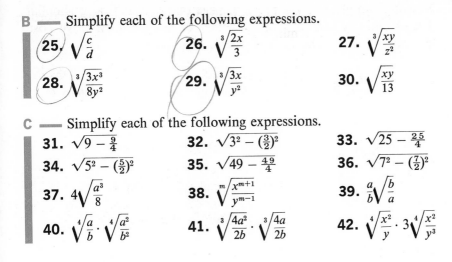

B —— Simplify each of the following expressions.

25. $\sqrt{\dfrac{c}{d}}$ **26.** $\sqrt[3]{\dfrac{2x}{3}}$ **27.** $\sqrt[3]{\dfrac{xy}{z^2}}$

28. $\sqrt[3]{\dfrac{3x^3}{8y^2}}$ **29.** $\sqrt[3]{\dfrac{3x}{y^2}}$ **30.** $\sqrt{\dfrac{xy}{13}}$

C —— Simplify each of the following expressions.

31. $\sqrt{9 - \dfrac{9}{4}}$ **32.** $\sqrt{3^2 - \left(\dfrac{3}{2}\right)^2}$ **33.** $\sqrt{25 - \dfrac{25}{4}}$

34. $\sqrt{5^2 - \left(\dfrac{5}{2}\right)^2}$ **35.** $\sqrt{49 - \dfrac{49}{4}}$ **36.** $\sqrt{7^2 - \left(\dfrac{7}{2}\right)^2}$

37. $4\sqrt{\dfrac{a^3}{8}}$ **38.** $\sqrt[m]{\dfrac{x^{m+1}}{y^{m-1}}}$ **39.** $\dfrac{a}{b}\sqrt{\dfrac{b}{a}}$

40. $\sqrt[4]{\dfrac{a}{b}} \cdot \sqrt[4]{\dfrac{a^2}{b^2}}$ **41.** $\sqrt[3]{\dfrac{4a^2}{2b}} \cdot \sqrt[3]{\dfrac{4a}{2b}}$ **42.** $\sqrt[4]{\dfrac{x^2}{y}} \cdot 3\sqrt[4]{\dfrac{x^2}{y^3}}$

6–12   Adding Radical Expressions

You know that you can use the distributive postulate to add the like terms $5x$ and $7x$.

$$5x + 7x = (5 + 7) \cdot x = 12x$$

You can use the distributive postulate also to add like radicals.

$$5\sqrt{y} + 7\sqrt{y} = (5 + 7) \cdot \sqrt{y} = 12\sqrt{y}$$

Note that the factor $\sqrt{y}$ appears in both terms. You must have the *same radical* if you are to use the distributive postulate in addition.

EXAMPLE 1. $3\sqrt{5} + 8\sqrt{5} - 2\sqrt{5} = (3 + 8 - 2)(\sqrt{5}) = 9\sqrt{5}$

EXAMPLE 2.

$$\begin{aligned}
3\sqrt{x} + 6\sqrt{y} - \sqrt{x} - 3\sqrt{y} &= 3\sqrt{x} - \sqrt{x} + 6\sqrt{y} - 3\sqrt{y} \\
&= (3 - 1)(\sqrt{x}) + (6 - 3)(\sqrt{y}) \\
&= 2\sqrt{x} + 3\sqrt{y}
\end{aligned}$$

EXAMPLE 3.

$$\begin{aligned}
\sqrt{48} + 6\sqrt{27} - 5\sqrt{12} &= \sqrt{16} \cdot \sqrt{3} + 6\sqrt{9} \cdot \sqrt{3} - 5\sqrt{4} \cdot \sqrt{3} \\
&= 4\sqrt{3} + 18\sqrt{3} - 10\sqrt{3} \\
&= (4 + 18 - 10)(\sqrt{3}) \\
&= 12\sqrt{3}
\end{aligned}$$

Note in Example 3 on the previous page that each radical is simplified first so that you can determine whether or not the distributive postulate can be used. The same is true in Example 4.

EXAMPLE 4.

$$\sqrt{\frac{2}{3}}+\sqrt{\frac{3}{2}}-\sqrt{\frac{1}{6}} = \frac{\sqrt{2}\cdot\sqrt{3}}{\sqrt{3}\cdot\sqrt{3}}+\frac{\sqrt{3}\cdot\sqrt{2}}{\sqrt{2}\cdot\sqrt{2}}-\frac{\sqrt{1}\cdot\sqrt{6}}{\sqrt{6}\cdot\sqrt{6}}$$

$$= \frac{\sqrt{6}}{3}+\frac{\sqrt{6}}{2}-\frac{\sqrt{6}}{6}$$

$$= \tfrac{1}{3}\sqrt{6}+\tfrac{1}{2}\sqrt{6}-\tfrac{1}{6}\sqrt{6}$$

$$= (\tfrac{1}{3}+\tfrac{1}{2}-\tfrac{1}{6})(\sqrt{6})$$

$$= \frac{(2+3-1)}{6}(\sqrt{6})$$

$$= \tfrac{4}{6}\sqrt{6}, \text{ or } \tfrac{2}{3}\sqrt{6}$$

Exercises

A — Add or subtract as indicated. The replacements for the variables are nonnegative in Exercises 5 and 6, but can be any real numbers in the remaining exercises.

1. $3\sqrt{2}+2\sqrt{2}-4\sqrt{2}$ 　　　　**2.** $5\sqrt{3}-2\sqrt{3}-6\sqrt{3}$

3. $6\sqrt{2}+8\sqrt{2}-9\sqrt{2}$ 　　　　**4.** $-3\sqrt{3}+4\sqrt{3}-10\sqrt{3}$

5. $5\sqrt{x}+6\sqrt{x}-11\sqrt{x}$ 　　　**6.** $\sqrt{4x}-\sqrt{x}-\sqrt{36x}$

7. $\sqrt{12}-\sqrt{27}+\sqrt{48}$ 　　　　**8.** $3\sqrt{18}-2\sqrt{32}-5\sqrt{50}$

9. $10\sqrt{8}-\sqrt{72}+3\sqrt{98}$ 　　　**10.** $3\sqrt[3]{8}-2\sqrt[3]{16}-6\sqrt[3]{54}$

11. $3\sqrt[3]{27}-\sqrt[3]{16}-6\sqrt[3]{54}$ 　　**12.** $10\sqrt{8}-3\sqrt{98}+6\sqrt{72}$

13. $\sqrt{\frac{2}{3}}+5\sqrt{\frac{1}{6}}-3\sqrt{\frac{3}{2}}$ 　　**14.** $\sqrt{\frac{36}{2}}-3\sqrt{\frac{49}{2}}-6\sqrt{\frac{25}{2}}$

15. $\sqrt{\frac{2}{3}}-3\sqrt{\frac{1}{6}}$ 　　　　**16.** $\sqrt{\frac{2}{36}}-3\sqrt{\frac{2}{49}}-6\sqrt{\frac{2}{25}}$

17. $\sqrt[3]{x}-3\sqrt[3]{y}+5\sqrt[3]{x}+2\sqrt[3]{y}$ 　**18.** $2\sqrt{18}-3\sqrt{48}-3\sqrt{98}$

19. $-\sqrt{20}+\sqrt{45}$ 　　　　　**20.** $3\sqrt[4]{48}-2\sqrt[4]{162}$

B — Add or subtract as indicated.

21. $\sqrt[3]{54}-3\sqrt[3]{128}-6\sqrt[3]{16}$ 　　**22.** $\sqrt[3]{-54}-3\sqrt[3]{-16}+4\sqrt[3]{128}$

23. $\sqrt{\frac{8}{9}}+2\sqrt{\frac{1}{2}}-3\sqrt{\frac{9}{8}}$ 　　**24.** $\sqrt{\frac{a}{b}}-\sqrt{\frac{b}{a}}$

25. $\sqrt{\frac{y}{x}}-\sqrt{\frac{x}{y}}-3\sqrt{xy}$ 　　**26.** $\sqrt[3]{xy^2}-3\sqrt[3]{x^4y^6}+\sqrt[3]{9x^2y^6}$

C **27.** In Exercises 24 and 25, when would the radicals not represent real numbers?

28. Perform this subtraction: $\sqrt{(a+b)^2c}-\sqrt{(a-b)^2c}$. What two things would you need to know about $(a+b)$ and $(a-b)$ to carry the subtraction further?

6–13 The Distance Formula

Look at the example below and try to discover a general method for finding the distance between any two points in the coordinate plane.

EXAMPLE 1. Find the distance from $A(-2, 3)$ to $B(4, -5)$.

The points are plotted and the line segment AB is drawn at the right. The dotted lines in color show the other two sides of right triangle ABC. Triangle ABC will be used to find $|\overline{AB}|$, the distance from A to B.

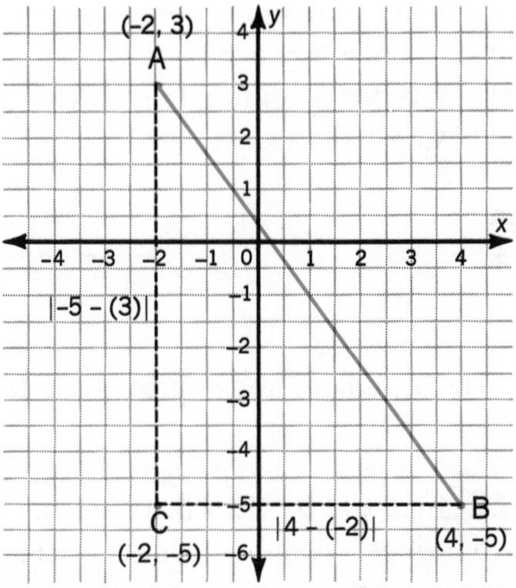

① Find the coordinates of C. They are the x coordinate of A and the y coordinate of B, or $(-2, -5)$.

② Find the length of $\overline{BC}$.

$$|\overline{BC}| = |4 - (-2)|$$
$$= 6 \text{ units}$$

③ Find the length of $\overline{CA}$.

$$|\overline{CA}| = |-5 - (+3)| = |-8|, \text{ or } 8 \text{ units}$$

④ Use the Pythagorean theorem to find $|\overline{AB}|$.

$$|\overline{AB}|^2 = |\overline{BC}|^2 + |\overline{CA}|^2$$

Let d represent $|\overline{AB}|$.

$$d^2 = 6^2 + 8^2$$
$$= 36 + 64$$
$$= 100$$

Hence, d is 10 or -10; but d must have the set of nonnegative numbers as its replacement set, since distance is nonnegative. The solution set for $d^2 = 6^2 + 8^2$ is $\{10\}$.

$$|\overline{AB}| = 10 \text{ units}$$

To obtain a **general distance formula,** choose any two points, (x_1, y_1) and (x_2, y_2), in the plane. One other vertex of a right triangle formed with these two points is (x_1, y_2). Why? The two legs of the right triangle have the measures $|x_2 - x_1|$ and $|y_2 - y_1|$. Then, by the Pythagorean theorem, the following sentences are true, where d is the distance between (x_1, y_1) and (x_2, y_2).

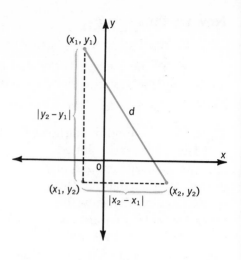

$$d^2 = |x_2 - x_1|^2 + |y_2 - y_1|^2$$
$$d = \sqrt{|x_2 - x_1|^2 + |y_2 - y_1|^2}$$
$$d = (|x_2 - x_1|^2 + |y_2 - y_1|^2)^{\frac{1}{2}}$$

The argument above proves the following theorem.

Theorem 6–10 The distance between any two points in the coordinate plane is found by (1) finding the difference between their x values and squaring it, (2) finding the difference between their y values and squaring it, and (3) adding the squares and then taking the nonnegative square root.

$$\forall P_1(x_1, y_1) \ \ \forall P_2(x_2, y_2) \ \ |\overline{P_1P_2}| = \sqrt{(x_2 - x_1)^2 + (y_2 - y_1)^2}$$

Why was it permissible to drop the absolute-value signs for $x_2 - x_1$? for $y_2 - y_1$?

EXAMPLE 2. Find the distance between $P_1(7, 3)$ and $P_2(2, 5)$.

$$(x_2 - x_1) = (2 - 7) = -5; \qquad (x_2 - x_1)^2 = 25$$
$$(y_2 - y_1) = (5 - 3) = 2; \qquad (y_2 - y_1)^2 = 4$$

$$|\overline{P_1P_2}| = \sqrt{(x_2 - x_1)^2 + (y_2 - y_1)^2}$$
$$|\overline{P_1P_2}| = \sqrt{25 + 4}$$
$$|\overline{P_1P_2}| = \sqrt{29}$$

Now try these

—— Use the Pythagorean theorem to find the distance between the points in each exercise.

1. (3, 7) and (8, −4)   **2.** (−5, −4) and (8, −2)

—— Use the distance formula to find the distance between the points in each exercise.

3. (1, 4) and (6, 9)   **4.** (−3, 2) and (2, −7)

Answers: **1.** $\sqrt{146}$ **2.** $\sqrt{173}$ **3.** $\sqrt{50}$ or $5\sqrt{2}$ **4.** $\sqrt{106}$

Exercises

A —— Find the distance between the points in each pair.

1. (−4, 5) and (5, −3)   **2.** (0, 7) and (−5, −8)
3. $(a, 2)$ and $(a, −7)$ **4.** $(9, b)$ and $(−5, b)$

5. Find the lengths of the three sides of a triangle with vertices at (7, 3), (5, −3), and (0, 6).

6. In the pictures at the opening of the chapter, there is a cable stretched between $A(2, 5)$ and $B(5, 1)$. How long is the cable?

B   **7.** The coordinates of each vertex of a quadrilateral are as follows.

$A(2, 7)$ $B(8, 3)$ $C(−4, −3)$ $D(5, −6)$

If $\overline{AB}$ and $\overline{CD}$ are opposite sides, find the lengths of all four sides. Is the quadrilateral a parallelogram? a rectangle? a square?

6–14   Solving Radical Equations

An equation such as $3 + \sqrt{x} = 6$ is a **radical equation.** To solve such an equation, you may add −3 to both sides and then square the sums to find a value for x. Solve $3 + \sqrt{x} = 6$.

Add −3 to each side. $\sqrt{x} = 3$
Square each side. $x = 9$

Check $3 + \sqrt{9} = 6$
$3 + 3 = 6$

Solution set: {9}

EXAMPLE. Solve $3\sqrt{2a-1}+4=7$.

Add -4 to each side. $\qquad 3\sqrt{2a-1}=3$
Square each side. $\qquad\quad 9(2a-1)=9$

Notice that the square of $3\sqrt{2a-1}$ is $3^2\cdot(\sqrt{2a-1})^2$ just as $(3x)^2$ is $3^2\cdot x^2$.

Use distributive postulate. $\qquad 18a-9=9$
Add 9 to each side. $\qquad\qquad\quad 18a=18$
Divide by 18. $\qquad\qquad\qquad\quad\ a=1$

Check $\ 3\sqrt{2(1)-1}+4=7$
$$3\sqrt{1}+4=7$$
$$3+4=7$$

Solution set: $\{1\}$

Squaring both sides of an equation sometimes gives a number that does not check in the original equation. When this is the case, the number is not a member of the solution set. For example, if you try to solve the equation $\sqrt{x}=-7$ by squaring both sides, you will get the equation $x=49$. Checking gives $\sqrt{49}=-7$. But $\sqrt{49}$ is the non-negative root of 49, so the solution does not check. The sentence $\sqrt{49}=-7$ is not true. In fact, the equation $\sqrt{x}=-7$ has ø as the solution set. You must check all solutions in the original equation.

Exercises

A — Solve and check each equation. If an apparent solution does not check, give the solution set as ø.

1. $3+\sqrt{x-1}=5$ **2.** $\sqrt{x}=6$ **3.** $8=\sqrt{x-9}$

4. $2\sqrt{x-5}=7$ **5.** $3-2\sqrt{x+4}=8$ **6.** $\sqrt{x}=-5$

7. $6-\sqrt{x-5}=2$ **8.** $5+\sqrt{x}=3$ **9.** $6+\sqrt{x}=13$

10. $8+2\sqrt{x}=0$ **11.** $7=3\sqrt{x}$ **12.** $8\sqrt{x}=4$

13. $\sqrt{\dfrac{n}{5}}=2$ **14.** $7=\dfrac{1}{\sqrt{y}}$ **15.** $8=\sqrt{5r+1}$

16. $\sqrt{1+2x}=\sqrt{5}$ **17.** $\sqrt{3y+2}=2\sqrt{y}$ **18.** $+4=\sqrt{7-2x}$

19. $3=\dfrac{9}{\sqrt{y-1}}$ **20.** $\dfrac{\sqrt{x+3}}{2}=\sqrt{x}$ **21.** $3\sqrt{s}=5\sqrt{3}$

22. $2\sqrt{x}=5$ **23.** $5\sqrt{x}=2$ **24.** $3=\dfrac{5}{4\sqrt{x}}$

25. $\dfrac{\sqrt{11-2a}}{3}=\sqrt{a}$ **26.** $5=\dfrac{15}{\sqrt{2a-3}}$ **27.** $\sqrt{7+3x}=-4$

B —— Which number in each pair is the larger? You should be able to answer these without taking the square root.

28. $\sqrt{49}$, $\sqrt{50}$ **29.** $\sqrt{24}$, $\dfrac{\sqrt{63}}{2}$ **30.** $\dfrac{3\sqrt{7}}{2}$, $2\sqrt{6}$

31. $\dfrac{2\sqrt{5}}{3}$, $\dfrac{4\sqrt{3}}{3}$ **32.** $\dfrac{4\sqrt{3}}{3}$, $\dfrac{5\sqrt{2}}{3}$ **33.** $\dfrac{4\sqrt{3a}}{b}$, $\dfrac{5\sqrt{2a}}{b}$, a, $b > 0$

—— Find the product.

34. $(2 + \sqrt{3})(2 - \sqrt{3})$ **35.** $(\sqrt{5} + \sqrt{2})(\sqrt{5} - \sqrt{2})$

36. $\dfrac{4}{(\sqrt{2} - \sqrt{3})} \cdot \dfrac{5}{(\sqrt{2} + \sqrt{3})}$ **37.** $\dfrac{8}{\sqrt{7} - \sqrt{3}} \cdot \dfrac{2}{\sqrt{7} + \sqrt{3}}$

C —— Write each of these fractions as a number with a denominator that is a rational number.

38. $\dfrac{2}{\sqrt{7}}$ **39.** $\dfrac{4}{\sqrt{2} + 3}$ **40.** $\dfrac{5}{\sqrt{5} - \sqrt{2}}$

41. $\dfrac{\sqrt{6} + \sqrt{3}}{\sqrt{6} - \sqrt{3}}$ **42.** $\dfrac{\sqrt{a}}{\sqrt{a} + \sqrt{b}}$ **43.** $\dfrac{\sqrt{a} + \sqrt{b}}{\sqrt{a} - \sqrt{b}}$

44. A rectangle of height 12 inches is inscribed in a circle with a radius of 10 inches. Find the area of the rectangle.

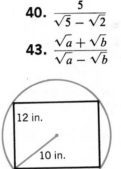

45. A man on a wharf 12 feet above the water pulls in a boat on the end of a rope. He had 20 feet of rope out and then pulled in 7 feet of rope. How far did he move the boat?

46. Each edge of the cube shown below measures 2 inches. Points A and C are the midpoints of the sides. What is the shortest distance from A to B to C, staying on the surface of the cube?

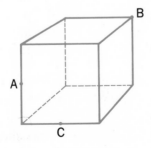

More Challenging Problems

1. Proclus, a Greek mathematician who lived about 460 B.C., showed that the sides of a right triangle, a, b, and c, can be expressed as $a = 2n + 1$; $b = 2n^2 + 2n$; and $c = 2n^2 + 2n + 1$, when n is any positive number. Use $a^2 + b^2 = c^2$ to show Proclus was correct.

━━ Perform the indicated operations.

2. $(a^{n+1} + 5)(a^{n-1} + 5)$

3. $(x - y)(x^{n-1} + x^{n-2}y + x^{n-3}y^2 + \cdots + x^2y^{n-3} + xy^{n-2} + y^{n-1})$

4. $\left(\dfrac{9.3x^2y^2 + 1.5x^3y + 5.7x^2y^3}{-0.03x^2y}\right)(0.3x + 0.3y)$

5. $\dfrac{0.216x^3 - 0.333x^2y + 0.198xy^2 - 0.081y^3}{0.72x^2 - 0.39xy + 0.27y^2}$

6. $\dfrac{3x^4y^8 - x^3y^6 - 4x^2y^4 + 32xy^2 - 24}{x^2y^4 - 2xy^2 + 4}$

7. $(a^5 - 243) \div (a - 3)$

8. $(a^4 - 16) \div (a - 2)$

9. $\dfrac{1 - x - 3x^2 - x^5}{1 + 2x + x^2}$

10. $\dfrac{2 - 3a - 6a^2 + a^4}{1 - 2a - 2a^2 + a^3}$

11. $(a^{\frac{n}{2}} + b^{\frac{n}{2}} + c^{\frac{n}{2}})^2$

12. $(c - 5)^3 - (c + 5)^2$

13. $(x^4 + y^4)^2 - (x^4 - y^4)^2$

14. $(x^n + y^n)^2 - (x^n - y^n)^2$

15. What is the quotient if 2^{100} is divided by 2^6?

CHAPTER REVIEW

1. Know the meaning of and be able to use each of the following words or phrases. The number shown after each word or phrase indicates where it is introduced, in case you need to review.

exponent (*258*)	radical sign (*271*)
base (*258*)	radicand (*271*)
power (*258*)	cube root (*271*)
positive integral	index (*271*)
exponent (*258*)	principal root (*271*)
zero exponent (*267*)	nth root (*272*)
negative integral	rational exponent, $\frac{1}{n}$ (*273*)
exponent (*267*)	rationalizing the
expanded notation (*268*)	denominator (*285*)
scientific notation (*268*)	distance
square root (*270*)	formula (*290*)
radical (*271*)	radical equation (*291*)

___ Name without using exponents.

2. 5^3 **3.** $(-2)^4$ **4.** $(-1)^7$

5. $8^{\frac{1}{3}}$ **6.** 7^{-1} **7.** 62^0

8. $(-1)^{\frac{1}{5}}$ **9.** $36^{-\frac{1}{2}}$ **10.** $(63)^{\frac{1}{2}}$

11. $(x^3) \cdot (x^4)$ means $(x \cdot x \cdot x) \cdot (x \cdot x \cdot x \cdot x)$ and equals $x^?$.

12. $\dfrac{a^7}{a^2}$ means $\dfrac{a \cdot a \cdot a \cdot a \cdot a \cdot a \cdot a}{a \cdot a}$ and equals $a^?$.

13. **a.** $m^a \cdot m^b = m^?$ $(m \neq 0)$ **b.** $m^a \div m^b = m^?$ $(m \neq 0)$

14. The product of 234 and 234 is 54,756. What is the positive square root of 54,756? What is the negative square root of 54,756?

15. The principal square root of 207.36 is 14.4. What is the square of 14.4? of -14.4?

___ Replace x and y with consecutive integers to make true sentences.

16. $x < \sqrt{42} < y$ **17.** $x < -\sqrt{42} < y$

18. $x < \sqrt{78} < y$ **19.** $x < -\sqrt{78} < y$

20. $x < \sqrt{93} < y$ **21.** $x < -\sqrt{93} < y$

___ Which of the following numbers have positive square roots that are larger than 10 but smaller than 100?

22. 138   **23.** 56   **24.** 938

25. 759   **26.** 7595   **27.** 12,714

28. Which one of the numbers in the set $\{-6, -3, 0, 3, 6\}$ satisfies the equation $2 + \sqrt{x + 3} = 5$?

___ Find the square of each of the following.

29. 213   **30.** 42.6   **31.** 0.0721

32. $29x^2y$ **33.** $4ab^2c^3$ **34.** $7m^4n^5$

35. Find a decimal approximating $\sqrt{132}$ to the nearest hundredth.

___ Find the indicated root in simplest form.

36. $\sqrt{49x^2}$ **37.** $\sqrt{\dfrac{81x^2}{144a^2}}$ **38.** $c\sqrt{(a - 7)^2}$

39. $\sqrt{405}$ **40.** $[(3x + 2)^2]^{\frac{1}{2}}$ **41.** $\sqrt[4]{\dfrac{16x^2}{81y^2}}$

42. $\sqrt{\frac{3}{7}}$ **43.** $\sqrt{\frac{5}{12}}$ **44.** $(\frac{12}{13})^{\frac{1}{2}}$

45. Change $\dfrac{\sqrt{3}}{\sqrt{11}}$ to an equivalent fraction with a denominator that is a rational number.

46. How many feet of fence are needed for Bobby's garden if it is shaped like the diagram in Figure 1?

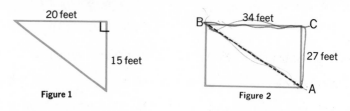

20 feet

15 feet

Figure 1

B   34 feet   C

27 feet

Figure 2   A

47. To the nearest tenth of a foot, how much farther is it from A to C to B than it is from A directly to B in Figure 2?

—— Simplify and add.

48. $14\sqrt{3} - 2\sqrt{12}$ **49.** $\sqrt{32} - \sqrt{8}$ **50.** $5\sqrt{18ab} + 2\sqrt{72ab}$

51. $5\sqrt{7} - 2\sqrt{7}$ **52.** $\sqrt{20} + \sqrt{45}$ **53.** $a\sqrt{128} - 5a\sqrt{32}$

—— Multiply or divide as indicated and leave the result in simplest radical form.

54. $\sqrt{3} \cdot \sqrt{27}$ **55.** $\sqrt{12} \div \sqrt{2}$

56. $4\sqrt{72} \div 3\sqrt{3}$ **57.** $4\sqrt{2} \cdot 3\sqrt{5}$

—— Solve and check the following equations. If you get an apparent solution that does not check, indicate that ø is the solution set.

58. $3\sqrt{x} - 4 = 5$ **59.** $14 - \sqrt{x} = 15$

60. $8 = 2\sqrt{x}$ **61.** $1 = \dfrac{2}{\sqrt{x} - 4}$

—— Find the distance between the points in each pair.

62. (3, 6) and (2, 11)   **63.** (−6, −5) and (−9, −8)

CHAPTER TEST

—— Simplify each of the following.

1. $x^3 \cdot x^5$ **2.** $x^8 \div x^2$

3. $(x^5)^3$ **4.** $(-2^7)(2^4)$

5. $x(3)^2$ **6.** $\left(\dfrac{x^3}{y^4}\right)^3$

—— Name each number without exponents.

7. $\left(\frac{4}{9}\right)^{\frac{1}{2}}$ **8.** $(-1)^{\frac{1}{6}}$

9. $-(121^{\frac{1}{2}})$ **10.** $(-125)^{\frac{1}{3}}$

11. 5^{-2} **12.** 17^0

—— Simplify each of the following expressions.

13. $\sqrt{3} \cdot \sqrt{4}$

14. $\sqrt{18}$

15. $\sqrt{a}(3 + \sqrt{6})$

16. $\sqrt[6]{64x^7}$

17. $\sqrt{\dfrac{16x}{9}}$

18. $\sqrt{\tfrac{1}{2}}$

19. $(\sqrt{2} + \sqrt{3})(\sqrt{2} - \sqrt{3})$

20. $\sqrt{6} - 3\sqrt{6} + 2\sqrt{6}$

21. $\sqrt[3]{\tfrac{24}{54}}$

22. $3\sqrt{18} - 3\sqrt{48} - 3\sqrt{98}$

—— Name each number with a rational denominator.

23. $\dfrac{2}{\sqrt{5}}$

24. $\dfrac{7}{3\sqrt{6}}$

25. $\sqrt{\tfrac{7}{12}}$

26. $\dfrac{4\sqrt{1}}{3\sqrt{14}}$

—— Solve for x.

27. $\sqrt{1 + 2x} = \sqrt{7}$

28. $8 + \sqrt{x + 2} = 17$

29. Find the distance from $(3, -5)$ to $(-7, 4)$.

—— Simplify the following radicals.

30. $\sqrt[3]{\dfrac{75}{27y^3}}$

31. $\sqrt{\dfrac{15x^2}{8}}$

32. $\left(\dfrac{26}{8x}\right)^{\frac{1}{3}}$

33. $\sqrt[3]{\dfrac{8x^2}{3x^3}}$

—— Use the distributive postulate to find the indicated products.

34. $(2\sqrt{x} - \sqrt{y})(\sqrt{x} + 3\sqrt{y})$

35. $(7 - 3\sqrt{x})(2 + 3\sqrt{x})$

36. $(\sqrt{x} + \sqrt{y})(\sqrt{x} - \sqrt{y})$

CUMULATIVE REVIEW

—— Give the letter of the response that best completes the sentence or answers the question.

1. If x is replaced by -3 and y by 4, what is the correct value of $6x - 5y$?

a. $(6 - 5)(-3 + 4)$

b. $(-18 - 5)4$

c. $(6 \cdot -3) - (5 \cdot 4)$

d. $(6 - 20)(-3)$

2. Which postulate for fractional numbers is illustrated by this sentence?

$$12(\tfrac{2}{3} + \tfrac{3}{4}) = 8 + 9$$

a. Associative postulate for addition.

b. Associative postulate for multiplication.

c. Distributive postulate.

d. Commutative postulate for multiplication.

3. Which sentence is true?

   a. The set {square, triangle, rectangle, parallelogram} is a subset of the set of quadrilaterals.

   b. {natural numbers} $\subseteq$ {rational numbers}

   c. {rational numbers} $\subseteq$ {integers}

   d. {the center of a circle} $\subseteq$ {circumference of a circle}

4. Which of the following is equivalent to {9, 10, 25, 3}?

   a. $\{\sqrt{100},\ \sqrt{625},\ \sqrt{81},\ \sqrt{9}\}$

   b. {5, 10, 15, 20, $\cdots$}

   c. {21, 19, 15, 11, 7}

   d. { }

5. Which second number is the negative of the first?

   a. $^+7$ and $-(^-7)$ **b.** $|\,^+3\,|$ and $|\,^-3\,|$

   c. $^+5$ and $|\,^-5\,|$ **d.** $-(^-6)$ and $+(^-6)$

6. Which sentence represents the difference of the two vectors shown here?

   a. $x - y = -6$ **b.** $x - y = -12$

   c. $x - y = +6$ **d.** $x - y = +12$

7. For which expression is $+8$ another name?

   a. $(-7 + 2)(-3)$ **b.** $(-7 - 2)(+3)$

   c. $-7(+2 - 3)$ **d.** $-2(-7 + 3)$

8. Which expression is equivalent to $-3m + \dfrac{n^2}{2} + 7m - \dfrac{3n^2}{2}$?

   a. $+4m - \dfrac{n^2}{2}$ **b.** $-10m - n^2$ **c.** $4m + n^2$ **d.** $4m - n^2$

9. In one pair of equations, the second equation is obtained by using the multiplication postulate for equations. Which pair is it?

   a. $3x - 2 = 5$ and $3x = 2 + 5$ **b.** $5x = -10$ and $x = -2$

   c. $4x + 5 = 7$ and $4x = 7 - 5$ **d.** $8 - \dfrac{x}{2} = \dfrac{3x}{2}$ and $8 = 2x$

10. If the replacement set is {3, 5, 7, 9, 11}, what is the solution set of $\dfrac{2x}{2} - 2 = 5$?

   a. $\varnothing$ **b.** {3, 5, 7}

   c. {7}   **d.** {3, 5, 7, 9, 11}

11. If the replacement set is the set of rational numbers, what is the solution set of the equation $\frac{3x}{4} - 7 = 2x + 9$?

    a. $\{12\frac{4}{5}\}$ **b.** $\{-12\frac{4}{5}\}$ **c.** $\{6\frac{4}{5}\}$ **d.** $\{5\frac{9}{11}\}$

12. Which sentence is true?

    a. $\forall x \in Q \quad x + 0 = 0$ **b.** $\forall x \in Q \quad \frac{2x}{3} = \frac{2}{3} + x$

    c. $\exists x \in Q \quad x - 2 = 2 + x$ **d.** $\exists x \in Q \quad \frac{2x}{3} = \frac{2}{3} + x$

13. Sam's age is three times that of his youngest sister, Ann. In 7 years he will be only twice as old. If you are to find Sam's and Ann's present ages, which equation correctly represents this problem?

    a. $3x - 7 = 2(x + 7)$ **b.** $3x + 7 = 2x + 7$
    c. $3(x + 7) = 2(x + 7)$ **d.** $3x + 7 = 2(x + 7)$

14. If the replacement set is the set of real numbers, what is the solution set of $3x + 2 = 5 \ or \ 3x + 2 > 5$?

    a. $\{x : x > 1\}$ **b.** $\{x : x \geq 2\frac{1}{3}\}$
    c. $\{x : x \geq 1\}$ **d.** $\{x : x = 2\frac{1}{2}\}$

15. Which ordered pair satisfies the equation $3x - 5y = 15$?

    a. $(5, 3)$ **b.** $(-5, 0)$ **c.** $(0, -3)$ **d.** $(0, 3)$

16. Which equation defines a linear function?

    a. $3xy = 2$ **b.** $3(x + y) = 2$
    c. $y(3x + 2) = 0$ **d.** $x(x + 2) = 3y$

17. If the graphs of the equations of a system are distinct lines with equal slopes, then the system is a(n)

    a. simultaneous system.   **b.** dependent system.
    c. inconsistent system.   **d.** consistent system.

18. Which equation has a graph with a y intercept of $(0, -2)$ and a slope of $-\frac{2}{3}$?

    a. $y = -\frac{2}{3}x + 2$ **b.** $y = -\frac{2}{3}x - 2$
    c. $y = x - 2$ **d.** $y = \frac{2}{3}x + 2$

19. In which quadrant of the coordinate plane do the graphs of the equations of the following system intersect?

$$\begin{cases} 2x - y = 8 \\ x + 3y = -3 \end{cases}$$

    a. First.   **b.** Second.   **c.** Third.   **d.** Fourth.

20. What rational number is named by $(-\frac{1}{3})^{-2}$?

    a. $\frac{1}{9}$ **b.** $-\frac{1}{9}$ **c.** 9   **d.** -9

21. Express 196.48 in scientific notation.

    a. 1.9648×10^{-2} **b.** 1.9648×10^{2}

    c. $19,648 \times 10^{2}$ **d.** 0.19648×10^{2}

22. What is the sum of $2\sqrt{8} + 3\sqrt{2}$?

    a. $11\sqrt{2}$ **b.** $5\sqrt{10}$ **c.** $5\sqrt{2}$ **d.** $7\sqrt{2}$

23. A simple closed path formed by the union of three or more line segments is a

    a. polygon.   **b.** triangle.   **c.** plane.   **d.** line.

24. Which of the following is not used to define a relation?

    a. Graph.   **b.** Equation.

    c. Set of ordered pairs.   **d.** The set of real numbers.

ENRICHMENT

A Computer Program for Linear Equations

In Chapter 5, you solved a linear equation by following a flow chart. In this chapter you will solve a linear equation by using the type of symbolic program that would be fed into a computer.

Basically, the parts of the computer are the Input, Operation, and Output; and Operation is subdivided into Memory, Control, and Arithmetic.

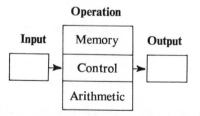

Into Input is fed information on punched cards or magnetic tape, and the information goes to Operation. Memory stores the information to be worked on. Arithmetic does the actual calculations. Control directs information between the other two sections of Operation and sends answers to Output, which prints out the answers on paper.

You and your pencil and paper will be the working parts of the computer, as well as the one who feeds it information. The information will be a list of code numerals, which would ordinarily be on separate punched cards. The information may be data or it may be instructions, but all information is in the form of a three-digit location numeral with a five-digit information numeral. If the three-digit numeral is 050 through 069 or 020 through 023, the information is data. Then the five-digit numeral that follows is just a decimal numeral. Thus,

$$051 — 00006$$

means that 6 is stored in location 051.

If the three-digit numeral is anything but 050–069 or 020–023, then the five-digit numeral is read as a two-digit numeral with a three-digit numeral. The two-digit numeral tells the operation to be performed on the data stored in the location indicated by the three-digit numeral that follows it. The code numbers for the operations that you, the computer, will perform are the following.

Code number	Operation
00	Register all zeros in Arithmetic.
01	Register in Arithmetic the number in the location that follows.
02	Add to the number in Arithmetic the number from the location that follows.
03	Subtract from the number in Arithmetic the number in the location that follows.
04	Multiply the number in Arithmetic by the number in the location that follows.
05	Divide the number in Arithmetic by the number in the location that follows.
06	Replace the number in the location that follows by the number in Arithmetic. Clear Arithmetic for further operations.
07	Print out the number in the location that follows.
08	Compare the number in Arithmetic with the number in the location that follows: Answer "Yes" if the numbers are equal; answer "No" if they are unequal.
09	If answer to previous comparison is "No," go to the location that follows and continue program from there.
10	Take absolute value of the number in Arithmetic.
11	Take square root of the number in Arithmetic.
12	Stop.

Thus, the first instruction piece of information will be as follows.

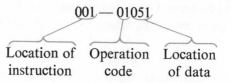

001 — 01051

Location of   Operation   Location
instruction   code   of data

001 means it is the first thing the computer will execute. 01 is read "Register in Arithmetic the number from the location that follows," which is 051. So you go to 051 and register whatever number it contains in Arithmetic. (*Register* means that you use the number and record it in a new location, but it is still in its old location for reuse.)

This program is going to allow you to solve from one to ten equations of the form $ax + b = 0$ ($a \neq 0$, $b \neq 0$). Thus, the data would be $a_1x + b_1 = 0$, $a_2x + b_2 = 0$, $\cdots$, $a_{10}x + b_{10} = 0$. Each a and b must be stored in a separate location and they have been assigned the locations 050 to 069.

$$050 — 0000a_1$$
$$051 — 0000b_1$$
$$052 — 0000a_2$$
$$053 — 0000b_2$$
$$\cdot \quad\quad \cdot$$
$$\cdot \quad\quad \cdot$$
$$\cdot \quad\quad \cdot$$
$$068 — 0000a_{10}$$
$$069 — 0000b_{10}$$

If fewer than ten equations are to be solved, 1 is inserted in place of a_n and 0 in place of b_n. This prevents division by 0 later in the program. Thus, if nine equations are given, the data would be the following.

$$\cdot$$
$$\cdot$$
$$\cdot$$
$$066 — 0000a_9$$
$$067 — 0000b_9$$
$$068 — 00001$$
$$069 — 00000$$

Before a program is written, a flow chart is drawn up as an outline of the steps to be covered in the program. This flow chart covers the steps needed for solving one equation, and then instructs the user to go back for new data and redo the same steps to solve the next equation.

This "going back" is known as a **loop.** A loop is an instruction to skip backward or forward over certain steps under certain conditions and is very useful in programming.

Flow Chart for Solving $ax + b = 0$ $(a \neq 0, b \neq 0)$

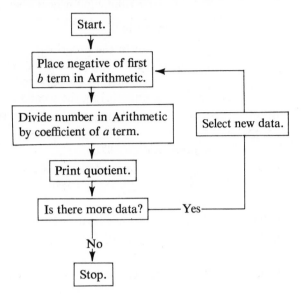

From the flow chart, the following step-by-step program is developed. As you read through the instructions, you will notice numbers and letters in parentheses. These are the results of solving the equation $a_1x + b_1 = 0$ and are, therefore, the general form of how the program works. The bracketed statements are further comments to clarify the procedure.

Location	Data or Instructions	Interpretation of Code Numeral
050 —	$0000a_1$	Put first x coefficient in 050.
051 —	$0000b_1$	Put first constant in 051.
.	.	.
.	.	.
.	.	.
068 —	$0000a_{10}$	Put tenth x coefficient in 068.
069 —	$0000b_{10}$	Put tenth constant in 069.
000 —	00000	Place all zeros in Arithmetic.
001 —	01051	Register number in 051 (b_1) in Arithmetic.
002 —	05050	Divide number in Arithmetic (b_1) by number in 050 (a_1).

(Continued on next page.)

003	—	04020	Multiply number in Arithmetic $\left(\frac{b_1}{a_1}\right)$ by number in 020 (-1).

003 — 04020   Multiply number in Arithmetic $\left(\frac{b_1}{a_1}\right)$ by number in 020 (-1).

004 — 06021   Move number in Arithmetic $\left(-\frac{b_1}{a_1}\right)$ to storage at 021. Clear Arithmetic for next operation.

005 — 07021   Print number in 021 $\left(-\frac{b_1}{a_1}\right)$.

[At this point in the program, the first equation is now solved. Instructions 006 through 014 prepare the computer to go back to 000 and start again, this time solving the second equation.]

006 — 01001   Register in Arithmetic the number in 001 (01051).

007 — 02022   Add to the number in Arithmetic (01051) the number in 022 (00002).

008 — 06001   Replace number in 001 (01051) by number now in Arithmetic (01053). Clear Arithmetic for next operation.

009 — 01002   Register in Arithmetic the number in 002 (05050).

010 — 02022   Add to number in Arithmetic (05050) the number in 022 (00002).

011 — 06002   Replace number in 002 (05050) by number now in Arithmetic (05052). Clear Arithmetic for next operation.

012 — 01023   Register in Arithmetic the number in 023 (05070).

013 — 08002   Compare number in Arithmetic (05070) with number in 002 (05052). Answer "Yes" or "No." (No)

014 — 09000   If answer to 013 is "No" (It is.), return to 000 and rerun. [If answer to 013 is "Yes," the program proceeds.]

015 — 12000   Stop.

020 — 0000$\bar{1}$ Put -1 in 020. [-1 is symbolized by $\bar{1}$.]

021 — 00000   Put all zeros in 021. [To be used for storage.]

022 — 00002   Put 2 in 022.

023 — 05070   Put 05070 in 023.

All the information is fed into the computer. As it is initially put in, the computer just "reads" the information and stores the data and instructions in the appropriate locations. Then the computer returns to the beginning of the program and proceeds through it in *strict ascending order*. Thus, it makes no difference that 050–069 comes before 000, 001, $\cdots$. The computer will begin the reading and execution of the program at 000, and will solve the equations one by one.

Now you, the programmer and the computer, can proceed to the exercises and solve the equations given.

Exercises

—— Solve the following equations by using the program. Your first step should be to label a sheet of paper "Memory" and make a list of locations 050–069 with the proper data stored. Also label a sheet of paper "Arithmetic" and one "Output." Be careful to do each step and to do it correctly.

1. $2x + 4 = 0, 3x - 9 = 0$

2. $2x + 6 = 0, 3x + 12 = 0, 5x - 10 = 0, 3x + 6 = 0$

3. $x - 1 = 0, 2x + 7 = 0, -x - 9 = 0, 5x - 25 = 0, 3x + 21 = 0,$
$-\frac{1}{2}x - 4 = 0, cx + e = 0, -5x + 1 = 0, -7x + 3 = 0, 8x + 24 = 0$

THE GROWTH OF MATHEMATICS

Archimedes

Archimedes (287?–212 B.C.) spent most of his life in the Greek city of Syracuse on the island of Sicily and is reputed to be *the* greatest mathematician of ancient times. Like Plato and others, he held applied mathematics in contempt. But he was a mechanical genius and often began with mechanical observations and then proceeded to his rigorous mathematical proofs. His discovery of the principles of floating bodies, that is, hydrostatics, is said to have been discovered as he was taking a bath. He leaped out of the bath and ran through the city crying "Eureka!" ("I have found it!")

He was familiar with the method of exhaustion and used it to *discover* the method for finding the areas of various regions, rather than to prove results as his predecessors had done; thus, he anticipated the calculus by two thousand years. Another major discovery was the law of the lever.

As a favor to his friend King Hiero, he built war machines that completely stunned a Roman army and put off the attack of Syracuse. But in another attack Archimedes was killed. On his tomb was inscribed, at his wishes, a sphere inside a circular cylinder, commemorating his discovery of the method for finding the volume of a sphere and its surface area.

Polynomials	Nonpolynomials
8	$4\sqrt{3x}$ $\quad -\sqrt{3x}$
$\sqrt{3}$ $\quad 3x$	$-3x^{\frac{3}{2}}$ $\quad \dfrac{5}{x}$
$-8x^2$	$\dfrac{x}{x^2-3}$
$-8x^2+3x+8$	
$x^3-8x^2+3x+\sqrt{3}$	$\dfrac{x+3}{x^2-6}$

Area is $(a + b)^2$, or
$a^2 + 2ab + b^2$.

$$(a+b)^2 = a^2 + 2ab + b^2$$

$$101^2 = (100+1)^2 = 100^2 + 2(100 \cdot 1)^2 + 1^2$$
$$= 10{,}000 + \ ? \quad + \ ?$$
$$= \ ?$$

$x + 2$ Area is $x^2 + 5x + 6.$

?

$2r$

r

Area shaded $= (2r)^2 - \pi r^2$
$= 4r^2 - \pi r^2$
$= (4 - \pi)(?)$

CHAPTER 7
POLYNOMIALS AND FACTORING

The diagrams show some uses of a subset of algebraic expressions called *polynomials*.

● Look at the examples in the upper left region to discover what a polynomial is. For polynomials, is any exponent of the variable negative? Is any exponent nonintegral? Does any polynomial involve division by the variable? How are polynomials different from nonpolynomials?

● In the upper right diagram, a and b represent positive numbers. What is the length of each side of the square? Why is the area of the square region $(a + b)^2$?

● Look at the center region. If the sentence $(a + b)^2 = a^2 + 2ab + b^2$ is true for any real numbers a and b, how is this sentence used to square 101 easily?

● In the lower left photograph, one side of the rectangle measures $x + 2$ units and the area of the rectangular region is $x^2 + 5x + 6$ units. What is the length of the other side? In other words, is there a polynomial that multiplied by $(x + 2)$ gives $x^2 + 5x + 6$?

● What is the area of the square in the lower right photograph? What is the area of the circle? What is the area of the shaded region? Can you name the area of the shaded region using two factors, one of which is $(4 - \pi)$?

In this chapter you will learn to answer questions such as these about products and factors of polynomials. You will also learn to solve some equations involving polynomial expressions.

7–1   Classifying Polynomials

By studying the chapter opening, you should arrive at the following definition.

> **Definition**   A <u>polynomial in one variable</u> is an algebraic expression formed by adding or multiplying numbers and the variable a finite number of times, so that there are only nonnegative integral exponents for the variable.

The replacement set for the variable in all polynomials in this chapter is the set of real numbers. The polynomial $2x^2 - 5$, for example, names a real number when any real number is chosen for x.

Polynomials may be in more than one variable, and the coefficients of polynomials may be any real numbers. Polynomials may be classified according to the specified subset of real numbers used as coefficients, as in the diagram.

Polynomials over the real numbers

$\sqrt{2}x^2 - 5$ with coefficients $\sqrt{2}$, -5

$x - \sqrt{2}$ with coefficients 1, $-\sqrt{2}$

> **Polynomials over the rational numbers**
>
> $\frac{2}{3}x - 9y$ with coefficients $\frac{2}{3}$, -9
>
> $0.5x^2 - 8$ with coefficients 0.5, -8
>
> > **Polynomials over the integers**
> >
> > $-7w^3 + 4r$ with coefficients -7, 4
> >
> > > **Polynomials over the
> > > nonnegative integers**
> > >
> > > $3x^2 + 2x + 9$ with coefficients 3, 2, 9
> > >
> > > 8 with coefficient 8
> >
> > $-3x$ with coefficient -3
>
> $\frac{3}{2}x^2 - 9x + 6$ with coefficients $\frac{3}{2}$, -9, 6

$3\frac{1}{2}s^2 - 9t + \frac{1}{2}u + v$ with coefficients $3\frac{1}{2}$, -9, $\frac{1}{2}$, 1

How does the diagram show that *all* the expressions are polynomials over the real numbers? Which expressions are polynomials
over the rational numbers? over the integers?

Another way to classify polynomials is by the number of **terms,** or
addends. Use the chart of prefixes
and examples to help you remember
the following names.

mono-	one	monotone
bi-	two	bicycle
tri-	three	tricycle

A **monomial** is a polynomial of one term: $2x^2$.
A **binomial** is a polynomial of two terms: $4a + 3$.
A **trinomial** is a polynomial of three terms: $16y^4 - 7y^3 - 4y^2$.

Classify each polynomial in the diagram as a monomial, a binomial,
or a trinomial.

Exercises

A —— Write *Polynomial* or *Nonpolynomial* to classify each of the
following expressions.

1. $3x^3 + 2x - 8$ **2.** $3x^{\frac{1}{2}} - 2x + 8$

3. $\sqrt{3}x^2 - 4x + 9$ **4.** $5m^{-2} + n^{-1} + 7$

5. $\frac{3}{x} - 5x^2 + 6$ **6.** $15x$

7. 39 **8.** $5\sqrt[3]{a^2} + 5b$

9. $\frac{a}{2} + 4$ **10.** $\dfrac{7}{2x - 5}$

—— For each of the following polynomials, write *Nonnegative
integers*, *Integers*, *Rational numbers*, or *Real numbers* to name the
coefficients. You may have more than one answer.

11. $5z^2 - 4z + 11$ **12.** $1.5x^3 - x + 12$

13. $4x + 5$ **14.** $\pi x^2 - 2$

15. $\frac{x}{3} - 28$ **16.** $\sqrt{25}w^4 - 3x^2 + 12y$

17. Give the least inclusive set of numbers for the coefficients
in Exercises 11–16.

—— Write *Monomial*, *Binomial*, or *Trinomial* to classify each polynomial.

18. $3x^3 + 3$ **19.** $2s^2 - 2t + 2$

20. a^5 **21.** $19 - 7x^2 + 5x$

22. $\sqrt[3]{11}r^2 + 11s$ **23.** $\dfrac{x^2}{3}$

24. $x^3 + x^2 - x$ and $\frac{x^2}{4} + \frac{x}{2} + (\frac{1}{2})^2$

25. $\sqrt{2}x^2 + 2x - 3$ and $\sqrt{8}x^3 + 3\sqrt{2}x^2 - 5$

26. $0.2x^4 - 0.5x^3 + 1$ and $1.2x^3 - 1.5x^2 + 1$

27. $\frac{2x^3}{3} + \frac{x}{6} + \frac{1}{2}$ and $3\sqrt{3}x^3 + \sqrt{27}x^2 - x$

7–2 Addition and Subtraction of Polynomials

When you add $2a$ and $3a$ to get $5a$, you are adding monomials. The monomials can be added, or combined, only if the variables are the same, that is, if they are *like terms*.

To add polynomials, you proceed in the same way — combining like terms.   The terms are usually arranged either in alphabetical order or in ascending and descending powers of the variable.

$$2b - 3d + 4a \quad \text{would be} \quad 4a + 2b - 3d,$$

in alphabetical order.

$$\tfrac{1}{2}y^2 - 3xy + 7x^2 - 4y^3 \quad \text{would be} \quad 7x^2 - 3xy + \tfrac{1}{2}y^2 - 4y^3;$$

the powers of x descend; the powers of y ascend; and it is in alphabetical order.

You will make fewer mistakes if you think of the sign as the sign for the coefficient of the term and think of all terms as being added.

EXAMPLE 1. Add $4a + 6b$ and $2a - 3b$.

Arrange the polynomials under one another and add.

$$
\begin{array}{r}
4a + 6b \\
2a - 3b \\
\hline
6a + 3b
\end{array}
$$

EXAMPLE 2. Add $-3x^2 + 7xy - 6y^2$ and $5xy + 3y^2 - 4x$.

Notice that the second polynomial has a term that the first does not.

$$
\begin{array}{l}
-3x^2 + 0 \ + \ 7xy - 6y^2 \quad \text{(Zero added for missing term.)} \\
\underline{\quad\ - 4x + \ 5xy + 3y^2} \quad \text{(Rearranged in ascending powers of } y.) \\
-3x^2 - 4x + 12xy - 3y^2
\end{array}
$$

To subtract polynomials, you proceed as in any subtraction example and add the additive inverse. The additive inverse of $6x^2$ is $-6x^2$. The additive inverse of $2n^2 + 3n^3m^2 - \frac{1}{2}m$ is $-2n^2 - 3n^3m^2 + \frac{1}{2}m$.

EXAMPLE 3. Subtract $a - b + c$ from $2a + b - c$.
Arrange the polynomials under one another.

$$2a + b - c$$
$$\underline{a - b + c}$$

Subtract.

$$2a + b - c$$
$$\underline{-a + b - c}$$
$$a + 2b - 2c$$

Now try these

—— Write the sum or difference in polynomial form.

1. $(4a - 3b) + (8a + 5b)$
2. $(4a^2 - 5ab - 6b^2) + (10ab - 6a^2 - 8b^2)$
3. $(6r + 9s) - (4r + 3s)$
4. $(h^2 + 6h + 9) - (25 + 10h + h^2)$

Answers: **1.** $12a + 2b$ **2.** $-2a^2 + 5ab - 14b^2$ **3.** $2r + 6s$ **4.** $16h - 16$

Exercises

A —— Add.

1. $4a - 3b + 5c$ **2.** $4r + 3s + t$ **3.** $6p - 4t + x$
$\,8a + 5b - 9c$ $\,6r + 9s + 5t$ $\,-7p + 8t + 6x$
$-p - 4t + 7x$

4. $5b + 4c + 8d,\ 8b - 7c - 6d,\ 3b - 4c$
5. $7x - 2y + 5z,\ 8y - 9z,\ 7x - 5y$
6. $5x + 7y - 10,\ 8y - 2x + 3,\ 2x - 10y + 4$
7. $4a^2 - 5ab - 6b^2,\ 10ab - 6a^2 - 8b^2,\ 10b^2 - 3a^2 - 7ab$
8. $a - b + c,\ b - c - a,\ c - a + b,\ a - 2b - c$
9. $4ab - 5bc + 6ac,\ 6bc - 7ab - 8ac,\ 10ab - bc - ac$
10. $x^2 + y^2 - z^2,\ 3z^2 - 2x^2 - 4y^2,\ 4y^2 + x^2 + z^2$
11. $x^2 - 6x + 7,\ 8x - 15 - x^2,\ 4x^2 + 6x - 9,\ 7x + 10$
12. $a^2 - 2ab + b^2,\ 2ab + a^2 + b^2,\ 4a^2 - 4ab - b^2,\ a^2 - b^2$
13. $a + 2b,\ 3b - 4c,\ 5a - 7c,\ 3b + 2d$

—— Write an algebraic expression, in simplest terms, for the perimeter of each of the following polygons.

14.

$3a$ $2a + 7$
$5b - 12$

15.

$2y + 3$
$x - 2$ $x - 2$
$2y + 3$

16.

$3x$ $4y - 1$
$3x$
$2y + 1$
$5y - 8$

17.

$3x$
$5m - 1$ $5m - 2$
$9x - 2$

18.

$5a$ $10b - 6$
$7a$ $10b - 6$

19.

$5b - 4$
$2a + 3$ $2a + 3$
$5b - 4$

—— Subtract.

20. $3a + 4$
     $2a + 9$

21. $7b - 5$
     $10b - 8$

22. $r + 8s$
     $r - 5s$

23. $7x - 3$
     $-2x - 9$

24. $3x^2 + 8y^2$
     $x^2 - 8y^2$

25. $5m^2 - 9n$
     $8m^2 - 10n$

26. $8a - 9xy$
     $-a + 9xy$

27. $a - b + c$
     $a + b - c$

28. $x^2 + 2x + 1$
     $x^2 - 2x + 1$

29. $2a + 0$
     $a - b$

30. $2x^2 - 4$
     $x + 2$

31. $x^3 + 0 + 0 + 8$
     $x^3 + x^2 - 2x + 0$

32. $x^2 + 6$
     $x^3 - 3$

33. $3x^2 - 6x$
     $2x^2 + 7$

34. $-4x^2 - x + 9$
     $3x^3 + x$

35. From $3a - 2b + 5c$, take $-2a + 5b - c$.

36. Subtract $6x^2 - 3xy + y^2$ from $8x^2 + 5xy - y^2$.

37. From $6ab - 2ac + 5bc$, take $10ab - 2bc + 3ac$.

38. Subtract $x^2 - 2xy + y^2$ from $x^2 + 2xy + y^2$.

39. From $x^2 - 2xy + y^2$, take $x^2 + 2xy + y^2$.

B **40.** From the sum of $x + 3y$ and $-3x - y$, subtract $x - y$.

41. Subtract $x^2 - y^2 - z^2$ from the sum of $2x^2 + 3y^2 - z^2$ and $4x^2 - 3y^2 + 5z^2$.

42. Take $a - b + 1$ from the sum of $a + c + 1$ and $a + b + 1$.

43. Subtract the sum of $(4x^3 + 2x^2 - 5)$ and $(15x - x^3 - x^2)$ from the difference of $(9 + 6x - 2x^2)$ and $(4x - 1 - 5x^3 + x^2)$.

44. If x is 3 inches, which is greater: the perimeter of a square whose sides each measure $3x - 1$ or the perimeter of a rectangle whose length is $x + 9$ and whose width is $2x - 3$? How much greater?

—— Combine like terms.

45. $2(a + 5) + 3(a + 5) - 4(a + 5) + 6(a + 5)$

46. $3a + 4 + 2(3a + 4) - 3(3a + 4)$

47. $8a + b - 5a + b - 2a + b$

48. When you add two polynomials over the set of nonnegative integers, will you obtain a polynomial over the same set? Show that your answer to the question is correct.

49. Repeat Exercise 48 for polynomials over the set of integers.

50. Repeat Exercise 48 for polynomials over the rational numbers.

51. Repeat Exercise 48 for polynomials over the real numbers.

52. What conclusion can you draw from the results in Exercises 48–51?

7–3   Products of Polynomials

The examples below show how products of polynomials may be found.

EXAMPLE 1. Find the product of $8x^2$ and $3x - 5$.

For the first step you may use the definition of subtraction, thinking of "$3x$ minus 5" as "$3x$ plus (-5)."

$$8x^2(3x - 5) = 8x^2[(3x) + (-5)]$$

Use distributive postulate. $\qquad\qquad = 8x^2(3x) + 8x^2(-5)$

Use associative and commutative
postulates and Theorem 6–1. $\qquad = 24x^3 - 40x^2$

Is the product of $8x^2$ and $3x - 5$ also a polynomial over the integers?

EXAMPLE 2. Multiply $x + 2$ and $x - 5$.

You start by thinking of $x + 2$ as one number in applying the distributive postulate. Think of $x + 2$ as a in $a(b + c) = ab + ac$.

$$a(b + c) \quad = \quad ab \quad + \quad ac$$
$$(x + 2)(x - 5) = (x + 2)(x) + (x + 2)(-5)$$

Use distributive postulate. $\qquad = x^2 + 2x - 5x - 10$

Use distributive postulate. $\qquad = x^2 + (2 - 5)x - 10$

Use definition of subtraction. $\qquad = x^2 - 3x - 10$

EXAMPLE 3. Find the product of $5t + 2n$ and $7t + 3n$.

$$(5t + 2n)(7t + 3n) = (5t + 2n)(7t) + (5t + 2n)(3n)$$
$$= 35t^2 + 14nt + 15nt + 6n^2$$
$$= 35t^2 + (14 + 15)nt + 6n^2$$
$$= 35t^2 + 29nt + 6n^2$$

If you prefer, you can write one polynomial under the other and multiply either from left to right or from right to left. The important thing is to keep like terms together.

$$
\begin{array}{l}
7t + 3n \\
5t + 2n \\
\hline
35t^2 + 15nt \longleftarrow 5t(7t + 3n) \\
\quad 14nt + 6n^2 \longleftarrow 2n(7t + 3n) \\
\hline
35t^2 + 29nt + 6n^2
\end{array}
\qquad
\begin{array}{l}
7t + 3n \\
5t + 2n \\
\hline
14nt + 6n^2 \\
35t^2 + 15nt \\
\hline
35t^2 + 29nt + 6n^2
\end{array}
$$

Since $35t^2 + 29nt + 6n^2$ is another name for $(5t + 2n)(7t + 3n)$, the two expressions should name the same number for every pair (t, n). You can substitute a pair of numbers to see if they produce the same results in both expressions. Let $t = 2$ and $n = 3$.

$$35t^2 + 29nt + 6n^2 \qquad\qquad (5t + 2n)(7t + 3n)$$
$$= (35 \cdot 4) + (29 \cdot 6) + (6 \cdot 9) \qquad = (10 + 6)(14 + 9)$$
$$= \quad 140 \quad + \quad 174 \quad + \quad 54 \qquad = \quad 16 \quad \cdot \quad 23$$
$$= 368 \qquad\qquad\qquad\qquad\qquad = 368$$

Although the results agree, this does not *prove* the answer is right. Why? The real reason for substituting is to remind you that the two expressions are names for the same number for *all* real numbers that replace t and n. In other words, the sentence

$$(5t + 2n)(7t + 3n) = 35t^2 + 29nt + 6n^2$$

is an identity.

Exercises

A Rename each product in polynomial form. Check Exercises 1–6 by letting a be 2 and b be 3.

1. $(a + 3)(a - 4)$ **2.** $(2a + 3b)(a - b)$

3. $(2a - 5)(3a + 2)$ **4.** $(a + 3)(a + 2)$

5. $(2a + 3)(3a - 2)$ **6.** $(a - 3b)(2a + 3b)$

7. $(a + b)(c + d)$ **8.** $(a - b)(c + d)$

9. $(a - b)(c - d)$ **10.** $(a + b)(c - d)$

11. $(3b - 4c)(3b + 4c)$ **12.** $(3b - 4c)(2c + 3d)$

13. $(4x - 5)(4x + 5)$ **14.** $(7n - 3)(7n + 3)$

15. $(3x - 4)(3x - 4)$ **16.** $(2a - 3b)(a - 4b)$

17. $(5x - 3y)(3x + 4y)$ **18.** $(a + b)(a - b)$

19. $(\frac{1}{2}x - y)(2x + y)$ **20.** $(\frac{1}{3}t - 5)(\frac{1}{3}t + 6)$

21. $(0.2u + 4)(5u - 0.3)$ **22.** $(1.6n - 9)(0.2n - 5)$

23. $(a^2 + b)(a^2 - 2b)$ **24.** $(x^2 - y^2)(x^2 + y^2)$

25. $(m^2 - 2n^2)(m^2 - 2n^2)$ **26.** $(4s - 3)(2s^2 + 3)$

27. $(a^3 + b^3)(3a^3 - b^3)$ **28.** $(2x^2 + 3y^2)(3x^2 + 2y^2)$

29. $(x - 3)^2$ **30.** $(2x + 3y)^2$

Find the area of each region outlined in red.

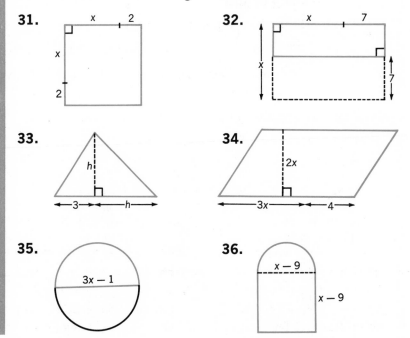

31.   **32.**

33.   **34.**

35.   **36.**

37. Note the difference in meaning in the expressions in **a** and **b**.

Expression	Meaning	Polynomial form
a. $(2x - 3)(3x + 4)$	$(2x - 3)$ times $(3x + 4)$	$6x^2 - x - 12$
b. $2x - 3(3x + 4)$	-3 times $(3x + 4)$ added to $2x$	$-7x - 12$

Check the work in **a** and **b** by substituting 5 for x in the expressions under **Expression** and **Polynomial form.**

— Rewrite each expression in polynomial form.

38. $(x + 5)(x - 7)$ **39.** $x + 5(x - 7)$

40. $y - 6(2y + 8)$ **41.** $(y - 6)(2y + 8)$

42. $2x + y(8x - 4y)$ **43.** $(2x + y)(8x - 4y)$

44. $7x - 9(3x - 4)$ **45.** $4 - (5x + 2)$

46. $2(8x + 3) - 5$ **47.** $5 - 2(8x + 3)$

B **48.** Look at the polynomials over the integers used as factors in Exercises 1–18. Is the product in every case also a polynomial over the integers? Is the set of polynomials over the integers closed with respect to multiplication?

49. Look at the polynomials over the rational numbers in Exercises 1–30. Is the set of polynomials over the rational numbers closed with respect to multiplication?

50. Write each product in polynomial form.

     a. $(x - 9)(2x + 3)$ **b.** $(2x + 3)(x - 9)$

Do you think multiplication of polynomials is commutative? Test some other examples.

C — Write each product in polynomial form.

Example. $(n^2 - 3n + 2)(n - 2)$

$$n^2 - 3n + 2$$
$$\underline{n - 2}$$
$$n(n^2 - 3n + 2) \longrightarrow n^3 - 3n^2 + 2n$$
$$-2(n^2 - 3n + 2) \longrightarrow \underline{\quad - 2n^2 + 6n - 4}$$
$$n^3 - 5n^2 + 8n - 4$$

51. $(x^2 - 2x + 1)(x - 1)$ **52.** $(x^2 + 2x + 1)(x + 1)$

53. $(x^2 - 2x + 1)(x + 1)$ **54.** $(x^2 + 2x + 1)(x - 1)$

55. $(x^2 - 6xy + 9y)(x - 3y)$ **56.** $(x^2 - 6x + 8)(x + 2)$

57. $(x^2 - 7xy + 12y^2)(x - 3y)$ **58.** $(n^3 - 5n^2 + 2)(n^2 - 2n)$

59. $(x^2 - xy + y^2)(x + y)$ **60.** $(x^2 + xy + y^2)(x - y)$

61. $(2 - 3a^2 - a)(a - 1)$

62. $(c - 2c^2 + 3)(2 + c)$

63. $(x^2 + x + 1)(x^2 - x + 1)$

64. $(x^3 + 3x^2 + 2x - 1)(x - 1)$

65. $(x^3 - 3x^2 + 3x - 1)(x - 1)$

66. $(5y^2 - 2 - 3y)(3 - y)$

67. $(3a^2 + 2 - 5a)(4a - 3)$

68. $(a^3 - 5 + 2a - 3a^2)(2 + a)$

69. If Q and R are polynomials over the rational numbers,

$$Q = ax^2 + bx + c \qquad \text{and} \qquad R = dx + e,$$

prove that QR is a polynomial over the rational numbers. (*Hint:* What kind of numbers are a, b, c, d, and e? Find the product, and use the postulates for rational numbers on page 31.)

7–4 Products of Binomials by Inspection

The product of two binomials, such as $2x - 7$ and $3x + 9$, is found so often in algebra that it is helpful to be able to write the product just from inspection of the two binomials.

Look at the examples below. When you first find the product, you have four terms, but the four can be simplified to three when the binomials have the same variables.

EXAMPLE 1. Find the product of $2x - 7$ and $3x + 9$ by inspection. Previously your work would have looked like the following.

$$
\begin{aligned}
(2x - 7)(3x + 9) &= (2x - 7)(3x) + (2x - 7)(9) \\
&= 6x^2 - 21x + 18x - 63 \\
&= 6x^2 + (-21 + 18)x - 63 \\
&= 6x^2 - 3x - 63
\end{aligned}
$$

Note that $-21x$ and $18x$ combine to give $-3x$. Which terms are multiplied to give $6x^2$? -63? $-21x$? $18x$?

To find the product by inspection, you need only

① multiply the first terms of each factor for the first term of the product,

② find the sum of the product of the inner terms (-7 and $3x$) and the product of the outer terms ($2x$ and 9) for the second term of the product,

③ multiply the last terms of each factor for the last term of the product.

EXAMPLE 2. Find $(4x + 1)(2x + 3)$ by inspection.

The first term is $4x(2x)$, or $8x^2$.
The second term is $1(2x) + 4x(3)$, or $+14x$.
The third term is $1(3)$, or $+3$.
The product is $8x^2 + 14x + 3$.

Compare this with the process written out in detail.

$$(4x + 1)(2x + 3) = (4x + 1)(2x) + (4x + 1)(3)$$
$$= 8x^2 + 2x + 12x + 3$$
$$= 8x^2 + (2 + 12)x + 3$$
$$= 8x^2 + 14x + 3$$

Now try these

1. In Exercises 2–10, the first and last terms of the product are given. In each exercise, how is the first term found? How is the last term found? Which terms of the factors will you multiply and then add to find the middle term?

—— Replace ● by + or −, and find the middle term in each product.

2. $(5a - 3)(2a - 2) = 10a^2$ ● _?_ $+ 6$

3. $(4a - 5)(5a - 1) = 20a^2$ ● _?_ $+ 5$

4. $(8x^2 - 3)(4x^2 + 5) = 32x^4$ ● _?_ $- 15$

5. $(2ab - 3)(3ab + 3) = 6a^2b^2$ ● _?_ $- 9$

6. $(5a - 3b)(2a + 3b) = 10a^2$ ● _?_ $- 9b^2$

7. $(6a + 2b)(9a - b) = 54a^2$ ● _?_ $- 2b^2$

8. $(3x - 2y)(2x - 5y) = 6x^2$ ● _?_ $+ 10y^2$

9. $(a - b)(a + b) = a^2$ ● _?_ $- b^2$

10. $(x - 5)(x + 5) = x^2$ ● _?_ $- 25$

Answers: **1.** Product of first terms of each factor; product of last terms of each factor; the two inner terms and the two outer terms. **2.** $-16a$ **3.** $-29a$ **4.** $+28x^2$ **5.** $-3ab$ **6.** $+9ab$ **7.** $+12ab$ **8.** $-19xy$ **9.** ± 0 **10.** ± 0

Exercises

A —— Write the products in polynomial form by inspection. Verify that you are correct in Exercises 1–6 by substituting -3 for x.

1. $(x + 5)(x + 3)$ **2.** $(x - 5)(x + 7)$

3. $(x + 2)(x - 2)$ **4.** $(x + 3)(x + 2)$

5. $(3x + 2)(5x + 7)$ **6.** $(3x + 4)(2x - 3)$

7. $(a - 2)(a + 3)$ **8.** $(y - 5)(y + 1)$

9. $(b - 7)(b + 3)$ **10.** $(2x + 5)(5x + 6)$
11. $(d + 4)(d - 5)$ **12.** $(m + n)(m - n)$
13. $(3y + 2)(4y + 3)$ **14.** $(2x + 5)(3x + 1)$
15. $(x + 3)(2x + 7)$ **16.** $(p + 9)(p + 11)$
17. $(3x - 4)(3x + 4)$ **18.** $(m - n)(p - q)$
19. $(b + 4)(b + 4)$ **20.** $(n - 2)(n + 2)$
21. $(m + 7)(m - 11)$ **22.** $(a + b)(2a - b)$
23. $(a - 2c)(a + 2c)$ **24.** $(3x - 2y)(3x + 2y)$
25. $(\frac{1}{2}x + 5)(6x - 10)$ **26.** $(\frac{1}{2}x - 3)(7x + 8)$
27. $(5a + 1)(\frac{1}{2}a + 4)$ **28.** $(\frac{1}{3}t + 8)(\frac{1}{4}t + 6)$
29. $(5x + \frac{2}{3})(6x + \frac{3}{2})$ **30.** $\left(\frac{x}{5} - 7\right)\left(\frac{x}{7} - 5\right)$
31. $(0.3u - 0.4)(0.5u - 0.1)$ **32.** $(1.8w - 2.4)(0.2u + 0.5)$
33. $(3x + 2)(x - 1)$ **34.** $(0.4m + 0.3n)(1.1m + 1.2n)$
35. $(x^2 + 2y)(x^2 - 2y)$ **36.** $(y^2 + 3)(y^2 + 3)$
37. $(2b + 3)(4b - 7)$ **38.** $(4y - 3)(4y - 3)$
39. $(4y - 3)(4y + 3)$ **40.** $(2a + 5)(2a + 3)$
41. $(4c - 7)(5c + 9)$ **42.** $(5x + 3)(x + 1)$
43. $(2f + 9)(3f + 7)$ **44.** $(7b + 2)(5b - 1)$
45. $(10p + 3)(6p - 1)$ **46.** $(8x + 3)(3x - 4)$
47. $(8r - 5)(7r + 5)$ **48.** $(2c - 9)(3c - 8)$
49. $(4x + 7)(5x - 3)$ **50.** $(x^2 - 4)(x^2 + 4)$
51. $(y^2 - 2)(y^2 + 2)$ **52.** $(7a - 2)(a + 8)$
53. $(a^2 - 3b)(a^2 + 2b)$ **54.** $(3x - 5y)(2x + 3y)$

B
55. $(\sqrt{2} + x)(\sqrt{2} - x)$ **56.** $(3^{\frac{1}{2}} - y)(3^{\frac{1}{2}} + y)$
57. $(\sqrt{2} + x)(\sqrt{2} + 2x)$ **58.** $(-3\sqrt{2} - y)(-4\sqrt{2} - y)$
59. $(\sqrt{2}x - 3)(\sqrt{2}x - 4)$ **60.** $(3^{\frac{1}{2}}a - b)(3^{\frac{1}{2}}a + 2b)$

C
61. $(3 - x^{\frac{1}{2}})(3 - x^{\frac{1}{2}})$ **62.** $(3\sqrt{2}x - 4)(-2\sqrt{2}x + 9)$
63. $(-\frac{7}{3}\sqrt{2} + x)(3\sqrt{2} - 2x)$
64. $(4\sqrt{2}x + 3\sqrt{3})(5\sqrt{2}x + 3\sqrt{3})$

65. Explain, using the areas of rectangular regions, how the drawing shows that $(a + 3)(a - 3) = a^2 - 9$ is true.

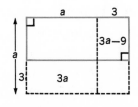

7–5 Squaring Binomials by Inspection

Multiply to see that each of the following is a true sentence.

    a. $(a - 5)^2 = (a - 5)(a - 5) = a^2 - 10a + 25$
    b. $(2x + 7)^2 = (2x + 7)(2x + 7) = 4x^2 + 28x + 49$
    c. $(x + y)^2 = (x + y)(x + y) = x^2 + 2xy + y^2$
    d. $(a - b)^2 = (a - b)(a - b) = a^2 - 2ab + b^2$

Look again at **c** and **d**. To square $x + y$, you square x, getting x^2, then take twice the product of x and y, getting $+2xy$, and then square y, getting $+y^2$. The square is the sum $x^2 + 2xy + y^2$. To square $a - b$, you square a, getting a^2, then take twice the product of a and $-b$, getting $-2ab$, and then square $-b$, getting $+b^2$. The square is $a^2 - 2ab + b^2$.

By following the pattern, you can square binomials by inspection.

①　Square the first term of the binomial.

②　Add to this twice the product of the first and last terms.

③　Add to this the square of the last term.

The shortcut for writing the square of a binomial can be used to square numbers also.

EXAMPLE 1. Square 32.

$$32^2 = (30 + 2)^2 = 30^2 + 2(30 \cdot 2) + 2^2$$
$$= 900 + \quad 120 \quad + 4 = 1024$$

EXAMPLE 2. Compute the square of 49.

$$49^2 = (50 - 1)^2 = 2500 - 100 + 1 = 2401$$

The advantage is that much of the work can be done "in your head."

Exercises

A ── Write the square as a trinomial by inspection. Verify that your answer is correct in Exercises 1–6 by substituting $-\frac{1}{2}$ for a.

    1. $(a + 3)^2$ **2.** $(a - 2)^2$ **3.** $(a - 5)^2$
    4. $(2a + 1)^2$ **5.** $(4a - 1)^2$ **6.** $(2a + 3)^2$
    7. $(5m - 1)^2$ **8.** $(5m + 3)^2$ **9.** $(7m - 4)^2$
    10. $(3x - y)^2$ **11.** $(x + 2)^2$ **12.** $(n + 3)^2$

13. $(x - y)^2$ **14.** $(x - 3)^2$ **15.** $(a - 5)^2$

16. $(n - 6)^2$ **17.** $(2x - 3)^2$ **18.** $(2x - 5)^2$

19. $(2x + y)^2$ **20.** $(y + 10)^2$ **21.** $(2x - 3y)^2$

22. $(3a - 2b)^2$ **23.** $(10a + 2)^2$ **24.** $(5c + 3d)^2$

25. $(2x^2 + 3y^2)^2$ **26.** $(5c^2 + 4y^3)^2$ **27.** $(a^2 - 3b^2)^2$

28. $(x^2y - 5)^2$ **29.** $(a^2 - 3)^2$ **30.** $(2a^2 + 3)^2$

—— Name with a decimal numeral.   Use your pencil to write only the answers.

31. $(20 + 1)^2$ **32.** $(100 - 1)^2$ **33.** $(50 + 2)^2$

34. $(20 - 1)^2$ **35.** $(1000 - 1)^2$ **36.** $(100 + 5)^2$

37. 98^2 **38.** 101^2 **39.** 19^2

B —— Each binomial below is a polynomial over the rational numbers.   Write the square as a trinomial over the rational numbers by inspection.

40. $(x + \frac{1}{2})^2$ **41.** $(x + \frac{1}{3})^2$ **42.** $(x - \frac{1}{6})^2$

43. $(2y + \frac{1}{2})^2$ **44.** $(6b + \frac{1}{2})^2$ **45.** $(5c + \frac{1}{3})^2$

46. $(9a + \frac{1}{6})^2$ **47.** $\left(x - \frac{a}{2}\right)^2$ **48.** $(y - \frac{1}{2}p)^2$

49. $\left(x + \frac{y}{2}\right)^2$ **50.** $\left(\frac{x}{2} + 4\right)^2$ **51.** $(5b - \frac{1}{4})^2$

—— Write as a trinomial over the real numbers.

52. $(x + \sqrt{3})^2$ **53.** $(2^{\frac{1}{2}} + m)^2$ **54.** $(3^{-\frac{1}{2}} - y)^2$

55. $(\sqrt{2}x + 2)^2$ **56.** $(3x - \sqrt{11})^2$ **57.** $(\sqrt{2}x - \sqrt{2})^2$

—— Find the area of the region enclosed in red.

58.   **59.**

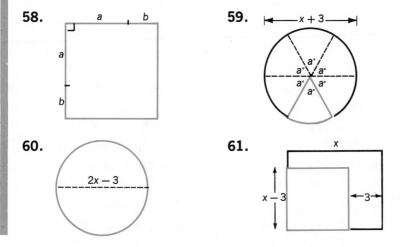

60.   **61.**

62. Examine the equations at the right and form a rule for squaring a number whose numeral ends in 5. Test the rule on 55, 25, and 15.

$$85^2 = 7225$$
$$35^2 = 1225$$
$$45^2 = 2025$$
$$65^2 = 4225$$

Now, treating the numbers as polynomials, find $(80 + 5)^2$, $(30 + 5)^2$, $(40 + 5)^2$, and $(60 + 5)^2$. Do you see why the rule you formulated works?

If t is the number of tens and 5 is the number of units, what is the number? What is its square? How does this prove that the rule works?

7–6 Product of $a + b$ and $a - b$

The product of binomials of the form $a + b$ and $a - b$ is easy to write by inspection. Note the examples below.

a. $(x + 7)(x - 7) = x^2 + 7x - 7x - 49 = x^2 - 49$
b. $(2x - 5)(2x + 5) = 4x^2 - 10x + 10x - 25 = 4x^2 - 25$
c. $(a + b)(a - b) = a^2 + ab - ab - b^2 = a^2 - b^2$

Can you see the pattern for finding the product of the sum and difference of two numbers? State it in your own words.

Now try these

—— Find the following products.

1. $(x + 1)(x - 1)$ **2.** $(a + 3)(a - 3)$
3. $(2r - 2)(2r + 2)$ **4.** $(\frac{1}{2}y + 8)(\frac{1}{2}y - 8)$

Answers: **1.** $x^2 - 1$ **2.** $a^2 - 9$ **3.** $4r^2 - 4$ **4.** $\frac{1}{4}y^2 - 64$

Exercises

A —— Find the following products. Verify that Exercises 1–6 are correct by replacing p with -5.

1. $(p + 7)(p - 7)$ **2.** $(p - 5)(p + 5)$
3. $(p + 8)(p - 8)$ **4.** $(2p + 5)(2p - 5)$
5. $(2p + 3)(2p - 3)$ **6.** $(3p + 5)(3p - 5)$
7. $(b + c)(b - c)$ **8.** $(c - 2)(c + 2)$
9. $(R - r)(R + r)$ **10.** $(2x + y)(2x - y)$
11. $(5x + 4y)(5x - 4y)$ **12.** $(7x - 6y)(7x + 6y)$

13. $(6x^2 - 7y)(6x^2 + 7y)$ **14.** $(a^2 + b^2)(a^2 - b^2)$

15. $(ab - c)(ab + c)$ **16.** $(y - x^2)(x^2 + y)$

17. $(\frac{1}{2} - 2x)(\frac{1}{2} + 2x)$ **18.** $(100 - 10)(100 + 10)$

19. $(2c + d)(2c - d)$ **20.** $(3c + 2d)(3c - 2d)$

21. $(5y - 4)(4 + 5y)$ **22.** $(x^2 + y^2)(x^2 + y^2)$

23. $(x^2 - y^2)(x^2 + y^2)$ **24.** $(x^2 - y^2)(x^2 - y^2)$

—— Name with a decimal numeral. Use your pencils to write only the answer.

25. $(20 + 1)(20 - 1)$ **26.** $(30 + 1)(30 - 1)$

27. $(100 + 2)(100 - 2)$ **28.** $(50 + 4)(50 - 4)$

29. $(10 + 5)(10 - 5)$ **30.** $(1000 + 1)(1000 - 1)$

31. $18 \cdot 22$ **32.** $101 \cdot 99$

33. $51 \cdot 49$ **34.** $51 \cdot 29$

—— Find the area of the region bounded by the red closed curve.

35.   **36.**

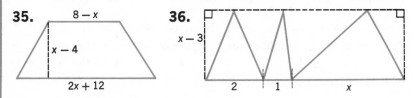

B —— Name as a polynomial over the real numbers.

37. $(3\sqrt{2}x - \sqrt{5})(3\sqrt{2}x + \sqrt{5})$

38. $(2^{\frac{1}{2}}a - 3 \cdot 2^{\frac{1}{2}}b)(2^{\frac{1}{2}}a + 3 \cdot 2^{\frac{1}{2}}b)$

39. $(2^{\frac{1}{3}}m - 5)(2^{\frac{1}{3}}m + 5)$

40. $[3 \cdot (-6)^{\frac{1}{3}}m - 5][3 \cdot (-6)^{\frac{1}{3}}m + 5]$

41. $[(x + \sqrt{2}) + 5][(x + \sqrt{2}) - 5]$

42. $[5 - (2x + \sqrt{5})][5 + (2x + \sqrt{5})]$

43. Can you find a pattern in the equations at the right for multiplying a number ending in 5 by a number 10 greater?

$$15 \times 25 = 375$$
$$35 \times 45 = 1575$$
$$85 \times 95 = 8075$$
$$55 \times 65 = 3575$$

Verify that the answers are correct by naming the factors as the product of $a + b$ and $a - b$, for example, $15 \times 25 = (20 - 5)(20 + 5)$. Can you explain now why the rule works?

Let t be the total number of tens in the greater number and 5 the number of units. What is the number? What is the smaller number? Find their product to prove your rule.

7–7 Factors of Numbers

Since $35 = 7 \cdot 5$ is true, 7 is a **factor** of 35 and also 5 is a factor of 35. In general, if $c = a \cdot b$ is true, then a is a factor of c, and b is a factor of c.

Below are some of the ways that 18 can be named as the product of two factors.

Whole-number factors	Integral factors	Rational-number factors
$18 = 1(18)$	$18 = -1(-18)$	$18 = \frac{1}{2}(36)$
$18 = 2(9)$	$18 = 1(18)$	$18 = \frac{1}{10}(180)$
$18 = 3(6)$	$18 = -2(-9)$	$18 = 10(1.8)$
$18 = 6(3)$	$18 = 2(9)$	$18 = -100(-0.18)$
$18 = 9(2)$	$18 = -3(-6)$	$18 = \frac{18}{7}(\frac{7}{1})$
$18 = 18(1)$	$18 = 3(6)$	$18 = \frac{1}{6}(108)$

The set of factors from the first column is $\{1, 18, 2, 9, 3, 6\}$. Can you find any whole-number factor of 18 not in the set?

Can you find any integral factor of 18 not in the following set of factors from the second column?

$$\{-1, -18, 1, 18, -2, -9, 2, 9, -3, -6, 3, 6\}$$

Is the set of integral factors of 18 finite or is it infinite?

The rational-number factors of 18 that are in the third column form the following set.

$$\{\tfrac{1}{2}, 36, \tfrac{1}{10}, 180, 10, 1.8, -100, -0.18, \tfrac{18}{7}, \tfrac{7}{1}, \tfrac{1}{6}, 108\}$$

Can you think of rational factors of 18 that are not in the set? Is the set of rational factors of 18 finite or infinite?

When you are asked to find the factors of a number, you must know whether you are to find the whole-number, integral, rational, or real factors. For example, $\frac{1}{2}$ has no whole-number factors, but it has an infinite number of rational or real factors. The number 17 is prime because its only whole-number factors are 1 and 17, but it would not be correct to say that a prime number has exactly two factors. You must specify that there are exactly two whole-number factors.

When a whole number is named as the product of prime-number factors or powers of prime factors, the number is expressed in **prime-factorization form**. The examples at the top of the next page show how a whole number can be named in prime-factorization form.

	METHOD I	METHOD II

$$\text{METHOD I} \qquad\qquad \text{METHOD II}$$
$$250 = 25 \cdot 10 \qquad\qquad 250 = 2 \cdot 125$$
$$= 5 \cdot 5 \cdot 2 \cdot 5 \qquad\qquad = 2 \cdot 5 \cdot 5 \cdot 5$$
$$= 2 \cdot 5^3 \qquad\qquad = 2 \cdot 5^3$$

Begin with any pair of whole-number factors greater than 1 and continue factoring until you have all primes. Then you have the prime-factorization form.

There is only one prime factorization for each composite whole number disregarding the order of the factors (recall that a **composite number** is any whole number greater than 1 that is not prime). This is the **unique factorization theorem.**

For negative numbers, the number is named as the product of -1 and the prime factors to get the prime-factorization form.

$$-125 = -1(125)$$
$$= -1(5 \cdot 5 \cdot 5)$$
$$= -1(5^3)$$

Exercises

A —— What whole-number factor makes each sentence true?

1. $36 = 9x$ **2.** $18 = 3y$ **3.** $100 = 2m$

4. $75 = 5a$ **5.** $m \cdot m = 49$ **6.** $a \cdot 100 = 100$

—— What rational-number factor makes each sentence true?

7. $\frac{1}{2}x = 10$ **8.** $(-3)x = 10$ **9.** $x \cdot x = 25$

10. $\frac{2}{3}x = \frac{5}{7}$ **11.** $\frac{1}{7}x = \frac{9}{15}$ **12.** $2\frac{1}{3}y = 6\frac{1}{9}$

—— What integral factor, if any, makes each sentence true?

13. $-2m = 36$ **14.** $7y = -56$ **15.** $-3a = -30$

16. $12a = -60$ **17.** $5a = 26$ **18.** $-17m = 17$

19. $-56q = 280$ **20.** $-7m = 0$ **21.** $3t = -204$

—— Name each number in prime-factorization form.

22. 36	**23.** 18	**24.** 21	**25.** 15	**26.** 42
27. 32	**28.** 45	**29.** 49	**30.** 9	**31.** 25
32. 28	**33.** 33	**34.** 44	**35.** 56	**36.** 396
37. 425	**38.** 500	**39.** 625	**40.** 1000	**41.** 960

B —— What real-number factor makes each sentence true?

42. $y\sqrt{5} = 5$ **43.** $16 = m \cdot 2$ **44.** $30 = x\sqrt{5}$

45. $8\frac{1}{2}r = 8$ **46.** $7\frac{1}{2}y = -7$ **47.** $4\frac{1}{2}t = 6$

48. $a\sqrt{3} = 9$ **49.** $v\sqrt[3]{5} = 5$ **50.** $k\sqrt[4]{2} = 2$

7–8　Monomial Factors of Polynomials

When you used the distributive postulate to find products, you wrote $a(b + c) = ab + ac$. You can also use the distributive postulate for factoring by using the symmetric property of equality, $ab + ac = a(b + c)$. The polynomial $ab + ac$ has the factors a and $b + c$. A factor such as a is a **common monomial factor** in the terms ab and ac. Look at these examples.

Finding products	Finding factors
$a(b + c) = ab + ac$	$ab + ac = a(b + c)$
$6(x + y) = 6x + 6y$	$6x + 6y = 6(x + y)$
$a(b + c + d) = ab + ac + ad$	$ab + ac + ad = a(b + c + d)$
$5x(3x^2-4x-1) = 15x^3-20x^2-5x$	$15x^3-20x^2-5x = 5x(3x^2-4x-1)$

In $6x + 6y$, 6 is the common monomial factor, and $x + y$ is the other factor. Notice that you usually do not factor the number when you are factoring a polynomial. You do not need to write $6x + 6y$ as $2 \cdot 3(x + y)$.

When you factor polynomials over the integers, it is customary to name the given polynomial as the product of two polynomials over the integers. You would not factor $6x + 6y$ as $12\left(\frac{x}{2} + \frac{y}{2}\right)$. If a polynomial does not have a polynomial factor over the integers, except 1, it is a **prime polynomial** with respect to the integers. For example, $6x + 5y$ is prime with respect to the integers and would not be factored as $5(\frac{6}{5}x + y)$.

Exercises

A —— One monomial factor of each polynomial is written, but one or more terms of the other factor have been left out. Write the complete second factor.

1. $3x + 6y = 3(\underline{\ ?\ } + 2y)$　　　　**2.** $4n - 2 = 2(2n - \underline{\ ?\ })$

3. $3b^2 - 24b = 3b(\underline{\ ?\ } - 8)$　　　**4.** $15ab^2 - 3b^2 = 3b^2(\underline{\ ?\ } - \underline{\ ?\ })$

5. $-3ax + 6ay = -3a(\underline{\ ?\ } - \underline{\ ?\ })$　　**6.** $p^2 - p = p(\underline{\ ?\ } - \underline{\ ?\ })$

7. $8y - 24 = 8(y - \underline{\ ?\ })$　　　　**8.** $8x^2y^2 - xy^2 = xy^2(\underline{\ ?\ } - \underline{\ ?\ })$

9. $x^2 - 3x^2y = x^2(\underline{\ ?\ } - \underline{\ ?\ })$　　**10.** $6a^2b - 3ab^2 = 3ab(\underline{\ ?\ } - \underline{\ ?\ })$

11. $3x^2 - 6xy + 9y = 3(\underline{\ ?\ } - \underline{\ ?\ } + \underline{\ ?\ })$

12. $-xy + 6x^2y - 4xy = -xy(\underline{\ ?\ } - \underline{\ ?\ } + \underline{\ ?\ })$

13. $8x + 8y + 2xy = 2(\underline{\ ?\ } + \underline{\ ?\ } + \underline{\ ?\ })$

14. $-5x^2 - 10y^2 = -5(\underline{\ ?\ } + \underline{\ ?\ })$

15. $4xy - 2x - 3x^3y = x(\underline{\ ?\ } - \underline{\ ?\ } - \underline{\ ?\ })$

—— One factor is given for each polynomial. Write the other factor. Check your factors by multiplying by inspection.

16. $5x + 20 = \underline{\ ?\ }(x + 4)$ **17.** $12y - 4 = \underline{\ ?\ }(3y - 1)$

18. $16m - 4m^2 = \underline{\ ?\ }(4 - m)$ **19.** $400x - x^2 = \underline{\ ?\ }(400 - x)$

20. $16x^2 - 2x = 2x(\underline{\ ?\ } - \underline{\ ?\ })$ **21.** $4ab - b = b(\underline{\ ?\ } - \underline{\ ?\ })$

22. $4ab + b = b(\underline{\ ?\ } + \underline{\ ?\ })$ **23.** $25x^2 - 20y^2 = \underline{\ ?\ }(5x^2 - 4y^2)$

24. $2mn - n = n(\underline{\ ?\ } - \underline{\ ?\ })$ **25.** $7x + 49xy = 7x(\underline{\ ?\ } + \underline{\ ?\ })$

26. $1000x^3 - x = x(\underline{\ ?\ } - \underline{\ ?\ })$ **27.** $a^3 + 2a^2b = a(\underline{\ ?\ } + \underline{\ ?\ } + \underline{\ ?\ })$

28. $8x^2 - 28x - 4 = \underline{\ ?\ }(2x^2 - 7x - 1)$

29. $5m - 10mn - 15 = \underline{\ ?\ }(m - 2mn - 3)$

30. $4x^3 + 6x^2 - 2x = 2x(\underline{\ ?\ } + \underline{\ ?\ } - \underline{\ ?\ })$

—— Factor the following polynomials over the integers. One factor should be the most inclusive factor common to all terms.

Example 1. $3x + 3y$

The most inclusive factor common to both terms is 3.

$$3x + 3y = 3(x + y)$$

Example 2. $7x^3 - 21x$

The most inclusive factor common to both terms is $7x$.

$$7x^3 - 21x = 7x(x^2 - 3)$$

Note that $7x^3 - 21x$, $7x$, and $x^2 - 3$ are all polynomials over the integers.

31. $7x + 7y$ **32.** $3a + 9b$ **33.** $8x - 4y$

34. $ax + bx$ **35.** $3x - am$ **36.** $9x^2 - 6y^2$

37. $4c + ac + bc$ **38.** $ay + by + 3y$ **39.** $d^2 + 2d + ad$

40. $ax - ay + a^2$ **41.** $5x - 10y + 15z^2$ **42.** $5m + 10m^2 + m^3$

43. $2\pi r^2 + 2\pi rh$ **44.** $a^2b + ab^2 + a^3b^3$ **45.** $4a^2 + 12ab + 4b^2$

B —— Some of the following polynomials have monomial factors over the integers. Factor those that have common monomial factors, and write *Prime polynomial* for those that do not.

46. $3a + b$ **47.** $7a^2b - 7ab$

48. $12n^2 - 4 + 16n$ **49.** $8x^2 - 3y^2$

50. $36x^2 - 18xy$ **51.** $14x^2 + 7xy + 21y^2$

52. $7n^2 - 8nm + 3n^2$

53. $9ab + a^2 + 2b^2$

54. $39a^3 - 52ab^2 + 65ac^2$

55. $27x^4 + 3x^3 + 9ax$

56. $9s - 13s^2 + 5t$

57. $25xy - 50xz + 100x$

58. $4x^2 - 8x + 6$

59. $3x^2 + 6xy - 2x^3$

60. $a^3 + 3a^2b + 3ab^2$

61. $14 - 42p + 7$

62. $3ab^2 - ab + 2a^2$

63. $8x^2 - 12xy - 16xz$

64. $ay^2 + ab + 3a$

65. $3x^3 - 15x^2 - 6x$

66. $8a^3 - 4ax^2 - 12a^2x^2$

67. $3a^2 + 4a^3 - 5a^4b$

68. $18ab^3c - 36a^2bc^3$

69. $4x^2y - 12xyz + 8xz^2$

7–9 Factoring the Difference of Two Squares

In a previous section, you found a pattern that led to the following products.

$$(a + b)(a - b) = a^2 - b^2$$
$$(4x + y)(4x - y) = 16x^2 - y^2$$
$$(5x - 3y)(5x + 3y) = 25x^2 - 9y^2$$

Explain why the polynomial form in each of these illustrations is called the difference of two squares.

You can reverse this pattern by the symmetric property of equality to find a pattern for factoring the difference of two squares.

Since the first term of the difference of two squares is the square of some expression, the first term of each factor must be the square root of the first square. Similarly, the second term of each factor is the square root of the second square. One factor must have + between the terms, and the other must have −, eliminating the possibility of a middle term in the polynomial.

EXAMPLE. Factor $25x^2 - 36y^2$.

① This is a difference of two squares, so you find the square root of the first term. $\qquad (5x \quad)(5x \quad)$

② Next, you find the square root of the second term. $\qquad (5x \quad 6y)(5x \quad 6y)$

③ Now fill in the signs. One has a plus sign, the other has a minus sign. Although it does not matter which comes first, you must have one of each.

$(5x + 6y)(5x - 6y)$
or
$(5x - 6y)(5x + 6y)$

Can the *sum* of two squares, say $a^2 + b^2$, be factored in the same manner? Rewrite $a^2 + b^2$ as $a^2 - (-b^2)$. Following the pattern for the difference of two squares, the factors would be $(a + \sqrt{-b^2})$ and $(a - \sqrt{-b^2})$. But b^2 is a positive number, so $-b^2$ is negative. Since a negative number does not have a real square root, $-b^2$ is not a real number. The *sum of two squares cannot be factored* over the set of real numbers.

Now try these

—— Factor each of the following polynomials.

1. $x^2 - 16$ **2.** $4r^2 - 1$ **3.** $9 - y^2$ **4.** $\dfrac{m^2}{4} - \dfrac{1}{4}$

Answers: **1.** $(x - 4)(x + 4)$ **2.** $(2r - 1)(2r + 1)$ **3.** $(3 - y)(3 + y)$
4. $\left(\dfrac{m}{2} - \dfrac{1}{2}\right)\left(\dfrac{m}{2} + \dfrac{1}{2}\right)$

Exercises

A —— Factor each of the following polynomials over the integers. Write *Prime polynomial* for each that cannot be factored over the integers.

1. $y^2 - 9$ **2.** $x^2 - 4$ **3.** $x^2 - 25$
4. $y^2 - 36$ **5.** $4x^2 - 9$ **6.** $9x^2 - 4$
7. $16y^2 - 36$ **8.** $-64 + 4x^2$ **9.** $x^2y^2 - a^2$
10. $y^6 - 36$ **11.** $9x^4y^2 - b^2$ **12.** $1 - 81y^2$
13. $x^2y^2 - z^2$ **14.** $-25 + 4x^2y^2$ **15.** $x^2 + y^2$
16. $x^2 - y^4$ **17.** $4x^2 + 16y^2$ **18.** $81x^2 - 9y^2$

—— Factor each polynomial over the rational numbers.

19. $\frac{1}{9}x^2 - 16$ **20.** $\frac{25}{36}a^2 - b^2$ **21.** $\frac{4}{9}x^2 - \frac{25}{36}y^2$
22. $\frac{121}{9}r^2 - s^2$ **23.** $-9 + x^2$ **24.** $-\frac{1}{16} + r^2$
25. $-25 + \frac{1}{64}b^2$ **26.** $\dfrac{a^2}{9} - \dfrac{b^4}{16}$ **27.** $\dfrac{4t^2}{49} - \dfrac{v^4}{81}$

28. The figure at the right shows a large square whose side is a units. Within the large square is a small square (in any position) whose side is b units. What is the area of the large square? What is the area of the small square? What is the area of the shaded surface between the two squares? Factor the expression for the shaded area.

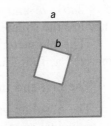

29. A small circle whose radius is r units is drawn within a large circle whose radius is R units. What is the area of the large circle? What is the area of the shaded part? Factor the expression for the shaded area.

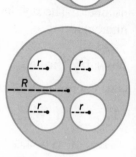

30. If four circular holes (radius r) are cut in a large circular plate of radius R, what is the area of the remaining surface in terms of R and r? Factor the expression for the shaded area.

B — Factor each polynomial over the real numbers.

Example. $x^2 - 5 = (x + \sqrt{5})(x - \sqrt{5})$

31. $y^2 - 7$ **32.** $x^2 - 11$ **33.** $a^2 - 27$

34. $x^2 - 50$ **35.** $36 - m^2$ **36.** $27 - r^2$

37. $150 - q^2$ **38.** $1 - 2x^2$ **39.** $t^2 - 5v^2$

— Factor each polynomial over the integers. (*Hint:* In Exercise 40, think of $a + b$ as one number x.)

40. $(a + b)^2 - c^2$ **41.** $c^2 - (a + b)^2$

42. $(r + s)^2 - t^2$ **43.** $(r + s)^2 - (t + u)^2$

44. $(x - a)^2 - (y - b)^2$ **45.** $4(x - a)^2 - 9(y + b)^2$

7–10   Factoring a Perfect Square Trinomial

A **perfect square trinomial** is the square of a binomial. Thus, $a^2 + 2ab + b^2$ and $a^2 - 2ab + b^2$ are perfect square trinomials because they are the squares of $a + b$ and $a - b$, respectively.

The characteristics of a perfect square trinomial may be summarized as follows.

① The first and third terms are perfect squares.

② The absolute value of the middle term is twice the product of the principal square roots of the first and third terms.

Having recognized a perfect square trinomial, you find its two **binomial factors** by reversing the process of squaring the binomial. The square root of the first term of the trinomial is the first term of the binomial factors. A square root of the third term of the trinomial is the second term of the binomial factors. The sign between the terms is determined by the signs of the trinomial. When the signs of the trinomial are all +, the sign in the binomial factor is +. When the signs of the terms alternate in the order +, −, +, the sign in the binomial is −.

EXAMPLE. Factor $4x^2 + 12x + 9$.

Note that the given polynomial follows the pattern described above for a perfect square trinomial. The terms $4x^2$ and 9 are perfect squares; $|12x|$ is equal to $2 \cdot \sqrt{4x^2} \cdot \sqrt{9}$. The first term of the trinomial is $4x^2$, so the square root of $4x^2$, or $2x$, is the first term of the binomial factor. The square root of the last term of the trinomial, 9, is 3. The signs are +, +, +, so the sign in the binomial factor is also +.

$$(2x \quad)(2x \quad)$$
$$(2x \quad 3)(2x \quad 3)$$
$$(2x + 3)(2x + 3)$$
$$\text{or}$$
$$(2x + 3)^2$$

Examine the following table for other examples.

Perfect square trinomial	Factors		Factored expression
$x^2 + 2xy + y^2$	$x + y$	$x + y$	$(x + y)^2$
$x^2 - 2xy + y^2$	$x - y$	$x - y$	$(x - y)^2$
$4x^2 - 12x + 9$	$2x - 3$	$2x - 3$	$(2x - 3)^2$
$x^4 + 2x^2y^2 + y^4$	$x^2 + y^2$	$x^2 + y^2$	$(x^2 + y^2)^2$

Exercises

A —— Each of the following trinomials is a perfect square. Write each one as the square of a binomial. One term of the binomial is written for you.

1. $a^2 + 4ab + 4b^2 = (a + \underline{?})^2$

2. $x^2 + 2xy + y^2 = (\underline{?} + y)^2$

3. $4x^2 - 4x + 1 = (2x - \underline{?})^2$

4. $b^2 - 8bc + 16c^2 = (b - \underline{?})^2$

5. $s^2 + 6st + 9t^2 = (s + \underline{?})^2$

6. $n^2 - 12n + 36 = (\underline{?} - 6)^2$

7. $4x^2 + 20x + 25 = (2x + \underline{?})^2$

8. $64x^2 - 16xy + y^2 = (\underline{?} - y)^2$

9. $25 - 10y + y^2 = (\underline{?} - y)^2$ **10.** $9a^2 - 24a + 16 = (\underline{?} - 4)^2$
11. $1 + 8b + 16b^2 = (\underline{?} + 4b)^2$ **12.** $a^2 - 6ab + 9b^2 = (\underline{?} - 3b)^2$

—— Replace ● with + or − to make the square of the binomial equal the trinomial.

13. $n^2 + 14n + 49 = (n ● 7)^2$ **14.** $x^2 - 16x + 64 = (x ● 8)^2$
15. $x^2 - 10x + 25 = (x ● 5)^2$ **16.** $p^2 - 10pq + 25q^2 = (p ● 5q)^2$
17. $a^2 + 8a + 16 = (a ● 4)^2$ **18.** $n^2 - 12n + 36 = (n ● 6)^2$
19. $a^2 - 16a + 64 = (a ● 8)^2$ **20.** $4x^2 - 12x + 9 = (2x ● 3)^2$
21. $b^2 - 6b + 9 = (b ● 3)^2$ **22.** $9 + 12x + 4x^2 = (3 ● 2x)^2$

—— Write each of these perfect square trinomials as the square of a binomial.   Check by squaring the binomial mentally.

23. $x^2 + 6x + 9$ **24.** $x^2 - 6x + 9$
25. $4x^2 - 12xy + 9y^2$ **26.** $4x^2 + 12xy + 9y^2$
27. $1 + 8x + 16x^2$ **28.** $1 - 8x + 16x^2$
29. $4x^2 - 4x + 1$ **30.** $4x^2 + 4x + 1$
31. $9y^2 + 12y + 4$ **32.** $9y^2 - 12y + 4$
33. $4a^2 - 4a + 1$ **34.** $4a^2 + 4a + 1$
35. $49a^2 - 84a + 36$ **36.** $4m^2 - 12m + 9$
37. $x^2 - 18x + 81$ **38.** $a^2 + 14a + 49$
39. $1 - 6b + 9b^2$ **40.** $4 - 20b + 25b^2$

B —— Factor over the integers.

Example. $(x^2 + 2xy + y^2) - z^2 = (x + y)^2 - z^2$
$$= (x + y - z)(x + y + z)$$

41. $(a^2 + 2ab + b^2) - c^2$ **42.** $c^2 - (a^2 + 2ab + b^2)$
43. $(x^2 - 2xy + y^2) - 9$ **44.** $16 - (x^2 - 2xy + y^2)$
45. $a^2 - 9 + 2ab + b^2$ (*Hint:* First rearrange the terms.)
46. $x^2 - 16 - 2xy + y^2$ **47.** $(x + y)^2 - (a^2 + 2ab + b^2)$

C —— Factor over the real numbers.

Example. $m^2 - 2\sqrt{11}m + 11 = (m - \sqrt{11})(m - \sqrt{11})$, or $(m - \sqrt{11})^2$

48. $a^2 + 2\sqrt{2}a + 2$ **49.** $x^2 - (y^2 + 2\sqrt{2}y + 2)$
50. $x^2 - 2\sqrt{3}x + 3$ **51.** $(x^2 - 2\sqrt{5}x + 5) - (y^2 + 2\sqrt{7}y + 7)$

52. In factoring the difference of two squares, what happens if you choose the negative square root of the first term?   Write $(-a + b)(-a - b)$ in polynomial form.

53. Note that $(-a + b) = -(a - b)$ is true and $(-a - b) = -(a + b)$ is true. Can you explain the result of Exercise 52 using this idea?

54. In factoring a perfect square trinomial, what happens if you choose the negative square root of the first term? Is $(-a + b)^2$ equivalent to $(a + b)^2$? Is $(-a - b)^2$ equivalent to $(a + b)^2$?

—— Factor each of the following in two ways.

55. $x^2 + 16x + 64$ **56.** $4t^2 - 49$ **57.** $36v^2 - 12v + 1$

7–11 Factoring $x^2 + (a + b)x + ab$

Consider the product of $x + a$ and $x + b$, where a and b are any real numbers.

$$(x + a)(x + b) = x^2 + (a + b)x + ab$$

Reversing the equation above by the symmetric property of equality, you can see that trinomials of the form $x^2 + (a + b)x + ab$ can be factored by finding two factors of the constant term whose sum is the numerical coefficient of the middle term, and adding them to x.

EXAMPLE 1. Factor $x^2 + 5x + 6$.

The set of factors of 6 is $\{1, 2, 3, 6\}$. Thus, the constant term could be $6 \cdot 1$ or $2 \cdot 3$.

Of these, the sum of one pair must give the coefficient of the middle term, 5. The sum of 2 and 3 is 5. Therefore, 2 and 3 are the second terms of the binomials.

$$(x \quad)(x \quad)$$
$$(x \quad 2)(x \quad 3)$$

Since the trinomial is of the form **+, +, +,** the sign in each binomial factor is +.

$$(x + 2)(x + 3)$$

EXAMPLE 2. Factor $x^2 - 5x - 24$.

The integral factors of -24 form the set

$$\{1, -1, 2, -2, 3, -3, 4, -4, 6, -6, 8, -8, 12, -12, 24, -24\}.$$

You do not need to write out the set. Of the factors of -24, the only pair whose product is -24 and whose sum is -5 is -8 and 3. These are the second terms of the binomial factors.

$$(x \quad)(x \quad)$$
$$(x + (-8))(x + 3)$$
$$(x - 8)(x + 3)$$

Explain why the signs in the binomials will be + and – whenever the sign of the last term of the trinomial is –.

In the following table you may examine further examples of factoring expressions of the form $x^2 + (a + b)x + ab$.

Trinomial	a, b	Factors		Factored expression
$x^2 + 3x + 2$	2, 1	$x + 1$	$x + 2$	$(x + 1)(x + 2)$
$x^2 + x - 30$	6, -5	$x + 6$	$x - 5$	$(x + 6)(x - 5)$
$x^2 - x - 30$	-6, 5	$x - 6$	$x + 5$	$(x - 6)(x + 5)$
$x^2 - 11x + 30$	-6, -5	$x - 6$	$x - 5$	$(x - 6)(x - 5)$

If the signs of a trinomial are $+$, $-$, $+$, in that order, what can you say about the signs in the binomial factors?

Some trinomials may be factored over the integers and some may not. For example, $x^2 - 2x - 24$ may be factored over the integers, but $x^2 + 3x + 1$ is prime with respect to the integers.

Now try these

—— For each of the following, what two integers will have the first number as their sum and the second number as their product?

1. 7, 12   **2.** −5, 6   **3.** 5, −24   **4.** −6, 5

5. −6, 9   **6.** −2, −15   **7.** −9, 18   **8.** 4, −32

9. −4, −32   **10.** −1, −72   **11.** 1, −72   **12.** −13, 36

Answers: **1.** 3, 4   **2.** −2, −3   **3.** −3, 8   **4.** −5, −1   **5.** −3, −3   **6.** −5, 3
     7. −3, −6   **8.** −4, 8   **9.** 4, −8   **10.** 8, −9   **11.** −8, 9   **12.** −4, −9

Exercises

A —— Factor each of the following expressions.

1. $x^2 + 7x + 12$ **2.** $x^2 - 5x + 6$

3. $x^2 + 5x - 24$ **4.** $x^2 - 6x + 5$

5. $x^2 - 6x + 5$ **6.** $x^2 - 2x - 15$

7. $x^2 - 4x - 32$ **8.** $x^2 - 13x + 36$

9. $x^2 + 4x - 32$ **10.** $x^2 - 9x + 18$

11. $x^2 + x - 72$ **12.** $x^2 - x - 72$

13. $x^2 + 10x + 21$ **14.** $x^2 - 6x + 8$

15. $x^2 + 14x + 48$ **16.** $x^2 - 8x + 15$

17. $x^2 + 6x + 8$ **18.** $x^2 + 10x + 16$

19. $x^2 + 2x - 8$ **20.** $x^2 - 5x - 14$

21. $y^2 + 9y + 18$ **22.** $y^2 - 17y + 66$

23. $x^2 + 2x - 15$ **24.** $y^2 - y - 156$

25. $x^2 + x - 56$ **26.** $y^2 + 6y - 72$
27. $3 - 4t + t^2$ **28.** $20 + 12v + v^2$
29. $-30 + 13w + w^2$ **30.** $51 - 20k + k^2$

B —— The following are the areas of rectangular regions expressed in terms of x, where x is an integer. If the length and width of each rectangle are also integers, find the dimensions in terms of x.

31. $x^2 - 169$ **32.** $x^2 + 13x + 12$
33. $x^2 - 13x + 12$ **34.** $x^2 - 4x + 4$

—— For each of the following, first factor out a common monomial, then factor the remaining trinomial into its binomial factors.

Example. $2x^2 - 10x + 12 = 2(x^2 - 5x + 6) = 2(x - 2)(x - 3)$

35. $3x^2 + 6x - 24$ **36.** $4x^2 - 32x + 60$
37. $2x^2 + 12x - 80$ **38.** $5y^2 - 45y - 110$
39. $2t^2 - 28t + 98$ **40.** $3x^3 - 33x^2 + 84x$

C **41.** For each of Exercises 31–34, determine the dimensions of the smallest rectangle that meets the other conditions.

7–12   Factoring $ax^2 + bx + c$

To factor a trinomial completely is to obtain any common monomial factors and the binomial factors (if the trinomial is not prime). For example, $2x^2 + 10x + 12$ may be factored as $(2x + 6)(x + 2)$ or as $(x + 3)(2x + 4)$, but it is only factored completely as $2(x + 3)(x + 2)$.

A trinomial such as $2x^2 + 7x + 5$ has no common monomial factor, and it is not in any of the forms discussed earlier. Yet it is not prime over the integers. In this case the first terms of the binomial factors must be $2x$ and x to produce a product of $2x^2$. The last terms must be 5 and 1 to produce a product of 5. Since the form is $+$, $+$, $+$, the sign in each binomial will be $+$. But it is not finished yet, because there are two different possible arrangements and only one of them is correct. The product of the correct factors should give a middle term of $7x$.

$(2x \quad)(x \quad)$

Only one of
$(2x + 1)(x + 5)$
or
$(2x + 5)(x + 1)$

$$1 \cdot x + 2x \cdot 5 = 11x$$
$$5 \cdot x + 2x \cdot 1 = 7x$$

Hence, $2x^2 + 7x + 5$ is factored completely as $(2x + 5)(x + 1)$.

In the case just given, the choices were limited, but often the problem involves several more choices. Skill in factoring expressions of the form $ax^2 + bx + c$ comes through thinking about each problem logically and through obtaining a lot of practice. The following examples will help.

EXAMPLE 1. Factor $8x^2 - 35x + 12$.

The first term can be factored into $8x$ and x or into $4x$ and $2x$. Notice that -35, the numerical coefficient of the middle term, is odd. This means that you will need some odd coefficients in the binomials to give two numbers whose sum will be an odd number. So start with $8x$ and x.

Since the pattern is $+, -, +$, both binomials will have $-$.

$(8x \quad)(x \quad)$
$(8x - \quad)(x - \quad)$

Possible pairs of factors for 12 are 1 and 12, 2 and 6, and 3 and 4. You can rule out 2 and 6 because they are both even. In fact, of the four combinations shown at the right, you can rule out the two in which odd numbers are multiplied by even numbers because you need an odd number in the middle term.

Only one of
$(8x - 1)(x - 12)$
$(8x - 12)(x - 1)$
$(8x - 3)(x - 4)$
$(8x - 4)(x - 3)$

Of the last possibilities, it is clear that $8x \cdot 12$ will give too large a middle term, so the logical answer is $(8x - 3)(x - 4)$. Check by multiplying.

Only one of
$(8x - 1)(x - 12)$
$(8x - 3)(x - 4)$

$(8x - 3)(x - 4)$

EXAMPLE 2. Factor $8x^2 + 10x - 3$.

The case is somewhat different. The pattern is $+, +, -$, so the signs in the binomials will be $+$ and $-$. It is usually best to put the signs in last when that happens. Since 3 has only odd factors and the middle term is even, $8x^2$ must be factored into $4x$ and $2x$. The factors of 3 are just 1 and 3. When these are tried, for $(4x \quad 1)(2x \quad 3)$, the products of the inner and outer terms will be $+2x$ and $-12x$ or $-2x$ and $+12x$. The other possibility gives $+6x$ and $-4x$ or $-6x$ and $+4x$. For the sum to be $+10x$, the choice must be $+12x$ and $-2x$ so the factored form of $8x^2 + 10x - 3$ is $(4x - 1)(2x + 3)$. Check by multiplying.

$(4x \quad)(2x \quad)$

Only one of
$(4x \quad 1)(2x \quad 3)$
or
$(4x \quad 3)(2x \quad 1)$

$(4x - 1)(2x + 3)$

When you are eliminating possibilities, you can do the work described here "in your head." With practice, you can soon learn which binomial factors are most likely for a given trinomial.

Now try these

Exercises

A —— Fill in the missing term or terms in the complete factorizations of the following trinomials.

1. $5x^2 + 9x - 18 = (5x - 6)(x + \underline{?})$

2. $4a^2 + 26a - 14 = 2(2a - \underline{?})(a + 7)$

3. $18n^2 + 21n - 4 = (6n - \underline{?})(3n + 4)$

4. $14x^2 - 13x - 12 = (7x + 4)(\underline{?} - 3)$

5. $40n^2 + n - 6 = (\underline{?} - 3)(\underline{?} + 2)$

6. $2a^2 + 7ab - 15b^2 = (2a - \underline{?})(a + \underline{?})$

7. $5a^2 + 2a - 7 = (5a + \underline{?})(a - \underline{?})$

8. $-3x^2 - 3x + 216 = -3(x + \underline{?})(x - \underline{?})$

9. $5(x^2 - 3x - 18) = 5(x - 6)(x + \underline{?})$

10. $3(2x^2 - 7x - 15) = 3(2x + \underline{?})(x - \underline{?})$

—— Factor completely each of the following trinomials.

11. $2x^2 + 11x + 4$ **12.** $3x^2 + 11x + 10$

13. $18y^2 + 6y - 4$ **14.** $15y^2 - y - 2$

15. $6y^2 - 17y + 12$ **16.** $42x^2 + 10x - 12$

17. $6x^2 + 5x - 4$ **18.** $9x^2 + 6x - 8$

19. $5x^2 - 16x + 3$ **20.** $8y^2 - 2y - 1$

21. $3y^2 + 4y - 7$ **22.** $x^2 - 4x - 32$

B —— Factor completely each of the following trinomials.

23. $8x^2 - 10xy + 3y^2$ **24.** $14x^2 - 57xy - 27y^2$

25. $18 - 9y - 35y^2$ **26.** $-21x^2 - 3x - 8$

27. $6x^2 + 21x + 18$ **28.** $40c^2 + 39cd - 40d^2$

29. $12x^2 - 29xy + 14y^2$ **30.** $56x^2 + 15x - 56$

31. $16a^2 + 56ab + 49b^2$ **32.** $3x^2 - 8xy - 3y^2$

33. $15x^4 - 10x^3 - 25x^2$ **34.** $18x^2 - 57x + 35$

35. $30s^2 + 39s - 9$ **36.** $4l^2 - 16l + 16$

7–13   Identifying Common Binomial Factors

Suppose you had to factor $a(b + c) + b(b + c)$. The binomial $(b + c)$ is a common factor of two terms. Think of $(b + c)$ as x.

$$a(b + c) + b(b + c) = ax + bx$$

Apply the distributive property.

$$ax + bx = (a + b)x$$

Therefore, $a(b + c) + b(b + c) = (a + b)(b + c)$ is true.

EXAMPLE 1. Factor $ax - xy - ac + cy$.

$$ax - xy - ac + cy = xa - xy - ca + cy$$

Apply distributive property. $= x(a - y) - c(a - y)$

Can you see why $-c$ is factored out of the last two expressions? Now let $(a - y)$ be k.

$$x(a - y) - c(a - y) = xk - ck, \text{ or } (x - c)k$$

Then go back to the original expression.

$$ax - xy - ac + cy = (x - c)(a - y)$$

EXAMPLE 2. Factor $4x - xy - 12 + 3y$.

$$\begin{aligned}
4x - xy - 12 + 3y &= 4x - yx - 12 + 3y \\
&= x(4 - y) - 3(4 - y) \\
&= (x - 3)(4 - y)
\end{aligned}$$

Notice that it makes no difference if you group in another way.

$$\begin{aligned}
4x - 12 - xy + 3y &= 4(x - 3) - y(x - 3) \\
&= (4 - y)(x - 3)
\end{aligned}$$

Exercises

A —— Factor each of the following expressions.

1. $d(e + f) + g(e + f)$ **2.** $x(b - c) - d(b - c)$

3. $a(b + 4) - c(b + 4)$ **4.** $x^2(a + b) + y^2(b + a)$

5. $rv + rw - sv - sw$ **6.** $km - kn - lm + ln$

7. $a(x + y) + b(x + y) + c(x + y)$ **8.** $ab + 5a - bc - 5c$

9. $10 + 2t - 5s - st$ **10.** $x^2(a + 3) - y^2(a + 3)$

11. $54g - 12gh - 45 + 10h$ **12.** $2xw - 6x + w - 3$

B — Factor each of the following expressions.

13. $\frac{2}{3}bc - \frac{14}{3}b + c - 7$ **14.** $\frac{3}{8}xy + \frac{3}{2}x - 8 - 2y$

15. $\sqrt{6} - 2s\sqrt{3} + r\sqrt{2} - 2sr$ **16.** $\frac{ac}{10} + \frac{3a}{5} - c - 6$

17. $2\sqrt{10} - 12ab - 3a\sqrt{2} + 8b\sqrt{5}$ **18.** $\frac{21}{5}x - \frac{3}{20}xy - 42 + \frac{3}{2}y$

Self-Test on Special Products and Factoring

The aim of this test is to see if you can correctly factor and multiply many different types of polynomials over the integers.

Cover *Column B*, factor the expression in *Column A*, and then check the answer in *Column B*.

Then cover *Column A*, multiply as indicated in *Column B*, and then check the answer in *Column A*.

Column A	Column B
1. $2a^2 + 14a + 24$	**1.** $2(a + 3)(a + 4)$
2. $5y^2 - 45$	**2.** $5(y + 3)(y - 3)$
3. $st^2 - st - 20s$	**3.** $s(t - 5)(t + 4)$
4. $7a^2 - 14a - 105$	**4.** $7(a - 5)(a + 3)$
5. $3x^2 + 12x + 45$	**5.** $3(x^2 + 4x + 15)$
6. $x^2 - 6x + 9$	**6.** $(x - 3)^2$
7. $6t^2 - 15t^3$	**7.** $3t^2(2 - 5t)$
8. $2 - 128t^2$	**8.** $2(1 + 8t)(1 - 8t)$
9. $ab^2 - ab - 72a$	**9.** $a(b - 9)(b + 8)$
10. $n^2 + 5n + 7$	**10.** Prime.
11. $3a^2 + a - 2$	**11.** $(3a - 2)(a + 1)$
12. $2a^2 - 5a + 3$	**12.** $(2a - 3)(a - 1)$
13. $a^2 + 25$	**13.** Prime.
14. $q^2 - 12q - 28$	**14.** $(q - 14)(q + 2)$
15. $2x^2 - 14x + 24$	**15.** $2(x - 3)(x - 4)$
16. $y^4 - 6y^2 - 16$	**16.** $(y^2 - 8)(y^2 + 2)$
17. $49c^2 + 70c + 25$	**17.** $(7c + 5)^2$
18. $5a^2 - 80$	**18.** $5(a + 4)(a - 4)$
19. $x^3 - x$	**19.** $x(x + 1)(x - 1)$
20. $a^4 - 16$	**20.** $(a + 2)(a - 2)(a^2 + 4)$
21. $1 - 4y^2$	**21.** $(1 + 2y)(1 - 2y)$
22. $x^2 + 4y^2$	**22.** Prime.
23. $3a^2 - a - 2$	**23.** $(3a + 2)(a - 1)$

7–14   Using Special Products to Solve Equations

Some equations are easily solved by using the special products you have learned because much of the work can be done mentally. Study the following examples.

EXAMPLE 1.   Solve $(x - 3)^2 = x^2 - 7x + 12$.

①   Square $(x - 3)^2$. $x^2 - 6x + 9 = x^2 - 7x + 12$

②   Add $-x^2 + 7x$. $x + 9 = 12$

③   Add -9. $x = 3$

$$\text{Check}\quad (3 - 3)^2 = 3^2 - 7(3) + 12$$
$$0 = 9 - 21 + 12$$
$$0 = 0$$

Solution set: $\{3\}$

EXAMPLE 2.   Solve $2(x - 5) - (x - 2)(x + 3) = 5 - (x - 4)^2$.

①   Multiply. $2x - 10 - (x^2 + x - 6) = 5 - (x^2 - 8x + 16)$

②   Apply distributive property. $2x - 10 - x^2 - x + 6 = 5 - x^2 + 8x - 16$

③   Combine like terms. $-x^2 + x - 4 = -x^2 + 8x - 11$

④   Add $x^2 - 8x + 4$. $-7x = -7$
$$x = 1$$

Solution set: $\{1\}$

Notice that before the distributive property is applied, the product of the binomials is kept in parentheses to help avoid errors in signs.
Check the solution of Example 2.

Exercises

A ▬ Solve for x.

1. $(x - 3)^2 = x^2 - 5x - 8$ **2.** $(2x - 3)^2 = 4x^2 - 6x - 3$

3. $(x + 5)^2 = x^2$ **4.** $(x + 3)^2 - (x + 5)^2 = 10$

5. $4 + (x - 9)^2 = 7 + x^2$ **6.** $(5x - 6)^2 = (4x + 1)^2 + 9x^2$

7. $(2x - 1)(x + 1) = x^2 + (x + 2)(x + 3)$

8. $3(x + 12) - (x - 4)^2 = 4 - x^2$

9. $(4x - 1)^2 - (2x + 3)^2 = (3x + 2)(4x - 5)$

10. $3(2x - 7) - (2x - 3)(2x - 1) = 5 - (2x - 5)^2$

11. $(3x - 4)^2 - (3x - 4)(2x + 5) = 5(3x - 4) + 3(x^2 - 12)$

12. $(15 - 8x)(15 + 8x) = 10 - (8x - 5)^2$

13. $(3x - 4)(3x + 4) = 9x^2 + 6x - 4$

14. $2(x + 2)(x - 3) + 3x^2 = 5x^2 + 2$

15. $(2x + 3)(2x - 3) + 5x = 4x^2 + 1$

B **16.** Find the number such that the square of 4 more than the number is the same as the square of the number.

17. Find two consecutive positive integers such that the difference of their squares is 51.

18. Find two consecutive odd positive integers such that the difference of their squares is 32.

19. Find two consecutive even positive integers such that the difference of their squares is 68.

7–15 Division of Polynomials

To be able to factor polynomials such as $x^3 - x^2 - 2x + 8$, it is helpful to be able to divide one polynomial by another. If you divide $x^3 - x^2 - 2x + 8$ by $x + 2$, for example, and get a polynomial for a quotient (it comes out "even"), then $x + 2$ and the quotient are factors of the original polynomial.

EXAMPLE 1. Divide $x^3 - x^2 - 2x + 8$ by $x + 2$ to see if $x + 2$ is a factor.

① Ask, By what must I multiply x in the divisor to get x^3 in the dividend? The answer is x^2. Write x^2 above x^3.

$$
\begin{array}{r}
x^2 \\
x + 2 \overline{)\, x^3 - x^2 - 2x + 8}
\end{array}
$$

② Multiply $x + 2$ by x^2, writing the answer below $x^3 - x^2 - 2x + 8$, like terms under one another. Then subtract as in ordinary division.

$$
\begin{array}{r}
x^2 \\
x + 2 \overline{)\, x^3 - x^2 - 2x + 8} \\
x^2(x+2) \rightarrow x^3 + 2x^2 \\
\hline
-3x^2 - 2x + 8
\end{array}
$$

③ Ask, By what must I multiply x in the divisor to get $-3x^2$? Write $-3x$ in the quotient.

$$
\begin{array}{r}
x^2 - 3x \\
x + 2 \overline{)\, x^3 - x^2 - 2x + 8} \\
x^3 + 2x^2 \\
\hline
-3x^2 - 2x + 8
\end{array}
$$

④ Multiply $x + 2$ by $-3x$, and subtract.

$$
-3x(x+2) \longrightarrow
\begin{array}{r}
-3x^2 - 6x \\
\hline
4x + 8
\end{array}
$$

(*Continued on next page.*)

POLYNOMIALS AND FACTORING   341

⑤ Ask, By what must I multiply x to get $4x$? Write 4 in the quotient, multiply $x + 2$ by 4, and subtract.

$$\begin{array}{r} x^2 - 3x + 4 \\ x + 2 \overline{\smash{\big)}\, x^3 - x^2 - 2x + 8} \\ \underline{x^3 + 2x^2} \\ 3x^2 - 2x + 8 \\ \underline{-3x^2 - 6x} \\ +4x + 8 \\ \underline{4x + 8} \\ 0 \end{array}$$

$4(x + 2) \longrightarrow 4x + 8$

Since the remainder is 0, $x + 2$ is a factor. Also, $x^2 - 3x + 4$ is a factor.

$$x^3 - x^2 - 2x + 8 = (x + 2)(x^2 - 3x + 4)$$

Check the answer by multiplying.

EXAMPLE 2. Is $(3a^2 - 7ab + 4b^2) \div (a - 2b)$ a polynomial?

Divide.

$$\begin{array}{r} 3a - b \\ a - 2b \overline{\smash{\big)}\, 3a^2 - 7ab + 4b^2} \\ 3a(a - 2b) \rightarrow 3a^2 - 6ab \\ \underline{-ab + 4b^2} \\ -b(a - 2b) \longrightarrow -ab + 2b^2 \\ \underline{2b^2} \end{array}$$

Since the remainder is not zero, the *quotient is not a polynomial.* Is the division correct? To check, the polynomial $3a^2 - 7ab + 4b^2$ should be equal to the product of $a - 2b$ and $3a - b$ plus the remainder, $2b^2$. Is the following true?

$$(a - 2b)(3a - b) + 2b^2 \stackrel{?}{=} 3a^2 - 7ab + 4b^2$$
$$(3a^2 - 7ab + 2b^2) + 2b^2 = 3a^2 - 7ab + 4b^2$$

Then the division is correct.

Exercises

A ▬▬ Divide to see if the second polynomial is a factor of the first.

1. $c^2 - 3c - 28$, $c - 7$ **2.** $6x^2 - 28x + 30$, $2x - 6$

3. $6x^3 + x^2 - 19x + 6$, $2x - 3$ **4.** $x^2 - 12x + 40$, $x - 6$

5. $a^3 + 6a^2 - 2a - 12$, $a^2 - 2$ **6.** $6a^2 - 13a + 7$, $2a - 3$

7. $x^2 + xy - 3y^2$, $x - y$ **8.** $p^2 - p - 32$, $p + 5$

9. $3a^3 + 8a^2b + 7ab^3 + 5b^3$, $3a + 2b$ **10.** $a^3 - 5a^2 + 2a + 8$, $a - 2$

B ── Divide the first polynomial by the second.

Example. $(x^3 + 6x + 20) \div (x + 2)$

There is no x^2 term. But when you write the dividend, there must be a term for each power of the variable. Thus, write the x^2 term with 0 as the coefficient and divide as usual.

$$
\begin{array}{r}
x^2 - 2x + 10 \\
x + 2 \overline{\smash{\big)}\ x^3 + 0x^2 + 6x + 20} \\
\underline{x^3 + 2x^2} \\
-2x^2 + 6x + 20 \\
\underline{-2x^2 - 4x} \\
10x + 20 \\
\underline{10x + 20} \\
0
\end{array}
$$

11. $x^3 + 4x - 3$, $x + 5$
12. $x^3 - 6x^2 + 1$, $x + 2$
13. $x^3 - 2x - 21$, $x - 3$
14. $x^3 - 8$, $x - 2$
15. $p^3 - 125$, $p - 5$
16. $x^4 + 4x^2 + 16$, $x^2 + 2x + 4$

More Challenging Problems

1. Find the square of $(a + b + c)$.

── Factor each polynomial.

2. $9a^4 - 12a^2b^2 + 4b^4$
3. $(x + y)^2 + (x + y) - 6$
4. $a^2 - 2ab + b^2 - b^2 + 2bc - c^2$
5. $(x^2 + 6x + 9) - (y - 1)^2$
6. $(m^2 + 2mn + n^2) - (9x^2 - 6xy + y^2)$
7. $4a^2 + 4ab + b^2 - 9c^2 + 12cd - 4d^2$
8. $x^2(2x - 3) - 2x(2x - 3) + (2x - 3)$

── One factor of each polynomial is written. Find the other factor by division.

9. $x^3 + y^3 = (x + y)(\underline{\ ?\ })$
10. $x^3 - y^3 = (x - y)(\underline{\ ?\ })$
11. $8a^3 - 27b^3 = (2a - 3b)(\underline{\ ?\ })$
12. $x^5 + 1 = (x + 1)(\underline{\ ?\ })$
13. $x^6 - y^3 = (x^2)^3 - y^3 = (x^2 - y)(\underline{\ ?\ })$

── Factor.

14. $a^3 + b^3$
15. $a^3 - b^3$
16. $125x^3 - 8y^3$
17. $64m^3 + 216n^3$
18. $a^6 - b^3$
19. $64a^6 + 27b^3$
20. $m^2 + n^2 + p^2 + 2mn + 2mp + 2np$ (*Hint:* See Exercise 1.)
21. Find the greatest common factor of $a^4 - 1$, $a^5 + a^3$, and $a^6 + 1$.

CHAPTER REVIEW

1. Know the meaning of and be able to use each of the following words or phrases. The number shown after each word or phrase indicates where it is introduced, in case you need to review.

polynomial in one variable (*308*)
term (*309*)
monomial (*309*)
binomial (*309*)
trinomial (*309*)
factor (*324*)

prime-factorization form (*324*)
unique factorization theorem (*325*)
common monomial factor (*326*)
prime polynomial (*326*)
perfect square trinomial (*330*)
binomial factor (*331*)

—— The diagram shows the relationship of the various sets of polynomials. To which set does each of the following belong?

2. $5x^2 - 2x + 3$
3. $x^2 + 7x + 10$
4. $8x^2 - 5x + 3$
5. $7x^2 - \frac{2}{5}x + \frac{3}{4}$

> Polynomials over the real numbers
>
> > Polynomials over the rational numbers
> >
> > > Polynomials over the integers
> > >
> > > > Polynomials over the nonnegative integers

6. Write an example of a
   a. monomial.   **b.** binomial.   **c.** trinomial.

—— Write the additive inverse for each of the following.

7. $-3x^2 + 5$ **8.** $2x^2 - 4x + 3$ **9.** $\frac{x^2}{3} + \frac{2}{3}x - 6$

10. Add $3x^2 - 2x + 5$ and $-7x^2 + 4x - 2$.
11. Add $8x^3 - 2$ and $-5x^2 - 3x + 6$.
12. Subtract $9x^2 - 2x + 7$ from $-2x^2 + 6x - 1$.
13. From $-19x^2 + 3$, take $15x^2 - 2x + 7$.
14. Find the sum of $3x - 7$, $5x^2 + 6$, and $-2x^2 + 3x$.
15. Subtract $17x - 2$ from $5x^2 - 2x + 8$.
16. What postulate has been used here?

$$-3x(2x + 7) = -3x(2x) + (-3x)(7)$$

Complete the multiplication.

____ Rename each product in polynomial form, by inspection if you can.

17. $(m^2 - 3)(m^2 + 4)$

18. $\left(\frac{n}{3} + 5\right)\left(\frac{2n}{3} - 4\right)$

19. $(7 - a)^2$

20. $(2x + 11)^2$

21. $(b - \frac{2}{3})(b + \frac{2}{3})$

22. $(3y^2 - 2)(3y^2 + 2)$

23. Why is $8x^2 - 3xy + y^2$ a prime polynomial? Why is $-18ab^2 + 13b$ not a prime polynomial?

24. Are the factors of a perfect square trinomial equal? Explain.

____ Given the following combinations of signs for a trinomial, what will the signs be in each of the binomial factors?

25. +, +, +   **26.** +, −, +   **27.** +, +, −   **28.** +, −, −

____ Completely factor the following.

29. $4x^2 - y^2$

30. $x^2 + 3x + 2$

31. $10x^2 + 7x - 12$

32. $16x^2 + 8xy + y^2$

33. Divide $21x^2 + 25x - 4$ by $3x + 4$.

CHAPTER TEST

____ Perform the operation indicated.

1. $(3x + 2)(5x - 9)$

2. $(8x - 3)(8x - 3)$

3. $(11x - 4)(11x + 4)$

4. $(5m + n)^2$

5. $2x(x^4 + 2x^3 + x^2 - 4x - 1)$

6. $(6r^3 - r + 10) - (3r^3 + 2r^2 - 5)$

7. $(2s^2 + st + 4t^2) + (5st - 6t^2 - s^2)$

8. $(x^2 + 3x - 54) \div (x + 9)$

9. $(6ab + 2bc) + (-3ac + 2ab) - (7bc - 2ac)$

10. $(x^3 + 3x^2 + 3x + 1) \div (x + 1)$

____ Completely factor the following polynomials.

11. $3x^4 - 2x^3 - 5x^2$

12. $4x^2 - y^2$

13. $x^2 + 10x + 25$

14. $25x^2y^2 - 36z^2$

15. $a(b + c) + d(b + c)$

16. $x^2 - 11x + 24$

17. $x^2 - 12x + 35$

18. $8mn - 3 + 12n - 2m$

____ Solve for x.

19. $(x + 3)(x - 5) = x^2 + 17x - 9$

20. $(2x + 1)^2 = 4(x^2 - 2x + 1)$

Diophantine Solutions of $a^2 + b^2 = c^2$

The Pythagorean theorem states that the relationship among the sides of a right triangle is $a^2 + b^2 = c^2$. The triple of numbers $a = 3$, $b = 4$, and $c = 5$ satisfies this equation; that is, $3^2 + 4^2 = 5^2$ is true. Now one may assign any value to a and any value to b and then compute c. For example, if a is 1 and b is 2, then c is $\sqrt{5}$. And even though $\sqrt{5}$ is an irrational number, it is an acceptable solution.

The Greek mathematician Diophantus (about A.D. 250) was very interested in solution sets for algebraic equations, but he insisted that the solutions be natural numbers. Algebraic equations whose solutions are restricted to the natural numbers have come to be called Diophantine equations. Actually, at the time of Pythagoras, 750 years before Diophantus, formulas were known that would produce natural-number solutions to the Pythagorean theorem. Check the following formulas by substituting them in the Pythagorean theorem.

$$a = n^2 - 1 \qquad\qquad b = 2n \qquad\qquad c = n^2 + 1$$

You know from working with the Pythagorean theorem that if a is 5 and b is 12, then c will be 13. But you will notice that $a = n^2 - 1$ never produces $a = 5$ no matter what natural number is assigned to n. Hence, the above formulas given by Pythagoras did not produce all the possible natural-number triples that satisfy $a^2 + b^2 = c^2$.

Euclid (about 300 B.C.) proposed the following formulas, which can be shown to produce all possible Pythagorean triples of the Diophantine type. In the formulas, p, q, and r may be assigned any natural numbers, provided that q is greater than r.

$$a = p(q^2 - r^2) \qquad\qquad b = p(2qr) \qquad\qquad c = p(q^2 + r^2)$$

Check to see that the formulas satisfy the Pythagorean theorem. Then if q is 3, r is 2, and p is 1, $p(q^2 - r^2)$ is $1(9 - 4)$, or a is 5. Are b and c equal to 12 and 13, respectively?

Exercises

1. Use the Pythagorean formulas to produce values for a, b, and c for several choices of n.

2. Let $p = 2$, $q = 4$, and $r = 3$. Determine the corresponding Diophantine triple from Euclid's formulas.

3. Can you find values of p, q, and r in Euclid's formulas for Diophantine triples that give the same triples as some n in Pythagoras' formulas?

4. Since p, q, and r may be any natural number ($q > r$), can you see how to derive Pythagoras' equations for a, b, and c from Euclid's equations? (*Hint:* See what happens if you let p be 1 and r be 1.)

THE GROWTH OF MATHEMATICS

Mathematics in the Eastern World

Although there is a long history of mathematical accomplishment in China, including a good system of numeration and a very early statement of the Pythagorean theorem, very little of Chinese thought reached the Western world directly. India, on the other hand, because of its geographical position was an important intermediary of ideas. It received ideas from the troops of Babylonians and Greeks who invaded the country, and the whole world benefited from Indian contributions to arithmetic and algebra carried to Europe by the Arabs.

The most important contributions of the Indians occurred between the sixth and thirteenth centuries A.D. Early in that period, they began to use zero as a number, giving rules for addition, subtraction, multiplication, and division, with zero included. (At least one Indian mathematician made the common mistake of thinking division of a number by zero gives the original number.)

Unlike the Greeks, Indian mathematicians did not worry about proof or logical niceties. They just proceeded to calculate on the assumption that no problems would develop. As a consequence, Indian mathematicians were the first to use negative numbers with freedom. They made no distinction in practice between rational and irrational numbers, so they developed sound rules for calculating with radicals.

In algebra, the Indians knew Diophantus' work and went considerably beyond it. They could solve all equations involving squares of the variable, and they worked with Diophantine equations involving two variables. Much of their later work in mathematics was applied to astronomy, and it involved quite modern methods of calculation.

x	−3	−2	−1	0	1	2	3
y	9	4	1	0	1	4	9

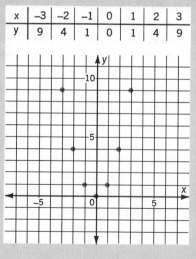

CHAPTER 8

QUADRATIC FUNCTIONS AND EQUATIONS

The curves pictured on the opposite page each illustrate one of the most interesting and useful of geometric curves, the parabola.

● The beam of a headlight is in the form of a cone. In the lower left drawing, the image of the car headlight on a wall perpendicular to the light is a circle. The image on the surface parallel to the light is a parabola.

● The path traveled by a basketball is a parabola. The boy throwing the ball in the center photograph is aiming for the hoop and has to determine a particular parabola if he wants the ball to go through the hoop. What is the path followed by a bullet or a rocket? What mathematics would you use to make a direct hit?

● If you completed the curve formed by the spray of water from the fountain, what curve would you have?

● The equation $y = x^2$ defines a quadratic function. The table above the graph at the lower right shows seven pairs of numbers that make $y = x^2$ true. How are the points arranged on the graph? Which number pair has a zero value for y? What is the x value for this pair?

● At the upper left is the graph for $y = x^2 - 4$ ($x \in$ R). The graph is in the form of what curve? What are the coordinates of the points at which the curve crosses the x axis? What are the coordinates of the lowest point? Can you tell what the highest point would be? What is the difference between this curve and the curve formed by the path of the basketball? What curve would result if you graphed $y = x^2 + 4$? How would you compare the two curves? How is the part of the curve on the right side of the y axis like the part of the curve on the left side of the y axis? How are they different?

8–1　Quadratic Functions and the Parabola

The following equations define quadratic functions.

   a. $y = x^2$ b. $y = -3x^2$

   c. $y = (\tfrac{1}{2}x - 3)^2$ d. $y = x^2 - 5x + 6$

> **Definition**　A quadratic function is the set of ordered pairs (x, y) such that $y = ax^2 + bx + c$ is true with $a \in R$, $b \in R$, $c \in R$, and $a \neq 0$.

Note that the definition above is designed to exclude the linear functions. Since a cannot be zero by definition, $y = 0x^2 - 5x + 6$ is a linear function and cannot be classified as a quadratic.

How can you be sure that **c** above is a quadratic function? Any equation of the form $y = ax^2 + bx + c$ is a **quadratic equation** and defines a quadratic function. By multiplying $(\tfrac{1}{2}x - 3)$ by $(\tfrac{1}{2}x - 3)$, you get the equation $y = \tfrac{1}{4}x^2 - 3x + 9$, a quadratic equation. What are a, b, and c in **a–d**?

A quadratic equation with all three terms is **a complete quadratic equation.** Quadratic equations of the form $y = ax^2$, $y = ax^2 + bx$, $y = ax^2 + c$ are **incomplete quadratic equations.**

Graph for $y = ax^2 + bx + c$

To graph a quadratic function, find ordered pairs that satisfy the defining equation and then locate the points whose coordinates are these ordered pairs.

EXAMPLE.　Graph $y = x^2 - 2x - 3$, where the domain is R.

①　For convenience, choose integers for x and find the corresponding number for y:

x	-2	-1	0	1	2	3	4
y	5	0	-3	-4	-3	0	5

Locate a point for each ordered pair. Then the graph, so far, consists of seven points, as shown in Figure 1.

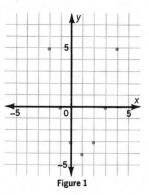

Figure 1

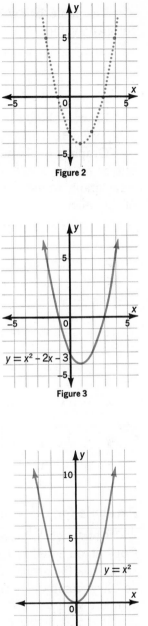

② If you choose rational numbers between the integers, you get many more
points, some of which are shown in
Figure 2.

③ If x is any real number, there will be
no holes in the graph.

Sketch a smooth curve over the
points to form the graph. The graph
for a quadratic equation is a **parabola.**
The arrows (Figure 3) show that the
parabola continues upward on both
sides.

Figure 2

Examine Figure 3. What happens
to y as x increases from 1 to 4? from 4
to 100? What happens to y as x increases
from -100 to -2? from -2 to 1? Since
y decreases on one side of the parabola
and increases on the other, there must be
a turning point. The turning point is
easily seen on the graph as the lowest, or
minimum, point, in this case, $(1, -4)$.
The turning point is called the **vertex** of
the parabola.

$y = x^2 - 2x - 3$

Figure 3

Parabola for $y = ax^2$

At the right is the graph for $y = x^2$,
$x \in R$. Copy the graph on graph paper.
On the same axes, draw the graph of
$y = 2x^2, x \in R$. Now compare the graphs.
Is the graph for $y = 2x^2$ wider or narrower
than the one for $y = x^2$? On the same
axes, draw the graph for $y = 3x^2$. How
do they compare?

If $a > 1$, how does the graph for
$y = ax^2$ compare with the graph for
$y = x^2$?

Do you think the graph for $y = \frac{1}{2}x^2$
is outside or inside the graph for $y = x^2$?
Draw it on the axes to be sure.

$y = x^2$

*Be sure to label your graphs clearly and keep them to use for future
exercises.*

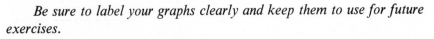

The table below shows corresponding numbers for x^2 and $-x^2$ for given values of x.

x	-3	-2	-1	0	1	2	3
x^2	9	4	1	0	1	4	9
$-x^2$	-9	-4	-1	0	-1	-4	-9

From looking at the table, what would you guess is the graph for $y = -x^2$? How does it compare with that for $y = x^2$?

Graph $y = x^2$ and $y = -x^2$ on the same axes. If you placed a mirror on the x axis so that the graph of $y = x^2$ were reflected in it, what graph would the reflection be? One graph is the mirror image of the other.

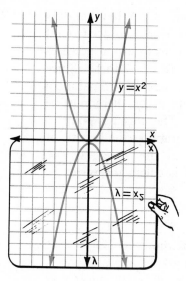

Parabola for $y = x^2 + c$

At the right is the graph of $y = x^2 + 4$. Copy it on graph paper. On the same axes, draw the graph of $y = x^2 - 4$. How do they compare? How do they both compare with $y = x^2$?

If $c > 0$, is the graph for $y = x^2 + c$ above or below that for $y = x^2$?

If $c < 0$, is the graph for $y = x^2 + c$ above or below that for $y = x^2$?

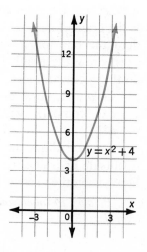

352   CHAPTER 8

Parabola for $y = (x + a)^2$

At the right is the graph for $y = (x - 2)^2$, or $y = x^2 - 4x + 4$. Is it to the right or to the left of the graph for $y = x^2$? On graph paper, draw the graph for $y = (x + 2)^2$. How does it compare with the graph for $y = x^2$?

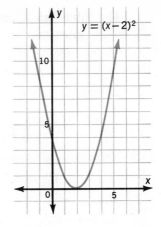

$y = (x - 2)^2$

Now try these

—— Is each function defined below a quadratic function? Write *Yes* or *No*. If *Yes*, give the numbers for a, b, and c; if *No*, tell why not.

1. $y = x^2$

2. $y = 3x^2 - \sqrt{7}x + 6$

3. $y = 0x^2 - 7x + 9$

4. $y - 3x^2 = 0$

5. $6x^2 - 7x + 6 - y = 0$

6. $y = (x - 3)^2$

7. $y = 4(x - 3)^2$

8. $y = (x - 2)(x - 3)$

9. $y = x^3 + x^2 + 7x$

10. $y = (x - 2)(x + 2)(x - 1)$

Answers: **1.** Yes; $a = 1, b = 0, c = 0$ **2.** Yes; $a = 3, b = -\sqrt{7}, c = 6$
3. No; $a = 0$ **4.** Yes ($y = 3x^2$); $a = 3, b = 0, c = 0$ **5.** Yes
($y = 6x^2 - 7x + 6$); $a = 6, b = -7, c = 6$ **6.** Yes ($y = x^2 - 6x + 9$);
$a = 1, b = -6, c = 9$ **7.** Yes ($y = 4x^2 - 24x + 36$); $a = 4, b = -24$,
$c = 36$ **8.** Yes ($y = x^2 - 5x + 6$); $a = 1, b = -5, c = 6$ **9.** No;
there is an x^3 term.   **10.** No; $y = x^3 - x^2 - 4x + 4$ has an x^3 term.

Checkpoint

What is a quadratic function? How does it differ from a linear function? Describe the graph for a quadratic function.

Exercises

A   **1.** Complete the table and graph $y = (x - 2)(x + 3)$ if the domain is the set of real numbers.

x	-5	-4	-3	-2	-1	0	1	2	3	4
y	14	6	0	?	?	?	?	?	?	?

Graph the following ($x \in$ R) by locating points using the x values given and then sketching a smooth curve.

2. $y = x^2 + 7$, $\{-4, -3, -2, -1, 0, 1, 2, 3, 4\}$

3. $y = x^2 - 6$, $\{-4, -3, -2, -1, 0, 1, 2, 3, 4\}$

4. $y = -x^2$, $\{-3\frac{1}{2}, -2\frac{1}{2}, -1\frac{1}{2}, 0, 1\frac{1}{2}, 2\frac{1}{2}, 3\frac{1}{2}\}$

5. $y = (x + 3)^2$, $\{-7, -6, -5, -4, -3, -2, -1, 0, 1\}$

6. $y = -x^2 - 4$, $\{-3, -2, -1, 0, 1, 2, 3\}$

7. $y = x^2 - x - 12$, $\{-3, -2, -1, 0, \frac{1}{2}, 1, 2, 3, 4\}$

Graph if the domain is R.

8. $y = 4x^2$

9. $y = -4x^2$

10. $y = x^2 - 5$

11. $y = x^2 + 5$

12. $y = (x - 1)(x + 1)$

13. $y = x^2 + 4x + 4$

B Graph the following pairs of parabolas, and tell whether or not they intersect. If they do intersect, give the coordinates of the point or points of intersection.

14. $y = x^2 + 1$, $y = -x^2 + 1$

15. $y = (x + 2)^2$, $y = (x - 2)^2$

16. $y = (x - 3)^2$, $y = -x^2 + 9$

17. $y = 5 - x^2$, $y = -x^2$

18. $y = x^2 - 2$, $y = -x^2 + 6$

Graph if the domain is R.

19. $y = 3(x - 1)(x + 2)$

20. $y = 2x^2 + 2x$

21. $y = 2x^2 - 7x - 4$

22. $y = x^2 - x - \frac{3}{4}$

C **23.** The function $y = (x - 1)(x + 2)(x - 3)$ is not quadratic. It is cubic.

a. Graph the function. Begin by using the following values for x.

$$x \in \{-4, -3, -2, -1, 0, 1, 2, 3, 4, 5\}$$

Then choose some other rational values for x to get other points. Sketch a smooth curve that contains all the points.

b. As x increases above 3, what happens to the values for y? What happens to the curve?

c. As x decreases below -2, what happens to y? What happens to the curve?

8–2   Zeros of a Function by Graphing

You have drawn the graph of a quadratic function by finding ordered pairs that satisfy the equation. Thus, you can also find ordered pairs of a function from looking at a graph.

EXAMPLE 1. Use the graph at the right to find the missing part of the following coordinates.

a. $(1, \underline{?})$ b. $(0, \underline{?})$
c. $(\underline{?}, -5)$ d. $(-1, \underline{?})$
e. $(4, \underline{?})$ f. $(\underline{?}, 0)$

To find the second number in $(1, \underline{?})$, start at 1 on the x axis. Then move vertically (in this case, down along the line $x = 1$) until you hit the curve. Looking at the y axis, y is -8 at this point; so the coordinates are $(1, -8)$.

For $(0, \underline{?})$, simply move along the y axis ($x = 0$). The point on the curve is $(0, -9)$.

For $(\underline{?}, -5)$, start at -5 on the y axis, since this time you know the y coordinate. Move horizontally until you hit the curve. There are two points on the curve: $(2, -5)$ and $(-2, -5)$.

For $(-1, \underline{?})$, the y coordinate is -8.

For $(4, \underline{?})$, the y coordinate is 7.

For $(\underline{?}, 0)$, you move along the x axis because this is the line $y = 0$. There are two points on the curve: $(3, 0)$ and $(-3, 0)$.

The point $(0, -9)$ where the curve crosses the y axis is called the **y intercept**, as it was for the graph of a line crossing the y axis. Then $(3, 0)$ and $(-3, 0)$, the points where the curve crosses the x axis, are called **x intercepts**.

Suppose a volley ball is thrown from a point 4 feet to the left of a net, and it traces the arc of the parabola $y = -x^2 + 16$. The ball is 16 feet high when it crosses the net. How high was it at the beginning of the throw? How high will it be when it hits the floor? How does the graph show this?

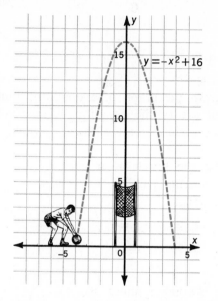

Where will the ball hit the floor? It will hit 4 units to the right of the net. If you think of a line on the floor as the x axis and the net as the y axis, you can see from the graph that the ball started at $(-4, 0)$ and will hit the floor at $(4, 0)$.

Now think of the parabola for $y = -x^2 + 16$ continuing below the x axis. The points $(-4, 0)$ and $(4, 0)$ are the intercepts of the graph. What is the value of the function, $y = -x^2 + 16$, when the x numbers of the coordinates for the intercepts are substituted in the function?

$$y = -(4)^2 + 16 \qquad y = -(-4)^2 + 16$$
$$= -16 + 16 \qquad\quad = -(16) + 16$$
$$= 0 \qquad\qquad\quad = 0$$

Finding the x number(s) that make the value of a function zero, $ax^2 + bx + c = 0$, is called finding the **zeros of a function.** As you saw in the example, this can be done by graphing to find the x intercepts.

Definition The <u>zero of a function</u> is a number for x in a set of ordered pairs of the form (x, y) such that y equals 0.

EXAMPLE 2. What are the zeros of $y = x^2 - 9$?

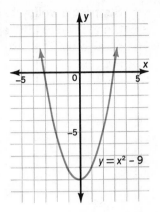

① Graph the function, as at the right.

② Find the zeros. The zeros are the numbers for x such that $0 = x^2 - 9$. From the graph, y is 0 where the curve crosses the x axis. The curve crosses at (3, 0) and (−3, 0). Hence, the zeros are 3 and −3.

Check

$$0 = 3^2 - 9 \qquad 0 = (-3)^2 - 9$$
$$0 = 9 - 9 \qquad 0 = 9 - 9$$

Exercises

A **1.** Use the graph to find the missing coordinate. If there are two answers, give both.

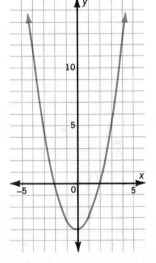

a. (0, _?_) **b.** (1, _?_)

c. (2, _?_) **d.** (3, _?_)

e. (−1, _?_) **f.** (−2, _?_)

g. (−3, _?_) **h.** (_?_, 12)

i. (_?_, 5) **j.** (_?_, −3)

k. (_?_, −4) **l.** (_?_, 0)

m. What are the zeros of the function graphed?

—— What values of x make y equal to zero for the functions graphed in Exercises 2–5? The functions are not all quadratic.

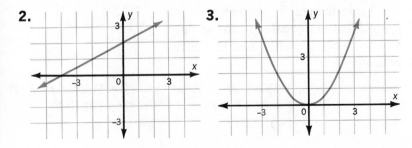

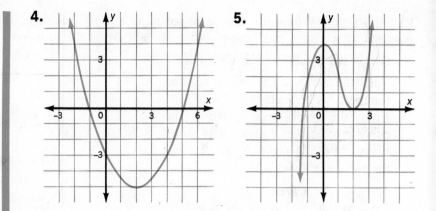

4. **5.**

— Use your graphs from Section 8–1 to find the zeros of these functions. If the graph does not cross the x axis, there is no real number for x such that y is 0. In such a case, write *No real zeros*.

6. $y = x^2$ **7.** $y = x^2 + 4$ **8.** $y = (x - 2)^2$

9. $y = x^2 + 7$ **10.** $y = x^2 - 6$ **11.** $y = (x - 2)(x + 3)$

12. $y = -x^2$ **13.** $y = (x + 3)^2$ **14.** $y = (x - 2)(x + 2)$

15. $y = 4x^2$ **16.** $y = -4x^2$ **17.** $y = (x - 4)(x + 3)$

B   **18.** Solve $x^2 - 2x - 24 = 0$ (that is, find the values for x that make the equation true) by graphing $x^2 - 2x - 24 = y$.

19. Find the zeros of $y = 2x^2 - 3x - 2$ to the nearest half.

8–3   Solving Quadratic Equations by Factoring

At the right is the graph of the function $y = x^2 + x - 6$. The polynomial $x^2 + x - 6$ can be factored as $(x + 3)(x - 2)$. Thus, $y = (x + 3)(x - 2)$ is an equivalent equation for the function.

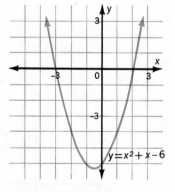

From the graph, you can see that $x = -3$ makes y equal to 0, and so does $x = 2$. This is easily checked algebraically.

$$y = (x + 3)(x - 2)$$
$$= (-3 + 3)(-3 - 2)$$
$$= 0 \cdot (-5), \text{ or } 0$$

$$y = (x + 3)(x - 2)$$
$$= (2 + 3)(2 - 2)$$
$$= 5 \cdot 0, \text{ or } 0$$

Solving $ax^2 + bx + c = 0$ $(a \neq 0)$ means to find the **solutions,** the number(s) for x that make the equation true. Putting the equation in factored form, you find the numbers that make $(x + c)(x + d) = 0$ true. You can do this by using Theorem 8–1.

Theorem 8–1 If the product of two real numbers, a and b, is zero, then $a = 0$ *or* $b = 0$ is true.

To find the solution set for $(x + c)(x + d) = 0$, use the compound sentence. It is helpful to have a symbol for *or*; $\vee$ is commonly used, and it is appropriate because it suggests $\cup$, the symbol for union.

$$(x + c = 0) \vee (x + d = 0)$$
$$(x = -c) \vee (x = -d)$$

The solution set for $x + c = 0$ is $\{-c\}$, and the solution set for $x + d = 0$ is $\{-d\}$. The solution for $(x + c = 0) \vee (x + d = 0)$ is $\{-c\} \cup \{-d\}, \{-c, -d\}$. Does this check? First try $-c$, and then $-d$.

$(x + c)(x + d) = 0$	$(x + c)(x + d) = 0$
$(-c + c)(-c + d) = 0$	$(-d + c)(-d + d) = 0$
$0 \cdot (-c + d) = 0$	$(-d + c) \cdot \quad 0 \quad = 0$
$0 = 0$	$0 = 0$

They are both true by Theorem 2–4. Now you can solve quadratic equations by factoring.

EXAMPLE 1. Solve by factoring: $a^2 - 3a - 10 = 0$.
First factor the equation and then find the solution set.

$$a^2 - 3a - 10 = 0$$
$$(a - 5)(a + 2) = 0$$
$$(a - 5 = 0) \vee (a + 2 = 0)$$
$$(a = 5) \vee (a = -2)$$

Check these solutions in the *original equation.*

Check $a = 5$.	*Check $a = -2$.*
$5^2 - (3 \cdot 5) - 10 = 0$	$(-2)^2 - (3 \cdot -2) - 10 = 0$
$25 - 15 - 10 = 0$	$4 + 6 - 10 = 0$
$25 - 25 = 0$	$10 - 10 = 0$
$0 = 0$	$0 = 0$

Solution set: $\{5, -2\}$

Remember that if the equation is not in the form $ax^2 + bx + c = 0$, you must put it in that form to get the solution set.

EXAMPLE 2. Solve $x^2 + x + 9 = x + 14$.

First make the equation equal to 0. Add $-x - 14$ to both sides.

$$
\begin{aligned}
x^2 + x + 9 &= x + 14 \\
-x - 14 &= -x - 14 \\
\hline
x^2 \qquad - 5 &= 0
\end{aligned}
$$

Then factor.

$$(x + \sqrt{5})(x - \sqrt{5}) = 0$$
$$(x + \sqrt{5} = 0) \vee (x - \sqrt{5} = 0)$$
$$(x = -\sqrt{5}) \vee (x = \sqrt{5})$$

Check $x = -\sqrt{5}$.

$$(-\sqrt{5})^2 + (-\sqrt{5}) + 9 = (-\sqrt{5}) + 14$$
$$5 + (-\sqrt{5}) + 9 = (-\sqrt{5}) + 14$$
$$(-\sqrt{5}) + 14 = (-\sqrt{5}) + 14$$

Check $x = \sqrt{5}$.

$$(\sqrt{5})^2 + \sqrt{5} + 9 = \sqrt{5} + 14$$
$$5 + \sqrt{5} + 9 = \sqrt{5} + 14$$
$$\sqrt{5} + 14 = \sqrt{5} + 14$$

Solution set: $\{-\sqrt{5}, \sqrt{5}\}$

You can see the advantage of algebraic methods. No graph would enable you to see that $-\sqrt{5}$ and $\sqrt{5}$ are zeros of $x^2 - 5 = y$.

Exercises

A — Solve by factoring. Leave any irrational numbers in radical form.

1. $x^2 - 5x - 6 = 0$ **2.** $x^2 - 5x + 6 = 0$

3. $x^2 - 3x - 10 = 0$ **4.** $x^2 = 100$

5. $n^2 = 81$ **6.** $y^2 + 7y = -12$

7. $y^2 - 8y - 9 = 0$ **8.** $a^2 - 36 = 0$

9. $c^2 - 49 = 0$ **10.** $3x^2 = 75$

11. $y^2 = 4y + 12$ **12.** $y^2 = -7y - 10$

13. $5a^2 + 3a - 2 = 0$ **14.** $3a^2 - 10a - 8 = 0$

15. $6a^2 + a - 2 = 0$ **16.** $9x^2 = 36$

17. $n^2 = 7$ **18.** $y^2 = 8$

19. $12a^2 - 6a - 6 = 0$ **20.** $3n^2 + 7 = 28$

21. $15a^2 = 13a + 20$ **22.** $4a^2 - 9 = 11$

23. $3x^2 - 2 = x^2 + 6$ **24.** $x^2 - 7 = 5 - 3x^2$

25. $24a^2 + 26a - 63 = 0$ **26.** $5x^2 - 2x = 3$

27. $5a^2 + 15 = 9a^2 - 13$ **28.** $8 - n^2 = 7n^2 - 16$

B —— Find the solution set by factoring. Irrational solutions may be left in radical form.

Example. Solve $\dfrac{n^2}{2} - \dfrac{n}{3} = \dfrac{9 - n}{3}$.

First multiply both sides by 6, the least common multiple of the denominators, to get rid of the denominators, and then simplify the equation.

$$6\left(\frac{n^2}{2}\right) - 6\left(\frac{n}{3}\right) = 6\left(\frac{9 - n}{3}\right)$$
$$3n^2 - 2n = 2(9 - n)$$
$$3n^2 - 2n = 18 - 2n$$
$$3n^2 - 18 = 0$$

Now divide both sides by 3. Then factor and find the solution set.

$$\frac{3n^2}{3} - \frac{18}{3} = \frac{0}{3}$$
$$n^2 - 6 = 0$$
$$(n + \sqrt{6})(n - \sqrt{6}) = 0$$
$$(n + \sqrt{6} = 0) \vee (n - \sqrt{6} = 0)$$
$$(n = -\sqrt{6}) \vee (n = \sqrt{6})$$

Solution set: $\{-\sqrt{6}, \sqrt{6}\}$

29. $x^2 + \dfrac{x}{15} = \dfrac{x^2 + 2}{5}$ **30.** $\dfrac{5x^2 + 1}{2} - \dfrac{2x - 3}{7} = 2$

31. $\dfrac{n^2}{3} - \dfrac{n}{2} = \dfrac{4 - 2n}{4}$ **32.** $\dfrac{n^2}{5} + \dfrac{n}{3} = \dfrac{n + 3}{3}$

33. $\dfrac{n^2}{5} + \dfrac{n}{3} + \dfrac{1}{30} = \dfrac{2n + 5}{6}$ **34.** $\dfrac{2n^2 - 1}{3} = \dfrac{1}{2}$

35. $9x^2 = 2$ **36.** $4x^2 = 3$

37. $\dfrac{x^2}{4} + 5 = \dfrac{x^2 + 2}{2}$ **38.** $\dfrac{5}{2x} = \dfrac{x}{6}$

39. $\dfrac{3x + 5}{5} = \dfrac{9 + x}{x}$ **40.** $\dfrac{n^2}{3} + \dfrac{3 - n^2}{4} = 5$

C   **41.** Prove Theorem 8–1. (*Hint:* Assume that one factor is *not* zero, and solve the equation for the other factor.)

8–4   Solving Incomplete Quadratic Equations

An incomplete quadratic such as $x^2 - 9 = 0$ can be solved by factoring.

$$x^2 - 9 = 0$$
$$(x + 3)(x - 3) = 0$$
$$(x + 3 = 0) \lor (x - 3 = 0)$$
$$(x = -3) \lor (x = 3)$$

Hence, $x^2 - 9 = 0$ is equivalent to $x = \pm 3$.

The example just given suggests that $x^2 = a$ is equivalent to $x = \pm\sqrt{a}$. It is easy to show that this is the case.

$$x^2 = a$$
$$x^2 - a = 0$$
$$(x - \sqrt{a})(x + \sqrt{a}) = 0$$
$$(x - \sqrt{a} = 0) \lor (x + \sqrt{a} = 0)$$
$$(x = \sqrt{a}) \lor (x = -\sqrt{a})$$
$$x = \pm\sqrt{a}$$

Theorem 8–2 Taking the square root of both sides of an equation produces an equivalent equation.

$$\forall x \in R \quad \forall a \in R \quad x^2 = a \text{ if and only if } x = \pm\sqrt{a}$$

This theorem may be used to solve $x^2 - 9 = 0$ in fewer steps. First rewrite as $x^2 = 9$. Take the positive and negative square root.

$$x = \pm 3$$

Solution set: $\{3, -3\}$

EXAMPLE 1. Solve $x^2 - 7 = 0$.

Add $+7$.	$x^2 = 7$
Take the square root.	$x = \pm\sqrt{7}$

Check $x = \sqrt{7}$.   *Check* $x = -\sqrt{7}$.

$$(\sqrt{7})^2 - 7 = 0 \qquad (-\sqrt{7})^2 - 7 = 0$$
$$7 - 7 = 0 \qquad\qquad 7 - 7 = 0$$

Solution set: $\{\sqrt{7}, -\sqrt{7}\}$

An incomplete quadratic equation of the form $ax^2 + bx = 0$ can be solved by factoring.

EXAMPLE 2. Solve $2x^2 - 4x = 0$.

Factor.	$2x(x - 2) = 0$
Use Theorem 8–1.	$(2x = 0) \lor (x - 2 = 0)$
	$(x = 0) \lor (x = 2)$

The solution set is $\{0, 2\}$. Check the solutions in the original equation.

Now try these

— Solve each equation.

1. $x^2 = 25$ **2.** $x^2 + x = 0$

3. $x^2 - 8 = 0$ **4.** $3x^2 = 15x$

Answers: **1.** $x = \pm 5$ **2.** $x = 0, x = -1$ **3.** $x = \pm\sqrt{8}$, or $\pm 2\sqrt{2}$
       4. $x = 0, x = 5$

Exercises

A — Give the solution set for each equation.

1. $x^2 = 16$ **2.** $y^2 - 4 = 0$

3. $l^2 - 11 = 0$ **4.** $n^2 - 7 = 12$

5. $m^2 + 2 = 3$ **6.** $7 - 2x^2 = -15$

7. $4c^2 = 36$ **8.** $3x^2 + 5 = 26$

9. $2r^2 = 200$ **10.** $2s^2 - 4s = 0$

11. $\frac{1}{2}z^2 = 32$ **12.** $x^2 + 7x = 0$

13. $x^2 - \frac{1}{2}x = 0$ **14.** $2x^2 = \frac{1}{2}$

15. $99 = b^2 - 22$ **16.** $3n^2 - n = 15 - n$

17. $4m^2 - 3 = 9$ **18.** $3y^2 + 5y = y^2$

19. $3z^2 = \frac{12}{9}$ **20.** $-2r - r^2 = 5r^2 + r$

B — Solve for x; a, b, and c are constants.

21. $x^2 = a + b$ **22.** $\frac{x^2}{a} = 1$

23. $\frac{x^2}{a} = b$ **24.** $ax^2 - 2ax = 0$

25. $4x^2 = a^2$ **26.** $\frac{ax^2}{b} = 1$

27. $\frac{ax^2}{b} = ac$ **28.** $\frac{ab^2}{x^2} = 1$

8–5 Perfect Square Trinomials

Suppose you are asked to solve $x^2 - 6x + 7 = 0$. Simple factoring cannot be used to solve this equation (Try it!), and graphing does not yield exact answers. You might apply Theorem 8–2 to give either $\sqrt{x^2 - 6x + 7} = 0$ or $\sqrt{x^2 - 6x} = \pm\sqrt{7}$, but this does not help unless you know how to find $\sqrt{x^2 - 6x + 7}$ or $\sqrt{x^2 - 6x}$ — and you do not. There is a method of solving $x^2 - 6x + 7 = 0$, however, and it does depend upon Theorem 8–2. You begin by transforming one side of the equation into a *perfect square trinomial*. That part of the solution process is the subject of this section. The completion of the solution process is given in the next section.

Recall that a perfect square trinomial over the rational numbers is the square of a binomial over the rational numbers.

Binomial				Trinomial

$$(x + 3)^2 = (x + 3)(x + 3) = x^2 + 6x + 9$$
$$(r - 5)^2 = (r - 5)(r - 5) = r^2 - 10r + 25$$
$$(y + b)^2 = (y + b)(y + b) = y^2 + 2by + b^2$$

The three binomials above consist of a variable and a constant. You can see that the first term of the trinomial is the square of the first term of the binomial.

$$x^2 \qquad r^2 \qquad y^2$$

The middle term is the variable with a coefficient. The coefficient of the middle term is twice the constant of the binomial.

$$6x = 2(3)x \qquad -10r = 2(-5)r \qquad 2by = 2(b)y$$

And the third term of the trinomial is the square of the second term of the binomial.

$$9 = (3)^2 \qquad 25 = (-5)^2 \qquad b^2 = (b)^2$$

Now suppose you are given an expression such as $x^2 - 6x$ (as in $x^2 - 6x = 7$). You should be able to supply a third term to $x^2 - 6x$ and make the expression a perfect square trinomial.

You know that the coefficient of the middle term is twice the constant of the binomial that would be squared to get the trinomial.

$$x^2 + 2(\underline{\ ?\ })x + (\underline{\ ?\ })^2 = (x + \underline{\ ?\ })^2$$

In this case the coefficient of the middle term is -6.

$$-6 = 2(\underline{\ ?\ })$$
$$-6 = 2(-3)$$

So the binomial is $(x - 3)^2$ and the last term of the trinomial would be $(-3)^2$, or 9.

$$(x - 3)^2 = x^2 + 2(-3)x + (-3)^2$$
$$= x^2 - 6x + 9$$

Then the constant of the binomial to be squared is one half the coefficient of the middle term of the perfect square trinomial, and the last term of a perfect square trinomial is the square of one half of the coefficient of the middle term, as symbolized here.

$$x^2 + bx + \left(\frac{b}{2}\right)^2$$

EXAMPLE. Complete $a^2 - 8a$ so it is a perfect square trinomial.

① The perfect square trinomial will be $a^2 - 8a + (\underline{\ ?\ })^2$.

② The coefficient of the middle term is -8. Thus, $\frac{1}{2}(-8)$ is -4.

③ The trinomial is $a^2 - 8a + (-4)^2$, or $a^2 - 8a + 16$.

Now try these

—— Supply the missing term to make each expression a perfect square trinomial.

1. $x^2 - 2x$ **2.** $x^2 + 14x$

3. $y^2 + 3y$ **4.** $z^2 - \frac{1}{3}z$

Answers: **1.** 1   **2.** 49   **3.** $\frac{9}{4}$ **4.** $\frac{1}{36}$

Exercises

A —— Find k.

1. $y^2 + (2 \cdot 7)y + k = (y + 7)^2$

2. $m^2 + (2 \cdot 9)m + k = (m + 9)^2$

3. $a^2 + 2(-5)a + k = (a - 5)^2$

4. $r^2 + (2 \cdot 9)r + k = (r + 9)^2$

5. $y^2 + 2(-\frac{1}{2})y + k = (y - \frac{1}{2})^2$

6. $x^2 + 2(-10)x + k = (x - 10)^2$

7. $x^2 + 6x + k = (x + 3)^2$

8. $y^2 + 10y + k = (y + 5)^2$

9. $x^2 - 12x + k = (x - 6)^2$

10. $m^2 - m + k = (m - \frac{1}{2})^2$

═══ Supply the third term to make each of the following expressions a perfect square trinomial. Then give the binomial that would be squared to get the trinomial.

11. $x^2 + 10x$ **12.** $y^2 - 8y$ **13.** $m^2 + 4m$

14. $a^2 + 2a$ **15.** $r^2 - r$ **16.** $x^2 + 12x$

17. $r^2 - 20r$ **18.** $a^2 + a$ **19.** $x^2 + 5x$

20. $x^2 - 11x$ **21.** $x^2 - \frac{2}{5}x$ **22.** $y^2 + 7y$

═══ For each of the following expressions, find the binomial that would be squared to give the expression as the first two terms of a perfect square trinomial.

23. $a^2 + 18a$ **24.** $y^2 - 22y$ **25.** $x^2 + 16x$

26. $x^2 - 3x$ **27.** $x^2 + \frac{4}{7}x$ **28.** $b^2 - 5b$

29. $x^2 + 8x$ **30.** $r^2 + \frac{1}{4}r$ **31.** $y^2 + \frac{1}{3}y$

32. $r^2 - 17r$ **33.** $a^2 + \frac{2}{3}a$ **34.** $x^2 - \frac{3}{4}x$

35. What must you add to $x^2 + ax$ to make it a perfect square trinomial? Then, using the addition property for equations, what would you add to both sides of $x^2 + ax = c$ to make the left side a perfect square trinomial?

═══ What number must you add to both sides of the following equation to make the left side a perfect square trinomial?

36. $x^2 + 4x = 5$ **37.** $x^2 - 8x = -15$

38. $a^2 - 5a = 16$ **39.** $s^2 + 10s = 24$

40. $x^2 + \frac{3}{4}x = -7$ **41.** $x^2 - 14x = -9$

42. $x^2 + \frac{4}{7}x = \frac{3}{7}$ **43.** $a^2 + 7a = 18$

44. To apply the method of this section to the general quadratic equation $ax^2 + bx + c = 0$, you must rewrite the equation in the form $x^2 + \frac{b}{a}x = -\frac{c}{a}$, so that the coefficient of x^2 is 1 and the constant is on the right. To do this,

① add the additive inverse of the constant term c to both sides of the equation, and

② divide both sides by a.

Performing these two steps with the equation $5x^2 - 11x + 10 = 0$, you get the following.

$$5x^2 - 11x = -10$$
$$x^2 - \tfrac{11}{5}x = -\tfrac{10}{5}$$

Now try the two steps with the equation $3x^2 + 7x - 9 = 0$.

— Change each of the following quadratic equations to the form $x^2 + \frac{b}{a}x = -\frac{c}{a}$, as in Exercise 44.

45. $7x^2 - 5x + 3 = 0$ **46.** $9x^2 - 6x = 4$

47. $8x^2 - 5x = 6$ **48.** $ax^2 = -bx - c$

49. $3x^2 + 4x = 5$ **50.** $6x^2 - 7x = -9$

51. $3x^2 + 5x + 1 = 0$ **52.** $7x^2 - 7x = 5$

8–6   Solving Quadratics by Completing the Square

The method of solving quadratic equations by **completing the square** involves making a perfect square trinomial of the left side of the equation and then using Theorem 8–2.   First, consider equations in which the coefficient of x^2 is 1.

EXAMPLE 1.   Solve $x^2 + 6x + 8 = 0$ by completing the square.

① Rewrite the equation to put on the left side only terms containing the variable.

$$x^2 + 6x + 8 - 8 = 0 - 8$$
$$x^2 + 6x = -8$$

② Make the left side of the equation a perfect square trinomial.   Remember to add the same number to both sides of the equation.

$$x^2 + 6x + (\tfrac{6}{2})^2 = -8 + (\tfrac{6}{2})^2$$
$$x^2 + 6x + 9 = -8 + 9$$
$$x^2 + 6x + 9 = 1$$

③ Factor the trinomial into its two equal binomial factors.

$$(x + 3)^2 = 1$$

④ Apply Theorem 8–2.

$$x + 3 = \pm\sqrt{1}, \text{ or } \pm 1$$

⑤ Find the two solutions.

$$(x + 3 = 1) \lor (x + 3 = -1)$$
$$(x = 1 - 3) \lor (x = -1 - 3)$$
$$(x = -2) \lor (x = -4)$$

⑥ Check in the original equation.

$$
\begin{array}{cc}
x = -2 & x = -4 \\
(-2)^2 + 6(-2) + 8 = 0 & (-4)^2 + 6(-4) + 8 = 0 \\
4 - 12 + 8 = 0 & 16 - 24 + 8 = 0 \\
-12 + 12 = 0 & -24 + 24 = 0
\end{array}
$$

Solution set: $\{-2, -4\}$

EXAMPLE 2. Solve $n^2 - 10 = 3n$.

① Rewrite the equation to put on the left side only terms containing the variable.

$$n^2 - 10 + 10 = 3n + 10$$
$$n^2 - 3n = 3n - 3n + 10$$
$$n^2 - 3n = 10$$

Follow steps ② through ⑥ as in Example 1. You should find that the solution set is $\{5, -2\}$.

Now try these

—— Find the solution set by completing the square.

1. $x^2 + 4x = 21$ **2.** $x^2 - 2x = 15$

3. $x^2 - 9 = -8x$ **4.** $x^2 + 3x = \frac{7}{4}$

Answers: **1.** $\{3, -7\}$ **2.** $\{5, -3\}$ **3.** $\{-9, 1\}$ **4.** $\{\frac{1}{2}, -3\frac{1}{2}\}$

Exercises

A —— Find the solution set by completing the square.

1. $x^2 + 4x = 12$ **2.** $x^2 + 6x = 27$

3. $n^2 - 8n = -15$ **4.** $n^2 - 2n - 8 = 0$

5. $a^2 - 6a + 8 = 0$ **6.** $x^2 + 8x = -12$

7. $a^2 + 4a = 5$ **8.** $b^2 + 10b = -16$

9. $x^2 - 14x = -40$ **10.** $x^2 - 12x = -35$

11. $x^2 - 10x = -24$ **12.** $c^2 + 2c = 15$

13. $x^2 - 16x = -60$ **14.** $x^2 - 16x = 17$

15. $a^2 - 3a = -2$ **16.** $x^2 - 7x + 12 = 0$

17. $x^2 - 7x + 10 = 0$ **18.** $x^2 - 9x = -18$

19. $a^2 - 3a = 10$ **20.** $n^2 + 6 = -5n$

21. $n^2 - 12 = n$ **22.** $x^2 - x = 6$

23. $x^2 + x = 6$ **24.** $x^2 - x = 30$

25. $y^2 + 3y = 4$ **26.** $y^2 - y = 2$

27. $p^2 + 5p = 0$ **28.** $x^2 = 3x$

B —— Solve for x by completing the square.

29. $x^2 + 2ax = b^2$ **30.** $x^2 - ax = c$

31. $x^2 - x = k$ **32.** $x^2 - 2x - 4d = 0$

33. $x^2 - \frac{1}{h}x = 3k$ **34.** $x^2 + \sqrt{b}x - b^2 = 0$

35. $x^2 + 4e^2bx - 2f = 0$ **36.** $x^2 + 3ax = \frac{4b^2}{3}$

8–7 Extension of Completing the Square

All of the quadratic equations you have solved by the method of completing the square have had 1 as the coefficient of the squared term. To use this method in solving quadratics with any number as the coefficient of the squared term, one more step is needed, as you will see in the following example.

EXAMPLE. Solve $2x^2 - 9x - 5 = 0$.

Using the multiplication property for equations, multiply both sides of the equation by the reciprocal of the coefficient of the squared term.

$$① \qquad 2x^2 - 9x - 5 = 0$$
$$(\tfrac{1}{2} \cdot 2x^2) - (\tfrac{1}{2} \cdot 9x) - (\tfrac{1}{2} \cdot 5) = (\tfrac{1}{2} \cdot 0)$$
$$1x^2 - \tfrac{9}{2}x - \tfrac{5}{2} = 0$$

Now the coefficient of the squared term is 1; proceed as before.

$$② \qquad x^2 - \tfrac{9}{2}x = \tfrac{5}{2}$$
$$③ \quad x^2 - \tfrac{9}{2}x + (\tfrac{1}{2} \cdot -\tfrac{9}{2})^2 = \tfrac{5}{2} + (\tfrac{1}{2} \cdot -\tfrac{9}{2})^2$$
$$x^2 - \tfrac{9}{2}x + \tfrac{81}{16} = \tfrac{5}{2} + \tfrac{81}{16}, \text{ or } \tfrac{121}{16}$$
$$④ \qquad (x - \tfrac{9}{4})^2 = \tfrac{121}{16}$$
$$⑤ \qquad x - \tfrac{9}{4} = \pm\sqrt{\tfrac{121}{16}}, \text{ or } \pm\tfrac{11}{4}$$
$$⑥ \quad (x - \tfrac{9}{4} = \tfrac{11}{4}) \lor (x - \tfrac{9}{4} = -\tfrac{11}{4})$$
$$(x = 5) \lor (x = -\tfrac{1}{2})$$
$$\textit{Solution set: } \{5, -\tfrac{1}{2}\}$$

Check to see that the solutions are correct.

Exercises

A — Solve the following equations by completing the square. Irrational solutions may be left in radical form.

1. $3n^2 - 2n = 1$
2. $2n^2 = n + 3$
3. $5n^2 + 2 = 11n$
4. $3x^2 - 2x = 8$
5. $2y^2 - 3y = 35$
6. $4n^2 + 4 = 17n$
7. $6p^2 - 9p = 27$
8. $2x^2 - 7x + 3 = 0$
9. $3a^2 + 8a + 5 = 0$
10. $2a^2 - 5a - 12 = 0$
11. $3x^2 - x - 2 = 0$
12. $2p^2 - 2p - 1 = 0$
13. $2a^2 + 3a = 17$
14. $3 = 6x^2 - x$

15. $1 - y = 3y^2$ **16.** $8y^2 - y = 3$

17. $2x^2 = 9x + 3$ **18.** $2x^2 - x - 2 = 0$

19. $3b^2 + 5b - 1 = 0$ **20.** $10y^2 - 41y = -4$

B —— Solve for x by completing the square.

21. $ax^2 + 2ax + a^2 = 0$ **22.** $2bx^2 + cx + 4d = 0$

23. $\sqrt{2}x^2 + ax = \dfrac{3c^2}{2}$ **24.** $g^2x^2 + \sqrt{h}x = -2l$

25. $\dfrac{1}{a}x^2 + \dfrac{1}{b}x + 2b = 0$ **26.** $ax^2 + bx + c = 0$

8–8   A Formula for Solving Quadratic Equations

By solving the general quadratic equation $ax^2 + bx + c = 0$ by the method of completing the square, you obtain two general solutions. The general solutions may then be used as formulas for finding the solutions of *any* quadratic equation.

Carefully examine the following solutions, one with numerals and the other with variables.

Solve $3x^2 - 16x + 5 = 0$.   Solve $ax^2 + bx + c = 0$.

① $x^2 - \dfrac{16}{3}x + \dfrac{5}{3} = 0$ $x^2 + \dfrac{b}{a}x + \dfrac{c}{a} = 0$

② $x^2 - \dfrac{16}{3}x = -\dfrac{5}{3}$ $x^2 + \dfrac{b}{a}x = -\dfrac{c}{a}$

③ $\left[\dfrac{1}{2}\left(-\dfrac{16}{3}\right) = -\dfrac{16}{6}; \left(-\dfrac{16}{6}\right)^2 = \dfrac{16^2}{6^2}\right]$ $\left[\dfrac{1}{2}\left(\dfrac{b}{a}\right) = \dfrac{b}{2a}; \left(\dfrac{b}{2a}\right)^2 = \dfrac{b^2}{4a^2}\right]$

$x^2 - \dfrac{16}{3}x + \dfrac{16^2}{6^2} = \dfrac{16^2}{6^2} - \dfrac{5}{3}$ $x^2 + \dfrac{b}{a}x + \dfrac{b^2}{4a^2} = \dfrac{b^2}{4a^2} - \dfrac{c}{a}$

④ $\left(x - \dfrac{16}{6}\right)^2 = \dfrac{16^2 - 60}{6^2}$ $\left(x + \dfrac{b}{2a}\right)^2 = \dfrac{b^2 - 4ac}{4a^2}$

⑤ $x - \dfrac{16}{6} = \pm\sqrt{\dfrac{16^2 - 60}{6^2}}$ $x + \dfrac{b}{2a} = \pm\sqrt{\dfrac{b^2 - 4a}{4a^2}}$

⑥ $x = +\dfrac{16}{6} \pm \dfrac{\sqrt{16^2 - 60}}{6}$ $x = -\dfrac{b}{2a} \pm \dfrac{\sqrt{b^2 - 4ac}}{2a}$

$x = \dfrac{+16 \pm \sqrt{16^2 - 60}}{6}$ $x = \dfrac{-b \pm \sqrt{b^2 - 4ac}}{2a}$

The solutions of the general quadratic equation are the following.

$$\left\{\dfrac{-b + \sqrt{b^2 - 4ac}}{2a}, \ \dfrac{-b - \sqrt{b^2 - 4ac}}{2a}\right\}$$

By using the plus-or-minus sign, you have one **quadratic formula,**
$x = \dfrac{-b \pm \sqrt{b^2 - 4ac}}{2a}$, that may be used to find the solutions of *any* quadratic equation.

EXAMPLE 1. Solve $3x^2 - 16x + 5 = 0$ by using the quadratic formula.
First you must know what a, b, and c are to use the quadratic formula.

$$a = 3 \qquad b = -16 \qquad c = 5$$

Then use the quadratic formula.

$$x = \frac{-b \pm \sqrt{b^2 - 4ac}}{2a}$$

$$x = \frac{-(-16) \pm \sqrt{(-16)^2 - 4(3)(5)}}{2(3)}$$

$$= \frac{16 \pm \sqrt{256 - 60}}{6}$$

$$= \frac{16 \pm \sqrt{196}}{6}, \text{ or } \frac{16 \pm 14}{6}$$

$$\left(x = \frac{16 + 14}{6}\right) \vee \left(x = \frac{16 - 14}{6}\right)$$

$$(x = 5) \vee (x = \tfrac{1}{3})$$

Check $x = 5$.	*Check* $x = \tfrac{1}{3}$.

$$\begin{array}{ll}
3(5)^2 - 16(5) + 5 = 0 & \qquad 3(\tfrac{1}{3})^2 - 16(\tfrac{1}{3}) + 5 = 0 \\
75 - 80 + 5 = 0 & \qquad \tfrac{3}{9} - \tfrac{16}{3} + 5 = 0 \\
-80 + 80 = 0 & \qquad -5\tfrac{1}{3} + 5\tfrac{1}{3} = 0
\end{array}$$

Solution set: $\{5, \tfrac{1}{3}\}$

EXAMPLE 2. Use the quadratic formula to solve $3x^2 + 2x - 3 = 0$.

$$a = 3 \qquad b = 2 \qquad c = -3$$

$$x = \frac{-b \pm \sqrt{b^2 - 4ac}}{2a}$$

$$x = \frac{-2 \pm \sqrt{(2)^2 - 4(3)(-3)}}{6}$$

$$x = \frac{-2 \pm \sqrt{4 + 36}}{6}, \text{ or } \frac{-2 \pm \sqrt{40}}{6}$$

Simplify the expression in the radical.

$$x = \frac{-2 \pm 2\sqrt{10}}{6}, \text{ or } -\tfrac{2}{6} \pm \tfrac{2}{6}\sqrt{10}, \text{ or } -\tfrac{1}{3} \pm \tfrac{1}{3}\sqrt{10}$$

The check is on the following page.

Check $x = -\frac{1}{3} + \frac{1}{3}\sqrt{10}$.

$$3(-\tfrac{1}{3} + \tfrac{1}{3}\sqrt{10})^2 + 2(-\tfrac{1}{3} + \tfrac{1}{3}\sqrt{10}) - 3 = 0$$
$$3[(-\tfrac{1}{3})^2 + 2(-\tfrac{1}{3} \cdot \tfrac{1}{3}\sqrt{10}) + (\tfrac{1}{3}\sqrt{10})^2] + 2(-\tfrac{1}{3} + \tfrac{1}{3}\sqrt{10}) - 3 = 0$$
$$3[\tfrac{1}{9} - \tfrac{2}{9}\sqrt{10} + \tfrac{1}{9}(10)] + (-\tfrac{2}{3} + \tfrac{2}{3}\sqrt{10}) - 3 = 0$$
$$\tfrac{3}{9} - \tfrac{6}{9}\sqrt{10} + \tfrac{30}{9} - \tfrac{2}{3} + \tfrac{2}{3}\sqrt{10} - 3 = 0$$
$$\tfrac{1}{3} + 3\tfrac{1}{3} - \tfrac{2}{3} - 3 - \tfrac{2}{3}\sqrt{10} + \tfrac{2}{3}\sqrt{10} =$$
$$+3\tfrac{2}{3} - 3\tfrac{2}{3} - \tfrac{2}{3}\sqrt{10} + \tfrac{2}{3}\sqrt{10} =$$

Check $x = -\frac{1}{3} - \frac{1}{3}\sqrt{10}$ to see that it is an exact solution.

Solution set: $\{-\frac{1}{3} + \frac{1}{3}\sqrt{10}, -\frac{1}{3} - \frac{1}{3}\sqrt{10}\}$

To find a *decimal approximation* for the solutions, you could look up $\sqrt{10}$ in the table on page 546 and compute the answer as follows.

$x \approx -\frac{1}{3} + \frac{1}{3}(3.162)$ $\qquad\qquad$ $x \approx -\frac{1}{3} - \frac{1}{3}(3.162)$
$= -0.333 + 1.054$, or 0.721 $\qquad$ $= -0.333 - 1.054$, or -1.387

Checking these values shows that they are only approximations.

Now try these

—— Use the quadratic formula to solve the following equations.

1. $x^2 - 4x - 5 = 0$ $\qquad$ **2.** $4x^2 + 12x = 7$ $\qquad$ **3.** $3x^2 - 5x - 4 = 0$

Answers: **1.** $x = 5$, $x = -1$ $\qquad$ **2.** $x = \frac{1}{2}$, $x = -\frac{7}{2}$ $\qquad$ **3.** $x = \dfrac{5 \pm \sqrt{73}}{6}$

Exercises

A —— Solve the following equations by the quadratic formula.

1. $x^2 - 4x = 21$ $\qquad\qquad$ **2.** $x^2 + 6x = 16$
3. $2x^2 - x - 3 = 0$ $\qquad$ **4.** $x^2 = 3x$
5. $p^2 - 4p = 0$ $\qquad\qquad$ **6.** $n^2 - 2n - 8 = 0$
7. $a^2 + 4a = 5$ $\qquad\qquad$ **8.** $6a^2 + 13a + 6 = 0$
9. $n^2 + 6 = -5n$ $\qquad\quad$ **10.** $2y^2 = 5y - 3$
11. $2x^2 + x = 3$ $\qquad\quad$ **12.** $y^2 + 3y = 4$
13. $y^2 - y = 2$ $\qquad\qquad$ **14.** $10b^2 + 7b - 12 = 0$
15. $2a^2 + 11a + 5 = 0$ $\qquad$ **16.** $x^2 + 6x = -9$

—— Solve the following by the quadratic formula and give an approximation for the solutions to the nearest hundredth.

17. $3n^2 - 2n = 2$ $\qquad\qquad$ **18.** $3x^2 - x - 3 = 0$
19. $2a^2 - 5a - 1 = 0$ $\qquad$ **20.** $2n^2 = n + 2$
21. $5n^2 + 3 = 11n$ $\qquad\quad$ **22.** $3b^2 + 5b + 1 = 0$

Solve the following by the quadratic formula. Simplify all answers. Irrational solutions may be left in radical form.

23. $x^2 - 2x = 4$ **24.** $x^2 + 2x = 1$

25. $x^2 + 4x = -2$ **26.** $x^2 + 6x + 3 = 0$

27. $x^2 - x - 1 = 0$ **28.** $x^2 + 3x + 1 = 0$

29. $2x^2 - 4x - 3 = 0$ **30.** $2x^2 + x - 5 = 0$

31. $3x^2 - 2x = 1$ **32.** $2x^2 + 7x + 2 = 0$

33. $6x^2 - 3x - 4 = 0$ **34.** $3x^2 + 10x + 5 = 0$

Use the quadratic formula to solve the following. Simplify all answers. Solve for x in Exercises 36, 41, and 46.

35. $2x^2 - 7x + 2 = 0$ **36.** $\frac{1}{a}x^2 + \frac{1}{b}x + \frac{1}{c} = 0$

37. $2x^2 - x - 1 = 0$ **38.** $3x^2 - 2x = 7$

39. $2y^2 - 3y = 4$ **40.** $4n^2 - 4 = n$

41. $\frac{1}{c}x^2 + dx = 2c$ **42.** $7x^2 - 3x - 1 = 0$

43. $9n^2 + 2 + 9n = 0$ **44.** $8n^2 + 7n - 2 = 0$

45. $4a^2 - 5 = 3a$ **46.** $3gx^2 - 2hx + k = 0$

8–9   Problems Involving Quadratic Equations

The conditions of the following exercises may be stated in terms of a quadratic equation, which you may then solve by any of the methods you have learned. Study the following Examples.

EXAMPLE 1. The altitude of a triangle is 3 units larger than its base. *The area is 9 square units.* Find the base and the altitude.

① Let x = number of units in the base.
Then $x + 3$ = number of units in the altitude.
Given   9 = number of square units in the area.
(Note that the replacement set for x is the set of positive real numbers.)

② Use these expressions in the formula for finding the area of a triangle.

$$\tfrac{1}{2}ba = A$$
$$\tfrac{1}{2}(x)(x + 3) = 9$$

(Continued on next page.)

③ Rewrite the equation in quadratic form.

$$\tfrac{1}{2}(x^2 + 3x) = 9$$
$$x^2 + 3x = 18$$
$$x^2 + 3x - 18 = 0$$

④ Solve the quadratic equation.   (Factoring is used here.)

$$(x - 3)(x + 6) = 0$$
$$(x - 3 = 0) \lor (x + 6 = 0)$$
$$(x = 3) \lor (x = -6)$$

⑤ Since x, the measure of the base, is a member of the set of positive real numbers, -6 is not in the solution set.   Does 3 satisfy the conditions of the problem?

$$x = 3$$
$$x + 3 = 6$$
$$\tfrac{1}{2}(3)(6) = 9$$
$$\tfrac{1}{2}(18) = 9$$
Solution set: $\{3\}$

⑥ The base is 3 units long and the altitude is 6 units long.

EXAMPLE 2.   **The sum of two numbers is 12.** *The sum of their squares is 80.*   Find each number.

① Let $\qquad n =$ one number.
Then $12 - n =$ the other number.

② Use the conditions of the problem to write an equation.

$$n^2 + (12 - n)^2 = 80$$
$$n^2 + 144 - 24n + n^2 = 80$$
$$2n^2 - 24n + 64 = 0$$
$$n^2 - 12n + 32 = 0$$

③ Solve the equation.

$$(n - 4)(n - 8) = 0$$
$$(n = 4) \lor (n = 8)$$

④ $\qquad$ *Check $n = 4$.* $\qquad\qquad$ *Check $n = 8$.*
$$4^2 + 8^2 = 80 \qquad\qquad 8^2 + 4^2 = 80$$
$$16 + 64 = 80 \qquad\qquad 64 + 16 = 80$$
Solution set: $\{4, 8\}$

⑤ Since $12 - 4 = 8$ and $12 - 8 = 4$, the two numbers are 4 and 8.

Exercises

A —— Write a quadratic equation for each problem and solve. Draw a figure to help you if appropriate.

1. One number is 3 units larger than another. Their product is 54. Find the numbers.

2. The square of a number is 56 more than the number itself. What is the number?

3. A number exceeds its square by $\frac{2}{9}$. Find the number.

4. The perimeter of a rectangle is 30 inches and its area is 54 square inches. What are its dimensions?

5. What is the length of a diagonal of a square if it is 3 inches longer than a side? (Use the Pythagorean theorem.) Approximate the answer to hundredths.

6. A man wished to fit three rods together in the shape of a right triangle. The hypotenuse was to be 2 inches longer than the base and 4 inches longer than the altitude. How long should he make each rod? Use the Pythagorean theorem.

$$(x - 2)^2 + (x - 4)^2 = x^2$$

7. The length of a rectangular piece of sheet metal is 3 times its width. What is its length if its area is 192 square inches?

8. The area of the front of the fireplace in the Wilson's living room is to be 1080 square inches. Its width is to be 6 inches longer than its height. What are its dimensions to be?

9. The product of two consecutive odd integers is 2703. What are the integers? (*Hint:* You can use $2n + 1$ and $2n + 3$. You should get a positive number and a negative number for the solutions of your equation. A pair of positive numbers and a pair of negative numbers satisfy the conditions of the problem.)

10. Find two consecutive even integers whose product is 1848. (*Hint:* You can use $2n$ and $2n + 2$.)

11. The difference in the squares of two consecutive odd integers is 56. What are the integers?

12. If a number is decreased by 18 times its reciprocal, the difference will be 7. What is the number?

13. The sum of a number and 15 times its reciprocal is 8. What is the number?

14. Two square playing spaces are marked off on a playground. The side of one playing space is 6 feet less than a side of the other playing space. The area of the two playing spaces is 1076 square feet. What is the length of a side of each playing space?

15. In the auditorium of Sally Bates's school, the number of seats in each row is 8 fewer than the number of rows. How many seats are in each row if the auditorium seats 609 persons?

16. There are two numbers such that one is 3 more than $\frac{1}{2}$ the other. The difference of the squares of the two numbers is 495. What are the numbers?

B —— Write a quadratic equation for each of the following problems and solve.

17. The numerator of a fraction is 1 less than its denominator. If the fraction is increased by 2 times its reciprocal, the sum will be $3\frac{5}{12}$. Find the numerator and the denominator.

18. The denominator of a fraction is 2 more than its numerator. If the fraction is increased by 3 times its reciprocal, the sum will be $5\frac{3}{5}$. Find the numerator and the denominator.

19. The area of the border in the figure at the right is 225 square feet. How wide is this border if the outside length is 25 feet and the outside width is 15 feet?

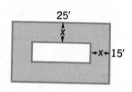

20. Sam and his father drove 294 miles to the State Fair. Sam drove the farm truck at an average speed of 7 miles per hour slower than his father drove the family car. It took Sam an hour longer than it did his father. What was Sam's rate? his father's rate?

21. An airplane flew a round-trip training flight from airport A to airport B. The distance between the two airports was 1200 miles. Going against the wind, the pilot flew 60 miles per hour slower than returning. It took one hour more time going than returning. What was the speed going and returning?

22. Mr. Fritz and Mr. Murphy can do a piece of work together in 5 hours. Alone Mr. Murphy can do the job in 3 hours less time than Mr. Fritz can do it alone. How many hours, to the nearest tenth, will it take each to do the job?

8–10 The Nature of the Solutions

Knowing the **nature of the solutions** of a quadratic equation is knowing if they are real or not and if there are two or only one.

From the graphs of quadratic functions, you can tell the nature of the solutions, or zeros, of the corresponding quadratic equations.

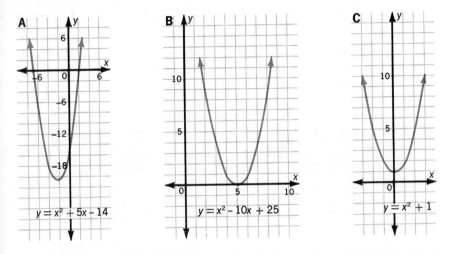

How many times does each graph cross the x axis in A? in B? in C? Then how many distinct real numbers make $x^2 + 5x - 14 = 0$ true? $x^2 - 10x + 25 = 0$ true? $x^2 + 1 = 0$ true?

For convenience, the solutions of $x^2 - 10x + 25 = 0$ are often said to be equal, because solving $x^2 - 10x + 25 = 0$ gives $+5$ and $+5$ as the solutions. However, there is only one *distinct* solution, $+5$.

Summary

Equation	Nature of solutions
$x^2 + 5x - 14 = 0$	Two distinct, real solutions.
$x^2 - 10x + 25 = 0$	One distinct, real solution (or two equal, real solutions).
$x^2 + 1 = 0$	No real solutions.

Using the quadratic formula yields the same results without graphing.

$$x^2 + 5x - 14 = 0 \qquad x = \frac{-5 \pm \sqrt{25 + 56}}{2}$$

Since $\sqrt{25 + 56}$ is *not equal* to zero, there are two real solutions, $\dfrac{-5 + \sqrt{81}}{2}$ and $\dfrac{-5 - \sqrt{81}}{2}$.

$$x^2 - 10x + 25 = 0 \qquad x = \frac{10 \pm \sqrt{100 - 100}}{2}$$

Since $\sqrt{100 - 100}$ is *equal* to zero, there is one distinct real solution, 5.

$$x^2 + 1 = 0 \qquad x = \frac{0 \pm \sqrt{0 - 4}}{2}$$

No real number equals $\sqrt{-4}$. You might try -2, but $(-2)^2$ is 4, not -4. Since $\sqrt{-4}$ is not a real number, $\frac{\pm\sqrt{-4}}{2}$ is not a real number, and there are no real solutions.

Can you see which portion of the quadratic formula determines the nature of the solutions? It is $b^2 - 4ac$. This number is the **discriminant** of the equation $ax^2 + bx + c = 0$. Why?

If $b^2 - 4ac > 0$, there are two distinct, real solutions for $ax^2 + bx + c = 0$.

If $b^2 - 4ac = 0$, there is one distinct, real solution (two equal, real solutions).

If $b^2 - 4ac < 0$, there are no real solutions.

Checkpoint

How can you use $b^2 - 4ac$ to determine the nature of the solutions of a quadratic equation?

Now try these

— Determine the nature of the solutions.

1. $2x^2 - 3x - 1 = 0$ **2.** $n^2 - 2n + 4 = 0$

3. $x^2 - 6x + 9 = 0$ **4.** $x^2 - 5x + 6 = 0$

Answers: **1.** Two distinct, real solutions. **2.** No real solutions. **3.** One distinct, real solution. **4.** Two distinct, real solutions.

Exercises

A —— Without solving, give the nature of the solutions of each of the following equations.

1. $x^2 + 2x + 8 = 0$ **2.** $3x^2 - 3x - 4 = 0$

3. $3y^2 - \frac{1}{3}y = \frac{2}{5}$ **4.** $x^2 = 5x + 5$

5. $3x^2 + 4x - \frac{3}{4} = 0$

6. $2y^2 - 4y = -2$

7. $x^2 - x + \frac{6}{25} = 0$

8. $20x = x^2 + 100$

9. $\frac{1}{2}x^2 - 16x + 132 = 0$

10. $4x^2 + 2x - 9 = 0$

B **11.** For what values of k will the graph of $x^2 + kx + 25 = y$ touch the x axis at just one point?

12. For what values of k are the solutions of $x^2 + 4x + k = 0$ real?

13. For what values of k will the graph of $x^2 + kx + 3 = y$ cut the x axis twice?

14. For what values of k will the graph of $kx^2 - 6x + 1 = y$ neither touch nor cross the x axis?

CHAPTER REVIEW

1. Know the meaning of and be able to use each of the following words or phrases. The number shown after each word or phrase indicates where it is introduced, in case you need to review.

quadratic function (*350*)

quadratic equation (*350*)

complete quadratic
  equation (*350*)

incomplete quadratic
  equation (*350*)

parabola (*351*)

vertex of a parabola (*351*)

y intercept (*355*)

x intercept (*355*)

zero of a function (*356*)

solution of a quadratic
  equation (*359*)

completing the square (*367*)

quadratic formula (*371*)

nature of the solution(s) of a
  quadratic equation (*377*)

discriminant (*378*)

—— The general form of the quadratic equation is $y = ax^2 + bx + c$. What is the value of a, b, and c in each of the following?

2. $y = -3x^2$

3. $y = 2x^2 + 5$

4. $y = 5x^2 - 2x + 7$

5. $y = -\frac{1}{4}x^2 + 9x$

6. Write an example of a complete quadratic equation; of an incomplete quadratic equation.

—— Describe the parabola that is the graph of each of the following; that is, tell which way it opens and give its vertex and x intercepts.

7. $y = 2x^2 - x - 15$

8. $y = 2x^2 - 3x$

9. $y = -5x^2$

10. $y = x^2$

—— What are the zeros of the following functions?

11. $3x^2 + 16x - 12 = 0$

12. $y = \frac{3x^2}{5}$

━━ Solve each equation by factoring.

13. $x^2 - 2x - 35 = 0$ 　　　　　　　　　 **14.** $2x^2 - x - 21 = 0$

15. If you are given the equation $(x - 5)(x + 2) = 0$, why does replacing x by 5 make the equation true?

16. What are the x intercepts of the graph of $y = 9x^2 - 29x + 6$?

━━ Make each of the following expressions a perfect square trinomial.

17. $x^2 - 9x$ 　　　　　 **18.** $x^2 - \frac{2}{5}x$ 　　　　　 **19.** $x^2 + 5x$

━━ Solve the following equations by completing the square.

20. $x^2 - 8x - 3 = 0$ 　　　　　 **21.** $x^2 - 5x = 4$

22. $15x^2 + 2x - 1 = 0$ 　　　　　 **23.** $7x^2 - 17x + 7 = 0$

24. Write the general form of a quadratic equation. Write the quadratic formula. Explain how the two are related.

━━ Use the quadratic formula to solve the following equations.

25. $4x^2 + 5 = 9x$ 　　　　　 **26.** $15x^2 - 7x - 2 = 0$

27. $2x^2 - 7x + 1 = 0$ 　　　　　 **28.** $x^2 - 11x = 0$

29. "The sum of a number, x, and 14 times its reciprocal is 9." You could use $x + \frac{14}{x} = 9$ to express the sum. Write the equation as a quadratic equation and find the number or numbers that satisfy it.

━━ Use the discriminant to give the nature of the solutions of the following.

30. $15x^2 - 16x - 15 = 0$ 　　　　　 **31.** $x^2 - 8x = -16$

32. $2x^2 - 3x + 3 = -11$ 　　　　　 **33.** $2x^2 = 32$

CHAPTER TEST ▐▬▬▬▬▬▬▬▬▬▬▬▬▬

━━ Make the following expressions perfect square trinomials by completing the square.

1. $x^2 + 6x$ 　　　 **2.** $x^2 - 12x$ 　　　 **3.** $n^2 - 2n$ 　　　 **4.** $r^2 + 7r$

━━ Solve the following quadratic equations.

5. $x^2 + 5x + 6 = 0$ 　　　　　 **6.** $a^2 - 6a - 7 = 0$

7. $3s^2 - 2s - 8 = 0$ 　　　　　 **8.** $\frac{1}{2}t^2 + \frac{1}{2}t - 15 = 0$

9. $x^2 - 5 = 0$ 　　　　　 **10.** $m^2 + 3m = 0$

11. $x^2 + 8x + 16 = 0$ 　　　　　 **12.** $y^2 - 14y = 1$

13. $2r^2 + r - 6 = 0$ 　　　　　 **14.** $4b^2 - 16 = 0$

15. For each of the following equations, choose the correct graph at the right.

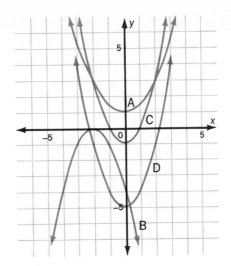

  a. $y = -x^2 - 4x - 4$
  b. $y = x^2 - 1$
  c. $y = \frac{1}{2}x^2 + 1$
  d. $y = x^2 - 5$

———— Graph each of the following parabolas, and tell whether the vertex is a minimum or a maximum point.

16. $y = -x^2 + 2$

17. $y = x^2 + 10x + 25$

———— Give the y intercept and the real zeros (if there are any) of the graphs of the following equations.

18. $3x^2 - 2x - 8 = y$

19. $-x^2 + 8x - 15 = y$

20. $x^2 + 4 = y$

21. $x^2 + 4x + 4 = y$

22. The length of a rectangle is 1 inch more than twice the width and the area is 55 square inches. Find the length and the width.

23. Separate 18 into two parts so that the sum of the squares of the parts will be 170.

ENRICHMENT

A Computer Flow Chart for Solving Quadratic Equations

In Chapter 5 there is a flow-chart analysis of the solution of the linear equation. Now you will work with a flow chart for the solution of the quadratic equation. Remember that the computer can add, subtract, multiply, divide, take square roots, give absolute values, and compare given numbers with each other or with given constants. These and only these operations may be included in the flow chart.

Submit $ax^2 + bx + c = 0$, $a \neq 0$, $b \neq 0$, $c \neq 0$, to the computer with a in location [1], b in location [2], and c in location [3]. Read through the flow chart and follow the steps for the algebraic solution in the left column below the chart. Then follow the numerical solution in the right column.

Flow Chart for Solving Quadratic Equations

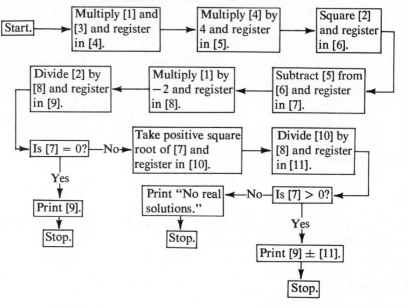

Solve $ax^2 + bx + c$.	Location	Solve $3x^2 + x + 4$
a	[1]	3
b	[2]	1
c	[3]	-4
ac	[4]	-12
$4ac$	[5]	-48
b^2	[6]	1
$b^2 - 4ac$	[7]	49
$-2a$	[8]	-6
$\dfrac{b}{-2a}$	[9]	$-\frac{1}{6}$
$\sqrt{b^2 - 4ac}$	[10]	7
$\dfrac{\sqrt{b^2 - 4ac}}{-2a}$	[11]	$-\frac{7}{6}$

[7] > 0	[7] = 0	[7] < 0	Print	
$\dfrac{b}{-2a} \pm \dfrac{\sqrt{b^2 - 4ac}}{-2a}$	$\dfrac{b}{-2a}$	"No real solutions."	Print result.	$-\frac{1}{6} \pm -\frac{7}{6}$

Exercises

1. Solve $6x^2 + 13x + 6 = 0$ by following the flow chart.

2. Solve $x^2 - 2x + 2 = 0$ by following the flow chart.

3. Suppose you want to solve an equation of the form $ax^2 + bx = 0$, $a \neq 0$, $b \neq 0$. You could solve it by using the flow chart for the general quadratic equation, but it is really too easy for that. Write a flow chart for solving $ax^2 + bx = 0$. (Remember that the computer will not factor $ax^2 + bx = 0$ into $x(ax + b) = 0$. You must only ask the machine to do the standard operations.)

4. You know that if the value of $b^2 - 4ac$, the discriminant, is less than zero, there are no real solutions to the quadratic equation. It is a waste of computer time to go through the entire program if there are no real-number solutions. Insert a step into the flow chart that will eliminate some steps and eliminate the time wasted.

THE GROWTH OF MATHEMATICS

When Mathematics Almost Disappeared

The Romans and the Greeks were very different in temperament. Although the Greeks had cultivated mathematics for its own sake, the Romans were only interested in "practical" mathematics. They paid little attention to the correct results of the Greeks, and as a consequence, many of the formulas they used were wrong. As the Roman Empire spread over most of the civilized world, so did the Roman attitude toward mathematics. With the gradual decline of the Empire, partial ignorance of mathematics gave way to even greater ignorance.

In the Middle Ages there were a few attempts to revive some of the Greek spirit in mathematics. Boethius (A.D. 480?–?524), born just after the fall of the Roman Empire, wrote an arithmetic and a geometry. Part of the geometry is a restatement of a few theorems from Euclid (without proof) and the remainder consists of the mostly incorrect formulas used by the Romans. For the next five or six centuries, these were about the only books on mathematics known in Europe. During this time most computation was done by means of finger-counting or using one form or another of the abacus. (The abacus could be used without any knowledge of mathematics.) In the monasteries there was sufficient arithmetic taught to enable the monks to calculate the dates of religious feasts. This state of affairs persisted until the twelfth century, when Arabic mathematics began to be known in Europe.

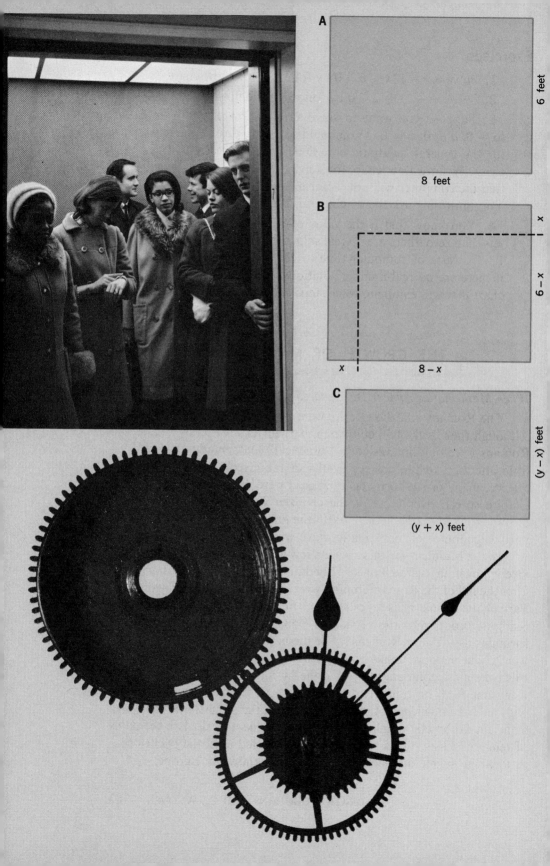

A

8 feet

6 feet

B

x

6 − x

x   8 − x

C

(y − x) feet

(y + x) feet

CHAPTER 9

RATIONAL EXPRESSIONS

● Diagram *A* at the left represents the floor of the elevator in the photograph. The dimensions of this rectangular floor are 8 feet by 6 feet. By counting, you know that there are seven people in the elevator. How would you find the number of square feet of floor space for each person in the elevator? Does $\frac{8 \times 6}{7}$ show the number of square feet of floor for each person? Name $\frac{8 \times 6}{7}$ as the ratio of two integers.

● Suppose the same seven people were to stand in an elevator with a smaller floor, as represented in *B*. What are the length and width of the smaller floor? Why does $\frac{(8 - x)(6 - x)}{7}$ show the number of square feet of floor space for each person? Rename $\frac{(8 - x)(6 - x)}{7}$ so that the numerator is a polynomial.

● What expression would you use if you want the number of square feet of floor space per person for any number of people, *y*, standing on floor *B*? for any number of people, *y*, standing on floor *C*?

● The radius of the larger gear in the photograph is a polynomial, $\frac{1}{4}x$. The radius of the smaller gear is the quotient of two polynomials, $\frac{x + 5}{15 - x}$. What is the ratio of the radius of the larger gear to the radius of the smaller?

● Write an expression for the area of the larger gear; for the area of the smaller gear; for the sum of the areas of both gears.

Each of the expressions used above to name the number of square feet per person and the expressions used with respect to the gears are rational expressions. In this chapter you will learn the meaning of rational expressions and how to perform operations on them.

9–1   Definition and Equality of Rational Expressions

Look at the examples below and try to formulate the definition of **rational expression.**

Rational expression		Nonrational expression	
a.	$\dfrac{480}{\sqrt{13}}$	b.	$\dfrac{\sqrt[3]{13y}}{1}$
c.	$\dfrac{x^2 - \sqrt{3}x + 480}{480}$	d.	$\dfrac{x^2 - \sqrt{5}x + 8}{480}$
e.	$\dfrac{y^2 - x^2}{y - x}$	f.	$\dfrac{y + \sqrt{x}}{y + \sqrt{x}}$
g.	$\dfrac{4x^3 - 3x^2 - 2x + 1}{x^2 + 3x - 9}$	h.	$\dfrac{3x^{\frac{1}{2}} - 9}{x + 3}$

Definition   A rational expression is one that can be expressed as the ratio of two polynomials, $\dfrac{P}{Q}$, where the numerical coefficients of Q are not all zero.

Tell why each expression in the table above either fits or does not fit the definition of rational expression. How can the definition of rational number help you remember the definition of rational expression? Tell how they are alike and how they are different.

If two rational numbers have either the same numerator or the same denominator, it is easy to tell whether or not the two rational numbers are equal.

$$\tfrac{2}{3} \neq \tfrac{1}{3} \quad \text{because} \quad 2 \neq 1$$
$$\tfrac{5}{6} \neq \tfrac{5}{7} \quad \text{because} \quad 6 \neq 7$$

In a similar way, equality of rational expressions with the same numerator or denominator can be determined. For example, for all real numbers for x,

$$\frac{x^2 - 5}{6} \neq \frac{x^2 - 4}{6} \quad \text{because} \quad x^2 - 5 \neq x^2 - 4.$$

For rational numbers with different numerators and denominators, equality is defined in a different way.

$$\tfrac{3}{4} = \tfrac{6}{8} \quad \text{because} \quad 3 \times 8 = 4 \times 6$$

Equality of any two rational expressions is defined in the same way.

Definition Two rational expressions $\frac{Q}{R}$ and $\frac{S}{T}$ are equal if and only if $Q \cdot T = R \cdot S$.

EXAMPLE. Use the definition of equality of rational expressions to show that $\frac{x^2 - 4}{x - 2}$ and $\frac{x + 2}{1}$ are equal.

$$\frac{x^2 - 4}{x - 2} \overset{?}{=} \frac{x + 2}{1}$$
$$(x^2 - 4)1 \overset{?}{=} (x - 2)(x + 2)$$
$$x^2 - 4 = x^2 - 4$$

Thus, $\frac{x^2 - 4}{x - 2}$ and $\frac{x + 2}{1}$ are equal. If x is 2, then $\frac{x^2 - 4}{x - 2}$ is not defined. Equality for rational expressions, however, was defined in such a way that the expressions are technically equal even when one (or both) are undefined for particular values of the variables.

Now try these

—— Use the definition of equality, and replace ● with = or ≠ to make true sentences.

1. $\frac{4m}{6m^2}$ ● $\frac{2}{3m}$

2. $\frac{x}{y}$ ● $\frac{xa}{ya}$

3. $\frac{x - y}{x}$ ● $\frac{-y}{1}$

4. $\frac{x - y}{2}$ ● $\frac{(x - y)(x + y)}{2(x + y)}$

5. $\frac{5x^2}{3x}$ ● $\frac{5x}{3}$

6. $\frac{a^2 + b^2}{a + b}$ ● $\frac{a + b}{1}$

Answers: **1.** = **2.** = **3.** ≠ **4.** = **5.** = **6.** ≠

Exercises

A —— Write *Rational* or *Nonrational* to describe each of the following expressions.

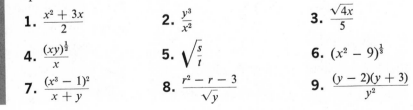

1. $\frac{x^2 + 3x}{2}$

2. $\frac{y^3}{x^2}$

3. $\frac{\sqrt{4x}}{5}$

4. $\frac{(xy)^{\frac{1}{2}}}{x}$

5. $\sqrt{\frac{s}{t}}$

6. $(x^2 - 9)^{\frac{1}{3}}$

7. $\frac{(x^3 - 1)^2}{x + y}$

8. $\frac{r^2 - r - 3}{\sqrt{y}}$

9. $\frac{(y - 2)(y + 3)}{y^2}$

—— Using the definition of equality of rational expressions, replace ● with = or ≠ to make true sentences.

10. $\dfrac{5}{8}$ ● $\dfrac{15}{24}$

11. $\dfrac{3}{7}$ ● $\dfrac{6}{13}$

12. $\dfrac{\sqrt{12}}{5}$ ● $\dfrac{\sqrt{3}}{2\frac{1}{2}}$

13. $\dfrac{15}{22}$ ● $\dfrac{7 \cdot 5}{11}$

14. $\dfrac{2\sqrt{2}}{9}$ ● $\dfrac{\sqrt{2}}{4}$

15. $\dfrac{\sqrt{6}}{\sqrt{15}}$ ● $\dfrac{\sqrt{2}}{\sqrt{5}}$

16. $\dfrac{x^2}{2}$ ● $\dfrac{x^3}{2x}$

17. $\dfrac{x+2}{y}$ ● $\dfrac{x+2}{xy}$

18. $\dfrac{r^2 - 6r + 9}{r - 3}$ ● $\dfrac{r+3}{1}$

19. $\dfrac{2a^2}{3a}$ ● $\dfrac{4a^3}{6a}$

20. $\dfrac{5b^3c}{2b}$ ● $\dfrac{2 \cdot 5b^2c^2}{c}$

21. $\dfrac{-4xy}{16x^2y^3}$ ● $\dfrac{1}{4xy^2}$

22. $\dfrac{x^2 - 4}{2x - 4}$ ● $\dfrac{x+2}{2}$

23. $\dfrac{y^2 - y - 2}{2y^2 - 5y + 2}$ ● $\dfrac{y+1}{2y-1}$

—— Add 7 to the numerator and denominator of each rational expression. Write a true sentence using = or ≠ to compare the original expression with the new one.

24. $\dfrac{5}{6}$ **25.** $\dfrac{x^2}{x}$ **26.** $\dfrac{x+4}{x}$ **27.** $\dfrac{x^2 - 7}{x - 7}$

—— Multiply the numerator and denominator of each rational expression by $x - 2$. Write a true sentence using = or ≠ to compare the original expression with the new one.

28. $\dfrac{x^3}{x}$ **29.** $\dfrac{x+2}{x-2}$ **30.** $\dfrac{x^2 - 4}{x + 4}$ **31.** $\dfrac{x^2}{y^2}$

9–2 Simplifying Rational Expressions

Using the definition of equality, it is easy to prove that a theorem you have used for rational numbers also applies to rational expressions.

Theorem 9–1 The numerator and denominator of a rational expression may be multiplied or divided by the same nonzero polynomial without changing the value of the expression.

$$\frac{P}{Q} = \frac{RP}{RQ}$$

By the definition of equality, the two rational expressions are equal if $P(RQ) = Q(RP)$ is true.

Statements	Reasons
1. $P(RQ) = (PR)Q$	1. Associative postulate of multiplication.
2. $(PR)Q = Q(PR)$	2. Commutative postulate of multiplication.
3. $Q(PR) = Q(RP)$	3. Commutative postulate of multiplication.

Thus, $P(RQ) = Q(RP)$ is true and $\frac{P}{Q} = \frac{RP}{RQ}$ is true.

EXAMPLE 1. Express $\frac{1}{2}$ as a rational number whose denominator is 6.

Method I

Use the multiplicative property of 1 to make the denominator 6.

$$\frac{1}{2} = 1 \times \frac{1}{2} = \frac{3}{3} \times \frac{1}{2} = \frac{3 \times 1}{3 \times 2} = \frac{3}{6}$$

Method II

Think: By what number is 2 multiplied to get 6? Then, multiply 1 by the same number, 3.

$$\frac{1}{2} = \frac{3 \times 1}{3 \times 2} = \frac{3}{6}$$

$$Check \quad 1 \times 6 = 2 \times 3$$
$$6 = 6$$

EXAMPLE 2. Express $\frac{4m}{6m^2}$ so that the numerator and denominator have only 1 as a common factor.

The process can be thought of in two ways.

Method I

Use the property of 1.

$$\frac{4m}{6m^2} = \frac{2m \cdot 2}{2m \cdot 3m} = \frac{2m}{2m} \cdot \frac{2}{3m} = 1 \cdot \frac{2}{3m} = \frac{2}{3m}$$

Method II

Factor the numerator and denominator and then divide both by the same number.

$$\frac{4m}{6m^2} = \frac{2m \cdot 2}{2m \cdot 3m} = \frac{2}{3m}$$

$$Check \quad 4m \cdot 3m \stackrel{?}{=} 6m^2 \cdot 2$$
$$12m^2 = 12m^2$$

The expression $\frac{2}{3m}$ is the simplest form of the rational expression $\frac{4m}{6m^2}$. A rational expression is in its **simplest form** when both polynomials of the rational expression have no common factors other than 1 or -1. To **simplify** an expression means to write the expression in its simplest form.

In the following example, the numerator and denominator are first written in factored form so the common factors are easily seen.

EXAMPLE 3. Simplify $\frac{x^2 + xy}{x^2 - xy}$.

Factor the numerator and denominator completely, and then divide both by the common factor.

$$\frac{x^2 + xy}{x^2 - xy} = \frac{x(x + y)}{x(x - y)} = \frac{x + y}{x - y}$$

There are no common factors of $x + y$ and $x - y$; so $\frac{x + y}{x - y}$ is the simplest form of $\frac{x^2 + xy}{x^2 - xy}$. Check to see that they are equal.

Remember that you always divide both numerator and denominator by the same *factor*. The rational expression $\frac{2a + 3}{a}$ cannot be simplified because $2a + 3$ and a have no common factor; that is, a is not a factor of the sum $2a + 3$.

Now try these

—— Is the second expression a factor of both the numerator and denominator of the rational expression? When your answer is *Yes*, simplify the rational expression and check, using the definition of equality.

1. $\frac{3 \cdot 5}{3 \cdot 6}$; 3

2. $\frac{a \cdot x}{a \cdot y}$; a

3. $\frac{3 + 7}{3}$; 3

4. $\frac{a + 5}{a}$; a

5. $\frac{x(x - 1)}{x}$; x

6. $\frac{3y^2 - y}{y}$; y

7. $\frac{6x - 6y}{6x + 6y}$; x

8. $\frac{6x - 6y}{6x + 6y}$; 6

9. $\frac{x^3 - 3}{x^3}$; x^3

Answers: **1.** Yes; $\frac{3 \cdot 5}{3 \cdot 6} = \frac{5}{6}$; $(3 \cdot 5) \cdot 6 = (3 \cdot 6) \cdot 5$ **2.** Yes; $\frac{a \cdot x}{a \cdot y} = \frac{x}{y}$; $(ax)y =$

$(ay)x$ **3.** No. **4.** No. **5.** Yes; $\frac{x(x - 1)}{x} = \frac{(x - 1)}{1}$; $x(x - 1) \cdot 1 =$

$x(x - 1)$ **6.** Yes; $\frac{3y^2 - y}{y} = \frac{y(3y - 1)}{y} = \frac{3y - 1}{1}$; $(3y^2 - y) \cdot 1 =$

$y(3y - 1)$ **7.** No. **8.** Yes; $\frac{6(x - y)}{6(x + y)} = \frac{x - y}{x + y}$; $[6(x - y)](x + y) =$

$[6(x + y)](x - y)$ **9.** No.

Exercises

A — Replace the ? by an expression to make a true sentence.

1. $\dfrac{8}{12} = \dfrac{?}{60}$ **2.** $\dfrac{24}{44} = \dfrac{6}{?}$ **3.** $\dfrac{6ab}{18a^2} = \dfrac{b}{?}$

4. $\dfrac{2x}{?} = \dfrac{x}{y}$ **5.** $\dfrac{?}{6a} = \dfrac{4}{3a}$ **6.** $\dfrac{2a}{a+b} = \dfrac{?}{6(a+b)}$

7. $\dfrac{b}{xy} = \dfrac{?}{ax^2y^2}$ **8.** $\dfrac{c-2}{2c+5} = \dfrac{c^2-2c}{?}$ **9.** $\dfrac{(x+y)(x-y)}{(x+y)(x+y)} = \dfrac{?}{x+y}$

— Simplify each of the following expressions.

Example. $\dfrac{6n^2}{15nm}$

Divide numerator and denominator by the common factor.

$$\frac{6n^2}{15nm} = \frac{3n \cdot 2n}{3n \cdot 5m} = \frac{2n}{5m}$$

10. $\dfrac{3 \cdot 5}{3 \cdot 4}$ **11.** $\dfrac{3 \cdot 4 \cdot 5}{3 \cdot 4}$ **12.** $\dfrac{6xy}{6}$

13. $\dfrac{6xy}{6x}$ **14.** $\dfrac{12}{18}$ **15.** $\dfrac{9}{12}$

16. $\dfrac{a^2}{ab}$ **17.** $\dfrac{24a}{36b}$ **18.** $\dfrac{12x}{15xy}$

19. $\dfrac{25x^2}{30x}$ **20.** $\dfrac{18x^2y}{24xy}$ **21.** $\dfrac{3xy}{24y}$

22. $\dfrac{y^7}{y^3}$ **23.** $\dfrac{y^5}{y^8}$ **24.** $\dfrac{30s^2}{20s}$

25. $\dfrac{7x^2}{6x}$ **26.** $\dfrac{r^2xy}{r^2xt}$ **27.** $\dfrac{6ab}{9a^2x}$

28. $\dfrac{2a^3b^2}{6a^2b^2}$ **29.** $\dfrac{-x^2y^3}{x^3y^2}$ **30.** $\dfrac{3a^4b^3}{9a^3b^3}$

31. $\dfrac{48ab^2c}{60a^2b^2}$ **32.** $\dfrac{-9xy}{30x^2y}$ **33.** $\dfrac{3 \cdot 5x}{2 \cdot 5y}$

34. $\dfrac{-30a^2bc}{-18a^3c}$ **35.** $\dfrac{36a^2b^3x^2}{-60a^2bx^5}$ **36.** $\dfrac{a(x+y)}{b(x+y)}$

37. $\dfrac{24}{15(x+y)}$ **38.** $\dfrac{m(x-y)^2}{e(x-y)}$ **39.** $\dfrac{30a}{25(x-a)}$

40. $\dfrac{36x}{15(x+2)}$ **41.** $\dfrac{15(a+b)}{6(2a+b)}$ **42.** $\dfrac{8(x-2y)}{18(2x-y)}$

Example. $\dfrac{3x^2 - xy}{xy + 3x^2}$

$$\frac{3x^2 - xy}{xy + 3x^2} = \frac{x(3x - y)}{x(y + 3x)} = \frac{3x - y}{y + 3x}$$

43. $\dfrac{3x - 6y}{9x + 12y}$ **44.** $\dfrac{a^2b - ab^2}{a^2b^2 + ab^2}$ **45.** $\dfrac{2ab + b^2}{a^2 - b^2}$

46. $\dfrac{6x - 6y}{6a + 6b}$ **47.** $\dfrac{ax + by}{ax - by}$ **48.** $\dfrac{2x - 10y}{2a - 2b}$

—— Tell whether the following statements are *True* or *False*.

49. $\forall x \neq 0 \quad \dfrac{6x^2}{x} = 6x$ **50.** $\forall x \neq 0 \quad \dfrac{8x^3}{2x^2} = 4x$

51. $\forall y \neq 2 \quad \dfrac{y}{y^2 - 2y} = \dfrac{1}{y - 2}$ **52.** $\forall a \neq \pm 3 \quad \dfrac{2a + 6}{a^2 - 9} = \dfrac{2}{a + 3}$

53. $\forall x \neq \pm\sqrt{6} \quad \dfrac{x^3 - 6x}{x^2 - 6} = x$ **54.** $\forall x, y \neq 0 \quad \dfrac{3x^4 y^2}{10x^2 y^2} = \dfrac{3x^2}{10y}$

B —— Simplify the following expressions.

Example. $\dfrac{a^2 - 9}{a^2 + 5a + 6}$

First factor, and then divide the numerator and denominator by the common factor.

$$\frac{a^2 - 9}{a^2 + 5a + 6} = \frac{(a - 3)\cancel{(a + 3)}}{(a + 2)\cancel{(a + 3)}} = \frac{a - 3}{a + 2}$$

55. $\dfrac{x^2 - y^2}{x^2 - 2xy + y^2}$ **56.** $\dfrac{3a + 3b}{a^2 + 2ab + b^2}$

57. $\dfrac{2x^2 + 6x + 4}{4x^2 - 12x - 16}$ **58.** $\dfrac{2x^3 - 2x^2 - 4x}{3x^3 + 3x^2 + 18x}$

59. $\dfrac{x^2 - 3x - 4}{2x^2 + 10x + 8}$ **60.** $\dfrac{2x^2 - 2x - 12}{x^3 - 5x^2 + 6x}$

61. $\dfrac{x^2 - 25}{x^2 - 10x + 25}$ **62.** $\dfrac{5a + 5}{a^2 + 7a + 6}$

63. $\dfrac{6x + 12}{x^2 - x - 6}$ **64.** $\dfrac{x^2 y - y}{x + 1}$

65. $\dfrac{3a^2 - 3}{a - 1}$ **66.** $\dfrac{a^2 + 1}{a + 1}$

C —— Express the following in simplest form.

67. $\dfrac{R^2 - r^2}{3r + 3R}$ **68.** $\dfrac{6a^2 + a - 15}{6a^2 - 13a + 6}$

69. $\dfrac{3a^2 - 27}{6a^2 + 15a - 9}$ **70.** $\dfrac{6a^2 + 42a + 72}{18 - 2a^2}$

71. $\dfrac{3a^2 - 12a - 15}{18 - 18a^2}$ **72.** $\dfrac{3x^2 - 27}{24 - 11x + x^2}$

73. $\dfrac{x^2 + 6xy + 9y^2}{x^2 - 9y^2}$ **74.** $\dfrac{16a^2 - 48ab + 36b^2}{ba^2 - 36b^2}$

75. $\dfrac{a^2 - 4a + 4}{4 - a^2}$ **76.** $\dfrac{4x^n (a + b)}{8x^{n-1}(a + b)^n}$

9–3 Multiplication of Rational Expressions

To multiply two rational numbers, you find the product of the numerators to determine the numerator of the product and you find the product of the denominators to determine the denominator of the product. The same holds true for rational expressions. The first theorem treats rational expressions with 1 in the numerator.

Theorem 9-2   The product of $\frac{1}{Q}$ and $\frac{1}{S}$, where $\frac{1}{Q}$ and $\frac{1}{S}$ are rational expressions, is $\frac{1}{QS}$.

The proof is left as an exercise.

Then the general theorem for multiplication of rational expressions can be stated.

Theorem 9-3   The product of $\frac{P}{Q}$ and $\frac{R}{S}$ is $\frac{PR}{QS}$.

$$\forall Q \neq 0 \quad \forall S \neq 0 \quad \frac{P}{Q} \cdot \frac{R}{S} = \frac{PR}{QS}$$

The proof is left as an exercise. Is the product of two rational expressions always a rational expression? Explain.

EXAMPLE 1. Find the product of $\frac{2x}{y}$ and $\frac{w}{3z}$.

$$\frac{2x}{y} \cdot \frac{w}{3z} = \frac{2xw}{3yz}$$

Remember to express the product in simplest form.

EXAMPLE 2. Simplify the product $\frac{3a^2b}{2ab^2} \cdot \frac{4abx}{9a^2by}$.

You can multiply the terms and then simplify the product or simplify and then multiply.

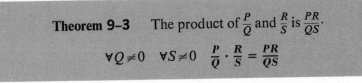

METHOD I

$$\frac{3a^2b}{2ab^2} \cdot \frac{4abx}{9a^2by} = \frac{12a^3b^2x}{18a^3b^3y}$$
$$= \frac{(6a^3b^2)2x}{(6a^3b^2)3by} = \frac{2x}{3by}$$

METHOD II

$$\frac{3a^2b}{2ab^2} \cdot \frac{4abx}{9a^2by} = \frac{\overset{1}{\cancel{3a^2b}}}{\underset{b}{\cancel{2ab^2}}} \cdot \frac{\overset{2x}{\cancel{4abx}}}{\underset{3y}{\cancel{9a^2by}}} = \frac{2x}{3by}$$

Can you see why only Method II from the previous page is used in Example 3 below?

EXAMPLE 3. Simplify $\dfrac{3a + 3b}{a - b} \cdot \dfrac{a + 2b}{a^2 + 2ab + b^2}$.

$$\frac{3a + 3b}{a - b} \cdot \frac{a + 2b}{a^2 + 2ab + b^2} = \frac{3\cancel{(a + b)}(a + 2b)}{(a - b)\cancel{(a + b)}(a + b)}$$

$$= \frac{3(a + 2b)}{(a - b)(a + b)}, \text{ or } \frac{3a + 6b}{a^2 - b^2}$$

You can see that the numerator and the denominator of each fraction were factored completely to make it easier to name the indicated product in lowest terms. When a product contains polynomial factors, as in Example 3, the answer may be left in either form shown above.

Now try these

— Find the product in simplest form.

1. $\dfrac{a^2}{b^2c} \cdot \dfrac{ab^2}{a}$

2. $\dfrac{5ab}{3x} \cdot \dfrac{12x^2}{10a^2b}$

3. $\dfrac{a + b}{a} \cdot \dfrac{a^2}{b}$

4. $\dfrac{m^2 - n^2}{m + n} \cdot \dfrac{m + n}{m - n}$

5. $\dfrac{x^2 - xy}{x - y} \cdot \dfrac{1}{x}$

6. $\dfrac{x - 2}{x - 5x + 6} \cdot \dfrac{x^2 - 9}{x^2 - 3x}$

Answers: 1. $\dfrac{a^2}{c}$ 2. $\dfrac{2x}{a}$ 3. $\dfrac{a(a + b)}{b}$ 4. $m + n$ 5. 1 6. $\dfrac{x + 3}{x^2 - 3x}$

Exercises

A — Write the product in simplest form.

1. $\dfrac{x}{y} \cdot \dfrac{my}{nx}$

2. $\dfrac{ab}{xy} \cdot \dfrac{x}{a^3b^2}$

3. $\dfrac{xy^2}{m^3n} \cdot \dfrac{m^2}{y^3}$

4. $\dfrac{a}{b} \cdot \dfrac{c}{d} \cdot \dfrac{ax}{by} \cdot \dfrac{y^2}{x^2}$

5. $\dfrac{7xy^2}{8x^2y} \cdot \dfrac{16xz^2}{49y^2z}$

6. $\dfrac{3}{x} \cdot \dfrac{x^2}{3}$

7. $\dfrac{4 \cdot 6}{2 \cdot 3^2} \cdot \dfrac{27}{2^2 \cdot 3}$

8. $\dfrac{3x}{d} \cdot \dfrac{c}{3x}$

9. $\dfrac{ab^2}{2} \cdot \dfrac{c}{abd}$

10. $(x + 2) \cdot \dfrac{x + 3}{x + 1}$

11. $(2x + 5) \cdot \dfrac{2x + 3}{2x - 5}$

12. $\dfrac{(x - 5)^2}{3(x - 5)}$

13. $x^2y \cdot \dfrac{8}{2x + 2xy}$

14. $\dfrac{3a - 3b}{10ab} \cdot \dfrac{50a^2b^2}{a^2 - b^2}$

15. $\dfrac{a + 1}{a + 2} \cdot \dfrac{a + 2}{a + 1}$

16. $(n + 3) \cdot \dfrac{n + 3}{n + 5}$

17. $(2x - 5) \cdot \dfrac{x + 7}{2x - 5}$

18. $\dfrac{a + 3}{a - 3} \cdot \dfrac{1}{a + 3}$

19. $n(a + b) \cdot \dfrac{1}{m(a + b)}$

20. $\dfrac{a^2 - 4b^2}{a^2 - b^2} \cdot \dfrac{3a^2b^2}{a + b}$

21. $\dfrac{a^2 + 5a}{a^2 - 16} \cdot \dfrac{a^2 - 4a}{a^2 - 25}$

22. $\dfrac{3x^2 - 48y^2}{2x^2 - 8y^2} \cdot \dfrac{3x^2 + 6y}{3x + 12y}$

23. $\dfrac{x^2 + 8x + 16}{x^2 - 9} \cdot \dfrac{x - 3}{x + 4}$

24. $\dfrac{a^2 - 3a - 10}{(a - 2)^2} \cdot \dfrac{a - 2}{a - 5}$

25. $\dfrac{9 - x^2}{x + 3} \cdot \dfrac{x}{3 - x}$

26. $\dfrac{24x^2}{3(x^2 - 4x + 4)} \cdot \dfrac{3x - 6}{2x}$

27. $\dfrac{x^2 - 6x + 5}{x - 1} \cdot \dfrac{x - 1}{x - 5}$

28. $\dfrac{c^2 - 6c}{c - 6} \cdot \dfrac{c + 3}{c}$

29. $\dfrac{x^2 - 24 - 2x}{x^2 - 30 - x} \cdot \dfrac{x + 5}{x^2 - 16}$

30. $\dfrac{9 - y^2}{r^3 - r} \cdot \dfrac{r - 1}{y + 3}$

B —— Write the product in simplest form.

31. $\dfrac{a^2 + 7ab + 10b^2}{a^2 + 6ab + 5b^2} \cdot \dfrac{a + b}{a^2 + 4ab + 4b^2} \cdot \dfrac{a + 2b}{1}$

32. $\dfrac{x^2 - y^2}{x^2 - 3xy + 2y^2} \cdot \dfrac{xy - 2y}{y^2 + xy} \cdot \dfrac{x(x - y)}{(x - y)^2}$

33. $\dfrac{2a - 3b}{a^2 + 4ab + 4b^2} \cdot \dfrac{4a^2 - 4b^2}{4a^2 - 9b^2} \cdot \dfrac{5a^2 + 10ab}{3ab - 3b^2}$

34. $\dfrac{6x - 3y}{4x^2 + 4xy + y^2} \cdot \dfrac{2x + y}{4x^2 - 4xy + y^2}$

35. $\dfrac{5m + 5n}{m^2 - n^2} \cdot \dfrac{m^2 - mn}{(m + n)^2}$

36. $\dfrac{x^2 - 3x - 18}{x^2 - x - 2} \cdot \dfrac{3x + 3}{x^2 - 2x - 15}$

37. $\dfrac{a^2 + 6a + 5}{a - 3} \cdot \dfrac{5a - 15}{a^2 + 4a - 5}$

38. $\dfrac{3a + 9}{3a^2 - 5a + 2} \cdot \dfrac{6a^2 - 7a + 2}{2a^2 + 3a - 18}$

39. $\dfrac{4x^2 - 9y^2}{6x^2 - 9xy} \cdot \dfrac{6xy}{4xy + 6y^2}$

40. $\dfrac{x^2 + 6x + 8}{x^2 + 4x + 14} \cdot \dfrac{x^2 + 5x + 6}{x^2 + 7x + 12}$

41. $\dfrac{a^2 + a - 2}{a^2 - 3a - 10} \cdot \dfrac{a^2 - 2a - 8}{a^2 - 7a + 12}$

42. $\dfrac{x^2 - 2xb + b^2}{b - 1} \cdot \dfrac{b^2 - 5b + 4}{x^2 - b^2}$

C —— Write the product in simplest form.

43. $\dfrac{x^2 - x - 1}{x - 1} \cdot \dfrac{x^2 - 1}{x} \cdot \dfrac{x^2 - x - 1}{x - 1}$

44. $\dfrac{a^2 - 5a + 6}{6a^2 - 17a + 5} \cdot \dfrac{6a^2 + 7a - 3}{2a^2 - 7a + 3} \cdot \dfrac{2a^2 - 7a + 5}{a^2 - 3a + 2}$

45. Begin the proof of Theorem 9–2 by multiplying each side of the equation by its multiplicative inverse QS. If both products equal 1, the multiplicative identity element, then $\dfrac{1}{Q} \cdot \dfrac{1}{S}$ and $\dfrac{1}{QS}$ have the same multiplicative inverse and they must be equal. Supply the reasons in the following proof.

Statements	*Reasons*
1. $(QS)\left(\frac{1}{Q}\right)\left(\frac{1}{S}\right) = \left[Q\left(\frac{1}{Q}\right)\right]$ $\times \left[S\left(\frac{1}{S}\right)\right]$	1. Associative and commutative postulates of multiplication.
2. $= 1 \times 1$, or 1	2. ?
3. $(QS)\left[\frac{1}{QS}\right] = 1,\ QS \neq 0$	3. ?
4. Thus, $\frac{1}{Q} \cdot \frac{1}{S}$ and $\frac{1}{QS}$ are equal.	4. ?

46. Theorem 9–3 can be proved by beginning with the left side of the equation and working to make it equal to the right side. Fill in the missing reasons.

Statements	*Reasons*
1. $\dfrac{P}{Q} \cdot \dfrac{R}{S} = \left(P \cdot \dfrac{1}{Q}\right)\left(R \cdot \dfrac{1}{S}\right)$	1. Postulate of division.
2. $\quad = P \cdot \left(\dfrac{1}{Q} \cdot R\right) \cdot \dfrac{1}{S}$	2. Associative postulate (applied twice).
3. $\quad = P \cdot \left(R \cdot \dfrac{1}{Q}\right) \cdot \dfrac{1}{S}$	3. _?_
4. $\quad = PR\left(\dfrac{1}{Q} \cdot \dfrac{1}{S}\right)$	4. _?_
5. $\quad = PR\left(\dfrac{1}{QS}\right)$	5. _?_
6. $\dfrac{P}{Q} \cdot \dfrac{R}{S} = \dfrac{PR}{QS}$	6. _?_

9–4 Division of Rational Expressions

It is easy to draw a diagram to show that $4 \div \frac{1}{2} = 8$ is true, or that there are eight halves in 4.

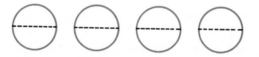

To make a diagram to illustrate the quotient for $\frac{2}{3} \div \frac{5}{7}$ would be more difficult. But the computation can be done easily by using the properties you have learned.

$$\frac{2}{3} \div \frac{5}{7} = \frac{\frac{2}{3}}{\frac{5}{7}} = \frac{\frac{2 \cdot 7}{3 \cdot 5}}{\frac{5 \cdot 7}{7 \cdot 5}}$$

Simplifying makes the denominator 1.

$$\frac{\frac{2 \cdot 7}{3 \cdot 5}}{1} = \frac{2}{3} \cdot \frac{7}{5} = \frac{14}{15}$$

Then,

$$\underbrace{\text{division}}_{\text{by } \frac{5}{7}} \quad \underbrace{\text{is the}}_{\text{same as}} \quad \underbrace{\text{multiplication}}_{\text{by } \frac{7}{5}.}$$

$$\frac{2}{3} \div \frac{5}{7} \quad = \quad \frac{14}{15} \quad = \quad \frac{2}{3} \cdot \frac{7}{5}$$

Notice that you multiplied by $\frac{7}{5}$, the reciprocal of the divisor $\frac{5}{7}$. In this way, the division process becomes a multiplication process. The same idea holds for division of rational expressions.

Theorem 9-4   To divide a rational expression $\frac{P}{Q}$ by a rational expression $\frac{R}{S}$, multiply $\frac{P}{Q}$ by the multiplicative inverse, or reciprocal, of $\frac{R}{S}$.

The proof will be left as an exercise.

Now try these

— Write the quotient in simplest form.

1. $\frac{a}{b} \div \frac{a}{c}$ **2.** $\frac{x^2y}{x} \div \frac{x}{y^2}$ **3.** $\frac{5a^2}{7b} \div \frac{15a^3}{14b^2}$ **4.** $\frac{x-y}{x+y} \div \frac{x^2-y^2}{2}$

Answers: **1.** $\frac{c}{b}$ **2.** y^3 **3.** $\frac{2b}{3a}$ **4.** $\frac{2}{x^2+2xy+y^2}$

Exercises

A — Find the quotients.   Express answers in lowest terms.

1. $\frac{x}{2} \div \frac{x}{4}$ **2.** $\frac{x}{4} \div \frac{x}{a}$ **3.** $\frac{2}{x} \div \frac{4}{x}$

4. $\frac{4}{x} \div \frac{2}{x}$ **5.** $\frac{x}{y} \div \frac{3}{y}$ **6.** $\frac{ad}{bc} \div \frac{a}{b}$

7. $\frac{a}{b} \div \frac{c}{d}$ **8.** $\frac{xy}{ab} \div \frac{xy}{bc}$ **9.** $\frac{1}{a} \div \frac{a}{b}$

10. $\frac{a}{x} \div \frac{c}{x}$ **11.** $\frac{1}{f} \div \frac{1}{g}$ **12.** $\frac{a}{x} \div \frac{x}{c}$

13. $\frac{8}{3a} \div 16$ **14.** $\frac{5x^2}{8xy} \div 15x$ **15.** $\frac{9ab^2}{8xy^2} \div \frac{3b^2}{2xy}$

16. $\frac{14a^2}{10b^2} \div \frac{21a^2}{15b^2}$ **17.** $\frac{5x}{12yz^2} \div \frac{15x^3}{18y^2z^2}$ **18.** $\frac{25x^2}{(3yz)^2} \div \frac{100x^3}{18yz^3}$

B — Find the quotients.   Express answers in lowest terms.

19. $\frac{x^2+x}{a} \div x^2$ **20.** $\frac{(a-b)(a+b)}{(x-y)(x+y)} \div \frac{a-b}{x+y}$

21. $\frac{a^2-b^2}{x^2-y^2} \div \frac{a+b}{x-y}$ **22.** $\frac{(2x)^3}{(4yz)^3} \div \frac{16x^2}{8y^2z^3}$

23. $\dfrac{3(x+y)^2}{x-y} \div 6(x+y)$

24. $\dfrac{x-y}{x+y} \div \dfrac{5x^2-5y^2}{3x-3y}$

25. $\dfrac{x^2+2x+1}{3x} \div (x+1)$

26. $\dfrac{a^3-6a^2+8a}{5x} \div \dfrac{2a-4}{10a-40}$

27. $\dfrac{5a^2-5ab}{ab+b^2} \div \dfrac{5a^2-5b^2}{b}$

28. $\dfrac{4x^2-4xy-3y^2}{3x^2y} \div \dfrac{2x^2-3xy}{6x^3}$

C —— Perform the indicated operations.

29. $\dfrac{x^2-y^2}{x^2} \cdot \dfrac{x+y}{x-y} \div \dfrac{x^2-y^2}{yx}$

30. $\dfrac{a^2-2ab+b^2}{ab} \cdot \dfrac{a+b}{a-b} \div \dfrac{a^2-b^2}{a^2}$

31. $\dfrac{a^3b^3}{a^3-ab^2} \div \dfrac{abc}{a-b} \cdot \dfrac{ab+bc}{ab}$

32. $\dfrac{xy-xz-x^2}{xyz} \cdot \dfrac{x^2y^2z^3}{yx-zx} \div x^3$

33. $\dfrac{2x^3}{2a+b} \div \dfrac{10a^2}{4a^2+4ab+b^2} \cdot \dfrac{12a+3b}{2a^2+ab}$

34. Prove Theorem 9–4. (*Hint:* Follow the numerical example on page 396.)

9–5   Least Common Multiple of Polynomials

Consider the rational numbers 4 and 6. The natural-number multiples of 4 are

$$\{4, 8, 12, 16, 20, 24, 28, 32, 36, \cdots\}.$$

The natural-number multiples of 6 are

$$\{6, 12, 18, 24, 30, 36, \cdots\}.$$

The multiples common to both 4 and 6 are

$$\{12, 24, 36, \cdots\}.$$

What is the least multiple in this last set? The **least common multiple** (LCM) of 4 and 6 is 12, because 12 is the least multiple of both 4 and 6; 12 is the least number that has both 4 and 6 as factors.

The same idea is used to define the least common multiple of polynomials.

Definition   The least common multiple (LCM) of two or more polynomials is the least polynomial that has each of the given polynomials as factors.

To find the LCM easily, first write each polynomial in factored form. Decide which factors are common to both polynomials. The factors that are not common factors are the "remaining" factors. The LCM is the product of all the common factors and the remaining factors.

EXAMPLE 1. Find the LCM of 8 and 12.

$$8 = \underline{2} \cdot \underline{2} \cdot 2$$
$$12 = \underline{2} \cdot \underline{2} \cdot 3$$

The factors common to both numbers are 2 and 2. The remaining factors are 2 and 3. The LCM, the product of these factors, is $2 \cdot 2 \cdot 2 \cdot 3$, or 24. The least number that has both sets of factors in it is 24.

EXAMPLE 2. Find the LCM of $6x^4y$ and $9x^2y^2$.

$$6x^4y = 2 \cdot \underline{3} \cdot \underline{x} \cdot \underline{x} \cdot x \cdot x \cdot \underline{y}$$
$$9x^2y^2 = 3 \cdot \underline{3} \cdot \underline{x} \cdot \underline{x} \cdot \underline{y} \cdot y$$

The common factors are $3 \cdot x \cdot x \cdot y$, or $3x^2y$.
The other factors are $2 \cdot x \cdot x \cdot 3 \cdot y$, or $6x^2y$.
Thus, the LCM is $3x^2y \cdot 6x^2y$, or $18x^4y^2$.

EXAMPLE 3. Find the LCM of $x^2 - 5x + 6$ and $x^2 + 2x - 8$.

$$x^2 - 5x + 6 = (x - 3)(x - 2)$$
$$x^2 + 2x - 8 = (x + 4)(x - 2)$$

The common factor is $(x - 2)$. The remaining factors are $(x - 3)$ and $(x + 4)$. The LCM is $(x - 2)(x - 3)(x + 4)$, or $x^3 - x^2 - 14x + 24$.

Now try these

—— Find the least common multiple for each of the following.

1. $6xy$, $9x^2$

2. 14, $2s^2t$, $4t^3$

3. $8a^2b$, $6ab^3$, $12abc$

4. $(x^2 - 4)$, $(x^2 + 3x + 2)$

Answers: **1.** $18x^2y$ **2.** $28s^2t^3$ **3.** $24a^2b^3c$ **4.** $(x - 2)(x + 2)(x + 1)$, or $x^3 + x^2 - 4x - 4$

Exercises

A —— Find the LCM of the following.

1. 6 and 2   **2.** 3 and 4   **3.** 2 and 5

4. 3 and 9   **5.** 5 and 6   **6.** 8 and 2

7. a and b **8.** x^2 and x **9.** ab and b^2

10. $2a^2$ and $12b^2$ **11.** $2a$ and $3a$ **12.** $6x$ and $3x$

13. $6p$ and $4p$ **14.** $2x$ and $3y$ **15.** ab^2 and a^2b

Example. $6a^2$, $15a$, and 18

    To find the LCM of three polynomials, find the LCM of two of them, and then find the LCM of the result and the third.

$$6a^2 = 3 \cdot 2 \cdot a \cdot a \qquad 15a = 3 \cdot 5 \cdot a$$
$$\text{LCM of } 6a^2 \text{ and } 15a \text{ is } 3a \cdot 2 \cdot a \cdot 5, \text{ or } 30a^2.$$
$$30a^2 = 3a \cdot 2 \cdot a \cdot 5 \qquad 18 = 3 \cdot 3 \cdot 2$$

    Notice that the only factor of 18 not already in $30a^2$ is the second 3. Thus, the LCM of $30a^2$ and 18 is $3a \cdot 2 \cdot a \cdot 5 \cdot 3$, or $90a^2$.

16. 9, 2, and 6   **17.** 8, 4, and 3   **18.** 5, 2, and 4

19. 5, 4, and 10   **20.** 12, 2, and 3   **21.** 16, 12, and 3

22. 5, 9, and 3   **23.** 7, 4, and 2   **24.** 6, 7, and 3

25. x^2, y, and y^2 **26.** x, y, and z **27.** x^2, xy, and y^2

B —— Find the LCM of the following.

28. $(x - y)$ and $(x + y)$ **29.** $(x^2 - y^2)$ and $(x - y)$

30. $(4a - 8b)$ and $(3a - 6b)$ **31.** $(9a^2 - 6)$ and $(15a^2 - 10)$

32. $(a + 4)$ and $(a + 2)$ **33.** $(2x + 2y)$ and $(x + y)$

34. $(x + 4)$ and $(x^2 - 16)$ **35.** $(x^2 - 4)$ and $(x + 2)^2$

36. $(x^2 - 5x + 6)$ and $(x^2 - 4x + 3)$

37. $(6a^2 - 5a - 6)$ and $(12a^2 + 11a + 2)$

38. $(8a^2 - 8a - 16)$ and $(10a^2 - 14a - 12)$

9–6 Addition and Subtraction of Rational Expressions

How do you find $\frac{2}{3} + \frac{5}{6}$? How do you find $\frac{5}{8} - \frac{1}{2}$?

    You have learned that to add or subtract rational numbers with unlike denominators, you rename the rational numbers so that they have like denominators. That denominator is called the **least common denominator** (LCD).

    The same principle is true in algebra. If the denominators of the rational expressions are unlike polynomials, you find the least common multiple of the polynomials, or the least common denominator of the rational expressions. Then proceed as in arithmetic to make the denominators alike, using the following theorem that was proved on page 389.

Theorem 9–1 The numerator and denominator of a rational expression may be multiplied or divided by the same nonzero polynomial without changing the value of the expression.

Study the following parallel arithmetic and algebraic examples.

Arithmetic	*Algebra*

A. Add $\frac{5}{8}$ and $\frac{1}{8}$.

$$\frac{5}{8} + \frac{1}{8} = \frac{5+1}{8} = \frac{6}{8}$$

A. Add $\frac{x}{x+y}$ and $\frac{3x}{x+y}$.

$$\frac{x}{x+y} + \frac{3x}{x+y} = \frac{x+3x}{x+y} = \frac{4x}{x+y}$$

B. Add $\frac{2}{3}$ and $\frac{4}{5}$.

① LCD is 15.

② $\frac{2}{3} = \frac{2 \cdot 5}{3 \cdot 5} = \frac{10}{15}$

  $\frac{4}{5} = \frac{4 \cdot 3}{5 \cdot 3} = \frac{12}{15}$

③ $\frac{10}{15} + \frac{12}{15} = \frac{22}{15}$, or $1\frac{7}{15}$

B. Add $\frac{a}{3b}$ and $\frac{c}{2d}$.

① LCD is $6bd$.

② $\frac{a}{3b} = \frac{a \cdot 2d}{3b \cdot 2d} = \frac{2ad}{6bd}$

  $\frac{c}{2d} = \frac{c \cdot 3b}{2d \cdot 3b} = \frac{3bc}{6bd}$

③ $\frac{2ad}{6bd} + \frac{3bc}{6bd} = \frac{2ad + 3bc}{6bd}$

C. From $\frac{1\frac{1}{2}}{8}$, subtract $\frac{\frac{1}{4}}{12}$.

① LCD is 24.

② $\frac{1\frac{1}{2}}{8} = \frac{1\frac{1}{2} \cdot 3}{8 \cdot 3} = \frac{4\frac{1}{2}}{24}$

  $\frac{\frac{1}{4}}{12} = \frac{\frac{1}{4} \cdot 2}{12 \cdot 2} = \frac{\frac{1}{2}}{24}$

③ $\frac{4\frac{1}{2}}{24} - \frac{\frac{1}{2}}{24} = \frac{4\frac{1}{2} - \frac{1}{2}}{24}$

  $= \frac{4}{24}$, or $\frac{1}{6}$

C. From $\frac{2a+b}{4ab}$, subtract $\frac{3a-2b}{6a}$.

① LCD is $12ab$.

② $\frac{2a+b}{4ab} = \frac{(2a+b) \cdot 3}{(4ab) \cdot 3} = \frac{6a+3b}{12ab}$

  $\frac{3a-2b}{6a} = \frac{(3a-2b) \cdot 2b}{6a \cdot 2b} = \frac{6ab-4b^2}{12ab}$

③ $\frac{6a+3b}{12ab} - \frac{6ab-4b^2}{12ab}$

  $= \frac{6a + 3b - (6ab - 4b^2)}{12ab}$

  $= \frac{6a + 3b - 6ab + 4b^2}{12ab}$

Note in Example C that the minus sign affects the whole numerator, $6ab - 4b^2$, and all the signs in it must be changed.

The following examples illustrate some other cases of adding or subtracting rational expressions.

EXAMPLE 1. Subtract $\frac{3x - y}{b}$ from $x + 2y$.

① Since the denominator for $(x + 2y)$ is 1, the LCD is b.

② $\left(\frac{x + 2y}{1} \cdot \frac{b}{b}\right) - \frac{3x - y}{b} = \frac{bx + 2by}{b} - \frac{3x - y}{b}$

$$= \frac{bx + 2by - (3x - y)}{b}$$

$$= \frac{bx + 2by - 3x + y}{b}$$

EXAMPLE 2. Combine $\frac{3}{x^2}$, $\frac{5}{2xy}$, and $-\frac{4}{3y^2}$.

① The LCD of x^2, $2xy$, and $3y^2$ is $3 \cdot 2 \cdot x \cdot x \cdot y \cdot y$, or $6x^2y^2$.

② $\frac{3}{x^2} + \frac{5}{2xy} - \frac{4}{3y^2} = \frac{3 \cdot 6y^2}{x^2 \cdot 6y^2} + \frac{5 \cdot 3xy}{2xy \cdot 3xy} - \frac{4 \cdot 2x^2}{3y^2 \cdot 2x^2}$

$$= \frac{18y^2}{6x^2y^2} + \frac{15xy}{6x^2y^2} - \frac{8x^2}{6x^2y^2}$$

$$= \frac{18y^2 + 15xy - 8x^2}{6x^2y^2}$$

EXAMPLE 3. $\frac{x + 1}{x^2 - 9} + \frac{4}{x + 3} - \frac{x - 1}{x - 3}$

① The factors of $x^2 - 9$ are $(x + 3)$ and $(x - 3)$, which are the other two denominators. So the LCD is $(x + 3)(x - 3)$.

② $\frac{x + 1}{(x + 3)(x - 3)} + \left(\frac{4}{x + 3} \cdot \frac{x - 3}{x - 3}\right) - \left(\frac{x - 1}{x - 3} \cdot \frac{x + 3}{x + 3}\right)$

$$= \frac{x + 1}{x^2 - 9} + \frac{4x - 12}{x^2 - 9} - \frac{x^2 + 2x - 3}{x^2 - 9}$$

$$= \frac{x + 1 + 4x - 12 - (x^2 + 2x - 3)}{x^2 - 9}$$

$$= \frac{5x - 11 - x^2 - 2x + 3}{x^2 - 9}, \text{ or } \frac{-x^2 + 3x - 8}{x^2 - 9}$$

Now try these

—— Find the LCD for the following expressions and rewrite them using the LCD.

1. $\frac{2a}{3}, \frac{7a}{5}$ **2.** $\frac{x}{2y^2}, \frac{3y}{x}$ **3.** $\frac{y + 1}{x}, \frac{2y}{x - 1}$

—— Perform the indicated operations.

4. $\frac{4}{x} + \frac{6}{y}$ **5.** $\frac{a}{2b} - \frac{3c}{b^2d}$ **6.** $\frac{5}{x} - \frac{2}{x + 1} + \frac{7}{y}$

1. 15; $\dfrac{10a}{15}, \dfrac{21a}{15}$　**2.** $2xy^2$; $\dfrac{x^2}{2xy^2}, \dfrac{6y^3}{2xy^2}$　**3.** $x(x-1)$ or x^2-x;

$\dfrac{(y+1)(x-1)}{x(x-1)}, \dfrac{2xy}{x(x-1)}$　**4.** $\dfrac{4y+6x}{xy}$　**5.** $\dfrac{abd-6c}{2b^2d}$

6. $\dfrac{7x^2+7x+3xy+5y}{xy(x+1)}$

Exercises

A ▬ Rewrite the following rational expressions, using the LCD.

1. $\dfrac{6x}{3}$ and $\dfrac{5x}{6}$

2. $\dfrac{x-2y}{6}$ and $\dfrac{2x-y}{7}$

3. $\dfrac{a}{a+b}$ and $\dfrac{b}{a-b}$

4. $\dfrac{2}{3x^2}$ and $\dfrac{3}{4xy}$

5. $\dfrac{x}{yz}, \dfrac{y}{xz}$, and $\dfrac{z}{xy}$

6. $\dfrac{1}{16-x^2}$ and $\dfrac{9}{4+x}$

▬ Find the value of each of the following if a is 3 and b is 2.

7. $\dfrac{1}{a}+\dfrac{1}{b}$

8. $\dfrac{3a}{a-b}-\dfrac{a+b}{a-b}$

9. $\dfrac{a+b}{b}-\dfrac{a+b}{a}$

10. $\dfrac{a}{a^2-b}-\dfrac{b}{b^2-a}$

11. $\dfrac{a-b}{a+b}-\dfrac{a+b}{a-b}$

12. $\dfrac{a^2}{a-1}+\dfrac{b^2}{a+1}$

13. Complete the following table by replacing each ? with the sum obtained by adding the rational expression in each row to the rational expression in each column.

		Column		
+		$\dfrac{a}{b}$	$\dfrac{c}{d}$	$\dfrac{x}{y}$
	$\dfrac{a}{b}$	?	$\dfrac{ad+bc}{bd}$	?
Row	$\dfrac{c}{d}$	$\dfrac{bc+ad}{bd}$	?	?
	$\dfrac{x}{y}$	?	?	$\dfrac{2x}{y}$

▬ In Exercises 14–17, indicate the letter of one of the following statements that justifies the result.

A. $\dfrac{P}{Q}=\dfrac{RP}{RQ}$, $R\neq 0$

B. $\dfrac{P}{R}+\dfrac{Q}{R}=\dfrac{P+Q}{R}$

C. $\dfrac{P}{Q}+\dfrac{R}{S}=\dfrac{PS+QR}{QS}$

D. $\dfrac{P}{Q}-\dfrac{R}{S}=\dfrac{PS-QR}{QS}$

14. $\dfrac{x+y}{a}+\dfrac{x}{a}=\dfrac{2x+y}{a}$

15. $\dfrac{3a-2b}{4}=\dfrac{-3a+2b}{-4}$

16. $\dfrac{5b}{3}-\dfrac{3b}{8}=\dfrac{31b}{24}$

17. $\dfrac{a}{b}+\dfrac{c}{d}+\dfrac{e}{f}=\dfrac{adf+bcf+bde}{bdf}$

Perform the operations indicated. Simplify your answer when possible.

18. $\dfrac{x^2}{7} + \dfrac{x^2}{6}$

19. $\dfrac{2x}{3} + \dfrac{5y}{2}$

20. $\dfrac{x^2y}{6} + \dfrac{xy^2}{5}$

21. $\dfrac{7ab}{10} - \dfrac{3a}{4}$

22. $\dfrac{2a+3}{6} - \dfrac{5a-7}{9}$

23. $\dfrac{3x-5}{4} + \dfrac{5x-3}{3}$

24. $\dfrac{4n-1}{5} - \dfrac{n+2}{4}$

25. $\dfrac{x^2-y^2}{3} - \dfrac{x^2+y^2}{8}$

26. $\dfrac{3c}{8} + \dfrac{b+c}{3}$

27. $\dfrac{1}{a} + \dfrac{1}{b}$

28. $\dfrac{2}{a} + \dfrac{3}{b}$

29. $\dfrac{1}{a} - \dfrac{1}{b}$

30. $\dfrac{4}{x} - \dfrac{5}{y}$

31. $\dfrac{a}{b} - \dfrac{c}{d}$

32. $\dfrac{3}{2c} + \dfrac{4}{6c}$

33. $\dfrac{5}{4a} - \dfrac{3}{8a}$

34. $3 + \dfrac{1}{a}$

35. $ax + \dfrac{b}{x}$

36. $3 + \dfrac{a}{b}$

37. $2x - \dfrac{x+y}{y}$

38. $\dfrac{7a}{10p} - \dfrac{2b}{5p}$

39. $\dfrac{5r}{4c} + \dfrac{4s}{5d}$

40. $\dfrac{3}{x} + \dfrac{5}{x^2}$

41. $\dfrac{4a}{b^2} - \dfrac{3a}{b}$

42. $\dfrac{3}{x} - \dfrac{5}{x^3} + \dfrac{2}{x^2}$

43. $\dfrac{a}{x^3} + \dfrac{b}{x^2} - \dfrac{c}{x}$

44. $\dfrac{5}{ab^2} - \dfrac{7}{a^2b}$

45. $a - \dfrac{b}{c}$

46. $\dfrac{a}{x} - (a-1)$

47. $a^2 - \dfrac{1}{a}$

48. $\dfrac{2}{xy} + \dfrac{3}{yz}$

49. $\dfrac{9}{mn} + \dfrac{3}{mn^2}$

50. $\dfrac{8}{x} + \dfrac{3}{xy}$

51. $\dfrac{1}{6p} - \dfrac{1}{4p} + \dfrac{1}{3p}$

52. $\dfrac{3}{b} + \dfrac{5}{2b} - \dfrac{11}{3b}$

53. $\dfrac{a+b}{b} - \dfrac{a-b}{a}$

54. $\dfrac{x+1}{2x} + \dfrac{2}{x}$

55. $v + \dfrac{m_1v_1}{m}$

56. $\dfrac{2x-1}{x} - \dfrac{x+3}{3x}$

57. $\dfrac{1}{2a^2} - \dfrac{5}{6ab} + \dfrac{7}{12b^2}$

58. $\dfrac{x}{2b} + \dfrac{2x}{b} - \dfrac{1}{b^2}$

59. $\dfrac{x-1}{3xy} + \dfrac{x^2-x}{9x^2y^2}$

60. $\dfrac{2a+1}{a} + \dfrac{3b+5}{b}$

61. $\dfrac{3a+5}{a} - \dfrac{2b-3}{b}$

62. $\dfrac{3x-y}{x} + \dfrac{4x+2y}{x}$

63. $\dfrac{4x+y}{x} - \dfrac{3x-4y}{x^2}$

64. $\dfrac{2y-3}{2y} + \dfrac{y-4}{3y}$

65. $\dfrac{5a-2b}{-a^2} + \dfrac{4a+3b}{-3a^2}$

66. $\dfrac{6r-2s}{-2s^2} - \dfrac{5r+2s}{s^2}$

B Combine as the signs indicate.

67. $\dfrac{5}{x+2} + \dfrac{3}{x-2}$

68. $\dfrac{5}{x+5} - \dfrac{3}{x-5}$

69. $\dfrac{2}{a+3} + \dfrac{5}{a+5}$

70. $\dfrac{2x}{x-y} - \dfrac{3y}{x+y}$

71. $\dfrac{a}{2a+2b} - \dfrac{b}{3a+3b}$

72. $\dfrac{4a}{6a-2b} + \dfrac{3b}{9a-3b}$

73. $\dfrac{2}{3t + 3s} + \dfrac{3}{5r - 5s}$

74. $\dfrac{3x}{2y - 3} - \dfrac{2x}{3y - 2}$

75. $\dfrac{x + 3}{x - 5} + \dfrac{x - 5}{x + 3}$

76. $\dfrac{a - 2}{a + 3} - \dfrac{a - 3}{a + 5}$

77. $\dfrac{x + 3}{x^2 - 4} + \dfrac{x - 5}{x + 2}$

78. $\dfrac{3a + 2}{3a + 6} - \dfrac{a - 2}{a^2 - 4}$

79. $\dfrac{a + b}{ax + ay} - \dfrac{a + b}{bx + by}$

80. $\dfrac{a - b}{a + b} - \dfrac{a}{a^2 - b^2}$

81. $\dfrac{x - y}{x + y} + \dfrac{4xy}{x^2 - y^2}$

82. $\dfrac{x + y}{x - y} - \dfrac{4xy}{x^2 - y^2}$

C — Perform the operation indicated.

83. $\dfrac{4a}{2a + 6} - \dfrac{a - 1}{a + 3}$

84. $\dfrac{x - 6y}{2x^2 + 5xy + 2y^2} - \dfrac{7}{x + 2y}$

85. $\dfrac{2m - 6}{2m^2 - 10m + 12} - \dfrac{5}{m - 3}$

86. $\dfrac{7}{a^2 + a - 2} - \dfrac{5}{a^2 - 4a + 3}$

87. $\dfrac{2x}{x^2 - 25} - \dfrac{4(x - 5)}{x - 5}$

88. $\dfrac{3}{y^2 + y - 6} + \dfrac{2}{y^2 - 4y + 4}$

89. $\dfrac{5}{a^2 - 2ab + b^2} + \dfrac{6}{a - b}$

90. $\dfrac{5}{3x - 3} + \dfrac{x}{2x + 2} - \dfrac{3x^2}{x^2 - 1}$

91. $\dfrac{x^2}{a^2 - b^2} + \dfrac{x}{(a - b)^2}$

92. $\dfrac{x^2}{x + y} - \dfrac{y^2}{x - y} - (x - y)$

9–7   The Signs in a Rational Expression

Any rational number, such as $\frac{4}{5}$, shown without a sign is understood to be positive.   Thus, you can think of $\frac{4}{5}$ as meaning $+\frac{+4}{+5}$. Three signs are associated with it.

Any rational expression has three signs.

① The sign of the rational expression.

② The sign of the numerator of the rational expression.

③ The sign of the denominator of the rational expression.

The three signs of the expression $-\dfrac{2x}{y^2}$ are

① $-$ for the rational expression, $\dfrac{2x}{y^2}$.

② $+$, understood, for the numerator, $2x$.

③ $+$, understood, for the denominator, y^2.

What are the three signs of $\dfrac{-2x}{y^2}$?

Study the following examples. Notice that, although the expressions have the same value, the signs differ.

a. $+\dfrac{+6x^2}{+2x} = +3x$

b. $+\dfrac{-6x^2}{-2x} = \dfrac{-1}{-1}\left(+\dfrac{-6x^2}{-2x}\right) = +\dfrac{+6x^2}{+2x} = +3x$

c. $-\dfrac{-6x^2}{+2x} = -1\left(-\dfrac{(-1)(-6x^2)}{+2x}\right) = +\dfrac{+6x^2}{+2x} = +3x$

d. $-\dfrac{+6x^2}{-2x} = -1\left(-\dfrac{+6x^2}{(-1)(-2x)}\right) = +\dfrac{+6x^2}{+2x} = +3x$

Since each rational expression equals $+3x$, they are all equal to each other.

$$+\frac{+6x^2}{+2x} = +\frac{-6x^2}{-2x} = -\frac{-6x^2}{+2x} = -\frac{+6x^2}{-2x}$$

From the examples, you can see that by introducing -1 twice as a factor in the coefficients, an expression may be changed to an equivalent expression.

> **Theorem 9–5** The factor (-1) may be introduced twice into any rational expression without changing the value of the expression.

First prove that $\dfrac{P}{Q} = -\dfrac{-P}{Q}$ is true.

Statements	Reasons
1. $\dfrac{P}{Q} = \dfrac{P}{Q}$	1. Reflexive property.
2. $\quad = \dfrac{-1}{-1} \cdot \dfrac{P}{Q}$	2. Theorem 9–1.
3. $\quad = \dfrac{-P}{(-1)Q}$	3. Postulate of multiplication.
4. $\quad = \dfrac{(1)}{(-1)} \cdot \dfrac{-P}{Q}$	4. Postulate of multiplication.
5. $\quad = -1\left(\dfrac{-P}{Q}\right)$, or $-\dfrac{-P}{Q}$	5. Definition of division of real numbers.

Thus, $\dfrac{P}{Q} = -\dfrac{-P}{Q}$ is true. Two of the signs have been changed.

Similarly prove that $\dfrac{P}{Q} = -\dfrac{P}{-Q}$ and $\dfrac{P}{Q} = \dfrac{-P}{-Q}$ are true.

The final statement for the entire proof would be that

$$\frac{P}{Q} = -\frac{-P}{Q} = -\frac{P}{-Q} = \frac{-P}{-Q} \text{ is true.}$$

What would the reason be?

This theorem is often helpful in combining rational expressions.

EXAMPLE. Combine $\dfrac{3}{x-y} - \dfrac{2}{y-x}$.

If $(y - x)$ were multiplied by -1, it would become $(-y + x)$, or $x - y$, and the rational expressions would have the same denominator. Remember that one more sign of the rational expression must be changed.

$$-\frac{2}{y-x} = -1\left(-\frac{2}{(-1)y-x}\right) = +\frac{2}{-(y-x)}$$

$$= \frac{2}{-y+x}, \text{ or } \frac{2}{x-y}$$

Notice that the $-$ sign in the denominator applies to the entire expression $y - x$. By removing the parentheses, $-(y - x)$ becomes $-y + x$, or $x - y$.

Now combine the rational expressions.

$$\frac{3}{x-y} + \frac{2}{x-y} = \frac{5}{x-y}$$

Could you have chosen to change the expression $\dfrac{3}{x-y}$ so that its denominator would be $(y - x)$ and then combine? Try it.

When you change the sign of a numerator or denominator that is a polynomial, be sure to distribute the (-1) factor over the entire polynomial. Thus, $\dfrac{-1}{-1} \cdot \dfrac{-2x^2 - 3x + 1}{-3x + 2}$ becomes $\dfrac{2x^2 + 3x - 1}{3x - 2}$.

When you change the sign of a numerator or denominator that is made up of factors, distribute the (-1) factor over *one* factor only.

$$\frac{-1}{-1} \cdot \frac{(a-b)(c+d)}{a(b-e)} = \frac{(-a+b)(c+d)}{a(-b+e)}$$

Changing more than one factor in either the numerator or denominator would be the same as multiplying by more than *one* (-1) factor, and that does not agree with the theorem. Which of the following expressions is the same as $\dfrac{(x-3)(x+2)}{5(x^2+y^2)}$?

a. $\dfrac{(x-3)(-x-2)}{-5(x^2+y^2)}$

b. $\dfrac{(x-3)(-x-2)}{-5(-x^2-y^2)}$

Now try these

— Tell whether or not the following pairs of rational expressions are equal.

1. $\dfrac{-ax^2}{by^3} = -\dfrac{ax^2}{by^3}$

2. $\dfrac{3+r}{s+2} = \dfrac{-3+r}{-s+2}$

3. $-\dfrac{x^2-9}{y^2+4} = \dfrac{-(x^2-9)}{y^2+4}$

4. $\dfrac{5xy}{-9y^2} = \dfrac{-5xy}{9y^2}$

Answers: **1.** Equal.　　**2.** Not equal.　　**3.** Equal.　　**4.** Equal.

Exercises

A — If the following pairs of rational expressions are equal, write *Equal*. If they are not equal, rewrite the second expression so it does equal the first.

1. $\dfrac{a}{b}$ and $\dfrac{-a}{-b}$

2. $\dfrac{3}{x^2}$ and $-\dfrac{-3}{x^2}$

3. $\dfrac{y}{9}$ and $\dfrac{-y}{9}$

4. $\dfrac{a+b}{-7}$ and $-\dfrac{a+b}{7}$

5. $\dfrac{x^2+y}{x}$ and $-\dfrac{x^2+y}{x}$

6. $\dfrac{ab+1}{a}$ and $\dfrac{ab+1}{-a}$

7. $\dfrac{3}{a-b}$ and $\dfrac{-3}{b-a}$

8. $\dfrac{c+d}{a}$ and $\dfrac{d-c}{a}$

9. $\dfrac{x}{(a-3)(a+5)}$ and $-\dfrac{x}{15-2a-a^2}$

10. $\dfrac{a+b}{a-b}$ and $\dfrac{a+b}{b-a}$

— Combine as indicated.

11. $\dfrac{a}{a-b} - \dfrac{b}{b-a}$

12. $\dfrac{5}{x^2} + \dfrac{7}{-x^2}$

13. $\dfrac{4}{x-2} + \dfrac{2}{2-x}$

14. $\dfrac{y}{y-3} + \dfrac{1}{3-y}$

15. $\dfrac{10}{2y-1} - \dfrac{6}{1-2y}$

16. $\dfrac{3a}{x-y} + \dfrac{2b}{y-x}$

B — Combine as indicated.

17. $\dfrac{a^2}{a^2-1} + \dfrac{a}{1-a}$

18. $\dfrac{4}{x-3} - \dfrac{x}{9-x^2}$

19. $\dfrac{a-b}{a+b} - \dfrac{a-b}{b+a}$

20. $\dfrac{2a+3b}{2} - \dfrac{a-b}{4}$

— Simplify these rational expressions.

21. $\dfrac{a-b}{b-a}$

22. $\dfrac{a+b}{b+a}$

23. $\dfrac{a^2-b^2}{b-a}$

24. $\dfrac{a^2-b^2}{b+a}$

25. $\dfrac{(x-2)(x-3)}{(3-x)(2-x)}$

26. $\dfrac{(a-b)^2}{(b-a)^2}$

9–8 Other Rational Expressions

Consider the following rational expressions.

a. $\dfrac{\frac{7}{8}}{4}$ b. $\dfrac{\frac{3}{4}}{\frac{7}{8}}$ c. $\dfrac{\frac{a}{b}-1}{c}$ d. $\dfrac{\frac{x}{x}}{y}$ e. $\dfrac{c-\frac{b}{a}}{b-\frac{a}{b}}$

There are two methods to write each of examples **a–e** as a rational expression in a simple form, that is, in a form without a rational expression $\frac{P}{Q}$ in its numerator or its denominator.

METHOD I: Make the numerator a single rational expression and the denominator a single rational expression. Then divide the single rational expressions.

$$\frac{3-\frac{x}{y}}{\frac{2x}{y}} = \frac{\frac{3y-x}{y}}{\frac{2x}{y}} = \frac{3y-x}{\cancel{y}} \cdot \frac{\cancel{y}}{2x} = \frac{3y-x}{2x}$$

METHOD II: Multiply the numerator and the denominator by a number or expression so that you will not have a rational expression in either the numerator or the denominator. That number or expression will be the LCD of all rational expressions in the numerators and denominators of the complex rational expressions.

$$\frac{3-\frac{x}{y}}{\frac{2x}{y}} = \frac{y}{y} \cdot \frac{\left(\frac{3}{1}-\frac{x}{y}\right)}{\left(\frac{2x}{y}\right)} = \frac{3y-x}{2x}$$

Now try these

—— Simplify the following expressions. Do Exercises 1–4 by Method I and Exercises 5 and 6 by Method II.

1. $\dfrac{\frac{x}{4}}{3}$

2. $\dfrac{b}{\frac{a}{b}}$

3. $\dfrac{\frac{x^2}{y^2}}{\frac{x}{y}}$

4. $\dfrac{\frac{x+y}{x}}{\frac{x^2-y^2}{x^2y}}$

5. $\dfrac{a+\frac{b}{c}}{b+\frac{c}{d}}$

6. $\dfrac{1-\frac{x}{y}}{\frac{1}{x}-\frac{1}{y}}$

Answers: **1.** $\dfrac{x}{12}$ **2.** $\dfrac{b^2}{a}$ **3.** $\dfrac{x}{y}$ **4.** $\dfrac{xy}{x-y}$ **5.** $\dfrac{acd+bd}{bcd+c^2}$ **6.** x

Exercises

A ——— Use either method to simplify the following rational expressions.

1. $\dfrac{\frac{1}{2}}{4}$

2. $\dfrac{20}{\frac{1}{4}}$

3. $\dfrac{\frac{2}{3}}{1\frac{1}{2}}$

4. $\dfrac{\frac{1}{2}-\frac{1}{3}}{\frac{1}{2}+\frac{1}{3}}$

5. $\dfrac{\frac{a}{b}+\frac{c}{d}}{ac}$

6. $\dfrac{\frac{a}{b}-\frac{c}{d}}{ad}$

7. $\dfrac{\frac{1}{x}-\frac{1}{y}}{\frac{1}{xy}}$

8. $\dfrac{\frac{1}{a}+\frac{1}{b}}{\frac{1}{ab}}$

9. $\dfrac{\frac{1}{a}-\frac{1}{b}}{\frac{1}{a}+\frac{1}{b}}$

10. $\dfrac{\frac{x}{y}-\frac{y}{x}}{x+y}$

11. $\dfrac{x+y}{\frac{1}{x}+\frac{1}{y}}$

12. $\dfrac{\frac{1}{y}-\frac{1}{x}}{x^2-y^2}$

13. $\dfrac{\frac{1}{x}-1}{x-x^2}$

14. $\dfrac{\frac{1}{y}-1}{\frac{1}{y}+1}$

15. $\dfrac{\frac{a}{b}-1}{a^2-b^2}$

16. $\dfrac{1-\frac{x^2}{y^2}}{x+y}$

17. $\dfrac{x+\frac{1}{x}}{x}$

18. $\dfrac{x}{x+\frac{1}{x}}$

19. $\dfrac{\frac{1}{x}-x}{x}$

20. $\dfrac{\frac{a^2-b^2}{2}}{a+b}$

21. $\dfrac{\frac{a}{b}-\frac{b}{a}}{a-b}$

22. $\dfrac{x-\frac{9}{x}}{x+3}$

23. $\dfrac{9-\frac{b}{y}}{-\frac{3}{y}}$

24. $\dfrac{-8a-\frac{7}{b}}{-\frac{9}{b}}$

B ——— Simplify the following.

25. $\dfrac{4xy-\frac{y}{2}+y}{-\frac{y}{3}}$

26. $\dfrac{\frac{12x^2y}{9z}}{\frac{4xy}{3z}}$

27. $\dfrac{\frac{36rs^2}{7r^2s^2}}{\frac{4rs}{21r^2s}}$

28. $\dfrac{\frac{a-b}{c}}{\frac{a+b}{3c}}$

29. $\dfrac{\frac{a+2}{2a}}{\frac{a-2}{a}}$

30. $\dfrac{\frac{x^2-25}{x}}{x-5}$

31. $\dfrac{\frac{x+2}{x-2}}{\frac{2x+4}{x^2-4}}$

32. $\dfrac{\frac{a}{b}-1}{\frac{a}{b}+1}$

33. $\dfrac{\frac{y}{x^2}+x}{xy+\frac{1}{x}}$

C — Simplify the following rational expressions.

34. $\dfrac{\dfrac{2}{x-1}+\dfrac{x-1}{x+1}}{1+\dfrac{1}{x}}$

35. $\dfrac{\dfrac{a-4}{a+4}-1}{\dfrac{a+4}{a-4}+\dfrac{2}{a+4}}$

36. $\dfrac{\dfrac{x-y}{x^2+y^2}-\dfrac{1}{x}}{\dfrac{x-y}{x^2+y^2}-\dfrac{1}{y}}$

37. $1+\dfrac{1}{x+\dfrac{1}{x+\dfrac{1}{x}}}$

More Challenging Problems

— Perform the indicated operations and simplify the results.

1. $\dfrac{x+y+\dfrac{y^2}{x}}{x+y+\dfrac{x^2}{y}}$

2. $1-\dfrac{m(m-n)}{1-mn}$

3. $\dfrac{x+\dfrac{y^3}{x^2}}{\dfrac{y^2}{x^2}-\dfrac{y}{x}+1}$

4. $\dfrac{\dfrac{x^2}{y^2}-1}{\dfrac{x^2}{y^2}+\dfrac{2x}{y}+1}$

5. $\dfrac{mx+my-2x-2y}{mx-my-2x+2y}$

6. $\dfrac{x^3+y^3}{4x^2+xy-3y^2}$

7. $\dfrac{a^3-b^3}{a^2b-a^2}\cdot\dfrac{2a}{\dfrac{a^2-b^2}{b^2-a^2}}$

8. $\dfrac{3^{n^2+1}}{3^{(n+2)^2}}\cdot\dfrac{3^{2(n-1)}}{3(n)^0}$

9. $\dfrac{1-x^3}{1+\dfrac{x}{1-\dfrac{x}{1+x}}}$

10. $\dfrac{2x+2}{x+1-\dfrac{x^2+x+1}{x+\dfrac{1}{x-1}}}$

11. $\dfrac{\dfrac{1-4x^2}{(2x+y)^2}\left[1+\dfrac{y+1}{2x-1}\right]}{\dfrac{1}{2x+y}-\dfrac{1}{2x-y}+\dfrac{1}{4x^2-y^2}}$

12. $\dfrac{x-6+\dfrac{4}{x-2}}{\left(\dfrac{1}{x+2}-\dfrac{x}{7x-4}\right)\left(x-\dfrac{x+8}{x-1}\right)}$

13. $\dfrac{\dfrac{1}{a^2}-\dfrac{1}{4d^2}-\dfrac{1}{a^3}-\dfrac{1}{8b^3}}{\dfrac{1}{a}+\dfrac{1}{2d}-\dfrac{1}{a^2}-\dfrac{1}{4b^2}}$

14. $1-\dfrac{2}{x+\dfrac{3}{x-\dfrac{4}{x}}}$

15. Find $\dfrac{x-y}{x+y}$ in terms of a and b if $x=\dfrac{a}{b+a}$ and $y=\dfrac{a-b}{-a}$.

— Solve.

16. $\dfrac{4x^2 + 8}{x^2 + 2x - 3} - \dfrac{6x + 1}{x + 3} = \dfrac{2x - 7}{1 - x}$

17. $\dfrac{15}{2x + 1} - \dfrac{5}{4x^2 - 1} + \dfrac{6}{2x - 1} = 0$

18. $\dfrac{1 + 2x}{x^2 - 4x - 21} = \dfrac{1 + x}{6 + 5x + x^2} + \dfrac{x + 5}{x^2 - 5x - 14}$

19. A storekeeper paid a dollars to two men, paying n times as many dollars to one as the other. How much did he pay each man in terms of a and n?

CHAPTER REVIEW

1. Know the meaning of and be able to use each of the following words or phrases. The number shown after each word or phrase indicates where it is introduced, in case you need to review.

rational expression (*386*)
simplifying a rational
   expression (*390*)
least common
   multiple (LCM) (*398*)

least common
   denominator (LCD) (*400*)
signs of a rational
   expression (*405*)

2. If $\dfrac{A}{B} = \dfrac{C}{D}$ ($B, D \neq 0$), which of the following statements is true?

  a. $AC = BD$ **b.** $A + C = B + D$
  c. $AD = BC$ **d.** $A + D = B + C$

3. By what process do you check the equality of two rational expressions?

— Tell if the following pairs of expressions are *Equal* or *Unequal*.

4. $\dfrac{x - 5}{x}, \dfrac{x^2 - 10x + 25}{x - 5}$

5. $\dfrac{10x^2 - 13x - 3}{2x - 3}, \dfrac{5ax + a}{a}$

6. $\dfrac{14x^2 - x - 3}{2x^2 - 7x + 3}, \dfrac{7x + 3}{x - 3}$

— Write the following expressions in simplest form.

7. $\dfrac{3a(x^2 - 4y^2)}{a(x - 2y)}$

8. $\dfrac{5x^2 - 38x - 63}{5x^2 + 2x - 7}$

9. State the theorem that permits you to write this product.

$$\frac{x-3}{x+4} \cdot \frac{x-2}{x+1} = \frac{x^2 - 5x + 6}{x^2 + 5x + 4}$$

10. What is the product of $\frac{7nx^3}{3n^2y^3}$ and $\frac{15y^2}{21x^2}$ in simplest form?

—— Supply the correct rational expression to make each of the following sentences true.

11. $\frac{3}{a} \div \frac{5}{b} = \frac{3}{a} \cdot \underline{\ ?\ }$

12. $\frac{4b^2}{-13ab} \div \frac{2b}{a} = \frac{4b^2}{-13ab} \cdot \underline{\ ?\ }$

13. What is the quotient in Exercise 11? in Exercise 12?

—— Perform the indicated operation. Write your answers in simplest form.

14. $\dfrac{7x-y}{-5x^2} - \dfrac{x-3y}{3x^2}$

15. $\dfrac{-2a}{4a-b} + \dfrac{3a}{\dfrac{b}{2} - 2a}$

16. $\dfrac{\dfrac{x-y}{xy}}{x^2 - y^2} \cdot xy$

17. $\dfrac{-3 + \dfrac{2}{a}}{\dfrac{a^2}{-3a+2}}$

18. Show that $\frac{x-y}{y-x}$ and -1 are equivalent.

19. The length of a rectangle is $3n + 4$. The width is $\frac{1}{3}$ the length. Write expressions for the perimeter and the area of the rectangle.

CHAPTER TEST

—— Replace ● with = or ≠ to make true statements.

1. $\dfrac{x-1}{y} \ ● \ \dfrac{x}{y}$

2. $\dfrac{x^2y}{x^3y} \ ● \ \dfrac{1}{x}$

3. $\dfrac{ax+ay}{bx+by} \ ● \ \dfrac{a(x+y)}{b(x+y)}$

4. $\dfrac{p^2 - 3p - 4}{2p^2 - 14p + 24} \ ● \ \dfrac{p+1}{p-3}$

5. $\dfrac{17+t^2}{-x^2y} \ ● \ -\dfrac{17+t^2}{x^2y}$

6. $\dfrac{5g^2h^3}{17i} \ ● \ -\dfrac{-5g^2h^3}{-17i}$

7. $\dfrac{2m^2 + mn}{4m^2n} \ ● \ \dfrac{2m+n}{4mn}$

8. $\dfrac{16a^2b^2c}{12a^3 + 6a} \ ● \ -\dfrac{-8b^2c}{6a^2 + 3}$

—— Perform the operations indicated. Simplify your answers.

9. $\dfrac{a^2 - 36}{10ab} \cdot \dfrac{2b}{a+b}$

10. $\dfrac{4a^4b^4}{a^2 - b^2} \div \dfrac{2a^3b^3}{a^2 - 2ab + b^2}$

11. $\dfrac{2x-3}{4x+5} + \dfrac{2x-5}{4x+5}$

12. $a - \dfrac{a+b}{b}$

13. $\dfrac{a - \dfrac{1}{b}}{a + \dfrac{1}{b}}$

14. $\dfrac{\dfrac{a}{b} - \dfrac{b}{a}}{\dfrac{a}{b} - 1}$

15. $\dfrac{a}{a - 2} - \dfrac{1}{a^2 - 4}$

16. $\dfrac{4}{x^2 - 5x + 6} - \dfrac{5}{x^2 + 2x - 15}$

17. $a - \dfrac{2}{a - 2} + 1$

18. $\dfrac{3a + 5}{a} - \dfrac{3b - 2}{b}$

19. $\left(\dfrac{1}{a^2} - \dfrac{1}{b^2}\right)\left(\dfrac{3a^2b}{b - a}\right)$

20. $\dfrac{x^2 - 5x - 6}{x^3} \cdot \dfrac{x}{x + 1}$

CUMULATIVE REVIEW

—— Give the letter of the response that best completes the sentence or answers the question.

1. What is the value of $\dfrac{2a + b}{-3c}$ if a is -4, b is 2, and c is -1?

   a. -2 **b.** $+2$ **c.** -6 **d.** $+6$

2. Which equation is represented graphically by a line with a slope of $-\frac{7}{4}$, passing through $(0, 3)$?

   a. $4y - 7x = 12$ **b.** $-4y + 7x = 12$

   c. $4y + 7x = 12$ **d.** $4y + 7x = -12$

3. If the cost of automobile tires is \$15 each, the cost, n, of any number of tires, t, may be represented as $n = 15t$. What is a sensible replacement set for t?

   a. The rational numbers.   **b.** The real numbers.

   c. The integers.   **d.** The natural numbers.

4. Given $\frac{a}{b}$ and $\frac{c}{d}$ with $a, c \in W$ and $b, d \in N$, which sentence is false?

   a. $\frac{a}{b} = \frac{c}{d}$ if $ad = bc$.   **b.** $\frac{a}{b} > \frac{c}{d}$ if $ad > bc$.

   c. $\frac{a}{b} > \frac{c}{d}$ if $bc > ad$.   **d.** $\frac{a}{b} < \frac{c}{d}$ if $ad < bc$.

5. If the replacement set is the set of integers, what is the solution set of $3x - 2 > 4$?

   a. $\{2, 3, 4, 5, \cdots\}$ **b.** $\{3, 4, 5, 6, \cdots\}$

   c. $\{1, 2, 3, 4, \cdots\}$ **d.** $\{-3, -4, -5, -6, \cdots\}$

6. Which graph correctly represents the solution set of $7x - 3(x + 5) < -3$? The replacement set is R.

a.

$$-5\ -4\ -3\ -2\ -1\ \ 0\ \ 1\ \ 2\ \ 3\ \ 4\ \ 5$$

b.

$$-5\ -4\ -3\ -2\ -1\ \ 0\ \ 1\ \ 2\ \ 3\ \ 4\ \ 5$$

c.

$$-5\ -4\ -3\ -2\ -1\ \ 0\ \ 1\ \ 2\ \ 3\ \ 4\ \ 5$$

d.

$$-5\ -4\ -3\ -2\ -1\ \ 0\ \ 1\ \ 2\ \ 3\ \ 4\ \ 5$$

7. Which postulate for the real numbers is illustrated by $3a^2b + 7a^2b = 10a^2b$?

a. Commutative.　　　　　b. Distributive.

c. Associative.　　　　　d. Additive identity.

8. Which of the following sentences is equivalent to $8 - 5x = -7x + 2$?

a. $-12x + 10 = 0$　　　　b. $2x = -3$

c. $2x = -6$　　　　　　　d. $\frac{7}{5}x = 6$

9. What is the solution set of $9x - 3 = 5(3x - 1)$?

a. $\{-\frac{1}{3}\}$　　　b. $\{\frac{1}{3}\}$　　　c. $\{3\}$　　　d. $\{-3\}$

10. What is the slope of the line that passes through the two points $(-6, 2)$ and $(3, -5)$?

a. $-\frac{7}{9}$　　　b. $\frac{7}{9}$　　　c. $\frac{9}{7}$　　　d. $-\frac{9}{7}$

11. Which number pair correctly completes the following?

$$\{(x, y) : 3x - 5y = 13\} \cap \{(x, y) : -x - 3y = 5\} = \{(\underline{?}, \underline{?})\}$$

a. $(-1, 2)$　　　b. $(-1, -2)$　　　c. $(1, -2)$　　　d. $(-2, 1)$

12. By what postulate are these two sentences equivalent?

$$(3n + 10) + 5n - 10 \quad \text{and} \quad 3n + (10 + 5n) - 10$$

a. Commutative.　　　　　b. Associative.

c. Distributive.　　　　　d. Transitive.

13. Which exponent theorem is illustrated by $3x^{\frac{1}{2}} \cdot 5x^{\frac{3}{4}} = 15x^{\frac{5}{4}}$?

a. $(xy)^n = x^n y^n$　　　　b. $x^{\frac{1}{n}} = \sqrt[n]{x}$

c. $(x^m)^n = x^{mn}$　　　　d. $x^m \cdot x^n = x^{m+n}$

14. To rationalize the denominator of $\dfrac{x^3}{x - \sqrt{2}}$, multiply numerator and denominator by $\underline{?}$.

a. $x - \sqrt{2}$　　b. $x + \sqrt{2}$　　c. $\sqrt{2}$　　d. $-\sqrt{2}$

15. Consider the following system of equations.

$$\begin{cases} -15x + 2y = -7 \\ 7x - 10y = 1 \end{cases}$$

The graph of which of the following equations passes through the intersection of the graphs of the equations in the system?

a. $x = -\frac{1}{2}$ **b.** $y = -\frac{1}{4}$

c. $2x + 1 = 0$ **d.** $2x - 1 = 0$

16. Which term makes $x^2 + 1\frac{1}{3}x$ a perfect square trinomial?

a. $\frac{2}{3}$ **b.** $-\frac{4}{3}$ **c.** $\frac{4}{9}$ **d.** $-\frac{4}{9}$

17. What are the correct factors of the polynomial $6a^3 - 9a^2b - 6ab^2$?

a. $3(a - 2b)(2a + b)$ **b.** $3a(a - 2b)(2a + b)$

c. $3a(a + 2b)(2a - b)$ **d.** $-3(a - 2b)(2a + b)$

18. What are the zeros of the function $y = 12x^2 + 17x - 5$?

a. $\frac{1}{4}$ and $\frac{5}{3}$ **b.** $\frac{1}{4}$ and $-\frac{5}{3}$

c. $-\frac{1}{4}$ and $\frac{5}{3}$ **d.** $-\frac{1}{4}$ and $-\frac{5}{3}$

19. What is the quotient of $x^2 - 9x + 8$ divided by $x - 1$?

a. $x + 9$ **b.** $x - 9$ **c.** $x - 8$ **d.** $x + 8$

20. Which of the following is equivalent to $\frac{a}{-b}$?

a. $-\frac{a}{b}$ **b.** $-\frac{a}{-b}$ **c.** $\frac{-a}{-b}$ **d.** $-\frac{-a}{b}$

ENRICHMENT

Continued Fractions

How are the following two expressions different?

a. $1 + \cfrac{1}{2 + \cfrac{1}{3 + \cfrac{1}{4 + \frac{1}{5}}}}$ **b.** $2 + \cfrac{1}{1 + \cfrac{1}{4 + \cfrac{1}{1 + \cfrac{1}{4 + \cfrac{1}{1 + \cfrac{1}{4 + \cdots}}}}}}$

Both **a** and **b** are **continued fractions** but **a** is a *terminating* continued fraction, since it has a definite last term. In this section the primary topic is simple terminating, continued fractions, generally symbolized as follows, where each a_i after a_1 must be an integer, and all numerators after a_1 are equal to 1.

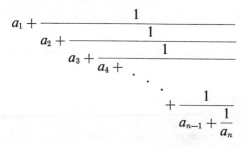

$$a_1 + \cfrac{1}{a_2 + \cfrac{1}{a_3 + \cfrac{1}{a_4 + \cfrac{\cdots}{}}}}$$
$$+ \cfrac{1}{a_{n-1} + \cfrac{1}{a_n}}$$

You may ask "Is a continued fraction such as **a** just invented or is it arrived at in a particular way? Does it have a particular value?" To determine its value, start at the bottom and add upward.

$$1 + \cfrac{1}{2 + \cfrac{1}{3 + \cfrac{1}{4 + \frac{1}{5}}}} = 1 + \cfrac{1}{2 + \cfrac{1}{3 + \frac{1}{21/5}}} = 1 + \cfrac{1}{2 + \cfrac{1}{3 + \frac{5}{21}}}$$

$$= 1 + \cfrac{1}{2 + \cfrac{1}{\frac{68}{21}}} = 1 + \cfrac{1}{2 + \frac{21}{68}} = 1 + \cfrac{1}{\frac{157}{68}} = 1 + \frac{68}{157} = \frac{225}{157}$$

Then **a** is the rational number $\frac{225}{157}$. Can $\frac{225}{157}$ be expanded back to a continued fraction? Begin by dividing 225 by 157.

$$\tfrac{225}{157} = 1 + \tfrac{68}{157}$$

You can make $\frac{68}{157}$ a rational expression with a numerator of 1 by making its multiplicative inverse the denominator.

$$\tfrac{225}{157} = 1 + \tfrac{68}{157} = 1 + \cfrac{1}{\frac{157}{68}}$$

Now you can divide 157 by 68 and continue the process.

$$1 + \cfrac{1}{\frac{157}{68}} = 1 + \cfrac{1}{2 + \frac{21}{68}}, \quad \text{or} \quad 1 + \cfrac{1}{2 + \cfrac{1}{\frac{68}{21}}}$$

$$= 1 + \cfrac{1}{2 + \cfrac{1}{3 + \frac{5}{21}}}, \quad \text{or} \quad 1 + \cfrac{1}{2 + \cfrac{1}{3 + \frac{1}{21/5}}}$$

$$= 1 + \cfrac{1}{2 + \cfrac{1}{3 + \cfrac{1}{4 + \frac{1}{5}}}}$$

Can you go any further with the expansion of $\frac{225}{157}$? If you express $\frac{1}{5}$ as $\dfrac{1}{\frac{5}{1}}$, you obtain $\frac{1}{5}$ again, so the process is ended. In general, when you reach a fraction that has a numerator of 1, the continued fraction has terminated.

Although the proof will not be given here, a theorem and its converse can be stated.

Theorem If n can be written as a simple terminating, continued fraction, then n can be written as a rational number.

The converse would read "If n can be written as a rational number, then n can be written as a simple terminating, continued fraction."

Exercises

1. Express these continued fractions as rational numbers.

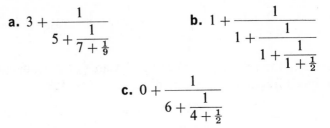

a. $3 + \dfrac{1}{5 + \dfrac{1}{7 + \frac{1}{9}}}$
b. $1 + \dfrac{1}{1 + \dfrac{1}{1 + \dfrac{1}{1 + \frac{1}{2}}}}$

c. $0 + \dfrac{1}{6 + \dfrac{1}{4 + \frac{1}{2}}}$

2. Expand these rational numbers as continued fractions.

a. $\frac{11}{9}$

b. $\frac{23}{17}$

c. $\frac{11}{15}$ $\left(\textit{Hint:}\ \text{Start with } a_1 = 0;\ \text{that is, } \frac{11}{15} = 0 + \frac{11}{15} = 0 + \dfrac{1}{\frac{15}{11}} = 0 + \dfrac{1}{1 + \frac{4}{11}},\ \text{and so forth.}\right)$

d. $-\frac{15}{7}$ (*Hint:* $-\frac{15}{7} = -3 + \frac{6}{7}$; now expand $\frac{6}{7}$ as shown in **c** and add.)

3. a. Express $\frac{83}{65}$ as a continued fraction.

b. Multiply both numerator and denominator of $\frac{83}{65}$ by 2 to obtain the equivalent fraction $\frac{166}{130}$. Express $\frac{166}{130}$ as a continued fraction.

c. Multiply $\frac{83}{65}$ by $\frac{3}{3}$ and express the equivalent fraction, $\frac{249}{195}$, as a continued fraction.

d. What do you notice about the three continued fractions for **a**, **b**, and **c**? If you add up each of the continued fractions, what one fraction will you obtain?

e. If you have done your computation correctly, you have illustrated a very interesting property of continued fractions. State it in your own words.

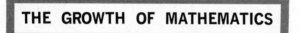

THE GROWTH OF MATHEMATICS

Algebra *Is an Arabic Word*

With the rapid rise of the Islam religion, starting in A.D. 622, the conquering Arabs soon came to occupy most of the intellectual centers of the ancient world. And because of their religion, they were faced with a number of problems, such as the calculation of the dates of religious festivals and the times for daily prayer, that required mathematics. Arab rulers answered the need by having translations made of the classical Greek works of mathematics. The Arabs were also in contact with India, so they were soon in possession of the flexible decimal place-value numeration system with the all-important zero. Thus, Arab mathematicians were in an excellent position to synthesize the known mathematical learning and to extend it.

The writer who was most successful at this synthesis was Muhammad ibn-Musa al-Khwarizmi (A.D. 780–?850). The Latin form of his name, *algorism*, came to mean "arithmetic" in Europe. Today, *algorism* denotes any definite procedure for solving a mathematical problem. Al-Khwarizmi's best-known book, *Restoration and Reduction*, was written in 830. When translated in the twelfth century, it reintroduced the work of Diophantus and introduced the work of the Indian writers on algebra to Europe. The word *algebra* derives from the Arabic title of this book, *al-jebr w'almuquabala*.

Many other Arabic writers contributed to arithmetic and algebra, but not extensively to geometry. They often gave geometric illustrations to explain why the algebraic operations were performed; however, they did not use proofs.

Some Arabic writers used negative numbers. They were able to solve all equations involving the square of a variable, but they did not know how to solve equations involving the cube of a variable. The main contribution of the Arabs was the preservation of the Greek works and the introduction of Indian mathematics to Europe.

CHAPTER 10

USING RATIONAL EXPRESSIONS

You know what a rational expression is, and now you will learn some of the many ways rational expressions are used in mathematics.

● Have you ever whirled a bucket of water around in a circle as the boy in the upper left photograph is doing? If you have, you should have found that the water did not spill out, even when the container was upside-down. This is because objects moving in circular paths tend to move away from the center of their motion. This tendency, called centrifugal force, can be measured by the formula $F = \frac{Mv^2}{gr}$. In this formula, F is the centrifugal force, M is the mass in pounds, v is the velocity in feet per second, g is a constant, 32.2 feet per second per second, and r is the radius of the circle in feet. Much work in science and business is aided by such rational expressions.

● If you were a traffic controller in a railroad yard, you would want to be sure that the two trains in the lower left photograph were on different tracks before they reached each other. Finding the time when they would meet can be solved by rational expressions.

● If an engineer had wanted to know before he started drilling how long the tunnel through the redwood would be, he would not have been able to measure it directly. If the tree trunk were circular, how would knowing its circumference help him to find the distance through the trunk? In this chapter, you will learn other methods of indirect measurement that involve triangles.

● The instrument being used in the upper right photograph is called a transit. It measures angles and enables the surveyor to calculate distances and other data. If you know two sides of a right triangle, how would you find the third, using methods that you already know? There are relationships between the acute angles and the sides of a right triangle that you will learn to use to make indirect measurements.

10–1 Equations with Rational Expressions

To solve $\frac{x}{2} + \frac{2x}{3} = \frac{5}{4}$, first multiply each term by the LCD, 12. Then you can easily solve the simplified equation for x.

$$12\left(\frac{x}{2}\right) + 12\left(\frac{2x}{3}\right) = 12\left(\frac{5}{4}\right)$$
$$6x + 8x = 15$$

In general, to solve equations with rational expressions, the procedure is the same. Multiply each term by the LCD and solve for the variable. Study the following examples.

EXAMPLE 1. Solve $\dfrac{x}{x + 6} = 13$.

① The LCD is $x + 6$.

② Multiply each term by $x + 6$.

③ Solve for x.

$$\frac{x}{x + 6} = 13$$
$$(x + 6)\left(\frac{x}{x + 6}\right) = (x + 6)(13)$$
$$x = 13x + 78$$
$$-12x = 78$$
$$x = -6\tfrac{1}{2}$$

$$Check \qquad \frac{-6\tfrac{1}{2}}{-6\tfrac{1}{2} + 6} = 13$$
$$\frac{-6\tfrac{1}{2}}{-\tfrac{1}{2}} = 13$$
$$\left(-\tfrac{13}{2}\right)\cdot\left(-\tfrac{2}{1}\right) = 13$$
$$13 = 13$$

EXAMPLE 2. Solve $\dfrac{2}{3x} + \dfrac{1}{2} = \dfrac{3}{4x}$.

① The LCD of $3x$, 2, and $4x$ is $12x$.

② Multiply each term by $12x$.

$$\frac{2}{3x} + \frac{1}{2} = \frac{3}{4x}$$
$$12x\left(\frac{2}{3x}\right) + 12x\left(\frac{1}{2}\right) = 12x\left(\frac{3}{4x}\right)$$
$$(4 \cdot 2) + (6x \cdot 1) = (3 \cdot 3)$$
$$8 + 6x = 9$$
$$6x = 1$$
$$x = \tfrac{1}{6}$$

$$Check \qquad \frac{2}{3\left(\tfrac{1}{6}\right)} + \tfrac{1}{2} = \frac{3}{4\left(\tfrac{1}{6}\right)}$$
$$\frac{2}{\tfrac{1}{2}} + \tfrac{1}{2} = \frac{3}{\tfrac{2}{3}}$$
$$\left(2 \cdot \tfrac{2}{1}\right) + \tfrac{1}{2} = \left(3 \cdot \tfrac{3}{2}\right)$$
$$4 + \tfrac{1}{2} = \tfrac{9}{2}, \text{ or } 4\tfrac{1}{2}$$

EXAMPLE 3. Solve $\dfrac{7}{x-4} = \dfrac{5}{x+2}$.

① The LCD is $(x-4)(x+2)$.

② Multiplying each term by the LCD gives the following equation.

$$(x+2)(7) = (x-4)(5)$$

③ Solve for x.

$$7x + 14 = 5x - 20$$
$$2x = -34$$
$$x = -17$$

④ Check to be sure.

Now try these

—— Solve.

1. $\dfrac{15}{2x} = 3$

2. $\dfrac{8}{x+2} = 8$

3. $\dfrac{a}{a+5} = \dfrac{1}{2}$

4. $\dfrac{4}{3x} + \dfrac{6}{5x} + \dfrac{3}{10} = \dfrac{1}{3}$

5. $\dfrac{2}{x+3} = \dfrac{4}{x+1}$

6. $\dfrac{x-4}{7} + \dfrac{2}{x-2} = 1$

Answers: **1.** $2\frac{1}{2}$ **2.** -1 **3.** 5 **4.** 76 **5.** -5 **6.** 9 or 4

Exercises

A —— Solve the following equations.

1. $\dfrac{2}{x} = 3$

2. $\dfrac{3}{a} = -4$

3. $\dfrac{2}{3x} = \dfrac{1}{9}$

4. $\dfrac{3}{2x} - \dfrac{1}{3} = \dfrac{5}{6x}$

5. $\dfrac{5}{6x} + 3 = \dfrac{1}{2x}$

6. $\dfrac{3}{10x} - \dfrac{3}{5} = \dfrac{2}{5x}$

7. $\dfrac{5}{n} - \dfrac{1}{2} = 2$

8. $\dfrac{4}{x} + \dfrac{3}{2x} = \dfrac{11}{6}$

9. $\dfrac{2n+1}{2n} - \dfrac{3n-2}{3n} = \dfrac{7}{12}$

10. $\dfrac{4}{2x} - 3 = \dfrac{-2}{5x} - \dfrac{3}{5}$

11. $\dfrac{4}{3x} - \dfrac{5}{2x} = 5 - \dfrac{1}{6x}$

12. $\dfrac{7}{4x} - 2 = \dfrac{3}{2x} - 4$

13. $\dfrac{3}{2} = \dfrac{x}{x+2}$

14. $\dfrac{b-2}{b+3} = \dfrac{3}{8}$

15. $\dfrac{x-7}{x+2} = \dfrac{1}{4}$

16. $\dfrac{5}{a+3} = \dfrac{2}{2}$

17. $\dfrac{a-1}{a-2} = 1.5$

18. $\dfrac{y}{y-3} = \dfrac{6}{3}$

19. $\dfrac{2}{x+3} = \dfrac{5}{x}$

20. $\dfrac{-3}{x+5} = \dfrac{1}{2}$

B — Solve.

21. $\dfrac{x}{3} + \dfrac{2x^2}{3x - 4} = \dfrac{9x - 2}{9}$

22. $\dfrac{2x - 1}{2} - \dfrac{x + 2}{2x + 5} = \dfrac{6x - 5}{6}$

23. $\dfrac{7}{x - 4} = \dfrac{5}{x - 2}$

24. $\dfrac{10}{x - 3} = \dfrac{9}{x - 5}$

25. $\dfrac{x + 5}{x - 3} + \dfrac{4}{x - 3} = 5$

26. $\dfrac{x + 2}{x + 4} = \dfrac{x + 6}{x - 8}$

27. $\dfrac{x - 1}{x + 1} = \dfrac{x + 3}{x + 10}$

28. $\dfrac{x - 3}{x + 5} = \dfrac{x - 2}{x + 2}$

C — Solve the following.

29. $\dfrac{3}{3x^2 - 3x - 28} = \dfrac{5}{5x^2 - x - 20}$

30. $\dfrac{x}{x^2 - 9} < 4 - \dfrac{4x}{x - 3}$

31. $\dfrac{2x + 1}{x - 1} - \dfrac{3x}{x + 2} = \dfrac{-x^2 - 2}{x^2 + x - 2}$

32. $\dfrac{a}{a - 2} = \dfrac{a + 3}{a + 2} - \dfrac{a}{a^2 - 4}$

33. $\dfrac{3(x - 4)}{4x^2 - 9} = \dfrac{3x}{4x^2 - 16x + 15}$

34. $\dfrac{1}{1 - x^2} + \dfrac{1}{x - 1} > 0$

35. $\dfrac{7x}{x^2 - 2x - 8} = \dfrac{3}{x - 4} + \dfrac{4x}{x^2 - 5x + 4}$

10–2 Problems with Rational Expressions

Some word problems can be solved by using one equation with one variable. Other problems are easier to solve by using two equations with two variables. And many problems can be worked by either method. By reading the conditions of the problem, you should be able to decide whether it is easier to express the given conditions in terms of one variable or in terms of two variables.

EXAMPLE 1. What number must be subtracted from the numerator and added to the denominator of $\frac{17}{22}$ to make a rational number equal to $\frac{5}{8}$?

The problem says "what number." State the condition in terms of one variable.

① Let x = unknown number.

$17 - x$ = new numerator.

$22 + x$ = new denominator.

② Then write the equation stated in the problem.

$$\frac{17 - x}{22 + x} = \tfrac{5}{8}$$

③ Solve for x. $8(22 + x) \left(\dfrac{17 - x}{22 + x} \right) = 8(22 + x)(\tfrac{5}{8})$

$$8(17 - x) = (22 + x)(5)$$
$$136 - 8x = 110 + 5x$$
$$-13x = -26$$
$$x = 2$$

Check $\dfrac{17 - 2}{22 + 2} \overset{?}{=} \tfrac{5}{8}$

$$\tfrac{15}{24} = \tfrac{5}{8}$$

When solving a problem using two equations with two variables, each of the two conditions is expressed in an equation. This gives two equations that can be solved by either the addition method or the substitution method that you learned earlier.

EXAMPLE 2. Separate 120 into two parts so that one part is $\tfrac{3}{5}$ of the other part. (To separate a number into two parts means to find two addends whose sum is that number.)

① Let x be *one part,*
      y be *the other part.*

② Use the two conditions of the problem to write two equations.
   I   Separate 120 into two parts. $x + y = 120$
   II One part is $\tfrac{3}{5}$ of the other part. $x = \tfrac{3}{5}y$

③ Choose a method to solve the problem.   Since x is given as $\tfrac{3}{5}y$, use the substitution method.

I $x + y = 120$
   $\tfrac{3}{5}y + y = 120$
   $\tfrac{8}{5}y = 120$
   $8y = 600$
   $y = 75$ *the other part*
II $x = \tfrac{3}{5} \cdot 75$
   $= 45$ *one part*

④ Check in the problem.

Exercises

A   **1.** What number must be added to the numerator and subtracted from the denominator of the rational number $\tfrac{17}{32}$ to make a rational number equal to $\tfrac{3}{4}$?

2. The numerator of a rational number is 3 smaller than its denominator; if 2 is added to the numerator, the value of the rational number becomes $\tfrac{3}{4}$. What is the rational number?

3. The denominator of a rational number is 7 more than its numerator. If the numerator is diminished by 6, the resulting rational number equals $\frac{1}{2}$. What was the original rational number?

4. Separate 95 into two parts so that one part is $\frac{2}{3}$ of the other.

5. One number is 4 more than another. The quotient of the larger divided by the smaller is $\frac{5}{2}$. Find the numbers.

6. One number is 7 less than another. The quotient of the larger divided by the smaller is $\frac{4}{3}$. Find the numbers.

7. Separate 72 into two parts so that their quotient is $\frac{2}{3}$.

8. What number added to both the numerator and the denominator of $\frac{3}{5}$ will make the value of the resulting rational number $\frac{3}{4}$?

9. The sum of two rational numbers is $\frac{11}{16}$, and one of them is $\frac{5}{6}$ of the other. Find the rational numbers.

10. The difference between two rational numbers is $\frac{1}{8}$. One rational number is $\frac{2}{3}$ of the other. Find the rational numbers.

11. Two integers are consecutive (n and $n + 1$). If 6 is added to the first and 2 is subtracted from the second, the quotient of the resulting integers is $4\frac{1}{2}$. Find the integers.

12. The numerator of a rational number exceeds its denominator by 3. If 1 is added to the denominator and 5 is subtracted from the numerator, the value of the rational number becomes $\frac{1}{2}$. What is the rational number?

13. The numerator of a rational number is 8 less than the denominator. If 3 is added to the numerator and 1 is subtracted from the denominator, the resulting rational number is $\frac{2}{5}$. What is the rational number?

14. The perimeter of a rectangle is 52 inches. How long is each side if the altitude is 2 inches more than $\frac{1}{3}$ the base?

15. Find three consecutive integers such that $\frac{1}{2}$ the first plus $\frac{2}{3}$ the second less $\frac{3}{4}$ the third will be 10.

B **16.** A is $\frac{5}{6}$ as old as B. Five years ago, A was $\frac{4}{5}$ as old as B was then. How old is A now? How old is B now?

17. The sum of the angles of any triangle equals 180°. If in a certain triangle, $\frac{3}{5}$ of the first angle equals 34° less than the second and $\frac{5}{6}$ of the first angle equals the third, how many degrees are there in each angle?

18. Susan is now $\frac{4}{5}$ as old as her older sister Jean. Four years ago she was $\frac{3}{4}$ as old as her sister. What are their present ages?

19. Gail is now 24 years younger than her mother. Eight years ago she was $\frac{1}{4}$ as old as her mother. What are their present ages?

20. A seed store has 300 pounds of lawn-seed mixture that is $\frac{3}{4}$ rye grass and $\frac{1}{4}$ blue grass. How much blue grass must be added to make a mixture that is $\frac{1}{2}$ rye grass and $\frac{1}{2}$ blue grass? (*Hint:* The amount of rye grass remains the same.)

21. Mr. Zack has $\frac{1}{3}$ of his savings invested at 5%, $\frac{1}{4}$ at 4%, and the rest at 6%. The total interest per year on these investments is \$372. How much does he have invested at each rate?

10–3 Work Problems

Work problems usually involve persons or machines working together at different rates of speed. The method for solving these problems involves deciding how much of the work an individual can do in a unit of time, such as a minute, an hour, or a day.

The following examples should help you.

EXAMPLE 1. Arthur can shovel snow from a sidewalk in 60 minutes and Jack can do it in 30 minutes. How long will it take them to do the job together?

① Let n = number of minutes for both to do the job together.

② Arthur can do $\frac{1}{60}$ of the job in 1 minute and

$\quad\quad \frac{n}{60}$ of the job in n minutes.

Jack can do $\frac{1}{30}$ of the job in 1 minute and

$\quad\quad \frac{n}{30}$ of the job in n minutes.

③ The sum of the parts of the job that each does in n minutes equals 1, the whole job.

$$\frac{\text{part done}}{\text{by Arthur}} + \frac{\text{part done}}{\text{by Jack}} = \text{whole job}$$

$$\frac{n}{60} \quad + \quad \frac{n}{30} \quad = 1$$

④ Multiply by the LCD, 60, and solve for n.

$$60\left(\frac{n}{60}\right) + 60\left(\frac{n}{30}\right) = 60(1)$$
$$n + 2n = 60$$
$$3n = 60$$
$$n = 20$$

⑤ They can do the job together in 20 minutes. Check the solution.

EXAMPLE 2. Jeff can do a certain job in 8 days. After working alone for 4 days, he is joined by Charlie and together they finish the work in 2 more days. How long would it take Charlie alone?

① If Jeff can do the job alone in 8 days, then he can do $\frac{1}{8}$ of the job in 1 day and $\frac{6}{8}$, or $\frac{3}{4}$, of the job in 6 days.

② Let n be the number of days it would take Charlie to do the job alone. Then

$\frac{1}{n}$ is the part of the job he can do in 1 day and

$\frac{2}{n}$ is the part of the job he can do in the 2 days he works with Jeff.

③ The sum of the parts done by Jeff and Charlie equals one whole job.

$$\frac{3}{4} + \frac{2}{n} = 1$$

④ Solve for n.

$$4n\left(\frac{3}{4}\right) + 4n\left(\frac{2}{n}\right) = 4n(1)$$
$$3n + 8 = 4n$$
$$-n = -8$$
$$n = 8$$

⑤ Check the solution with the conditions of the problem to be sure you are correct.

Exercises

A **1.** One man can make a sidewalk in 4 days, and another can do it in 4.5 days. How long will it take them working together?

2. A large pipe can empty a tank in 5 minutes, and a smaller pipe can empty it in 8 minutes. How long would it take to empty the tank if both pipes were draining the tank?

3. Mike can do a piece of work in 3 days, Ted in 5 days, and Kevin in 8 days. If all three work together, how long will it take them to do the work?

4. To remove the dirt for a building foundation, a contractor is using a large diesel shovel and a small one. If the large one can do the whole job in 6 days and the small one can do it in 9 days, how long will it take them together?

5. Mr. Hall estimates he can paint Mrs. Smith's house alone in 6 days. One of his helpers could paint it alone in 8 days and the other helper could paint it alone in 10 days. How long will it take all three working together?

6. One machine can complete an order for bolts in 7 hours and another machine can do it in 5 hours. How long will it take both machines to finish the job after the slower machine has been working alone for $3\frac{1}{2}$ hours?

B **7.** How long will it take Mary and Alice to perform a job together if Mary takes 12 days alone and Alice takes 8 days?

8. It takes 4 minutes to fill a certain bathtub and 8 minutes to empty it when it is full. With the drain open and the tub empty, how long will it take to fill the tub?

10–4 Motion Problems

If you have ever rowed a boat, you know it seems easier to row and the boat goes faster if you go with the current, rather than against it.

Similarly, pilots of aircraft are glad to pick up a tailwind, a wind from behind the plane, since they can complete their flight in less time. The speed of the plane with respect to the ground (the ground speed) is the usual air speed plus the speed of the wind. On the other hand, a headwind, a wind at the front of the plane, cuts the speed.

The following example involves varying rates of motion.

EXAMPLE. The air speed of an airplane is 225 miles per hour. Flying from city A to city B, it has a tailwind of 25 miles per hour. It takes 3 hours longer to fly from B to A than from A to B. How far is it between the two cities?

(1)   Let n = distance between A and B.
    250 mph = speed from A to B.
    200 mph = speed from B to A.

Then $\frac{n}{250}$ = number of hours to fly from A to B,

    $\frac{n}{200}$ = number of hours to fly from B to A.

(2) Since it takes 3 hours longer to fly from B to A than from A to B, the following equation is true.

$$\frac{n}{200} - \frac{n}{250} = 3$$

(*Continued on next page.*)

③ Multiply by the LCD, 1000, and solve for n.

$$1000\left(\frac{n}{200}\right) - 1000\left(\frac{n}{250}\right) = 1000(3)$$
$$5n \quad - \quad 4n \quad = 3000$$
$$n = 3000 \text{ miles}$$

Exercises

A **1.** Jake can row at the speed of 6 mph in still water. In a river where the current is 3 mph, it takes him 4 hours longer to row x miles upstream than the same distance downstream. Find x.

2. Tim can average 12 mph with his motor boat in still water. In a river with a current of 4 mph, it takes him 9 hours to travel from point A to point B and return. Find the distance from A to B.

3. On a trip between two cities, an airplane took $3\frac{1}{2}$ hours flying at a speed of 360 mph with the wind. The return trip between the cities took $4\frac{1}{2}$ hours and the speed and direction of the wind was the same. Find the speed of the airplane on the return trip. What was the speed of the wind?

4. James drove his car 300 miles in the same time that Edgar drove his car 270 miles. James drove 5 miles an hour faster than Edgar. Find the speed of each.

5. An automobile traveled $\frac{1}{5}$ as fast as an airplane. The airplane required $\frac{1}{2}$ hour less time to go 900 miles than the automobile required to go 210 miles. Find the speed of each.

6. A motorist drove 120 miles at a certain rate. Driving back, he doubled his rate, and took 3 hours less time. Find his rate going.

7. Allan can drive his car over a route in 5 hours, and John can drive his car over the same route in 4 hours. How long would it take them to meet if they started at opposite ends at the same time?

═══════════════════ **Racetrack Puzzle** ═══════════════════

Two bike riders, Robinson and Brown, start at the same time and race on a circular track. Robinson can circle the track in 6 minutes and Brown in 4 minutes. From the beginning of the race, how many minutes will it be before Brown overtakes Robinson?

10–5 Solving Rational Equations for One of the Variables

On a loan of $500 for one year, Mr. Frederick pays $30 interest. He wants to figure out the rate of interest he pays. He knows the formula for finding the interest, $prt = i$, and uses that to obtain a new formula for the rate of interest.

Both sides of the equation are divided by pt so r appears in terms of the other three variables.

Then, this new formula can be used to find the rate of interest.

$$prt = i$$
$$\frac{prt}{pt} = \frac{i}{pt}$$
$$r = \frac{i}{pt}$$
$$r = \frac{\$30}{\$500 \times 1}, \text{ or } \frac{30}{500}$$
$$r = \tfrac{6}{100}, \text{ or } 6\%$$

Many of the formulas used by scientists, engineers, and business-men contain rational expressions. For instance, in physics, you would use the formula

$$\frac{1}{R} = \frac{1}{r_1} + \frac{1}{r_2} + \frac{1}{r_3}$$

to find the combined resistance of three electric circuits in parallel connection. Or you might use the formula

$$V = \tfrac{1}{6}h(B + b + 4M)$$

to find the volume of a prismatoid. Even if you do not completely understand the formulas, you can solve for any variable; and if you were given values for the variable, you could use the formula.

You should notice that some formulas contain such letters as R and r or B and b. The capital and lower-case letters are different variables, just as a and b or x and y are different variables. The same is true when **subscripts** are used to differentiate between variables; for example, C_L, C_a, r_1, and r_2 all represent different quantities. (These are read "C sub L," "C sub a," "r sub 1," "r sub 2.")

The following examples show how to change the form of an equation by solving for one variable in terms of the others, just as $prt = i$ was solved for r.

EXAMPLE 1. Solve for a in the equation $s(a + b) = c$.

$$s(a + b) = c$$

① Use distributive property. $\quad sa + sb = c$

② Add $-sb$. $\qquad\qquad\qquad sa = c - sb$

③ Multiply by $\dfrac{1}{s}$. $\qquad\qquad a = \dfrac{c - sb}{s}$

EXAMPLE 2. Solve for n in the equation $\frac{n+2}{c} = \frac{n+c}{b}$.

① Multiply by bc.

$$bc\left(\frac{n+2}{c}\right) = bc\left(\frac{n+c}{b}\right)$$
$$b(n+2) = c(n+c)$$
$$bn + 2b = cn + c^2$$

② Get terms with n on one side.

$$bn - cn = c^2 - 2b$$

③ Factor to have n by itself.

$$n(b-c) = c^2 - 2b$$

④ Solve for n.

$$n = \frac{c^2 - 2b}{b - c}$$

Now try these

—— Solve for n.

1. $na + n = cd$ **2.** $\frac{n}{x} + 1 = x - d$ **3.** $\frac{n-a}{b} = \frac{n}{2}$

Answers: **1.** $n = \dfrac{cd}{a+1}$ **2.** $n = x^2 - dx - x$ **3.** $n = \dfrac{-2a}{b-2}$, or $\dfrac{2a}{2-b}$

Exercises

A —— Solve for the required variable in terms of the other variables.

1. $i = prt$ Solve for r. **2.** $s = \dfrac{W}{L}$ Solve for L.

3. $M = \dfrac{bh^3}{3}$ Solve for b. **4.** $v = \dfrac{S}{T}$ Solve for T.

5. $s = \dfrac{ah}{r}$ Solve for a. **6.** $v = \dfrac{bh^3}{3}$ Solve for h.

7. $I = \dfrac{bd^3}{a}$ Solve for b. **8.** $A = \dfrac{F}{M}$ Solve for M.

9. $A = \frac{1}{2}bh$ is the formula for finding the area of a triangle. Solve it for b.

10. $I = \frac{E}{R}$ is called Ohm's Law and is used to determine electric current flowing through a circuit. Find R.

11. $F = \frac{Mv^2}{gr}$ is the formula used to compute centrifugal force, the kind of force you feel when a car goes around a curve. Solve for g.

12. $K = \frac{1}{2}mv^2$ is used to find kinetic energy, the energy of a moving body. Solve for m.

13. $V = \frac{4}{3}\pi r^3$ is used to find the volume of a sphere. Solve for π.

14. $S = \frac{1}{2}gt^2$ enables you to compute the distance an object falls in time t. Solve for g.

15. $A = p + prt$ is used by bankers to calculate your total savings principal, plus interest. Solve for p.

—— Solve for n.

16. $2n + a = b$

17. $2n - a = b$

18. $an - b = c$

19. $n(a - b) = c$

20. $n(a + b) + c = d$

21. $an - bn = c$

22. $an - bn + cn = d$

23. $an + bn + c = d$

24. $\frac{1}{3}n + a = b$

25. $\frac{1}{3}n + a = n$

26. $\frac{n}{a} = b$

27. $\frac{n}{a} = \frac{b}{c}$

B —— Solve for n.

28. $\frac{n}{a} + \frac{b}{c} = d$

29. $\frac{a}{c} = n + bn$

30. $\frac{n}{a + b} = c$

31. $\frac{n}{a + b} = c - n$

32. $\frac{1}{n} = \frac{1}{a} + \frac{1}{b}$

33. $\frac{1}{n} = \frac{1}{a} - \frac{1}{b}$

34. $\frac{1}{f} = \frac{1}{p} + \frac{1}{q}$ is used to determine the focal length of a lens. Solve for f.

35. If you wanted to find the sum of an infinite number of terms in a sequence such as $\frac{1}{2}, \frac{1}{4}, \frac{1}{8}, \cdots$, you could use the formula $S = \frac{a}{1 - r}$. Solve this for r.

36. If you wanted to find a certain term of the sequence 5, 7, 9, 11, $\cdots$, you would use the formula $l = a + (n - 1)d$. Solve for n.

37. What is the sum of the first one hundred even integers? The formula $S = \frac{n}{2}(a + e)$ would aid you in finding the sum. Express the formula in terms of a.

38. $M = \frac{25}{f} + \frac{25}{d}$ is used to determine the magnifying power of a simple microscope. (*25* is 25 centimeters, the distance for the most distinct image.) Express this formula in terms of d.

—— Solve for the required variables.

39. $r = \frac{v^2pL}{a}$ Solve for p and for a.

40. $R = \frac{WL - x}{L}$ Solve for W, for L, and for x.

41. $f = \frac{gm - t}{m}$ Solve for g, for m, and for t.

42. $S = \frac{rl - a}{r - l}$ Solve for r, for l, and for a.

C **43.** Assume that all variables in the formula $f = \frac{gm - t}{m}$ represent positive numbers. If the value of m is increased and g and t remain fixed, is the value of f *increased* or *decreased*? What happens if t is negative and m is increased? Give evidence to support your answer.

44. The formula for the coefficient of lift, used in aerodynamics, is $C_L = \dfrac{L}{\frac{P}{2} SV^2}$.   Solve for S. Then find the value of S when $L = 864$, $P = .003$, $C_L = .1$, and $V = 120$.

45. The formula $W = C_L \frac{P}{2} SV^2$ can be changed in order to find the velocity needed to sustain the weight of an airplane under certain conditions. Solve for V^2. Then find V when $W = 1500$, $C_L = .43$, $P = .002$, and $S = 200$.

10–6   Indirect Measurement

One application of rational expressions occurs in the study of **trigonometry.** Although *trigonometry* means "measurement of triangles," its application is extensive and is not limited to measuring triangles.

For now, the next few sections will acquaint you with how trigonometry is used to measure triangles and how triangle relationships can be used to measure distances indirectly.

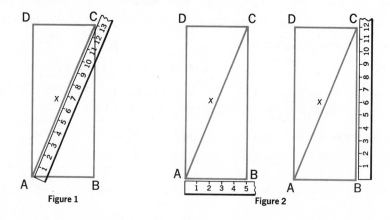

Figure 1   Figure 2

In Figure 1 at the bottom of the previous page, the measure of diagonal AC is found by **directly** measuring the length. The "measure of $\overline{AC}$" is written symbolically as $|\overline{AC}|$.

In Figure 2, $|\overline{AC}|$ is found **indirectly**. Sides AB and BC are measured directly as 5 inches and 12 inches, respectively. Then these lengths are used with the Pythagorean theorem to find the length of the diagonal AC.

$$
\begin{aligned}
|\overline{AC}|^2 &= |\overline{AB}|^2 + |\overline{BC}|^2 \\
&= (5)^2 + (12)^2 \\
&= 25 + 144, \text{ or } 169 \\
|\overline{AC}| &= \sqrt{169}, \text{ or } 13
\end{aligned}
$$

You may want to use indirect measurement either for convenience or out of necessity, for example, to find the length of a bridge to span a river or to find the length of a tunnel to be dug through a mountain.

To make measurements indirectly, you use direct measurements and a known relation between the direct measurements and the unknown.

Exercises

A   **1.** To find the area of a table top, Tom used a square piece of cardboard one foot on a side, making it one square foot in area. He applied it to the table top and found the number of square units needed to cover the top of the table.

a. Is he measuring directly or indirectly?

b. What is the unit of measurement?

c. How many 1-foot squares could Tom place on the table top?

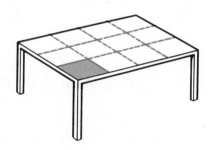

2. Byron measured the length and width of the table directly with a ruler and then used these lengths to find the area.

a. If the length is measured as 4 feet and the width as 3 feet, find the area using the formula $A = lw$.

b. In this case, was the area measured directly? Explain.

c. What measurements were made directly?

d. What measurement was obtained indirectly?

3. The diameter of a circular sand box was measured as 11 feet.

a. Write the formula for the relation between the diameter and circumference of a circle.

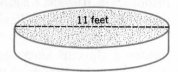

b. Find the circumference of the sand box.

c. Did you find the circumference directly or indirectly?

4. It took the Halls 8 hours to make a trip of 375 miles by car.

a. Write the formula showing the relation among time, t, distance, d, and rate, r.

b. Find their average rate of travel.

c. Did you find their average rate of travel directly or indirectly? Explain.

5. Dolores wants to put marble tiles on a circular table top so she can use it as a chess board.

a. The diameter of the table is 14 inches. Using the formula $A = \pi r^2$, find the area in square inches.

b. If the tiles are 1-inch squares, does the number for the area tell you the number of tiles you will need to cover the table top?

c. If you know that one side of the playing area is 8 inches, how many tiles will you need to cover it? Can you find the answer directly? indirectly? Which is easier?

10–7   Angles and Triangles

At the right is an **angle,** which is formed by two rays with a common endpoint. This angle is called angle A, which may be written $\angle A$, and is formed by $\overrightarrow{AB}$ and $\overrightarrow{AC}$. Rays AB and AC are the **sides** of the angle, and point A is the **vertex.**

The measure of an angle is determined by comparing it with a unit angle. One unit that is used to measure angles is the degree. With the degree as a unit, it takes 90 unit angles to make a **right angle.**

You know that if you join three points by segments, the figure formed is a triangle. By joining points A, B, and C, you form triangle ABC, written $\triangle ABC$.

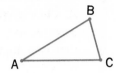

The sum of the measures of the angles of a triangle is 180°. An angle whose measure is less than 90° is an **acute angle.** An angle whose measure is greater than 90° is an **obtuse angle.**

A triangle that has a right angle is a **right triangle.** The right angle is shown by the symbol ⌐ in the triangle. Since the sum of the measures of the angles of a triangle is 180°, the other two angles of a right triangle must be acute angles.

For $\triangle XYZ$ at the right,

$$|\angle X| + |\angle Y| + |\angle Z| = 180°.$$

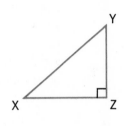

If $|\angle Z|$ is 90° and $|\angle X|$ is 40°, you can find the measure of $\angle Y$ indirectly.

$$
\begin{aligned}
|\angle X| + |\angle Y| + |\angle Z| &= 180° \\
40° + |\angle Y| + 90° &= 180° \\
|\angle Y| + 130° &= 180° \\
|\angle Y| &= 50°
\end{aligned}
$$

In order to distinguish the three sides of a right triangle, they are named as shown in the figure.

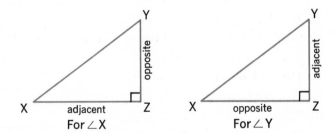

In a right triangle, the side opposite the right angle is called the **hypotenuse** to distinguish it from the *sides.*

Exercises

A **1.** Name the vertex of the angle at the right. What are the two sides of the angle?

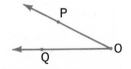

2. If $\overrightarrow{OP}$ and $\overrightarrow{OQ}$ are each made 4 inches longer, is the measure of $\angle O$ smaller, larger, or the same?

3. In △*XYZ* at the right, ∠*Z* is a right angle and | ∠*X* | is 35°. What is | ∠*Y* |?

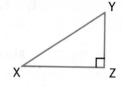

4. One of the angles of a right triangle measures 68°. What is the measure of the other two angles?

5. a. Triangle *ABC* is a right triangle. If | ∠*A* | is 70°, what is | ∠*B* |? Is the sum of | ∠*A* | and | ∠*B* | equal to 90°?

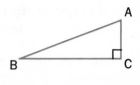

b. If one acute angle of a right triangle measures 33°, the other acute angle measures _?_°. The sum of the measures of the two acute angles is _?_°.

c. What is the sum of the measures of the two acute angles in a right triangle?

d. If one acute angle of a right triangle measures *x*°, the other acute angle measures _?_°.

6. Use triangle *ABC* at the right to complete these statements.
  a. The side opposite ∠*A* is _?_.
  b. The side adjacent to ∠*A* is _?_.
  c. The side opposite ∠*B* is _?_.
  d. The side adjacent to ∠*B* is _?_.
  e. The hypotenuse is _?_.

7. Use right triangle *MNP* to complete these statements.
  a. The side opposite ∠*M* is _?_.
  b. The side adjacent to ∠*M* is _?_.
  c. The side opposite ∠*N* is _?_.
  d. The side adjacent to ∠*N* is _?_.
  e. The hypotenuse is _?_.

B **8.** One acute angle of a right triangle measures 10° more than 3 times the measure of the other acute angle. What are the measures of the three angles?

9. In △*ABC*, | ∠*A* | is 7° less than twice | ∠*B* |, and | ∠*C* | is 3° more than 5 times | ∠*B* |. What are | ∠*A* |, | ∠*B* |, and | ∠*C* |?

10. The measure of one angle of a triangle is 40° more than ½ the measure of a second angle and 20° less than a third angle. If the first angle measures 60°, find the measures of the other two angles.

10–8   The Tangent Ratio

When a rational number $\frac{a}{b}$ is used to represent the division of one number by another, the quotient, $a \div b$, is called the *ratio of a to b*. A **ratio** is the comparison of two numbers by division.

Look at the right triangles below. From the following experiment, you will discover an important idea about right triangles.

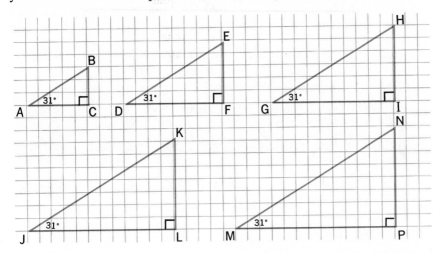

You can see that one angle of each triangle is 31° and that you can find the length of each side of the triangles by counting the number of units in that segment.

On a piece of paper, copy the following chart. In the first column, write the length of the side adjacent to the 31° angle. Then find, to the nearest tenth, the ratio of the measures of the two sides. Record your results in the third column. The first one is done for you.

Right triangle	Length of side opposite 31° angle	Length of side adjacent to 31° angle	$\left\| \frac{\text{opposite side}}{\text{adjacent side}} \right\|$
ABC	3	5	$\frac{3}{5}$, or .6
DEF			
GHI			
JKL			
MNP			

Look at your results and then answer the following questions.

a. Are the lengths of the sides opposite the 31° angle the same in any two triangles?

b. Are the lengths of the sides adjacent to the 31° angle the same in any two triangles?

c. What is the ratio $\dfrac{|\text{ side opposite 31° angle }|}{|\text{ side adjacent to 31° angle }|}$? Will this be the same for any 31° angle? Can you explain the results?

If two angles of one triangle are equal in measure to two angles of another triangle, the triangles are **similar.** The ratio of the measures of the corresponding sides of similar triangles is *always the same.*

The five triangles that you used for your ratio experiment each had a 31° angle and a 90° angle. Thus, they are all similar, and the ratio $\dfrac{|\text{ opposite side }|}{|\text{ adjacent side }|}$ is always the same. This ratio is called the **tangent.**

> **Definition** For any given acute angle of a right triangle, the ratio of the measure of the side opposite the angle to the measure of the side adjacent to the angle is called the <u>tangent.</u>

The abbreviation for *tangent* is **tan.** The tangent of 20° is *tan 20°.* For $\triangle ABC$, the following ratios hold.

$$\tan |\angle A| = \frac{|\overline{BC}|}{|\overline{AC}|}, \text{ or } \frac{a}{b}$$

$$\tan |\angle B| = \frac{|\overline{AC}|}{|\overline{BC}|}, \text{ or } \frac{b}{a}$$

Direct measuring of the lengths of the sides of a triangle and computation of the tangent is time consuming and often produces inaccurate results. Because tangent values are widely used, tables of such values have been prepared for easy reference. The *Table of Sine, Cosine, and Tangent Values* appears on page 547. The values of the tangents of angles from 0° to 89° are computed to four decimal places, as you can see in the portion of the table reproduced at the right. Now study the examples on the following page.

ANGLE	SINE	COSINE	TANGENT
40	.6428	.7660	.8391
41	.6561	.7547	.8693
42	.6691	.7431	.9004
43	.6820	.7314	.9325
44	.6947	.7193	.9657
45	.7071	.7071	1.0000
46	.7193	.6947	1.0355
47	.7314	.6820	1.0724
48	.7431	.6691	1.1106
49	.7547	.6561	1.1504

EXAMPLE 1. Find the tangent of 41°.

In the column headed ANGLE, find 41°. Directly opposite 41°, in the column headed TAN, read .8693.

$$\tan 41° \approx .8693$$

Nearly all values in the table are approximations.

EXAMPLE 2. What is the measure of the angle whose tangent is 1.1106?

In the column headed TAN, find 1.1106. Directly opposite 1.1106, in the column headed ANGLE, read 48°.

$$\tan 48° \approx 1.1106$$

The measure of the angle whose tangent is 1.1106 is 48°.

EXAMPLE 3. A flagpole is side BC in $\triangle ABC$ pictured at the right. Point A is 42 feet from point C and $|\angle A|$ is 47°. How high is the flagpole?

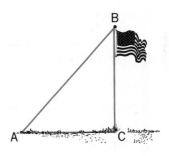

The problem states the measure of an angle of a right triangle and the measure of the side adjacent to the given angle. You are to find the measure of the side opposite the given angle. Thus, you can use the tangent ratio.

$$\tan |\angle A| = \frac{|\overline{BC}|}{|\overline{AC}|}$$

$$\tan 47° = \frac{|\overline{BC}|}{42}$$

From the table, tan 47° is approximately 1.0724.

$$1.0724 \approx \frac{|\overline{BC}|}{42}$$

$$(1.0724)(42) \approx |\overline{BC}|$$

$$45.0408 \approx |\overline{BC}|$$

The height of the flagpole to the nearest foot is about 45 feet.

Now try these

—— Use the table of values on page 547 to find x.

1. $\tan 76° \approx x$ **2.** $\tan 10° \approx x$

3. $\tan x \approx 1.3270$ **4.** $\tan x \approx .5774$

5. Using $\triangle ABC$ at the right, find tan $|\angle B|$ and $|\overline{BC}|$ to the nearest foot.

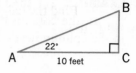

Answers: **1.** 4.0108   **2.** .1763   **3.** 53°   **4.** 30°   **5.** 2.4751; 4 feet

Checkpoint

1. What are similar triangles?

2. What is true about corresponding sides of similar triangles?

3. What is the definition of the tangent ratio?

Exercises

A —— Use the table on page 547 to find the following.

1. tangent of 20°   **2.** tan 22°   **3.** tangent of 40°

4. tangent of 45°   **5.** tan 55°   **6.** tangent of 70°

—— Find the tangent of each of the following angle measures.

7. 5°   **8.** 25°   **9.** 37°

10. 80°   **11.** 85°   **12.** 89°

—— Find x.

13. tan $x \approx .5774$ **14.** tan $x \approx 1.7321$ **15.** tan $x \approx .1228$

16. tan $x \approx .6009$ **17.** tan $x \approx 1.6003$ **18.** tan $x \approx 2.2460$

19. Refer to the table and complete the following sentence: As the measure of an angle increases from 0° to 89°, the tangent of the angle measure __?__ (increases or decreases) from .0000 to __?__.

20. The triangle in the figure below is a right triangle. Use the tangent ratio to find the distance between Tom's home and John's home, directly through the park.

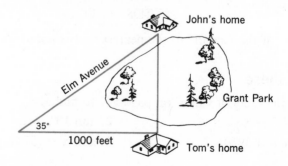

Find the length, *x*, of the indicated side in each of the following figures.

21.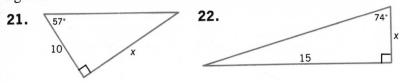

22.

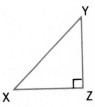

23. In right triangle *XYZ*, | ∠*X* | is 45°. Since the sum of | ∠*X* |, | ∠*Y* |, and | ∠*Z* | is 180°, | ∠*Y* | is also 45°. If two angles of a triangle have the same measure, the sides opposite these angles have the same length and the triangle would be called an isosceles triangle.

Triangle *XYZ* is isosceles and | $\overline{XZ}$ | = | $\overline{YZ}$ | is true.

$$\tan | \angle X | = \frac{| \overline{YZ} |}{| \overline{XZ} |} = \underline{\ ?\ } \qquad \tan | \angle Y | = \frac{| \overline{XZ} |}{| \overline{YZ} |} = \underline{\ ?\ }$$

The tangent of 45° is equal to 1.

24. The tangent of 90° is not given in the table. Experiment with several triangles like those below to see what happens to the lengths of the opposite (opp.) and adjacent (adj.) sides as the angle gets larger.

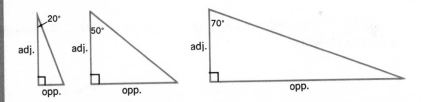

Can you explain why the tangent of 90° is not given?

25. To the nearest foot, how long is $\overline{DF}$, in △*DEF* below?

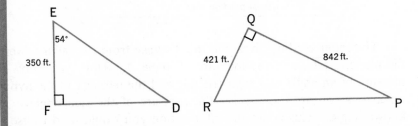

B 26. In △*PQR* above, what is | ∠*P* |, to the nearest degree?

27. Use Figure 1 below to find the length of $\overline{BC}$ to the nearest foot.

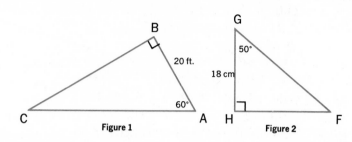

Figure 1

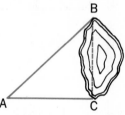

Figure 2

28. To the nearest centimeter, find the length of $\overline{HF}$ in Figure 2.

29. In the figure at the right, angle C is the right angle of $\triangle ABC$. What measurements could you make to find $|\overline{BC}|$, the distance across the pool?

30. Using the figure for Exercise 29, find $|\overline{BC}|$ if $|\angle A|$ is 42° and $|\overline{AC}|$ is 240 feet.

10–9   The Sine and Cosine Ratios

Suppose you wish to know the height of a plane, as illustrated in the figure below.

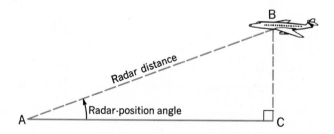

The radar reading gives you the distance from the radar tower to the plane, $|\overline{AB}|$, and the measure of angle A. Thus, you know the measure of an angle of a right triangle and the measure of the hypotenuse, and you are looking for the measure of the side opposite the known angle. This is not the information you would need to use the tangent ratio.

Or suppose your problem is to find the distance across the widest part of the mouth of a volcano. By considering $\triangle ABC$, you can find $|\angle A|$ and it is 35°, and you know that the measure of $\overline{AB}$, the hypotenuse, is 650 feet. The length you wish to find is that of the side adjacent to the known angle. This, too, is not the information you would need to use the tangent ratio.

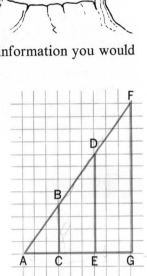

There are two other ratios you can use with the right triangle.

$$\frac{|\text{ side opposite } \angle A\ |}{|\text{ hypotenuse }|}$$

$$\frac{|\text{ side adjacent to } \angle A\ |}{|\text{ hypotenuse }|}$$

Apply these two ratios to the three right triangles shown at the right. You can find the lengths of the legs of the right triangles by counting the units. Then use the Pythagorean theorem to find the length of the hypotenuse.

Complete the following chart by replacing ? with your results.

	$\triangle ABC$	$\triangle ADE$	$\triangle AFG$
side opposite $\angle A$	$|\overline{BC}| = 4$	$|\overline{DE}| = \underline{?}$	$|\overline{FG}| = 12$
side adjacent to $\angle A$	$|\overline{AC}| = \underline{?}\,3$	$|\overline{AE}| = 6$	$|\overline{AG}| = \underline{?}\,9$
hypotenuse	$|\overline{AB}| = 5$	$|\overline{AD}| = \underline{?}\,10$	$|\overline{AF}| = 15$
$\dfrac{|\text{ opposite side }|}{|\text{ hypotenuse }|}$	$\dfrac{|\overline{BC}|}{|\overline{AB}|} = \underline{?}$	$\dfrac{|\overline{DE}|}{|\overline{AD}|} = \underline{?}$	$\dfrac{|\overline{FG}|}{|\overline{AF}|} = \underline{?}$
$\dfrac{|\text{ adjacent side }|}{|\text{ hypotenuse }|}$	$\dfrac{|\overline{AC}|}{|\overline{AB}|} = \underline{?}$	$\dfrac{|\overline{AE}|}{|\overline{AD}|} = \underline{?}$	$\dfrac{|\overline{AG}|}{|\overline{AF}|} = \underline{?}$

The three triangles in the figure are similar and, therefore, the ratios of the measures of their corresponding sides should be equal. Do your results support this?

Then, for any given acute angle of a right triangle, the ratio $\dfrac{|\text{opposite side}|}{|\text{hypotenuse}|}$ is always the same and the ratio $\dfrac{|\text{adjacent side}|}{|\text{hypotenuse}|}$ is always the same.

Definition For any given acute angle of a right triangle, the ratio of the measure of the side opposite the angle to the measure of the hypotenuse is called the <u>sine.</u>

Definition For any given acute angle of a right triangle, the ratio of the measure of the side adjacent to the angle to the measure of the hypotenuse is called the <u>cosine.</u>

Checkpoint

1. What is meant by the sine ratio?

2. What is meant by the cosine ratio?

Exercises

A ▬▬ Use the table of values on page 547 to find approximations for the sine and the cosine of the following angles.

1. 35°	**2.** 42°	**3.** 54°
4. 83°	**5.** 72°	**6.** 61°

▬▬ Find x.

7. $\sin x \approx .1392$	**8.** $\sin x \approx .3907$	**9.** $\sin x \approx .6561$
10. $\sin x \approx .7547$	**11.** $\sin x \approx .9135$	**12.** $\sin x \approx .9962$

13. Look at your results for Exercises 7–12. As the size of an acute angle increases, does the sine ratio increase or decrease?

▬▬ Find x.

14. $\cos x \approx .9336$	**15.** $\cos x \approx .7660$	**16.** $\cos x \approx .5299$
17. $\cos x \approx .1736$	**18.** $\cos x \approx .0175$	**19.** $\cos x \approx .9877$

20. Look at the cosine values in the table. As the size of an acute angle increases, does the value of the cosine increase or decrease?

21. Now you can solve the problems mentioned at the beginning of the section.

a. The distance from the tower to the plane is 3000 feet, and angle *A* measures 20°.

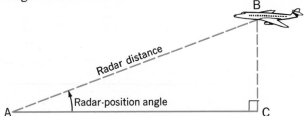

The height of the plane is the measure of the side opposite the 20° angle and you know the hypotenuse. Use the sine ratio.

$$\sin |\angle A| = \frac{|\overline{BC}|}{3000}$$

$$.3420 \approx \frac{|\overline{BC}|}{3000}$$

Solve for $|\overline{BC}|$.

b. Finding the distance across the mouth of the volcano is finding the measure of a side adjacent to a given acute angle of a right triangle, also given the measure of the hypotenuse. Use the cosine ratio.

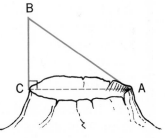

$$\cos 35° = \frac{|\overline{AC}|}{650}$$

$$.8192 \approx \frac{|\overline{AC}|}{650}$$

Solve for $|\overline{AC}|$.

22. Use the triangle below to find the following values.

a. $\tan |\angle A| = \underline{\ ?\ }$

b. $\cos |\angle A| = \underline{\ ?\ }$

c. $\cos |\angle B| = \underline{\ ?\ }$

d. $\tan |\angle B| = \underline{\ ?\ }$

e. $\sin |\angle A| = \underline{\ ?\ }$

f. $\sin |\angle B| = \underline{\ ?\ }$

g. To the nearest degree, what is $|\angle A|$ and $|\angle B|$?

C   14 m   B

3.49 m

A

23. John's kite string is 196 feet long and makes an angle of 42° with the horizontal in the figure below. How high above the ground is the kite?

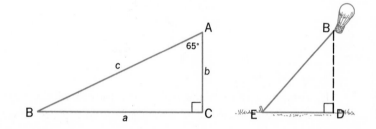

24. In the figure above, $\overline{AB}$ represents a wire supporting a telephone pole, $\overline{BC}$. Find $|\overline{AB}|$.

B   25. In $\triangle ABC$ below, c is 75 feet and $|\angle A|$ is 65°. What is b?

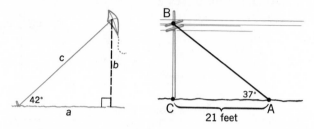

26. In the figure at the right above, the balloon at B is anchored to the ground at a point E by a wire. The wind blows the balloon so the wire makes an angle of 48° with the ground. If point D, directly under the balloon, is 260 feet from E, how long is the wire?

27. How far above the ground is the balloon in Exercise 26?

28. The scouts of the Wolf Patrol want to know the distance across a pond. They laid off $\overline{CA}$ at right angles to $\overline{BC}$. They extended $\overline{CA}$ until they came to a point A from which they could measure $\overline{AB}$. They measured $\overline{AB}$ and the angle A. If $|\overline{AB}|$ is 580 feet and $|\angle A|$ is 57°, find $\overline{BC}$.

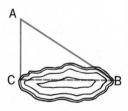

29. The railroad that runs to the summit of Pike's Peak makes, at the steepest place, an angle of 27° with the horizontal. How many feet would you rise in walking 100 feet up the railroad track?

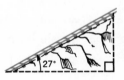

30. The ladder in the figure is 20 feet long and reaches the wall at a point 18 feet from the ground. To the nearest degree, what is the measure of the angle that the ladder makes with the house?

─── Exercises 31–36 refer to *right triangles.* Make a drawing for each: *a* is the side opposite ∠*A*, *b* is the side opposite ∠*B*, and *c* is the side opposite ∠*C* (which is a right angle).

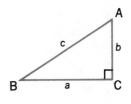

31. Find *c* when *a* is 26 inches and | ∠*A* | is 54°.
32. Find *c* when *a* is 8.4 centimeters and | ∠*A* | is 62°.
33. Find *a* when *c* is 65 yards and | ∠*A* | is 45°.
34. Find *b* when *c* is 100 feet and | ∠*A* | is 35°.
35. Find *b* when *c* is 42 miles and | ∠*B* | is 30°.
36. Find *a* when *c* is 78 meters and | ∠*A* | is 54°.

37. If | $\overline{XY}$ | is 110 feet and | ∠*YXZ* | is 27°, what is *d* in Figure 1?

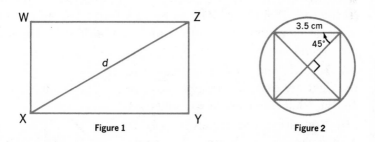

Figure 1   Figure 2

C **38.** The diagonals of a square are perpendicular to each other, as shown in Figure 2 above. If a circle is circumscribed about the square, the diagonals are also diameters of the circle. Find, by means of the cosine ratio, the radius of a circle circumscribed about a square whose side is 3.5 centimeters.

39. Use the Pythagorean theorem to check your answer to Exercise 38.

10–10 Solving Problems Using the Three Trigonometric Ratios

The following problems will give you practice in using all three trigonometric ratios — sine, cosine, and tangent. In solving these problems, you should first make a drawing, if no illustration is given, to show the parts that you know and the parts you wish to find. Then decide which ratio you should use to find the unknown part.

Exercises

A **1.** Refer to the figure given at the right and complete: Given b and $|\angle A|$, you can find a by using the _?_ ratio. Given b and $|\angle A|$, you can find the measure of the hypotenuse, c, by using the _?_ ratio. Given a and $|\angle A|$, you can find b by using the _?_ ratio, or you can find the measure of the hypotenuse, c, by using the _?_ ratio. Given $|\angle B|$ and a, you can find b by using the _?_ ratio, or you can find the measure of the hypotenuse, c, by using the _?_ ratio.

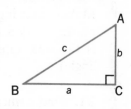

2. To find the distance across a pond between two points, M and N, Jack measured off 620 feet on a line MR perpendicular to segment MN. He found $|\angle MRN|$ to be 35°. Find $|\overline{MN}|$.

3. Some girl scouts measured the height of a mound. They stretched a string from a point, A, at the bottom of the mound to the top, T, finding $|\overline{AT}|$ to be 72.5 feet. The measure of the angle of elevation of the top from point A is 35°. How high is the mound?

4. If $|\overline{AB}|$ and $|\overline{BC}|$ in the figure at the right are each 30 feet and $|\overline{BD}|$ is 18 feet, what is the measure of angle A?

5. You are given rectangle $ABCD$ with diagonal $\overline{AC}$ drawn. The angle between $\overline{AD}$ and $\overline{AC}$ measures 31° and $|\overline{AD}|$ is 16.3 inches. How long is $\overline{AC}$?

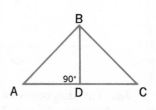

B **6.** Find the angle of elevation of the sun to the nearest degree when a church steeple 200 feet high casts a shadow 80 feet long.

7. From the top of a cliff 3500 feet above a lake, the angle of depression of the nearest shore is 18°. Find the distance from the top of the cliff to the edge of the lake.

8. In the figure at the right, $|\overline{AB}|$ is 215 feet, $|\angle A|$ is 35°, $|\angle C|$ is 65°, and the angles at D are right angles. How long are $\overline{BD}$ and $\overline{BC}$?

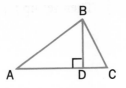

10–11   Interpolation in a Trigonometric Table

The measure of an acute angle in a right triangle is not always a whole number of degrees. Values less than one degree are measured in minutes and seconds. Sixty minutes make one degree and sixty seconds make one minute. The expression 29° 34′ 11″ is read "twenty-nine degrees, thirty-four minutes, and eleven seconds." In such cases, it is not possible to read the value of the tangent, sine, or cosine of an angle directly from the table of values.

Similarly, if the value of a trigonometric ratio for an angle is not given in the table, it is not possible to read the measure of the angle directly from the table.

To find in-between values, a process called **interpolation** is used.

EXAMPLE 1. Find tan $22\frac{1}{2}°$.

Since $22\frac{1}{2}°$, or 22° 30′, is halfway between tan 22° and tan 23°, assume that tan 22° 30′ is halfway between tan 22° and tan 23°. With this assumption, you can set up a proportion using the differences between the values. The result will give you values that are satisfactory for most practical purposes.

① Write the values you are concerned with in table form.

$$\text{tan } 22° \approx .4040$$
$$\text{tan } 22° \, 30' \approx \underline{\ ?\ }$$
$$\text{tan } 23° \approx .4245$$

② Consider 22° and 23° as 22° 00′ and 23° 00′, respectively. Find the differences between the angle measures and the tangent values. The differences are shown by the brackets.

$$60'\begin{bmatrix}30'\begin{bmatrix}\text{tan } 22° \, 00' \approx .4040 \\ \text{tan } 22° \, 30' \approx \underline{\ ?\ }\end{bmatrix}x \\ \text{tan } 23° \, 00' \approx .4245\end{bmatrix}.0205$$

(Continued on next page.)

③ Then set up a proportion.

$$\frac{30}{60} \approx \frac{x}{.0205}$$

$$\frac{1}{2} \approx \frac{x}{.0205}$$

$$2x \approx .0205$$

$$x \approx .01025$$

Thus, .01025 is the difference between tan 22° and tan $22\frac{1}{2}°$.

④ Add the difference to the value of tan 22° to get the value of tan $22\frac{1}{2}°$.

$$\text{tan } 22\frac{1}{2}° \approx .4040 + .01025$$

$$\approx .41425 \approx .4142$$

Note that here you added the difference because the tangent gets larger as the angle measure gets larger. But if this were the cosine, you would have to subtract the difference. Why?

EXAMPLE 2. What is the angle whose cosine is .8124?

① Look in the table to find two values between which .8124 falls and put your information in table form.

$$\text{cos } 35° \approx .8192$$

$$\text{cos } \underline{?} \approx .8124$$

$$\text{cos } 36° \approx .8090$$

② Find the differences.

$$60' \left[x \begin{bmatrix} \text{cos } 35° \ 00' \approx .8192 \\ \text{cos } \underline{?} \approx .8124 \end{bmatrix} .0068 \\ \text{cos } 36° \ 00' \approx .8090 \end{bmatrix} .0102 $$

③ Set up a proportion.

$$\frac{x}{60} \approx \frac{.0068}{.0102}$$

$$\frac{x}{60} \approx \frac{2}{3}$$

$$3x \approx 120$$

$$x \approx 40$$

④ The angle whose cosine is .8124 is approximately 35° 40′.

Always round your answers to the nearest whole number of minutes or, in the case of the decimal value, to a 4-place decimal.

Now try these

— Between what two values in the table will the following sine values fall?

1. .6049   **2.** .9175   **3.** .3201

4. Repeat Exercises 1–3, considering the values as cosine values.

— Between what two values in the table will the following tangent values fall?

5. 2.7841   **6.** .9056   **7.** .2511

8. Find the angle whose sine is .4722.

Answers: **1.** .6018 and .6157   **2.** .9135 and .9205   **3.** .3090 and .3256   **4.** .6157 and .6018; .9205 and .9135; .3256 and .3090   **5.** 2.7475 and 2.9042   **6.** .9004 and .9325   **7.** .2493 and .2679   **8.** 28° 11′

Exercises

A —— By interpolation, find the value of each ratio.

1. $\tan 39\frac{1}{2}°$ **2.** $\cos 54\frac{1}{2}°$ **3.** $\sin 26\frac{1}{4}°$

4. $\tan 38.7°$ **5.** $\sin 73.4°$ **6.** $\cos 72.6°$

—— By interpolation, find x.

7. $\cos x = .9763$ **8.** $\cos x = .6364$ **9.** $\cos x = .8039$

10. $\sin x = .2840$ **11.** $\sin x = .8351$ **12.** $\sin x = .9542$

13. $\tan x = 2.2208$ **14.** $\tan x = .2357$ **15.** $\tan x = 1.0488$

16. How tall is a tree that casts a shadow of 60 feet when the angle of elevation of the sun is $35\frac{1}{2}°$?

17. Figure 1 below shows a triangle inscribed in a circle; $|\angle OAB|$ is 30°, $\overline{OB}$ is perpendicular to $\overline{AC}$, and $|\overline{AB}| = \frac{1}{2}|\overline{AC}|$. How long is side AC if the radius of the circle is 6.3 inches?

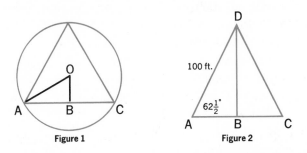

Figure 1   Figure 2

18. In Figure 2 above, how long is $\overline{AC}$ if $\overline{DB}$ is perpendicular to $\overline{AC}$ and $|\overline{AB}| = |\overline{BC}|$?

CHAPTER REVIEW ▐▬▬▬▬▬▬▬▬▬

1. Know the meaning of and be able to use each of the following words or phrases. The number shown after each word or phrase indicates where it is introduced, in case you need to review.

trigonometry (*434*)   right triangle (*437*)
direct measurement (*435*)   hypotenuse (*437*)
indirect measurement (*435*)   ratio (*439*)
angle (*436*)   similar triangles (*440*)
sides (*436*)   tangent (*440*)
vertex (*436*)   sine (*446*)
right angle (*436*)   cosine (*446*)
acute angle (*437*)   interpolation (*451*)
obtuse angle (*437*)

2. By what do you multiply both sides of the following equation to obtain an equation without rational expressions?

$$\frac{x}{3} + \frac{x}{4} = \frac{13}{12}$$

3. What is the lowest common denominator for $\frac{8}{x-2} = \frac{7}{x-7}$? Solve the equation.

▬▬ Solve the following equations.

4. $\dfrac{7x-2}{4x} - \dfrac{2x+3}{3x} = \dfrac{5}{12}$

5. $\dfrac{x-2}{x+3} = \dfrac{x+5}{x-7}$

6. The numerator of a rational number is 2 smaller than the denominator. If the numerator is increased by 9 and the denominator is multiplied by 3, the rational number equals $\frac{2}{3}$. What is the number?

7. The Mammouth Dairy has an old machine that fills cartons with milk at the rate of 1000 in 15 minutes. Their newer machine fills 1000 cartons in 9 minutes. How long will it take both machines working together to fill 1000 cartons with milk?

8. Mr. Deluca drove 400 miles in heavy traffic going on a vacation trip. He returned home in much lighter traffic and was able to drive at a rate that was a fourth faster. The return trip took him two hours less time. What was his rate of speed going on the trip?

9. What operation do you perform to change each equation into the next equivalent equation?

$$x + \frac{y}{5} = y \rightarrow 5x + y = 5y \rightarrow -4y = -5x \rightarrow y = \frac{5x}{4}$$

10. The formula for the area of a trapezoid is $A = \frac{h(B+b)}{2}$. Solve this formula for B.

11. Before cutting down a large tree in his yard, Mr. Jacobs measured the circumference of its trunk and computed its diameter by using the formula $C = \pi d$. After cutting down the tree, he measured the diameter as 27 inches. Which was an indirect measurement? Should the two measures have been the same?

12. What is the name of an angle whose measure is 90°? whose measure is greater than 90°? less than 90°?

13. Which two of the following triangles are similar?

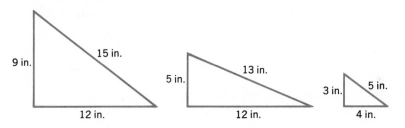

For each of the three pairs of corresponding sides of the similar triangles, write the ratio of the lengths. Are the three ratios equal?

14. For the triangle at the left below, write the ratio that represents tan 30°; sin 60°; cos 30°.

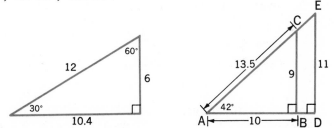

15. Look at triangle ABC above. What is tan $|\angle A|$? Does the ratio $\frac{9}{10}$ approximately represent tan 42°? Does the ratio $\frac{11}{|AD|}$ represent tan 42°? What is $|\overline{AD}|$? What is $|\overline{BD}|$?

— Draw $\triangle ABC$, $|\angle B| = 90°$. Then answer Exercises 16–19 using $\triangle ABC$.

16. If you are given $|\angle A|$ and $|\overline{AB}|$, would you use the tangent, sine, or cosine ratio to find $|\overline{BC}|$?

17. Given $|\angle A|$ and $|\overline{BC}|$, what ratio would you use to find $|\overline{AC}|$?

18. Given $|\angle A|$ and $|\overline{AC}|$, what ratio would you use to find $|\overline{BC}|$? $|\overline{AB}|$?

19. Given $|\angle C|$ and $|\overline{BC}|$, what ratio would you use to find $|\overline{AC}|$?

20. Using the table on page 547, interpolate to find x to the nearest 10 minutes if $\tan x = 2.8355$.

21. Interpolate to find $\sin 54.8°$ to the nearest ten-thousandth.

CHAPTER TEST

1. The formula $V = \frac{1}{3}\pi r^2 h$ is used to find the volume of a cone. Express this formula in terms of h.

2. To determine the total surface area of a cylinder, you can use the formula $T = 2\pi r(r + h)$. Express this formula in terms of h.

—— Solve the following equations for x.

3. $\dfrac{2}{x} = \dfrac{6}{x + 5}$

4. $\dfrac{4 - x}{4} = \dfrac{6}{2 - x}$

5. $\dfrac{x - 2}{x + 4} = \dfrac{x - 1}{x - 3}$

6. One number is 6 less than the other. If 5 is subtracted from both numbers, the quotient of the larger divided by the smaller is $\frac{4}{3}$. What are the numbers?

7. Using the triangle at the right, write each of these ratios.

    a. $\sin |\angle A| = \underline{\,?\,}$ **b.** $\tan |\angle A| = \underline{\,?\,}$

    c. $\cos |\angle A| = \underline{\,?\,}$ **d.** $\tan |\angle B| = \underline{\,?\,}$

    e. $\sin |\angle B| = \underline{\,?\,}$ **f.** $\cos |\angle B| = \underline{\,?\,}$

8. One angle of a right triangle measures 70° and the side adjacent to it measures 19 feet. To the nearest tenth of a foot, what is the measure of the side opposite the 70° angle?

9. If you want the top of the 30-foot ladder shown to be 25 feet from the ground, to the nearest degree, what must the measure of angle O be? If you want the bottom to be 20 feet from the building, what must the measure of angle O be?

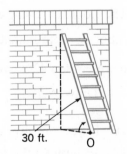

10. Jack can mow his lawn in 6 hours. His younger brother Frank can mow it in 10 hours. How long will it take them to mow the lawn if they work together?

11. Find sin 56° 50′.

12. Find cos 28° 30′.

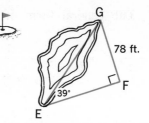

78 ft.

13. Shady Golf Course has a very large water trap. Using the figure at the right, find the length, $|\overline{GE}|$, of the water trap to the nearest foot.

ENRICHMENT

Convergents of Continued Fractions

As you saw in Chapter 9, a continued fraction has the form

$$\frac{p}{q} = a_1 + \cfrac{1}{a_2 + \cfrac{1}{a_3 + \cfrac{1}{a_4 + \vphantom{\cfrac{1}{1}}}}} \quad . \quad \text{For} \quad 1 + \cfrac{1}{2 + \cfrac{1}{3 + \cfrac{1}{4 + \frac{1}{5}}}},$$

$$+ \cfrac{1}{a_{n-1} + \cfrac{1}{a_n}}$$

$\frac{p}{q}$ is $\frac{225}{157} \approx 1.433121$, which you found by adding from the bottom up. Suppose you add from the top down. What values do you get? Call the values of these partial quotients c_n.

$$c_1 = 1 \qquad c_2 = 1 + \tfrac{1}{2}, \text{ or } \tfrac{3}{2} \qquad c_3 = 1 + \cfrac{1}{2 + \frac{1}{3}} = 1 + \cfrac{1}{\frac{7}{3}}, \text{ or } \tfrac{10}{7}$$

$$c_4 = 1 + \cfrac{1}{2 + \cfrac{1}{3 + \frac{1}{4}}} = 1 + \cfrac{1}{2 + \cfrac{1}{\frac{13}{4}}} = 1 + \cfrac{1}{2\frac{4}{13}} = 1 + \cfrac{1}{\frac{30}{13}}, \text{ or } \tfrac{43}{30}$$

$$c_5 = \tfrac{225}{157}$$

If you expressed each value as a decimal, you would see that the values are getting closer and closer to 1.433121. The values are *converging* to c_5. For this reason, the partial quotients are called the **convergents** of the continued fractions. The convergents have some interesting properties and they can be used to solve equations.

The general form of the convergents is $c_1 = \dfrac{p_1}{q_1} = a_1$; $c_2 = \dfrac{p_2}{q_2} =$

$a_1 + \dfrac{1}{a_2}$; $c_3 = \dfrac{p_3}{q_3} = a_1 + \dfrac{1}{a_2 + \dfrac{1}{a_3}}$; $c_4 = \dfrac{p_4}{q_4} = a_1 + \dfrac{1}{a_2 + \dfrac{1}{a_3 + \dfrac{1}{a_4}}}$; $c_5 = \dfrac{p_5}{q_5} = \dfrac{p}{q}$.

The following is a chart of the convergents of $\frac{225}{157}$.

n	1	2	3	4	5
a_n	1	2	3	4	5
p_n	1	3	10	43	225
q_n	1	2	7	30	157

An interesting pattern results if you cross-multiply, following the arrows, and subtract the products.

$$q_1 p_2 - q_2 p_1 = (1 \cdot 3) - (2 \cdot 1) = 1$$
$$q_2 p_3 - q_3 p_2 = (2 \cdot 10) - (7 \cdot 3) = -1$$
$$q_3 p_4 - q_4 p_3 = (7 \cdot 43) - (30 \cdot 10) = 1$$
$$q_4 p_5 - q_5 p_4 = (30 \cdot 225) - (157 \cdot 43) = -1$$

The pattern of 1 and -1 is true for convergents in general, although this will not be proved here. The pattern can be represented by the formula $q_n p_{n+1} - q_{n+1} p_n = (-1)^{n+1}$ and is a help in solving equations.

Suppose you are given $5m + 7n = 3$, an equation of the form $am + bn = c$, where a, b, and c are integers, and you want to find integers for m and n that make the equation true. In a simple case like this, you can determine by trial and error that $m = 2$ and $n = -1$ satisfy the equation, and so do $m = 9$ and $n = -6$.

But it might take quite a few trials and errors to solve $31x + 11y = 2$. A more definite method of solution is needed. You can use continued fractions to develop a method for solving such linear equations.

Use the coefficients of the variables to form a fraction greater than 1; in this case it is $\frac{31}{11}$. Then expand this fraction into a continued fraction, find the convergents, and make a chart as at the right.

n	1	2	3	4
a_n	2	1	4	2
p_n	2	3	14	31
q_n	1	1	5	11

Cross-multiply and subtract using the equation $q_n p_{n+1} - q_{n+1} p_n = (-1)^{n+1}$.

$$(1 \cdot 3) - (1 \cdot 2) = 1$$
$$(1 \cdot 14) - (5 \cdot 3) = -1$$
$$(5 \cdot 31) - (11 \cdot 14) = 1$$

Notice that if the terms of the last equation on the previous page are slightly rearranged, you have

$$31(5) - 11(14) = 1,$$

which corresponds very closely to the original equation. Substituting a for 31 and b for 11, you may write $5a - 14b = 1$. Then multiplying by 2 and changing the sign of the b term gives $10a + (-28)b = 2$, which is the same as $10(31) + -28(14) = 2$ and the problem is solved: $m = 10$ and $n = -28$.

Exercises

1. Calculate the convergents for the following continued fraction. Fill in a chart and check $q_n p_{n+1} - q_{n+1} p_n = (-1)^{n+1}$.

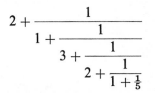

$$2 + \cfrac{1}{1 + \cfrac{1}{3 + \cfrac{1}{2 + \cfrac{1}{1 + \frac{1}{5}}}}}$$

2. Use continued fractions to find integral solutions for the following equations. Follow the example in the discussion.

a. $17m - 6n = 1$ **b.** $54m + 13n = 2$

c. $31m - 15n = 1$ **d.** $74m - 253n = 1$

THE GROWTH OF MATHEMATICS

New Ideas in Trigonometry

The first trigonometric tables were done before Euclid's time, and trigonometry was actively studied and improved by various mathematicians in Alexandria and in India. The chief purpose of trigonometry was to aid in astronomical calculations.

Johann Müller (1436–1476), a German astronomer, reintroduced the study of trigonometry in European mathematics. Müller is usually known as Regiomontanus, the Latin name of the city of Königsberg, where Müller was born. One of the contributions of Müller to trigonometry was the calculation of tables for very small differences in measure, thus producing more precise values of the trigonometric functions. He was also actively involved in collecting and translating Greek mathematical works that had been preserved in manuscript.

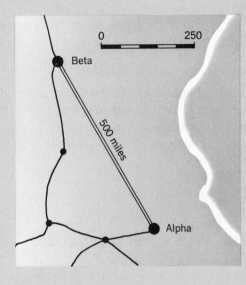

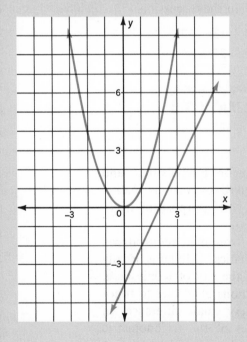

CHAPTER 11

RELATIONS AND FUNCTIONS

Relations and functions are among the most interesting and most useful parts of mathematics. In this chapter you will learn some of the general properties of relations and functions as well as the specific properties of a few special relations and functions.

● In the upper left region on the opposite page, a man is enlarging a photograph. Think of a ray of light from the bulb in the enlarger passing through the negative. Does the ray suggest a point on the enlargement that corresponds to a point on the negative? Is every point on the negative associated with a point on the enlargement by a ray? This illustrates the idea of a mapping.

● Look at the map in the upper right region. You know that the relation between distance, rate, and time is $d = rt$. At an average rate of 100 mph, how many hours will it take for the trip from Alpha to Beta? how many hours at 10 mph? This example illustrates inverse variation.

● Two functions that you have studied are graphed in the lower left region. How can you show that each is a function? What is the name of each?

● The graphs shown in the lower right region are of functions that are probably new to you. Trace each with your finger. How do the graphs differ from those at the left? How is the graph of the exponential function similar to the graph of the logarithmic function? How do they differ?

● The oscilloscope in the center of the page displays a curve that is the graph of the sine function. This curve often appears in nature as well as in science and mathematics.

11–1 Mappings

You are familiar with maps of various kinds, such as road maps, political maps, and weather maps. The primary purpose of a map is to represent on a smaller (or larger) scale some particular characteristic of the object being mapped — direction and type of highway for the road map; relative position and size of countries for the political map; and temperature, humidity, and air pressure for the weather points in the drawing. The way the map is made can be thought of as the **rule** for making the association between points of the real object and the points on the map.

EXAMPLE 1. Give a method for mapping a football field.

Rule

① Choose a point above the center of the field. Label it A.

② Choose a plane parallel to the field between A and the field. The position of the plane will determine the size of the map.

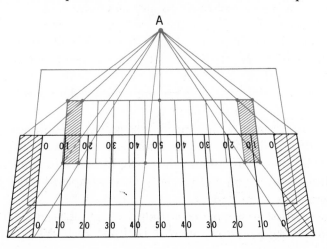

③ Draw the line segments from A to points on the field.

④ The intersection of the plane and the set of these segments is the map.

Each point of the football field is mapped to exactly one point in the drawing according to this plan. Note that the map will be smaller than the football field. How would you change the plan to get an enlargement of the football field?

EXAMPLE 2. Give a plan for mapping the rooms in a one-story house.

Rule

① Choose a plane passing through the house parallel to the floor at a height such that it passes through each window and each door.

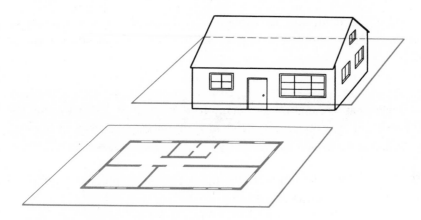

② The intersection of the plane and the house is the map.

Many points of the house are mapped into a single point on the map. For example, all of the points in a segment perpendicular to the floor become one point on the map. Also, the map is the same size as the floor of the house. You could reduce the size by repeating the method described in Example 1.

The two examples illustrate the mathematical idea of a **mapping.**

> **Definition** A mapping is a rule that associates the elements of one set, called the domain, with elements from a second set. The second set associated with elements in the domain is called the range or the image.

Notice that there are three components in the definition: two sets and one rule. In Example 1, the first set, or domain, is the set of points on the football field. The other set, or range, is the set of points on the map. The rule is the way the mapping was done.

In Example 1, each point in each set was mapped into one and only one point in the other set. Such a mapping is called a one-to-one mapping.

Definition A mapping is <u>one-to-one</u> whenever each element in the range is the image of one and only one element in the domain and each element in the domain maps into one and only one image element in the range.

Use the definition to explain why Example 1 is a one-to-one mapping. Is Example 2 a one-to-one mapping of the house into the map?

Definition A mapping is <u>many-to-one</u> when at least two elements in the domain are matched with one element in the range.

Explain why Example 2 is a many-to-one mapping. Example 3 illustrates a one-to-many mapping.

EXAMPLE 3. Illustrate the mapping for which the set of positive integers is mapped into the set of integers with each element in the first set matched with its square root from the second set.

The domain is the set of perfect-square integers, the range is the set of integers except 0, and the rule is to associate each element in the domain with its square root.

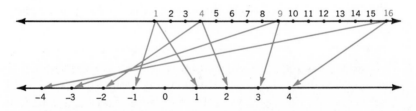

In this case each perfect square is mapped to two integers. Notice that only perfect squares are mapped. Explain why 0 is not in the image set.

Definition A mapping is <u>one-to-many</u> when at least one element in the domain is matched with two or more elements in the range.

Checkpoint

1. What three components are needed to define a mapping?

2. What is the meaning of the word *many* in the expression *one-to-many*?

3. What is the difference between one-to-many and many-to-one?

4. Describe the conditions for a one-to-one mapping.

Exercises

A —— Give the range for each mapping. State whether each mapping is one-to-one, one-to-many, or many-to-one. Draw diagrams for each exercise similar to that in Example 3 on page 464.

Domain	Second set	Rule
1. {0, 2, 4, 6, 8, 10}	Positive integers	Add 1.
2. {1, 2, 3, 4, 5}	Positive integers	Multiply by 5.
3. {25, 20, 15, 10}	Positive integers	Divide by 5.
4. {−7, 3, 5, 7, −3, 0}	Integers	Take absolute value.
5. {2, 7, 9, 8}	Real numbers	Take principal square root.

6. Suppose the domain of a mapping is the set of children in the United States, the range is the set of men in the United States, and the rule is *Fathers are matched with children.* How would you describe the mapping: as one-to-one, as many-to-one, or as one-to-many?

7. Let the set of cars on the New York State Thruway form the domain and the set of tires form the range. *Cars are matched with the tires on them.* How would you describe the mapping?

8. Is there a one-to-one mapping of the real numbers with the points on a line? Explain.

B **9.** A graph is the image that results when pairs of numbers are mapped with points in the plane. Look at the drawing.

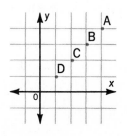

Domain: {(1, 1), (2, 2), (3, 3), (4, 4)}
Image: {A, B, C, D}

On to what point is each pair mapped?

10. Is there a one-to-one mapping of the even numbers with the set of positive integers? Explain.

11. Is there a one-to-one mapping of the rational numbers with the set of points on a line? Explain.

12. Is there a one-to-one mapping of the set of ordered pairs of real numbers with the points on a plane?

━━ Sketch a graph of the mapping defined by the equation or inequality when the set of real numbers is mapped with the set of real numbers according to the following rules. In each case, give the domain and range.

13. $y = |x|$

14. $y = |x + 2|$

15. $|y| = x$

16. $|y + 2| = x$

17. $y = x^2$

18. $x = y^2$

19. $y > x^2$

20. $x + y \leq 10$

21. Which mappings in Exercises 13–20 are one-to-one? one-to-many? many-to-one?

C ━━ Think of the possible ordered pairs formed using the given domain and range. Then write the ordered pairs in the relation defined by the rule.

	Domain	Range	Rule
22.	$\{5, 10, 12\}$	$\{1, 11\}$	$>$
23.	$\{8, \sqrt{19}\}$	$\{2\sqrt{5}, \sqrt{64}, \sqrt{81}\}$	$<$
24.	$\{5\sqrt{3}, -2\sqrt{6}\}$	$\{\sqrt{24}, \sqrt{75}\}$	$\neq$

11–2 Ordered Pairs

A *relation* has been defined as a set of ordered pairs. A *function* has been defined as a relation with the first elements in the pairs all different. Shown below are some relations involving pairs of numbers. Why is the relation R_1 not a function? Why are R_2, R_3, and R_4 relations that are also functions?

a. $R_1 = \{(10, 9), (10, 8), (10, 7), (10, 6), (10, 5)\}$

b. $R_2 = \{(1, 1), (2, 4), (3, 9), (4, 16), (5, 25)\}$

c. $R_3 = \{(-3, 3), (-2, 2), (-1, 1), (0, 0), (1, 1), (2, 2), (3, 3)\}$

d. $R_4 = \{(-5, -3), (-3, -1), (-1, 1), (1, 3), (3, 5), (5, 7)\}$

Each relation in **a–d** can be shown by using an equation or inequality and set-builder notation. Which set at the right has each relation in **a–d** as a subset?

e. $\{(x, y) : y = x + 2\}$
f. $\{(x, y) : y = \|x\|\}$
g. $\{(x, y) : y = x^2\}$
h. $\{(x, y) : y < x\}$

The sets defined in **e–h** show that some relations can be defined by equations. In fact, the two functions you have studied most thoroughly, the *linear* and *quadratic*, are defined by using equations. A *linear* function is defined as the set of ordered pairs (x, y) such that $y = mx + b$, $m \neq 0$ and $x \in R$, and the *quadratic* function is defined as $y = ax^2 + bx + c$, $a \neq 0$ and $x \in R$.

It appears that relations and mappings have a lot in common. In fact, every relation can be thought of as a mapping, and vice versa. The *domain* of a relation is simply the set of first elements of the pairs. The *range*, or *image*, is the set of second elements. What are the domain and range in each of **a–d**?

The domain and range of a relation need not be sets of numbers.

i. $R_5 = \{$(New York, Albany), (Michigan, Lansing),
(California, Sacramento), (Virginia, Richmond)$\}$

j. $R_6 = \{$(General Motors, Chevrolet), (Ford, Lincoln),
(Chrysler, Plymouth), (American, Rambler)$\}$

What is the domain and range of each relation in **i** and **j**? Give a verbal rule describing the domain; the range. Is each a function?

Checkpoint

1. What is a relation? a function?

2. Can *some* relations be defined by equations or inequalities? Can *all* relations be defined by equations or inequalities?

3. What is the replacement set for the linear function? the quadratic function? How is each function defined?

Exercises

A —— List the domain and range for each relation in Exercises 1–4.

1. $\{(1, 10), (1\frac{1}{4}, 10), (1\frac{1}{2}, 10), (1\frac{3}{4}, 10), (1\frac{7}{8}, 10)\}$

2. $\{(1, 1), (4, 2), (9, 3), (16, 4), (25, 5)\}$

3. $\{$(Indiana, Indianapolis), (Ohio, Columbus),
(Alabama, Montgomery), (Pennsylvania, Harrisburg)$\}$

4. {(feathers, chicken), (hair, human), (scales, fish),

(feathers, bird), (hair, dog)}

5. Which relations in Exercises 1–4 are functions?

6. Give a mathematical sentence or a verbal description of the way the pairs were formed in Exercises 1–4.

7. The equation $y = 3x + 4$ defines a relation between x and y. Complete the table showing seven number pairs that satisfy $y = 3x + 4$. Then draw the graph of this portion of the relation on the x and y axes. The replacement set for x is {0, 1, 2, 3, 4, 7, 10}.

When x is	0	1	2	3	4	7	10
then y is	4	7	?	?	?	?	?

Is this relation a function?

8. The perimeter of a regular hexagon is related to the length of one side. The relation is defined by $p = 6s$. Complete the table below showing several pairs of numbers that satisfy $p = 6s$ when $s \in$ {0, 1, 2, 3, 4, 5, 6}. Then graph the relation with s on the horizontal axis and p on the vertical axis.

When s is	0	1	2	3	4	5	6
then p is	0	6	?	?	?	?	?

—— The tables below define relations. Study each table and then write an equation that defines each relation. Which relations are functions?

9.

n	3	4	5	6	7	8
d	0	1	2	3	4	5

10.

w	1	2	3	4	5	6
c	5	10	15	20	25	30

11.

q	2	3	4	5	6	7
p	5	7	9	11	13	15

12.

x	0	1	2	3	4	5	6
y	−1	1	3	5	7	9	11

—— List the set of ordered pairs of numbers for each relation graphed below. Is the relation a function?

13.   **14.**

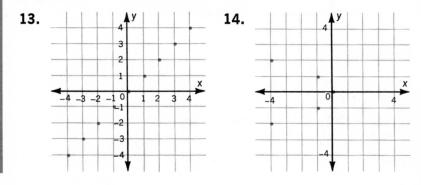

Sketch the graph on a plane of the relations defined by the following inequalities if the replacement set is the set of real numbers.

15. $y < -1$ **16.** $x > 2$ **17.** $-3 < |x| < 3$

18. $y > 1$ **19.** $x < -2$ **20.** $0 < |y| < 1$

Below are graphs of six relations. Which are functions?

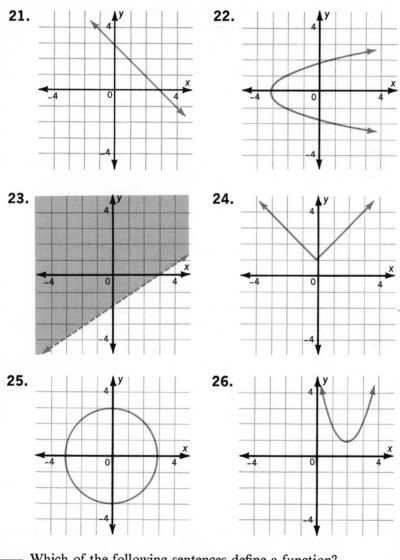

21.

22.

23.

24.

25.

26.

Which of the following sentences define a function?

27. $y = 7x - 9$ **28.** $x = y + 8$ **29.** $y < x$

30. $0 \cdot y + x = 9$ **31.** $y = x^2 + 7$ **32.** $x = y^2$

B — Graph each of the following relations where the domain is {−4, −3, −1, 0, 1, 2, 3, 4}. Indicate which are functions.

33. $\{(x, y) : y = x\}$

34. $\{(x, y) : |x| = 3y\}$

35. $\{(x, y) : x + y \geq 1\}$

36. $\{(x, y) : x^2 = y\}$

37. In the Bunch family there are three young children, Willy, Sally, and Jim. Suppose the replacement set for the elements in the ordered pairs is the set of children. What ordered pairs would result using *is a brother of* to define the relation between the first and second elements? Is the relation a function?

— Using the same children as in Exercise 37 and Mr. Bunch, list the ordered pairs for each relation defined as follows.

38. is the father of

39. is the sister of

40. is the son of

41. is the daughter of

42. is the mother of

43. Which relations in Exercises 38–42 are functions?

11–3   Graphs of Relations

You learned earlier that a relation defined by a set of ordered pairs can be graphed. When the relation is defined by an equation, the graph of the relation is found by plotting all the ordered pairs that satisfy the equation.

A relation may be symbolized with a letter such as *R, f, g, h,* or some other letter. You might use *f* to denote the relation defined by the equation $y = 2x + 3$, which is shown in graph A below. The letter *g* might denote the relation graphed in B.

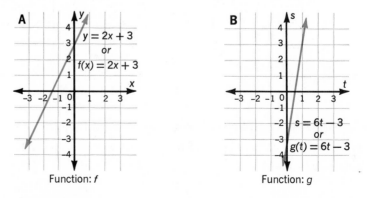

A $y = 2x + 3$
or
$f(x) = 2x + 3$

Function: *f*

B $s = 6t - 3$
or
$g(t) = 6t - 3$

Function: *g*

When a relation is a function, there is a special way of showing range elements. For the function f the image of 2 is 7, since $2(2) + 3$ is equal to 7. This is shown by writing $f(2) = 7$, read "f at two equals seven." In general, $f(x) = y = 2x + 3$ describes the function, so $f(x)$ is another way to denote y. Notice that $f(x)$ does *not* mean "f times x" when f is the name of a function. In B, the expression $g(t)$ means the value of g from the range for the given value of t, so $g(t) = 6t - 3$ is another way to describe the function.

Notice that this notation is usually restricted to functions. If this notation is used for a relation that is not a function, say $u(v) = \pm v$, then $u(2)$ denotes the set $\{-2, 2\}$.

Can you identify the type of function graphed in A and B on the previous page? It is the linear function. Recall its definition and also that of the quadratic function.

> A **linear function** is a function defined by the equation $y = mx + b$, where m, b, and x are real numbers, $m \neq 0$.
>
> A **quadratic function** is a function defined by the equation $y = ax^2 + bx + c$, where a, b, c, and x are real numbers, $a \neq 0$.

It can be proved that every linear function has a graph that is a line; and every line in the coordinate plane not parallel to the y axis is the graph of a linear function. Similarly, the graph of every quadratic function is a parabola; and every parabola whose axis of symmetry is parallel to the y axis is the graph of a quadratic function.

The graph of any relation with numbers may be drawn by plotting the ordered pairs on the coordinate plane. Many numerical relations are neither linear nor quadratic, but are easily graphed.

EXAMPLE 1. Graph the function defined by the following.

$$g(x) = \begin{cases} -2 \text{ when } x < 0 \\ 0 \text{ when } x = 0 \\ 2 \text{ when } x > 0 \end{cases}$$

By looking at the values x can have, you can see that the domain is the set of real numbers. The range, or image set, of the function is $\{-2, 0, 2\}$. Some typical ordered pairs are given in the table below.

x	-50	-2	-0.0001	0	0.0001	5	200
$g(x)$	-2	-2	-2	0	2	2	2

Explain why g is a function. Is it one-to-one? The graph is on the following page.

Here is the graph of g.

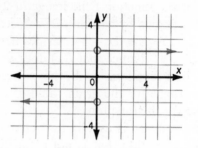

EXAMPLE 2. Graph the relation defined by

$$S = \{(x, y) : y = x + 2 \text{ or } y = 3x^2\}.$$

If a relation is defined by two or more equations joined by *or*, the graph is found by graphing each equation. The union of all these points is the graph of the relation. Using union symbolism, the relation is $S = \{(x, y) : y = x + 2\} \cup \{(x, y) : y = 3x^2\}$.

Is the graph in Example 2 the same as the graph of this relation?

$$\{(x, y) : y = x + 2 \text{ and } y = 3x^2\}$$

How do you graph sentences joined by *and*?

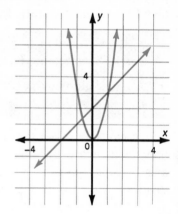

Now try these

—— If $f(x) = 2x + 6$, find

1. $f(-1)$. **2.** $f(\frac{1}{2})$. **3.** $f(p)$.

—— If $f(x) = x^2 - 2x + 6$, find

4. $f(0)$. **5.** $f(1)$. **6.** $f(-2)$.

—— If $g(x) = \dfrac{2x}{x + 3}$, find

7. $g(0)$. **8.** $g(0.25)$. **9.** $g(-3)$.

10. Describe the graph of a linear function.

11. Describe the graph of a quadratic function.

Answers: **1.** 4 **2.** 7 **3.** $2p + 6$ **4.** 6 **5.** 5 **6.** 14 **7.** 0 **8.** $\frac{2}{13}$, or $0.\overline{153846}$
9. -3 is not an element of the domain, so $g(-3)$ is not defined.

Exercises

A —— If g is the function defined by $y = -2x + 3$, find

1. $g(0)$.   **2.** $g(\frac{1}{2})$.   **3.** $g(-2)$.   **4.** $g(3)$.

—— If f is the function defined by $y = 6 - x^2$, find

5. $f(-2)$.   **6.** $f(-1)$.   **7.** $f(0)$.   **8.** $f(1)$.

—— If f is a function defined by $f(x) = x^2 - 2x + 3$, find

9. $f(0)$.   **10.** $f(-1)$.   **11.** $f(-3)$.   **12.** $f(5)$.

—— Draw the graphs of the relations defined below, and give the domain and range of each relation in Exercises 17–24. State whether or not the relation is a function.

13. $f(x) = 5x - 1;\ -2 < x \le 1$ **14.** $h(x) = |x|;\ -5 \le x \le 5$

15. $g(x) = \frac{1}{3}x - 2;\ -3 \le x \le 3$ **16.** $t(x) = -|x|$

17. $f(x) = \begin{cases} 3 \text{ when } x < 0 \\ -3 \text{ when } x > 0 \end{cases}$ **18.** $f(x) = \begin{cases} 1 \text{ when } x > 0 \\ 0 \text{ when } x = 0 \\ -1 \text{ when } x < 0 \end{cases}$

19. $g(x) = x - 2 \text{ or } g(x) = x$ **20.** $f(x) = -x \text{ and } t(x) = x$

21. $f(x) = x^2 + 5x + 6$ **22.** $g(x) = x^2 + 11x + 30$

23. $f(x) = x^2 - 2x - 3$ **24.** $h(x) = 2x^2 - 5x + 2$

25. $f(x) = -2x^2 - 2x - 12$ **26.** $g(x) = 6x^2 + 9x - 6$

27. Describe the graph of $y = mx + b$ when m is 0; when b is 0; when both m and b are 0.

28. As $|a|$ increases, what happens to the graph of $y = ax^2$?

29. Would the graph of $y = -\frac{1}{2}x^2$ be inside or outside the graph of $y = -x^2$?

30. What point do all graphs of $y = ax^2$ for different values of a have in common?

31. What is the slope and y intercept of the linear function whose graph passes through $(-2, -3)$ and $(4, 4)$?

32. Assuming that the domain of the function in Exercise 31 is {real numbers}, what is its range?

33. Determine m and b if the graph of $f(x) = mx + b$ is the line segment joining $(-5, 6)$ and $(3, 4)$.

—— Determine the equation that defines the linear function whose graph passes through the points whose coordinates are as follows.

34. $(0, 0)$ and $(1, 2)$ **35.** $(5, 2)$ and $(3, -7)$

36. $(-1, 2)$ and $(3, 4)$ **37.** $(-3, -5)$ and $(2, -4)$

38. What is the y intercept of the graph of $y = x^2 + 3$?

39. What is the y intercept of $y = x^2 - 3$?

40. For any given value of x, is the point on $f(x) = x^2 - 1$ one unit lower than on $f(x) = x^2$? Explain.

B ── If $f(x) = 3x$, find x if

41. $f(x) = 3$.   **42.** $f(x) = 6$.   **43.** $f(x) = -9$.   **44.** $f(x) = -3$.

── If t is the function defined by $t(x) = x^2 - 2x - 20$, find

45. $t(a)$.   **46.** $t(c)$.   **47.** $t(a - c)$.   **48.** $t(2a)$.

── If $f(x) = 2x + 1$, find x if

49. $f(x) = 0$.   **50.** $f(x) = 1$.   **51.** $f(x) = -1$.   **52.** $f(x) = -2$.

── If h is a function defined by $y = |x|$, find x if

53. $h(x) = 2$.   **54.** $h(x) = -2$.   **55.** $h(x) = 0$.   **56.** $h(x) = k$.

── Draw the graph of each of the following equations and state whether or not the equation defines a function.

57. $f(x) = 1; \frac{1}{2} \le x \le 2$

58. $f(x) = \begin{cases} 2 \text{ when } 1 \le x \le 3 \\ 1 \text{ when } 1 \le x \le 2 \end{cases}$

59. $f(x) = |x| (-5 \le x \le 5)$ or $f(x) = -x(-3 \le x \le 3)$

60. $f(x) = \begin{cases} -2 \text{ when } -3 \le x < 3 \\ x \text{ when } -2 \le x \le 2 \\ x + 1 \text{ when } 0 \le x < 1 \end{cases}$

61. Explain why moving a vertical line across the graph of a relation shows whether or not it is a function.

62. How do you obtain the range from the graph of the function? How do you obtain the domain from the graph of the function?

63. If f is a function that maps each real number x into the real number $x^2 + 5$, list ten ordered pairs in the function. Graph f.

64. The function g maps any real number r into $(r + 1)(r - 1)$. Draw the graph of the function.

C ── If $f(x) = 2x^2 + 3x - 6$ and $g(x) = x^2 + 4$, find

65. $f(x) + g(x)$.   **66.** $f(x) - g(x)$.

67. $g(x) - f(x)$.   **68.** $f(x) + 2g(x)$.

69. $\frac{f(x)}{g(x)}$.   **70.** $\frac{g(x)}{f(x)}$.

71. $f(g(x))$.   **72.** $f(f(x).)$

73. $2f(x) - g(x)$.   **74.** $3f(x) + 2g(x)$.

11–4 Inverse Variation

You know that the faster the speed, the less time it takes to make a trip. For a trip of 480 miles, the relationship between rate of travel (speed) and time can be shown by the equation $rt = 480$. The table below shows six number pairs that satisfy this relation.

r	80	60	40	30	20	10	5
t	6	8	12	16	24	48	96

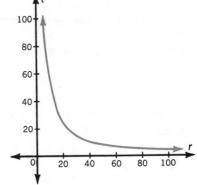

Is the relation a function? Notice that the domain can include only positive numbers. What is the range? As the values for t increase, do the values for r increase or decrease? As the values for r increase, do the values for t increase or decrease?

In Chapter 4 you learned that the function of *direct variation*, $y = kx$, has the following properties. As the values for x increase, the values for y increase, and as the values for x decrease, the values for y decrease. Every value for y is a constant times every value for x. Clearly, the relation $rt = 480$ exhibits a kind of variation that is the opposite of direct.

When the product of two variables is a nonzero constant, an increase in the values of one variable will cause a decrease in the values of the other one. Also, a decrease in the values of one variable will cause an increase in the values of the other one.

Definition <u>Inverse variation</u> is a variation of two related variables such that the product of the variables is a nonzero constant. The function of inverse variation may be defined by

$$y = \frac{k}{x}, \, k \neq 0,$$

or equivalently by

$$xy = k, \, k \neq 0.$$

The constant k is the constant of variation.

The equation $rt = 480$ implies that r **varies inversely as t.** As a function, you might write $f(t) = r = \frac{480}{t}$. Notice that it is also true that t varies inversely as r, since $t = \frac{480}{r}$ is true.

Often it is convenient to express direct variations in terms of a proportion. For example, for two pairs of numbers (x_1, y_1) and (x_2, y_2) that satisfy $y = kx$, you can write the following true statements.

(1) $y_1 = kx_1$, or $\frac{y_1}{x_1} = k$ (2) $y_2 = kx_2$, or $\frac{y_2}{x_2} = k$

Then, because each left side equals k, you get the following proportion.

$$\frac{y_1}{x_1} = \frac{y_2}{x_2}$$

Similarly, there is a connection between proportions and inverse variation. Consider (x_1, y_1) and (x_2, y_2) that satisfy $xy = k$.

Upon substituting, the following statements are true.

(1) $x_1y_1 = k$ (2) $x_2y_2 = k$

Therefore, $x_1y_1 = x_2y_2$ is true. Why? This leads to $\frac{x_1}{x_2} = \frac{y_2}{y_1}$. Why?

Exercises

A ▬▬ Use the equation $rt = 300$ to complete the following sentences.

1. The formula $rt = 300$ is an example of _?_ (direct, inverse) variation.

2. When t is 5, r is _?_. When t is 10, r is _?_. When a value of t is doubled, the value of r is _?_.

3. When t is 15, r is _?_. When t is $7\frac{1}{2}$, r is _?_. When a value of t is halved, the value of r is _?_.

4. When r is 50, t is _?_. When r is 100, t is _?_. When a value of r is doubled, the value of t is _?_.

5. When r is 50, t is _?_. When r is 25, t is _?_. When a value of r is halved, the value of t is _?_.

▬▬ Mary has $3.00 to spend for candy and she always spends the whole amount. There is a relation between the number of pieces, n, she can buy and the cost per piece, c, in cents. The relation can be shown by the equation $nc = 300$. Use this relation to complete the following sentences.

6. If c is 2, n is _?_. If c is 6, n is _?_. If the cost per piece is tripled, the number she can buy is _?_.

7. If c is 12, n is ___. If c is 3, n is ___. If the cost per piece is divided by 4, the number of pieces she can buy is ___.

8. If n is 10, c is ___. If n is 50, c is ___. If the number she buys is multiplied by 5, the cost per piece is ___.

9. If n is 20, c is ___. If n is 5, c is ___. If the number she buys is divided by 4, the cost per piece is ___.

10. Does c vary inversely as n? Does n vary inversely as c?

11. Which of the following are examples of inverse variation?

    a. $xy = 6$ **b.** $x + y = 6$ **c.** $x - y = 6$

    d. $\dfrac{x}{y} = 6$ **e.** $x = \dfrac{10}{y}$ **f.** $x = 10y$

    g. $x - y = 10$ **h.** $x + y = 10$ **i.** $y = 250x$

    j. $y = 430x - 5$ **k.** $xy + y = 8$ **l.** $y = \dfrac{42}{x}$

12. Shown below is the graph of $xy = 24$ when the replacement set for x and y is R. Explain why there are two curves in the graph. Why is $xy = 24$ the equation of a function? When you think of the function as $f(x) = \dfrac{24}{y}$, explain why 0 is in neither the domain nor the range.

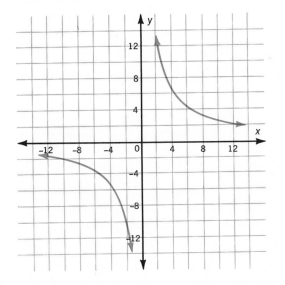

13. Draw a graph for each example of inverse variation in Exercise 11. Are the graphs lines or are they some other kind of curve?

14. There is an infinite number of rectangles that have an area of 400 square feet. Write an equation that shows the relation between the length, l, and the width, w, of rectangles with an area of 400 square feet.

—— Use the equation from Exercise 14 to complete the following.

15. If l increases, then w _?_.

16. If l decreases, then w _?_.

17. If a certain value of l is doubled, the value of w is _?_.

18. If a certain value of w is multiplied by 3, the value of l is _?_.

19. If a certain value of l is multiplied by $\frac{1}{2}$, the value of w is _?_.

—— If you invest \$1000, you might be interested in the length of time and the rate of interest required to earn \$200 on the investment. The equation $200 = 1000rt$ expresses the relation between r, the rate of interest per year, and t, the time in years the \$1000 is invested. Use this formula for Exercises 20–25.

20. Make a table showing the pairs of numbers for r and t when t is any member of the set $\{1, 2, 3, 4, 5, 6, 7, 8, 9, 10\}$.

21. To earn \$200 in 5 years, the rate of interest must be _?_.

22. To earn \$200 in 1 year, the rate of interest must be _?_.

23. Use the ten number pairs for r and t from Exercise 20 to graph ten points of the relation. Do the points lie along a straight line? Sketch a smooth curve containing the points.

24. If the number of years required to earn \$200 increases, does the rate of interest increase or decrease?

25. If the rate of interest increases, does the time increase or decrease?

26. If y varies inversely as x, and y is 12 when x is 4, what is the constant of variation? Write the equation that shows the relation between x and y.

27. For rectangles of the same area, the base varies inversely as the height. What is the constant of variation when the base is 10 feet and the height is 12 feet? Write the equation that shows the relation between base and height for rectangles that have this area.

—— If y varies inversely as x, find the constant of variation and write the equation showing the relation between x and y for each of the following.

28. $y = 7$ when $x = 6$

29. $y = 4$ when $x = 12$

30. $y = \frac{3}{4}$ when $x = \frac{2}{3}$

31. $y = -5$ when $x = 2$

32. $y = -8$ when $x = -5$

33. $y = -5\frac{1}{4}$ when $x = -8\frac{1}{3}$

—— Each of these equations is an example of inverse variation.

a. $xy = 10$　　　**b.** $xy = \frac{1}{2}$　　　**c.** $x = \dfrac{12}{y}$　　　**d.** $xy = .01$

34. Find two number pairs that satisfy each equation.

35. For each equation, find the ratio of the x numbers of the pairs and the ratio of the y numbers of the pairs.

36. Are the two ratios equal?

37. Is one of the ratios equal to the multiplicative inverse of the other one?

B —— Which of the following are examples of direct variation and which are examples of inverse variation?

38.

x	−4	−2	0	2	4	6
y	−12	−6	0	6	12	18

39.

x	−5	−3	−1	1	3	5
y	15	9	3	−3	−9	−15

40.

x	−12	−6	−2	−1	1	2	4	6	12
y	−2	−4	−12	−24	24	12	6	4	2

41.

x	−5	−2	1	4	7	10
y	3	6	9	12	15	18

42.

x	−10	−4	0	4	8	12
y	$-7\frac{1}{2}$	−3	0	3	6	9

43.

x	−5	−2	0	3	4	5	10
y	50	8	0	18	32	50	200

44. $P = 4s$　　The perimeter of a square equals 4 times the length of a side.

45. $t = \dfrac{400}{r}$　　To travel 400 miles at r miles per hour requires t hours.

46. $d = 50t$　　The distance traveled at 50 miles per hour equals 50 times the number of hours.

47. $f = 3y$　　The number of feet in any length equals 3 times the number of yards.

48. $AR = 1000$　　The amount of the taxable value of property times the tax rate equals $1000 in taxes.

49. $l = 6e$　　The length of the 6 edges of any cube equals 6 times the length of any edge.

50. $b = \dfrac{96}{a}$ The base of any rectangle with an area of 96 square inches equals 96 divided by the altitude of the rectangle.

51. $C = 2\pi r$ is the formula for the circumference of a circle in terms of its radius. Complete: The circumference of a circle varies _?_ (directly, inversely) as its radius. What is C if r is 10? 100?

—— If y varies inversely as the square of x, then $y = \dfrac{k}{x^2}$, or $yx^2 = k$, is true. Find the constant of variation and write the equation showing the relation for each of the following.

52. $y = 6$ when $x = 2$ **53.** $y = 2$ when $x = 1$

54. $y = 8$ when $x = 4$ **55.** $y = 4$ when $x = -3$

56. $y = -5$ when $x \doteq -4$ **57.** $y = 3\frac{1}{2}$ when $x = 5\frac{3}{4}$

58. The formula for the area of a circle is $A = \pi r^2$. Complete this table showing pairs of numbers for r and A. A varies *directly as the square* of r.

r	1	2	3	4	5	6	7	8	9	10
A	π	4π	9π	16π	_?_	_?_	_?_	_?_	_?_	_?_

—— Use the results of Exercise 58 to complete the following.

59. If any number for r is doubled, the number for A is _?_.

60. If any number for r is multiplied by 5, the number for A is _?_.

61. A circle with a radius of $7\frac{1}{2}$ inches has an area _?_ times the area of a circle with a radius of 15 inches; _?_ times the area of a circle with a radius of 30 inches.

62. If an object is dropped from some height, the approximate distance it will fall in any number of seconds is expressed by the formula $d = 16t^2$. Complete the following table showing the relation between d and t. Does d vary directly as t, inversely as t, or directly as the square of t?

t	1	2	3	4	5	6
d	16	64	144	_?_	_?_	_?_

—— Use the results of Exercise 62 to complete the following.

63. If t is doubled, d is _?_.

64. If t is tripled, d is _?_.

65. If t is halved, d is _?_.

C **66.** The formula for the volume of any sphere is $V = \frac{4}{3}\pi r^3$. You can say of a variation such as this that the volume varies *directly* *as the cube* of the radius. Complete: If r is doubled, V is _?_. If r is halved, V is _?_.

67. The frequency of vibration of a string (of given length and size) varies *directly as the square root* of the tension (pounds of pull) on the string. This may be written as the formula $f = k\sqrt{t}$. If k is 60, what is f when t is 49? when t is 25?

68. The frequency of vibration of a string (uniform length and tension) varies *inversely as the square root* of its weight. Express this relation in a formula, using k to represent a constant. Given that k is 508, what is f when w is 4?

11–5   Inverses of Relations and Functions

Consider the relation $S = \{(1, 2), (2, 3), (4, 5), (5, 6)\}$. The domain of S is $\{1, 2, 4, 5\}$. What is the range? Note that the relation may also be viewed as a mapping.

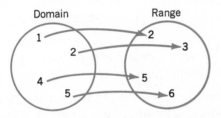

In any mapping, the rule may be reversed to give another mapping. For example, to read a road map, you reverse the rule by using the map to picture the physical world. To reverse the rule for S, you merely need to put the arrowheads at the other end of the curves. The domain and range are then interchanged.

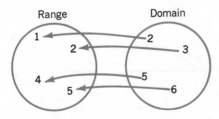

The result may then be written as the relation

$$\{(2, 1), (3, 2), (5, 4), (6, 5)\}.$$

Because of the way the relation {(2, 1), (3, 2), (5, 4), (6, 5)} was formed from S, it is called the **inverse** of S. It is symbolized as S⁻¹ and read "S inverse." Observe that S⁻¹ is the relation whose members were obtained by interchanging the coordinates of each ordered pair of S.

> **Definition** The <u>inverse of a relation</u> S is a relation S⁻¹ that is obtained by interchanging the coordinates of every ordered pair of the given relation S.

Since functions are relations, the inverse of a function may be given the same definition. The inverse of f is f^{-1}. Notice that by interchanging coordinates, the domain of f becomes the range of f^{-1} and the range of f becomes the domain of f^{-1}.

The inverse of a function is not always a function itself. Explain why *the inverse of a function is also a function if and only if no horizontal line intersects the graph of the function in more than one point.*

When a function is defined by an equation, such as $y = 2x$, the equation of the inverse can be found by interchanging x and y. This has the effect of interchanging the coordinates. Then solve for y to represent the function in $y = f(x)$ form as follows.

$$y = 2x$$
$$\text{Interchange } x \text{ and } y. \quad x = 2y$$
$$\text{Solve for } y. \quad y = \tfrac{1}{2}x$$

You can show that $y = \tfrac{1}{2}x$ is the inverse of $y = 2x$ by comparing the solutions. Typical solutions of $y = 2x$ are (1, 2), (3, 6), and (4.5, 9). When the coordinates of these pairs are reversed, they become (2, 1), (6, 3), and (9, 4.5), which are solutions of $y = \tfrac{1}{2}x$.

A relation and its inverse may also be compared by looking at their graphs, shown in Figure 1.

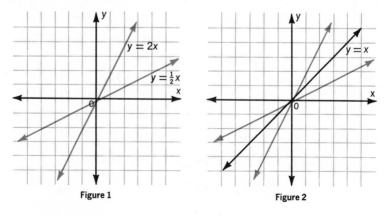

Figure 1

Figure 2

When you look at the two graphs in Figure 1 in conjunction with the graph of $y = x$, Figure 2, an important and useful relationship becomes apparent. If the graph were folded along the line defined by $y = x$, the relation and its inverse would coincide. The graph of R^{-1} is the reflection of the graph of R in relation to the graph of $y = x$. This is true for the graphs of any relation and its inverse.

Exercises

A ▬ Give the inverse of each of the following relations.

1. R = {(1, 3), (2, 4), (3, 6), (4, 8)}
2. S = {(1, 0), (2, 0), (3, 0), (4, 0), (5, 0)}
3. T = {(1, 0), (1, 1), (1, 2), (1, 3), (1, 4), (1, 5)}
4. U = {(1, 1), (2, 2), (3, 3), (4, 4), (5, 5), (6, 6)}
5. V = {(1, 2), (2, 1), (3, 4), (4, 3), (5, 6), (6, 5)}
6.

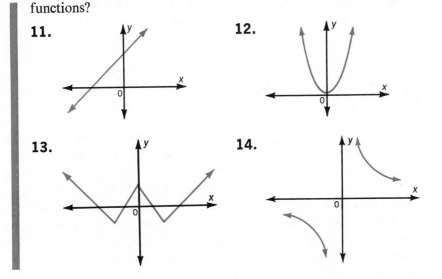

7. $f = \{(x, y) : y = 3x\}$
8. $g = \{(x, y) : y = 2x + 1\}$
9. $h = \{(x, y) : y = -4x - 5\}$
10. $F = \{(x, y) : y = x^2\}$

B ▬ Which of the functions graphed below have inverses that are functions?

11.

12.

13.

14.

Which of the relations graphed below that are not functions have inverses that are functions?

15.

16.

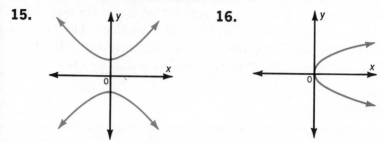

What are the coordinates of the reflections of the following points if the points are reflected through the line $y = x$?

17. $(4, -2)$ **18.** $(-2, 6)$ **19.** $(3, 3)$ **20.** $(3, -5)$

Find and graph the ordered pairs of each function. Graph the inverse of each function by reflecting each point through the line $y = x$.

21. $y = x, \quad x \in \{1, 2, 3\}$ **22.** $y = 2x, \quad x \in \{2, 4, 6\}$

23. $y = -x, \quad x \in \{1, 3, 5\}$ **24.** $y = x + 1, \quad x \in \{0, 1, 2, 3\}$

25. Find the equation that defines the inverse of each of the functions in Exercises 21–24.

C **26.** Does the set $\{(1, 2), (3, 2), (2, 1)\}$ define a function? Is it one-to-one? One-to-many? Is its inverse a function?

27. Does the set $\{(1, 2), (2, 3), (3, 4)\}$ define a function? Is it one-to-one or one-to-many? Is its inverse a function?

28. From Exercises 26 and 27, can you tell what kind of function has an inverse that is also a function?

11–6 Exponential Functions

You have previously studied exponents and can find the decimal place-value representation of such expressions as 3^2, 5^{-1}, and $16^{\frac{1}{2}}$. Any real number can be used as an exponent, although you have learned only how to use the rational numbers so far. Thus, it is possible to find a value of an expression such as 10^x for any real replacement for x. For any real number x, a solution of $y = 10^x$ may be obtained. There is only one value of y for each value of x. Hence, the equation $y = 10^x$ defines a function, known as an **exponential function.**

The table below shows several pairs of numbers that satisfy $y = 10^x$. Approximations are given for y when x is not an integer.

x	-3	-2	-1	0	0.2	0.4	0.6	0.8	1	1.2	1.4
y	$\frac{1}{1000}$	$\frac{1}{100}$	$\frac{1}{10}$	1	1.6	2.5	4.0	6.3	10	16	25

The solutions from the table can be plotted to form a partial graph of the function. By drawing a smooth curve through these points, you obtain the graph of the function.

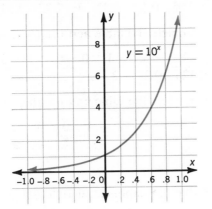

Look at the graph and answer these questions.

a. As the values for x increase, do the values for y increase or decrease?

b. As the values for x decrease, do the values for y increase or decrease?

c. Do you think that the curve crosses the x axis?

d. At what point does the curve cross the y axis?

Notice that although the values of y increase and decrease along with the values of x, this is not the same as direct variation. In this case they do not increase or decrease at proportional rates. In fact, the values for y increase very much for large values of x, but very little for small ones. The curve crosses the y axis at $(0, 1)$ because $1 = 10^0$. The curve will not cross the x axis because $0 = 10^x$ has no solution.

Other exponential functions can be obtained by substituting another number for 10. For example, $y = 2^x$, $y = e^x$ (where $e \approx 2.71828$), and $y = 3^x$ all define exponential functions.

Definition An exponential function is a function defined by $f(x) = b^x$, where the number b, called the base, is greater than zero but not equal to one.

Exercises

A   **1.** What is the domain and range of $y = 10^x$? Use the table of values given at the beginning of this section.

—— Graph the following exponential functions and draw smooth curves through each set of points, $x \in R$.

2. $y = e^x$ Use this table of values.

x	−3	−2	−1	0	1	2	3
y	0.05	0.14	0.37	1	2.72	7.39	20.1

3. $y = 2^x$ Complete the table and use these values.

x	−4	−3	−2	−1	0	1	2	3	4	5	10
y	0.06	0.125	0.25	?	?	?	?	?	?	?	?

4. $y = 3^x$ Complete the table and use these values.

x	−4	−3	−2	−1	0	1	2	3	4
y	?	?	?	?	?	?	9	27	81

5. $y = 5^x$

B   **6.** Is it true that no exponential function $y = b^x$ crosses the x axis?

—— Exercises 7–11 refer to $y = 10^x$.

7. As x increases from 0 to 1, y increases from _?_ to _?_.

8. As x increases from 1 to 2, y increases from _?_ to _?_.

9. Is the rate of increase of y in an interval greater than or less than the corresponding increase in x for that interval?

10. Does the graph appear to get steeper as x increases?

11. Will the graph eventually reach a point where it stops curving and becomes a straight line?   Explain.

12. In the definition of an exponential function, $y = b^x$, the restriction $b \neq 1$ is made.   Suppose b is 1.   Then what kind of function is defined?   Graph this function.

13. Graph $y = 10^x$ and $y = (\frac{1}{10})^x$ on the same set of axes.

—— Use the graphs in Exercise 13 to answer the following questions.

14. Are both graphs smooth curves?

15. When $b > 1$ and x increases, does y increase or decrease?

16. When $0 < b < 1$ and x increases, does y increase or decrease?

17. Do the graphs show points in common?   If so, which ones?

18. Describe the domain and range of the graph of $y = (\frac{1}{10})^x$.

19. Draw the reflection of the graph of $y = b^x$, $b > 1$, if the reflection is through the line $y = x$. At what point does the reflected curve intersect the x axis? What is the relationship between $y = b^x$ and the function whose graph is the reflected curve?

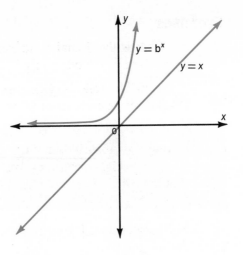

11–7   Logarithmic Functions

In the figure below, the dashed curve is the reflection of the graph of $y = 10^x$ in the graph of $y = x$. The dashed curve represents the inverse of $y = 10^x$. Since for each value for x, there is exactly one value for y, the inverse is a function also. The inverse is a **logarithmic function**. It is defined by $x = 10^y$, or by $y = \log_{10} x$ (read "y equals the logarithm of x to the base ten" or "y equals log base ten x").

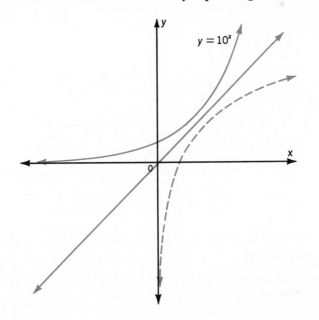

The inverse of any exponential function is a logarithmic function.

Exponential function	Logarithmic function
$y = 2^x$	$x = 2^y$, or $y = \log_2 x$
$y = e^x \ (e \approx 2.71828)$	$x = e^y$, or $y = \log_e x$
$y = 3^x$	$x = 3^y$, or $y = \log_3 x$

Definition A <u>logarithmic function</u> is a function defined by $y = \log_b x$, which means $x = b^y$, where b is greater than zero and not equal to one. The value of b is the <u>base</u> of the function.

For b greater than 1, the graph is similar to the one at the right. Notice that as the values for x increase, so do the values for y. Similarly, as the values for x decrease, so do the values for y. What is the x intercept? Based upon your work with exponential functions, do you think there is a y intercept?

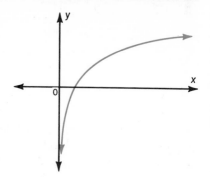

Exercises

A ━━━ Use the graph of $y = \log_{10} x$ to answer Exercises 1–7.

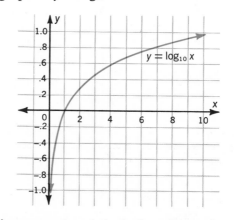

1. When x is greater than 1, is the logarithm of x a positive or a negative number?

2. When x is between 0 and 1, is the logarithm of x a positive or a negative number?

3. At what point does the curve cross the x axis? What is the logarithm of the number 1?

4. As x gets closer and closer to 0, what happens to the graph?

5. When x equals 10, what is the value of y?

6. What is the domain of $y = \log_{10} x$?

7. What is the range of $y = \log_{10} x$?

B —— Use the graph of $y = \log_e x$ ($e \approx 2.71828$) to answer the following questions.

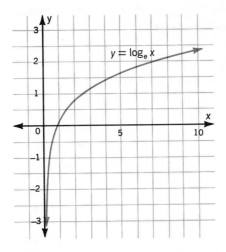

8. When x is greater than 1, is the logarithm of x a positive or a negative number?

9. When x is 1, what is $y = \log_e x$?

10. When x is between 0 and 1, is the logarithm of x a positive or a negative number?

11. Can x equal 0? Why or why not?

12. What is the domain of $y = \log_e x$?

13. What is the range of $y = \log_e x$?

—— From the graphs of $y = \log_{10} x$ and $y = \log_e x$, certain common properties are apparent for the general logarithmic function $y = \log_b x$, $b > 1$. Complete the following for that function.

14. As x increases, y _?_. As x decreases, y _?_.

15. The domain of $y = \log_b x$ is {positive real numbers} and the range is _?_.

16. When x is greater than 1, the logarithm of x is _?_ (positive, negative, or zero).

17. When x equals 1, the logarithm of x is _?_ (positive, negative, or zero).

18. When $0 < x < 1$ is true, the logarithm of x is _?_ (positive, negative, or zero).

19. When x equals the base b, y equals _?_.

20. The graph of $y = \log_b x$, $b > 1$, gets closer and closer to the _?_ axis, but never crosses it.

C —— Use the table of values prepared below to draw the graphs of the given function. Draw a smooth line through the points. Check with the graphs drawn in parts A and B of this exercise set.

21. $y = \log_{10} x$

x	1	2	3	4	5	6	7	8	9	10
y	0	0.30	0.48	0.60	0.69	0.77	0.84	0.90	0.95	1.00

22. $y = \log_e x$

x	1	2	3	4	5	6	7	8	9	10
y	0	0.69	1.09	1.38	1.60	1.79	1.94	2.07	2.19	2.30

11–8 Computation with Logarithms

The value of a logarithmic function for a particular replacement for x is called the **logarithm** of the replacement. Logarithms are exponents; the value of $y = \log_{10} x$ is the number y such that $x = 10^y$ is true.

For every property of exponents, there is a corresponding property of logarithms. The following table shows how these properties are related for the operations of multiplication, division, and raising to a power.

Operation	Exponents	Logarithms
Multiplication	$a^m \cdot a^n = a^{m+n}$ (Add exponents.)	$\log xy = \log x + \log y$ (Add logarithms.)
Division	$\dfrac{a^m}{a^n} = a^{m-n}$ (Subtract exponents.)	$\log \dfrac{x}{y} = \log x - \log y$ (Subtract logarithms.)
Raising to a power	$(a^m)^n = a^{mn}$ (Multiply exponents.)	$\log x^y = y \log x$ (Multiply the logarithm by the power.)

State in words the properties of the logarithm of a product, of a quotient, and of a power.

Use of these properties simplifies computation, as can be seen from the following examples.

EXAMPLE 1. Use logarithms to find 3.25×1.63.

Since 10 is the base of the numeration system, it is convenient to use logarithms to base 10. A table of logarithms to base 10, called **common logarithms,** is provided on pages 548 and 549.

Find log 3.25 in the table. First locate 3.2 in the column headed N. In this same row, in the column headed 5, you will find 5119. Notice that the columns represent different hundredths places and that the decimal points are omitted for each logarithm. Since 3.25 is between $10^0 = 1$ and $10^1 = 10$, log 3.25 is between 0 and 1; so 5119 means 0.5119. Using the table in a similar way, you can also determine that log 1.63 is approximately 0.2122. Now apply the property of the logarithm of a product.

$$\log 3.25 \approx 0.5119$$
$$\log 1.63 \approx 0.2122$$
Add the logarithms. $\qquad \overline{0.7241}$

The logarithm of the product is approximately 0.7241. Use the table to find the logarithm nearest 0.7241. It is 0.7243. The entry 7243 is in the 5.3 row and the 0 column. Hence, 0.7243 is the approximate logarithm of 5.30.

Therefore, 3.25×1.63 is approximately 5.30. For most purposes the error caused by the various approximations is so small that it can be ignored. For example, the exact product of 3.25 and 1.63, found in the ordinary way, is 5.2975.

EXAMPLE 2. Use logarithms to find $\frac{8.75}{2.36}$.

$$\log 8.75 \approx 0.9420$$
$$\log 2.36 \approx 0.3729$$
Subtract the logarithms. $\qquad \overline{0.5691}$

The difference, 0.5691, is the logarithm of the quotient. In the table, 0.5691 corresponds most nearly to the number 3.71. Therefore,

$$\frac{8.75}{2.36} \approx 3.71$$

is true.

EXAMPLE 3. Find 1.27^4.

Use the property of powers.

$$\log 1.27 \approx 0.1038$$
$$\log 1.27^4 = 4 \log 1.27$$
$$4 \log 1.27 \approx 0.4152$$
$$1.27^4 \approx 2.60$$

Exercises

A —— Use the table to find the common logarithms of the following numbers.

1. 3.92   **2.** 1.31   **3.** 3.21   **4.** 5.06

5. 2.01   **6.** 7.91   **7.** 9.00   **8.** 4.59

—— Perform the indicated computation using logarithms.

9. 3.92×1.31 **10.** $\frac{5.06}{2.01}$

11. $(3.21)^2$ **12.** 5.21×1.63

13. 2.32×2.54 **14.** $(1.21)^5$

15. 3.23×2.62 **16.** $(3.51)(1.82)$

17. $\frac{(7.91)}{(3.82)}$ **18.** $(1.23)^3$

19. $(1.01)^4$ **20.** $\frac{8.71}{2.83}$

21. $\frac{9.00}{3.78}$ **22.** $(1.11)^3$

23. $(2.65)(3.27)$ **24.** 4.86×1.01

11–9 Trigonometric Functions

The equation $y = \sin x$ shows the relation between a number of degrees, x, and the ratio of the measure of the side opposite an acute angle in a right triangle to the hypotenuse. This ratio is y, the sine of the angle. In the table of values of the trigonometric functions, you may think of the column headed *Angle* as x and the column headed *Sine* as y. For each angle x, is there one and only one number for y? There is only one such number, so $y = \sin x$ defines a function. Some of the number pairs are shown in the table below.

When x is	0°	10°	20°	30°	40°	50°	60°	70°	80°	90°
Then y is	.000	.1736	.3420	.5000	.6428	.7660	.8660	.9397	.9849	1.0000

The graph of $y = \sin x$ is shown below $(0° \leq x \leq 90°)$.

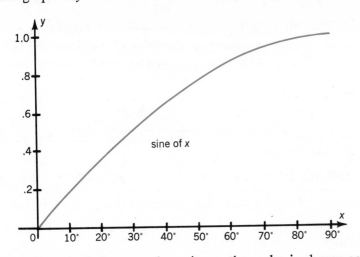

The relationship between the units on the scales is chosen so that one unit on the vertical axis is approximately equivalent to 57° on the horizontal axis. The reasons for this will become apparent in later courses. As you study trigonometric functions further, you will extend the domain of the sine function to the full set of real numbers. For $\{x : 0° \leq x \leq 360°\}$, the graph of $y = \sin x$ looks like the following.

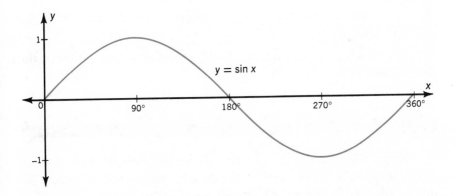

Exercises

A — Use the table of values on page 547 in these exercises.

1. Complete this table showing ten number pairs that satisfy the equation $y = \cos x$.

When x is	0°	10°	20°	30°	40°	50°	60°	70°	80°	90°
y is	1.0000	.9848	?	?	?	?	?	?	?	?

RELATIONS AND FUNCTIONS   493

2. Draw a graph of the function defined by $y = \cos x$ when the domain is $0 \le x \le 90°$.

3. The equation $y = \tan x$ shows the relation between x, the number of degrees, and y, the tangent of x. From the table you can see that the tangent is undefined for an angle of 90° because it involves division by 0. Then, 90° is not a possible choice for x. For every other number for x, is there one and only one number for y? Does $y = \tan x$ define a function?

4. Complete this table showing ten number pairs that satisfy the equation $y = \tan x$.

When x is	0°	10°	20°	30°	40°	50°	60°	70°	80°	89°
y is	?	?	?	?	?	?	?	?	?	?

5. Draw a graph of $y = \tan x$ when the domain is $0° \le x < 90°$. Notice that x cannot be 90°.

B **6.** Complete this table showing ten number pairs that satisfy the equation $y = 3(\sin x)$. Each number for y is 3 times the value of $\sin x$.

When x is	0°	10°	20°	30°	40°	50°	60°	70°	80°	90°
y is	.0000	.5208	1.0260	?	?	?	?	?	?	?

7. Make a table and draw the graph of $y = 3(\sin x)$ when the domain is $0° \le x \le 90°$.

8. Make a table and draw the graph of $y = 3(\cos x)$ when the domain is $0° \le x \le 90°$.

CHAPTER REVIEW

1. Know the meaning of and be able to use each of the following words or phrases. The number shown after each word or phrase indicates where it is introduced, in case you need to review.

rule (*462*)
mapping (*463*)
domain (*463*)
range, or image (*463*)
one-to-one mapping (*464*)
many-to-one mapping (*464*)
one-to-many mapping (*464*)

inverse variation (*475*)
inverse of a relation (*482*)
exponential function (*485*)
logarithmic function (*488*)
logarithm (*490*)
common logarithm (*491*)
trigonometric function (*492*)

2. The perimeter P of a square is related to its side s by the equation $P = 4s$. Express this same relation by a graph, a table, a sentence, and a set of ordered pairs (s, P).

3. Consider the relation $R = \{(1, 2), (2, 3), (4, 5), (6, 7)\}$. What is the domain of the relation? What is the range?

4. If $f(x) = \frac{2x - 3}{x}$, find $f(-2)$ and $f(3)$.

5. Draw the graph of the function g defined by the following.

$$g(x) = \begin{cases} -3 \text{ when } x < 0 \\ 0 \text{ when } x = 0 \\ 2 \text{ when } x > 0 \end{cases}$$

6. Draw the graph of $f(x) = 3x - 2$ for the domain $-2 \leq x \leq 2$.

7. When $b = 0$ in $y = mx + b$, what kind of variation exists between x and y?

8. Express inverse variation as a proportion showing that y varies inversely as x.

9. What is the equation of the line about which a relation can be folded to get its inverse?

10. Given an equation that defines a function, how do you form the equation that defines the inverse of this function?

11. State *four* of the properties of the graph $y = b^x$.

12. State *four* of the properties of the graph $y = \log_b x$.

13. State the property of a logarithm of a product, a quotient, and a power.

14. Define each trigonometric function you have studied.

CHAPTER TEST

1. Define the relation $y = 2x$ by a table, a graph, and a set of ordered pairs.

2. Using the graph of the function f defined at the right, find the domain and the range of f.

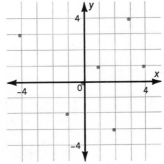

Each mapping in Column I illustrates a special kind of function. Find its name in Column II. More than one answer may be used.

COLUMN I

COLUMN II

3.

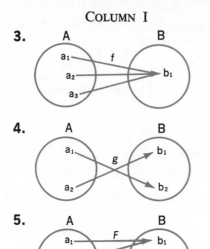

a. One-to-one function.

4.

b. Many-to-one function.

5.

c. Constant function.

6. Determine m and b of $y = mx + b$ such that its graph passes through $(-2, 1)$ and $(3, 4)$.

7. If y varies inversely as x, and y is 30 when x is 6, write the equation that shows the relation between x and y.

8. Determine which of the functions graphed below have inverses that are functions.

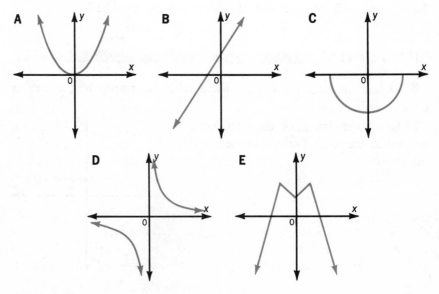

9. If $f(x) = 2x^2 - 3x + 1$, find $f(-1)$ and $f(t)$.

10. If $f = \{(1, 5), (-2, 3), (4, 6), (7, 8)\}$, then what is f^{-1}?

11. If $f(x) = 3x - 1$, determine the equation that defines its inverse.

—— Name each function graphed below.

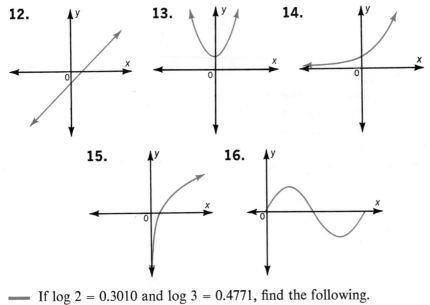

12. **13.** **14.**

15. **16.**

—— If $\log 2 = 0.3010$ and $\log 3 = 0.4771$, find the following.

17. $\log (2 \cdot 3)$ **18.** $\log \frac{3}{2}$ **19.** $\log 3^2$ **20.** $\log \sqrt{2}$

ENRICHMENT

Resolution of Forces Using Trigonometry

When vectors were presented after Chapter 4, you were dealing with the vector components of the force on an object. Seldom does an engineer measure his force vectors by their components; rather he measures the magnitude with a force gauge, and the direction is given by the configuration of the structure. Thus, the usual situation is that the force diagram will contain magnitudes and angles, or magnitudes and physical dimensions, from which he must determine the horizontal and vertical components by using trigonometry.

In analyzing a structure on which forces are exerted, the engineer uses a **free-body diagram.** A free-body diagram shows only the external forces felt by the body. If all the forces being considered operate on the same point, the diagram is called a **point diagram.** For example, suppose there is a box weighing 200 pounds, resting on a ramp inclined at angle θ. The base of the ramp is 30 feet and its upper end is 10 feet from the base, making the length of the ramp $10\sqrt{10}$.

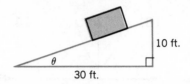

The forces external to the box are the pull of gravity and the force exerted on the box by the plane. This can be expressed as a point diagram. Place one axis labeled H parallel to the inclined plane; the other axis labeled V is perpendicular to this. Let the center of gravity of the box be the origin.

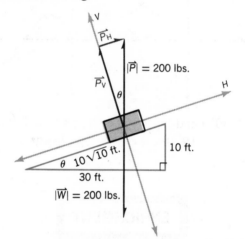

The force of gravity produces a weight of 200 pounds, $|\overrightarrow{W}|$, directed toward the center of the earth. Since the box is not moving, the plane must be opposing this force with another 200-pound force, marked $|\overrightarrow{P}|$. What is $\overrightarrow{P}$? Actually the plane is doing two things to the box: it is lifting it, and it is preventing it from sliding by friction. So there are two forces: one parallel to the V axis and one parallel to the H axis. How much is each force? Before you can determine the magnitude of each force, notice the right triangles in the diagram. One is the inclined plane itself, and the other is the force diagram: $\overrightarrow{P}$, $\overrightarrow{P_H}$, $\overrightarrow{P_V}$. Since the angle of inclination of the plane and the angle between $\overrightarrow{P}$ and $\overrightarrow{P_V}$ are both θ, the triangles are similar, which implies that the ratios of corresponding sides are equal and the corresponding trigonometric values will be equal.

First, find the sine and cosine of θ for the "ramp" triangle.

$$\sin \theta = \frac{10}{10\sqrt{10}}, \quad \text{or} \quad \frac{1}{\sqrt{10}} \qquad \cos \theta = \frac{30}{10\sqrt{10}}, \quad \text{or} \quad \frac{3}{\sqrt{10}}$$

The sine and cosine of θ for the force triangle are the following.

$$\sin \theta = \frac{|\overrightarrow{P_H}|}{200} \qquad \cos \theta = \frac{|\overrightarrow{P_V}|}{200}$$

Equate the values and solve for the unknown forces.

$$\frac{|\overrightarrow{P_H}|}{200} = \frac{1}{\sqrt{10}} \qquad\qquad \frac{|\overrightarrow{P_V}|}{200} = \frac{3}{\sqrt{10}}$$

$$|\overrightarrow{P_H}| = \frac{200}{\sqrt{10}} \approx 63 \text{ pounds} \qquad |\overrightarrow{P_V}| = \frac{600}{\sqrt{10}} \approx 190 \text{ pounds}$$

Thus, you have used the physical dimensions of a system to determine the forces acting. Now suppose a series of forces are acting on a point and the magnitude and direction angles are given for the forces. How would you determine the resultant of the forces? You could determine the horizontal and vertical components by using trigonometry, thus determining the endpoints of the vector, and then add by vector addition.

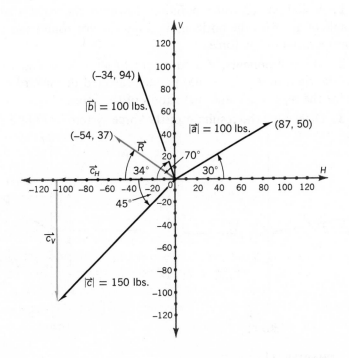

You have been given the coordinates for all the vectors in the figure on the previous page except $\vec{c}$. Determine $|\vec{c_H}|$ and $|\vec{c_V}|$ as follows.

$$\sin 45° = \frac{|\vec{c_V}|}{150} \qquad\qquad \cos 45° = \frac{|\vec{c_H}|}{150}$$
$$|\vec{c_V}| = \sin 45° \cdot 150 \qquad\qquad |\vec{c_H}| = \cos 45° \cdot 150$$
$$= .7071 \cdot 150 \qquad\qquad\qquad = .7071 \cdot 150$$
$$\approx 107 \text{ pounds} \qquad\qquad\qquad \approx 107 \text{ pounds}$$

Thus, the coordinates of the endpoint of $\vec{c}$ are $(-107, -107)$. Be careful to use the correct sign for the coordinates.

Then the resultant, $\vec{R}$, will be

$$\vec{R} = (87 - 34 - 107, \, 50 + 94 - 107) = (-54, 37).$$

The magnitude of $\vec{R}$, $|\vec{R}|$, is found by the Pythagorean theorem and the angle of inclination is found by trigonometry.

$$|\vec{R}| = \sqrt{(-54)^2 + 37^2} = \sqrt{4285} \approx 65$$
$$\tan \theta = \tfrac{37}{54} \approx .6852$$
$$\theta \approx 34°$$

Thus, $\vec{R}$ is as shown in red in the figure.

Exercises

1. A 400-pound force pointing down to the right makes an angle of 30° with the horizontal. Find the horizontal and vertical components of the force.

2. The components of a force are $|F_H| = 60$ pounds directed to the right and $|F_V| = 100$ pounds directed downward. Determine the magnitude and inclination of the force.

3. Determine the resultant of the force system in Figure 1.

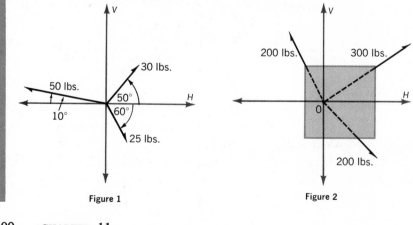

Figure 1

Figure 2

4. In Figure 2 at the bottom of the previous page, forces are applied to a metal plate so that their lines of action all meet in a point, 0. In this case the effect of the force system is equivalent to one with the same forces actually applied at 0. Find the resultant of the force system both in ordered-pair form and in the form of a magnitude and inclination angle.

5. A barrel weighing 500 pounds is on an inclined plane that rises 10 feet from a base 50 feet in length. What force must be applied to the barrel to keep it from rolling down the incline?

THE GROWTH OF MATHEMATICS

The Cubic Quarrel

Equations involving the third power of the variable and no higher powers are called cubic equations. While mathematicians in India and in the Arabic countries had been able to solve all quadratic equations sometime before A.D. 1000, cubic equations had been solved in only a few special cases by the beginning of the sixteenth century. When the general solution to cubic equations was finally reached, it led to mathematical intrigues up and down the Italian Peninsula.

In 1505 in Bologna, Scipione Ferro (1465–1526) discovered a way to solve some kinds of cubic equations. He told one of his pupils of the solutions, but he did not publish the results. In 1530 Niccolò Tartaglia (1500?–1557) announced that he could solve some cubic equations, so Ferro's pupil challenged him to a mathematical duel. The pupil proposed thirty problems that, as it happened, all were of the kind Tartaglia knew how to solve. Tartaglia proposed thirty problems of another type. His opponent could not solve them, so Tartaglia was declared the winner. Tartaglia could not solve the problems he had proposed either, but, working in Venice, he did manage the general solution of cubic equations in 1541. In the spirit of the times, he announced he had the solution but refused to tell what it was.

Geronimo Cardano (1501–1576), known in English as Jerome Cardan, became interested in the quarrel between Tartaglia and Ferro's pupil. Cardan lured Tartaglia to Milan with false promises, and, on a pledge of strict secrecy, obtained the general solution from him. Then in 1545, Cardan published it as his own. Naturally, another mathematical duel was set up, but it became a near riot between supporters of Cardan and those of Tartaglia. It is believed that Tartaglia won, but the general solution is known as "Cardan's solution."

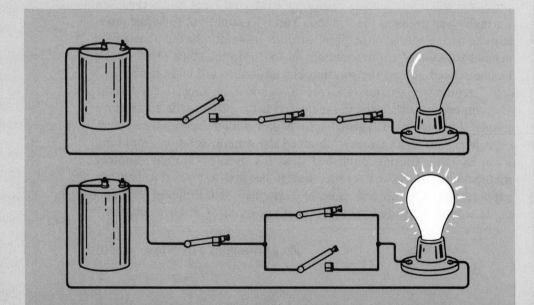

CHAPTER 12

LOGIC AND PROOF

Much of the reading, writing, and speaking done by a person involves a chain of reasons and a conclusion. The science concerned with the principles of correct reasoning is logic.

● A lawyer presenting a case before a court depends mainly on logic. Point by point, he tries to convince the judge and jury that his conclusion is the correct conclusion. Consider the following statements.

> Object A was stolen from Mr. X.
> Object A was found in the possession of Mr. Z.
> If Mr. Z has object A, then he must have stolen it from Mr. X.

Is this reasoning enough to convince you that Mr. Z is the thief? What if someone gave him object A, or he found object A on the street? More arguments are needed to complete the chain.

● The electric circuits pictured at the bottom of the page have switches that regulate the current going from the battery to the light bulb. If the switch is closed, the current can pass through the wire. If it is open, the current cannot pass through that wire. One switch in the top circuit is open and one switch in the bottom circuit is open. Why is the bulb lit in the bottom circuit but not in the top circuit? You will see in this chapter how the switches in the circuit can be used to represent statements and the bulb's being on or off will tell you if the logical conclusion is true or false.

● Advertising campaigns sometimes rely on a person's drawing more than the obvious conclusion from an ad. What do many toothpaste advertisers hope you will think after viewing their ads? Probably, that if you use their toothpaste, in addition to having clean teeth and fewer cavities, you will have a lovely smile and a sparkling personality. But there is nothing in the evidence to prove this. In this chapter you will see how logic is applied to reasoning and proofs.

12–1 Statements

The primary components of logic are sentences that can be classified as true or false. Such sentences are called **statements.** Listed below are six sentences, three of which, **d–f,** are statements.

a. x is an even number.
b. He is in my class.
c. 6 + x = 10

d. 8 is an even number.
e. This book is an algebra book.
f. 6 + 5 = 11

Why can sentences **a–c** not be classified as true or false?

> **Definition** A <u>statement</u> is a sentence that makes an assertion that is either true or false.

In mathematics and logic, you only need to consider sentences that are statements and open sentences that become statements when the variable is replaced by an element from its replacement set. Thus, you will not work with such nonstatements as "Close the door" or "Does 6 + x equal 10?"

An open sentence such as $x + 2x = 3x$ becomes a statement if the variable is quantified. Thus, $\forall x \in R \quad x + 2x = 3x$ is a statement.

In logic, letters are used as variables as they are in algebra. But instead of representing a number, the letter represents a simple statement. Lower-case letters, such as p, q, r, and s, will be used in general statement forms, whereas capital letters represent particular statements. The following diagram compares the use of x as a variable for numbers and q as a variable for statements.

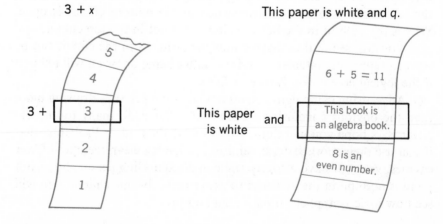

Exercises

A —— Identify the sentences that are statements.

1. Red is a color.   **2.** Frank is 14 years old.

3. She is a cheerleader.   **4.** $2 + 9 = 11$

5. $\forall a \in R \quad a + 0 = a$ **6.** There are 366 days in a leap year.

7. $x + y = xy$ **8.** Every month has 30 days.

9. All birds can fly.   **10.** Q is a false statement.

—— Identify the sentences.   Which are also statements?

11. In the universe.

12. $\exists y \in R \quad y + 2 = 5$

13. $7 \div 8$

14. c is an element of $\{a, b, c\}$.

15. The set of real numbers is a subset of set X.

16. There is a one-to-one correspondence between points on a line and the real numbers.

17. Are all elephants.

18. If x is 1, 2, or 3, $x + 1 < 5$ is true.

19. $\frac{2}{3} = \frac{3}{9}$

20. Of all the countries he visited.

12–2   Conjunctions and Disjunctions

The statements in Section 12–1 can be classified as **simple statements**. Simple statements joined by a connective, such as *and* and *or*, form **compound statements**. A compound statement with the connective *and* is a **conjunction**. *This paper is white* is joined by *and* with three statements to form three conjunctions.

This paper is white   *and*   q.
This paper is white   *and*   8 is an even number.
This paper is white   *and*   This book is an algebra book.
This paper is white   *and* $6 + 5 = 11$

If the symbol $\wedge$ is used for *and* and p is used to represent *This paper is white*, the conjunctions can be symbolized as $p \wedge q$. The conjunction $p \wedge q$ is true only when p is true and also q is true. Are the three conjunctions above true?

Study the tables below. At the left is a table of simple statements for p and q in all the possible combinations of true and false statements. At the right is a table with just the **truth values**, that is, T for true and F for false, of the statements and the conjunctions. It is called a **truth table.** Why is the conjunction true only for the first case?

p	q	p	q	Conjunction $p \wedge q$
Snow is white.	Grass is green.	T	T	T
Snow is white.	Grass is purple.	T	F	F
Snow is blue.	Grass is green.	F	T	F
Snow is blue.	Grass is purple.	F	F	F

The compound statement formed by two simple statements joined by *or* is a **disjunction.** The symbol $\vee$ is used for *or.* The *or* in logic means the same as *either ... or ... or both* in ordinary language. Hence, $p \vee q$ is true when p is true, when q is true, or when both p and q are true.

Use the same simple statements as above to explain why the disjunction is false only in the last case shown in the truth table.

Notice that the T's and F's in the left part of the table always appear in the same pattern, including all the possible combinations of T and F.

p	q	Disjunction $p \vee q$
T	T	T
T	F	T
F	T	T
F	F	F

You have used both conjunctions and disjunctions when you solved compound sentences such as $x < 5$ *and* $x > 3$ and $x < 5$ *or* $x > 3$. To solve the compound sentences, you found the numbers that make true compound statements. The solution set for the compound sentence can be denoted using *intersection* or *union* of sets.

EXAMPLE 1. Find the solution set for $(x < 5) \wedge (x > 3)$.

Compound sentence	Some compound statements
$(x < 5) \wedge (x > 3)$	$(2 < 5) \wedge (2 > 3)$
	$(3 < 5) \wedge (3 > 3)$
	$(3\frac{1}{2} < 5) \wedge (3\frac{1}{2} > 3)$
	$(4 < 5) \wedge (4 > 3)$
	$(4\frac{7}{8} < 5) \wedge (4\frac{7}{8} > 3)$
	$(5 < 5) \wedge (5 > 3)$
	$(6 < 5) \wedge (6 > 3)$

Solution set: $\{x : x < 5\} \cap \{x : x > 3\}$

Which replacements for x make $x < 5$ true? Which replacements for x make $x > 3$ true? The numbers shown in red are in the solution set of the compound sentence; that is, they are in the intersection of the two sets that make each of the simple sentences true. The entire solution set is shown in set-builder notation and by the following number-line graph.

Use the same process to explain the following example.

EXAMPLE 2. Find the solution set for $(x < 5) \lor (x > 3)$.

Solution set: $\{x : x < 5\} \cup \{x : x > 3\}$

Thus, the numbers that make true conjunctions can be denoted by using intersection of sets, and the numbers that make true disjunctions can be denoted by using union of sets.

Checkpoint

1. Explain the symbols $\land$ and $\lor$.

2. What is a compound statement?

3. What is a conjunction? a disjunction?

Exercises

A —— Form the conjunction of each pair of statements given below. Indicate whether the statement formed is *True* or *False*.

1. $2 \times 5 = 10$; $3 \times 8 = 36$

2. $6 + 8 = 14$; $3 + 2 = 5$

3. $8 \times 7 = 55$; $5 + 4 = 8$

4. $17 = 3 \times 5 + 2$; $32 = 6 + 2 \times 4$

5. $18 = 4 \times 4 + 2$; $16 = 3 \times 5 + 1$

—— Form the disjunction of each pair of statements given below. Indicate whether the statement formed is *True* or *False*.

6. $5 > 2$; $-3 < -4$

7. $3 - 2 = 0$; $5 \div \frac{1}{5} = 1$

8. $3 \neq 2$; $-6 \not> -5$

9. $5(1 + 8) = 5 + 40$; $8 \div 2 = 2 \div \frac{1}{2}$

10. $-2 \div 0 = 0$; $5 \times 0 = 1$

——— Find and graph the solution set for each of the following compound sentences. The replacement set is R.

11. $x > 6$ *and* $x < 10$

12. $x + 4 = -1$ *or* $x + 2 < 5$

13. $4(x + 1) = 12$ *and* $x = 2$

14. $2x + 3 < 4$ *or* $x + 5 = -4$

15. $3x + 9 < 7$ *and* $2x + 3 > -2$

——— Make truth tables for the following compound statements.

16. $p \vee q$	**17.** $p \wedge q$	**18.** $p \wedge r$
19. $q \wedge r$	**20.** $q \vee r$	**21.** $p \vee r$

22. If p and q are true and r is false, tell whether the compound statements in Exercises 16–21 are *True* or *False*.

B **23.** The truth value of a disjunction can be represented by an electrical circuit wired in parallel as shown in the diagram. B is the battery; p and q are switches; L is the light.

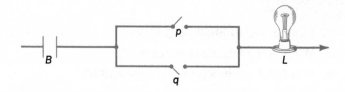

An open switch at both p and q indicates that current cannot flow from B to L. If either p or q or both are closed, the current can flow from B to L and the light will be on.

Given the following positions for switches p and q, indicate whether the light will be *On* or *Off*.

a. p is open; q is open. **b.** p is open; q is closed.

c. p is closed; q is open. **d.** p is closed; q is closed.

24. Summarize your results from Exercise 23 by completing the table at the right. T means the switch is closed, or the light is on. F means the switch is open, or the light is off.

Compare your results with the truth table for a disjunction.

Switch		Light
p	q	
T	T	
T	F	
F	T	
F	F	

25. The truth value of a conjunction can be represented by an electric circuit wired in series as shown in the diagram.

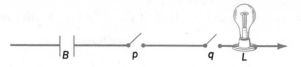

Using this circuit, write *On* or *Off* for **a–d** in Exercise 23. Then summarize your results in a table as in Exercise 24. Compare the table with the truth table for a conjunction.

12–3 Conditionals

A teacher made the following statement to illustrate what is called a **conditional statement**.

If your test score is *A*, then you have no homework.
    P   *Q*

> **Definition** A <u>conditional</u> is a compound statement made up of two statements joined in *If . . . then . . .* form.

The conditional *If p, then q* is symbolized as $p \rightarrow q$, which is read "*p* implies *q*."

To determine the truth value of $p \rightarrow q$, look at the tables below.

> *P*: Your test score is *A*.
> *Q*: You have no homework.

Interpret $P \rightarrow Q$ as "The teacher kept his promise."

		Did the teacher keep his promise?
Your test score is *A*.	You have no homework.	Yes
Your test score is *A*.	You have homework.	No
Your test score is not *A*.	You have no homework.	Yes
Your test score is not *A*.	You have homework.	Yes

The first, second, and fourth results are easy to see. What about the third? The reason for *Yes* in the third is that the teacher only promised what would happen if your test score *was* A. Logically, you cannot conclude that a false promise was made if your test score was not *A*. So the answer is *Yes*.

The results are summarized in the following truth table.

| | | Conditional |
		$p \rightarrow q$
p	q	$p \rightarrow q$
T	T	T
T	F	F
F	T	T
F	F	T

A conditional is false only when p is true and q is false. Use the conditional "If it is raining, then I use my umbrella" to verify the truth table for conditionals.

In ordinary language, a conditional statement would be interpreted as meaning that p *causes* q to happen. This is not the case in logic. Statements p and q are independent statements with no causal connection intended between them. They can be treated as separate parts.

Suppose p and q are switched. Then the statement would be $q \rightarrow p$.

Definition The <u>converse</u> of a conditional is the statement formed by interchanging p and q in $p \rightarrow q$. The converse of $p \rightarrow q$ is $q \rightarrow p$.

EXAMPLE 1. Is the converse of "If a number is divisible by 4, then the number is an even number" true?

P: A number is divisible by 4.
Q: The number is an even number.
$Q \rightarrow P$: If a number is an even number, then the number is divisible by 4.

The converse, $Q \rightarrow P$, is false because not all even numbers are divisible by 4.

EXAMPLE 2. What is the converse of "If today is July 4, then today is Independence Day"? Is it true or false?

P: Today is July 4.
Q: Today is Independence Day.
$Q \rightarrow P$: If today is Independence Day, then today is July 4.

The converse is true.

If a conditional and its converse are both true, they can be combined into one true statement called a **biconditional.** The connective is *if and only if.*

> *Conditional:* If today is July 4, then today is Independence Day.
> *Converse:* If today is Independence Day, then today is July 4.
> *Biconditional:* Today is July 4 if and only if today is Independence Day.

The symbol for *if and only if* is ↔. The conjunction can be expressed symbolically as follows.

$$(p \to q) \land (q \to p)$$
$$p \leftrightarrow q$$

The truth table below summarizes the results for the conditional, its converse, and the biconditional. Cover those three columns and see if you can give the correct truth values before looking at the results.

p	q	$p \to q$	$q \to p$	$p \leftrightarrow q$
T	T	T	T	T
T	F	F	T	F
F	T	T	F	F
F	F	T	T	T

EXAMPLE 3. Form the conditional, converse, and biconditional for the statements below. Identify each as true or false.

P: x is an even number.
Q: x is divisible by two.
$P \to Q$: If x is an even number, then x is divisible by two.　　　T
$Q \to P$: If x is divisible by two, then x is an even number.　　　T
$P \leftrightarrow Q$: x is an even number if and only if x is divisible by two.　　T

Checkpoint

1. What is a conditional? the converse of a conditional?
2. What is a biconditional? When is a biconditional true?

Now try these

—— Is each implication true or false?
1. If 2×3 equals 6, then $5 + 2$ equals 7.
2. If a is an integer, then a is a rational number.

3. Is the converse of each statement in Exercises 1 and 2 true or false?

4. Form the biconditional for the statement in Exercise 2. Is it true or false?

Answers: **1.** T **2.** T **3.** T; F **4.** *a* is an integer if and only if *a* is a rational number; F.

Exercises

A —— You are given the following statements.

P: E is a vowel.
Q: There are six days in a week.
R: The product of 2 and 1 is 21.
S: All ridable bicycles have wheels.

Write a conditional statement in *If . . . then . . .* form for each of the following symbolic statements. Indicate whether each is *True* or *False*.

1. $P \rightarrow Q$ **2.** $Q \rightarrow S$ **3.** $S \rightarrow P$
4. $Q \rightarrow R$ **5.** $R \rightarrow P$ **6.** $S \rightarrow R$

7. Write out the converse for each of the statements in Exercises 1–6. Indicate whether each is *True* or *False*.

—— Which pairs of statements combine to form a biconditional that is true?

8. P: You travel to Mexico.
Q: You drive a car to Mexico.

9. P: A triangle is equilateral.
Q: A triangle is equiangular.

10. P: x is a prime number.
Q: x is not divisible by 5.

11. P: x is an odd integer.
Q: x is an integer not divisible by 2.

12. P: This flower is a rose.
Q: This flower is red.

13. P: 9 is a factor of n.
Q: 3 is a factor of n.

B —— Using the four statements at the beginning of this exercise set indicate whether the following statements are *True* or *False*.

14. $(P \wedge Q) \rightarrow R$ **15.** $(P \vee R) \rightarrow S$
16. $(R \wedge P) \rightarrow Q$ **17.** $S \rightarrow (R \vee Q)$
18. $P \rightarrow (Q \vee S)$ **19.** $(R \wedge S) \rightarrow P$

12–4 Negation

The **negation** of a simple statement is formed by inserting *It is false that* . . . at the beginning of the statement. This is the same as negating the verb, as shown in the following examples.

Statement	Negation
P: 5 is an odd number.	*It is false that* 5 is an odd number. 5 is *not* an odd number.
Q: $\sqrt{2}$ is a rational number.	*It is false that* $\sqrt{2}$ is a rational number. $\sqrt{2}$ is *not* a rational number.

Statement *P* is true. Is its negation true? Is the negation of a true statement ever true?

Statement *Q* is false. But its negation is true. Is the negation of a false statement always true?

The negation of *p* is symbolized as $\sim p$ and is read "not *p*."

If both parts of a conditional are negated, another type of statement called the **inverse** is formed. The inverse of $p \rightarrow q$ is $\sim p \rightarrow \sim q$.

EXAMPLE. Write the inverse of the following statement: If a number is divisible by 6, then the number is an even number.

$$P: \text{A number is divisible by 6.}$$
$$Q: \text{The number is an even number.}$$
$$\sim P \rightarrow \sim Q: \text{If a number is not divisible by 6, then the number is not an even number.}$$

In this case, the inverse is not true. Look at the truth table below and explain why.

p	q	$\sim p$	$\sim q$	$\sim p \rightarrow \sim q$
T	T	F	F	T
T	F	F	T	T
F	T	T	F	F
F	F	T	T	T

Negations of disjunctions and conjunctions are a little more complicated.

The disjunction "Snow is white *or* ice is cold" is true if *either* of its statement parts is true. The negation is "It is false that snow is white *or* ice is cold"; that is, it is false that one or the other or both are true. Thus, both parts are false, and the negation can be written "It is false that snow is white *and* it is false that ice is cold."

$$\sim(p \lor q) \quad \text{is} \quad \sim p \land \sim q$$

The negation of a disjunction is a conjunction formed from the negation of both parts of the disjunction.

The conjunction "Snow is white *and* ice is cold" is true only when *both* parts are true. The negation is "It is false that snow is white *and* ice is cold." Since the conjunction is false if *one or the other or both parts* are false, the negation can be written "It is false that snow is white *or* it is false that ice is cold."

$$\sim(p \land q) \quad \text{is} \quad \sim p \lor \sim q$$

The negation of a conjunction is a disjunction formed from the negation of both parts of the conjunction.

The reasoning above uses practical examples to show that $\sim(p \lor q)$ and $\sim p \land \sim q$ are **logically equivalent** statements. Another way is to make a truth table for each statement. If the truth values for the statements are exactly alike, then the *statements are logically equivalent*. If p is logically equivalent to q, you can write $p \leftrightarrow q$. Note that the symbol is the same as that for the biconditional, as the meaning is the same.

Cover all but the first two columns of the truth tables below and see if you can correctly complete them.

p	q	$p \lor q$	$\sim(p \lor q)$
T	T	T	F
T	F	T	F
F	T	T	F
F	F	F	T

p	q	$\sim p$	$\sim q$	$\sim p \land \sim q$
T	T	F	F	F
T	F	F	T	F
F	T	T	F	F
F	F	T	T	T

Compare the last columns in each table. Are they exactly alike? Then $[\sim(p \lor q)] \leftrightarrow [\sim p \land \sim q]$ is true.

Exercises

A — Form the negation of each of the following statements and determine if each negation is true or false.

1. A square has four sides that are congruent.

2. An integer is a rational number.

3. A rational number is an irrational number.

4. A function is a set of ordered pairs.

5. An irrational number is a real number.

6. The number of natural numbers exceeds the number of even natural numbers.

7. $5 \times 3 - 4 \div 2 + 1 = 14$

8. Zero is a positive integer.

9. $\log_{10} 0 = 0$

10. Two perpendicular lines intersect.

— First determine the truth value of each conditional. Then write its inverse and determine its truth value.

11. If a number is divisible by 9, then it is a multiple of 3.

12. If a triangle is equilateral, then three sides of the triangle are the same length.

13. If $3 + 2 = 5$, then $2(3 + 2) = 2(5)$.

B — Form the negation of the following conjunctions and disjunctions.

14. Math is fun *and* logic is easy.

15. Winter is cold *or* summer is warm.

16. $x > 2$ *and* $x < 5$

17. $3 \times 5 = 4$ *or* $6 - 2 = 4$

18. $23 = 3 + 4 \times 6$ *and* $13 = 4 \times 2 + 5$

— Replace each _?_ by the symbol that completes each statement so that it is true.

19. $\sim(p \lor r) \leftrightarrow \sim p \underline{\ ?\ } \sim r$

20. $\sim(r \land s) \leftrightarrow \sim r \underline{\ ?\ } \sim s$

21. $\sim p \land \sim q \leftrightarrow \underline{\ ?\ } \lor \underline{\ ?\ }$

22. $\sim s \lor \sim t \leftrightarrow \underline{\ ?\ } \land \underline{\ ?\ }$

23. $\underline{\ ?\ }(q \land r) \underline{\ ?\ } \sim q \lor \sim r$

24. Make a truth table for $\sim(p \land q)$ and for $\sim p \lor \sim q$. How do the truth values for the statements compare?

25. Make a truth table to show that the inverse of $p \to q$ may be false when $p \to q$ is true.

26. The statement $\sim q \to \sim p$ is called the **contrapositive** of $p \to q$. As you can see, it is formed by both negating and switching the two parts of the conditional. Make a truth table to show that $p \to q$ is logically equivalent to $\sim q \to \sim p$.

27. Make truth tables to show that the converse and inverse of a given conditional are logically equivalent.

28. Write the converse, inverse, and contrapositive of the following conditionals.

    a. $\sim p \to q$ **b.** $p \to \sim q$

    c. If the temperature of water is lower than 32° F, the water will freeze.

29. The following truth table involves three statements, so eight rows of T's and F's are needed. The pattern in the three columns is the same as it was for the two-statement table: the first column has the first half T's and the second half F's; the second column has one fourth of the column T's, one fourth F's, and so forth; the third column has one eighth of the column T's, one eighth F's, which here means alternating T and F.

Replace each ? by T or F to correctly complete the chart.

p	q	r	$p \wedge q$	$(p \wedge q) \to r$
T	T	T	T	?
T	T	F	?	?
T	F	T	?	T
T	F	F	F	?
F	T	T	?	?
F	T	F	?	T
F	F	T	F	?
F	F	F	?	T

12–5   Tautologies

Sometimes statements are combined and the resulting statement is true, regardless of the truth values of the original statements. A statement form that has this property is called a **tautology**.

The example on the following page illustrates the idea of a tautology.

EXAMPLE. Show that $p \lor {\sim}p$ is a tautology.

Construct a truth table. Under p, write the possible values: T and F. Then fill in the other columns with the truth values for negation and disjunction.

p	${\sim}p$	$p \lor {\sim}p$
T	F	T
F	T	T

The third column indicates that whether the value of p is true or false, the disjunction is always true. Thus, it is a tautology.

The statement $p \lor {\sim}p$ is known as the **Law of the Excluded Middle.** An example would be "Today is Monday *or* today is not Monday." You can see that this is always true.

Exercises

A —— Use truth tables to show that the following statements are tautologies.

1. ${\sim}({\sim}p) \leftrightarrow p$ **2.** $(p \leftrightarrow q) \leftrightarrow [(p \to q) \land (q \to p)]$

3. $(p \land q) \to p$ **4.** $(p \land {\sim}q) \lor {\sim}(p \land {\sim}q)$

—— Use truth tables to show whether or not the following are tautologies.

5. ${\sim}p \lor p$ **6.** $q \lor q$

7. $p \land p$ **8.** ${\sim}({\sim}q) \lor {\sim}q$

9. $(p \land q) \land ({\sim}p \lor q)$ **10.** ${\sim}({\sim}p) \land {\sim}p$

B **11.** At the right is the truth table for $p \land {\sim}p$. The truth value of the conjunction is always false. A statement that is always false is a **contradiction.**

p	${\sim}p$	$p \land {\sim}p$
T	F	F
F	T	F

Construct a truth table to show that ${\sim}(p \lor {\sim}p)$ is a contradiction.

—— Construct a truth table to show whether each of the following statements is a tautology, a contradiction, or neither.

12. $p \lor (q \lor r) \leftrightarrow (p \lor q) \lor r$

13. $[(p \to q) \land (q \to r)] \to (p \to r)$

14. ${\sim}[(p \lor q) \to (q \lor p)]$

15. It is false that if John is 21 and all men 21 or over can vote, then John can vote.

16. $2 + 7 = 9$ *or* $10 \div 2 = 6$ implies that $10 \div 2 = 6$ *or* $2 + 7 = 9$.

12–6 Quantifiers

Sets M and B are illustrated in the diagram. The sets are described below by sentences using **quantifiers.**

a. *All* numbers in M are prime.

b. *Each* number in M is prime.

c. *Any* number in M is prime.

d. *Some* number in B is prime.

e. *There exists* a number in B that is prime.

f. *At least one* number in B is prime.

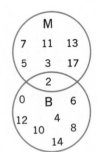

Sentences **a–c** use *all, each,* and *any* to denote exactly the same meaning, and they indicate the same quantification, or the same number of members. This quantification is shown, as you know, by the symbol ∀. Thus, the following sentence is true.

$$\forall x \in M \quad x \text{ is prime.}$$

In sentences **d–f,** the quantifiers are *some, there exists,* and *at least one.* In ordinary usage, *some* usually means "at least two but not all." But in logic *some* means the same as *there exists* and *at least one;* that is, it could denote one or all, but at least one. The quantification is shown by the symbol ∃. The following sentence is true.

$$\exists x \in B \quad x \text{ is prime.}$$

Negation and Quantifiers

Why is the sentence "All numbers in M are odd" false? It takes only one counterexample to make the *all* statement false, and in this case, 2 makes it false. Hence, "It is false that all numbers in M are odd" is equivalent to "At least one number in M is not odd."

> **The negation for a quantified statement using *all, each,* or *any* is a quantified statement using *some, there exists,* or *at least one* with the verb negated.**

Suppose you had to decide if the statement "There exists a multiple of 20 in set B" were true or false. You would examine all the members in set B and conclude that the statement is false. You could then say any of the following were true.

All numbers in B *are not* multiples of 20.
No number in B *is* a multiple of 20.
Each number in B *is not* a multiple of 20.

> **The negation for a quantified statement using *some, there exists*, or *at least one* is a quantified statement using *all, each*, or *any* with the verb negated.**

Note that *All x is not* . . . could also be worded *No x is* . . .

Exercises

A ■— Write T or F for each statement. Then form the negation of each statement and label it T or F.

1. All numbers are negative.

2. At least one rational number is not an integer.

3. Some triangles have three sides congruent.

4. Each graph represents a relation.

5. All terminating decimals are rational numbers.

6. Some straight lines represent functions.

7. All numbers that cannot be expressed as the ratio of two integers are irrational numbers.

8. Some numbers are not whole numbers.

9. Any directed line segment is a vector.

10. Some numbers make $x^2 - 5x + 6 = 0$ true.

Example. $\exists x > 2 \quad x + x = x^2$

The statement is false.
The negation is $\sim(\exists x > 2 \quad x + x = x^2)$
or $\forall x > 2 \quad \sim(x + x = x^2)$
or $\forall x > 2 \quad x + x \neq x^2$.
The negation is true.

11. $\forall x \quad x + 2x = 3x$ **12.** $\exists x \quad x + 7 = 19\frac{1}{2}$

13. $\exists x \quad x + x > x + 9$ **14.** $\forall x \quad |x| \geq x$

15. $\forall x \quad |x| \geq 0$ **16.** $\exists x \quad x^2 + 5x + 6 = 0$

17. $\exists x \in R \quad x^2 = 2$ **18.** $\exists x \quad 9x - 5x = 4x$

—— Replace each _?_ below by $\forall x \in R$ or $\exists x \in R$ to make the statement true.

19. _?_ $\quad x + x = 2x$

20. _?_ $\quad x^2 + 4x - 12 = 0$

21. _?_ $\quad \frac{4x}{x} = 4$

22. _?_ $\quad x \cdot x = x^2$

23. _?_ $\quad (x + 6)(x - 5) = x^2 + x - 30 = 0$

B —— Indicate whether each of the following is true, T, or false, F.

24. $\forall x \in R \quad \forall y \in R \quad x + y = y + x$

25. $\exists x \in R \quad \frac{x}{0} = 1$

26. $\forall x \in R, \, x \neq 0 \quad x \cdot \frac{1}{x} = 1$

27. $\exists x \in R \quad 2x - x = 2$

28. $\forall x \in R \quad \forall y \in R \quad \forall z \in R \quad (x - y) - z = x - (y - z)$

29. $\exists x \in R \quad |x - 3| = -1$

30. $\forall x \in R \quad x^2 - x + 11$ is a prime number.

31. $\exists x \in R \quad 2x + x = 2x$

32. $\forall x \in R \quad (3x - x = 2x) \wedge (4x = 20)$

33. $\forall x \in R \quad (3x > 2x) \wedge (|x| > 0)$

34. $\exists x \in R \quad \left(\frac{x}{6} = 0\right) \wedge (6 \cdot x = 0)$

35. $\exists x \in R \quad \exists y \in R \quad (x + y = 10) \wedge (x - y = 10)$

36. $\exists x \in R \quad \exists y \in R \quad (5x + y = 8) \wedge (5y = 40 - 25x)$

C **37.** If $[\sim\forall x \quad \sim(x + 1 = 1 + x)] \leftrightarrow [\exists x \quad x + 1 = 1 + x]$ can be abbreviated to $\sim\forall\sim \, \leftrightarrow \, \exists$, abbreviate $[\forall x \quad x \cdot 1 = 1 \cdot x] \leftrightarrow [\sim\exists x \quad \sim(x \cdot 1 = 1 \cdot x)]$ in the same way.

38. Make abbreviated forms for the two general statements regarding negation and quantifiers in this section.

12–7 Definitions and Undefined Terms

Proof in mathematics begins with certain undefined elements or terms, postulates (assumed statements) about the elements, and definitions of new elements or terms. A theorem is established using the principles of logic with postulates and definitions. Subsequent theorems may use previously proved theorems.

In this section, you will take a more careful look at the way definitions are formulated and at the role of undefined terms.

Four statements are listed below. One is a good definition of *square*. Which is it?

a. A square is a four-sided figure.

b. A square is a figure that has four congruent sides. (Note: *Congruent* means "having the same measure.")

c. A square is a rectangle having two adjacent sides congruent.

d. A square is a figure that has four congruent sides, four congruent angles, and two congruent diagonals.

Most people would agree that c is the best definition. The reason is most easily seen by looking at the following chart. The left column gives characteristics of a good definition, the right column discusses c.

1. The technical words used to define the term should have been defined previously or they should be in the set of undefined terms.	Technical words previously defined would include *rectangle*, *adjacent sides*, and *congruent*.
2. The term being defined should be placed in the smallest previously defined set to which it belongs.	Why was *rectangle* chosen as the smallest previously defined set instead of *quadrilateral* or *parallelogram*?
3. Just enough characteristics are given to distinguish it from other elements in the same set.	Does *two adjacent sides congruent* distinguish the elements called squares from all the other rectangles? The characteristic that all sides are congruent was not included because this can be proved as a theorem.
4. The statement is reversible; that is, separating the statement into two statements p and q produces $p \leftrightarrow q$.	P: A figure is a square. Q: A rectangle has two adjacent sides congruent and one right angle. $P \rightarrow Q$: If a figure is a square, it is a rectangle with two adjacent sides congruent and one right angle. $Q \rightarrow P$: If a rectangle has two adjacent sides congruent and one right angle, the figure (or rectangle) is a square. Since $P \rightarrow Q$ and $Q \rightarrow P$ are true, $P \leftrightarrow Q$ is true.

You can trace the technical words used in any definition back to undefined terms. For example, *rectangle* can be traced back to the undefined terms *point, line, plane,* and *between* as shown in the diagram below.

point ⎤
line ⎥ → Curve → Closed curve → Polygon → Quadrilateral → Rectangle
plane ⎥
between ⎦ → Line segment

Begin with the undefined terms and define each subsequent term, using only the undefined terms or your previous definitions.

Exercises

A — The following statements define terms that you have used in algebra. Each statement lacks at least one of the properties of a good definition. Which properties are lacking? Formulate an acceptable definition.

1. A *function* pairs members of the domain with members of the range.

2. A *rational number* is a number of the form $\frac{a}{b}$ where $b \neq 0$.

3. A *variable* is a symbol.

4. A nonterminating, nonrepeating decimal is a *real number*.

5. An *equation* is a statement like $4x + 1 = 6$.

— State each definition in an acceptable *If . . . then . . .* form. Then write its converse. Are both statements you wrote true?

6. An *inequality* is a statement that two numbers or algebraic expressions are not equal.

7. An *exponential function* is a function defined by $y = b^x$, where $b \neq 1$ and $b > 0$.

8. The *cosine* of an acute angle is the ratio

$$\frac{|\text{ side adjacent to acute angle }|}{|\text{ hypotenuse }|}.$$

9. An *irrational number* is a number that cannot be expressed as the ratio of two integers.

10. The *square root* of a number is one of its two equal factors.

B — Justify each of the following statements with a definition you learned earlier in the course.

11. The number $0.14\overline{14}$ is a rational number.

12. $\sqrt{2}$ is an irrational number.

13. The sine of angle A in Figure 1 is $\frac{a}{c}$.

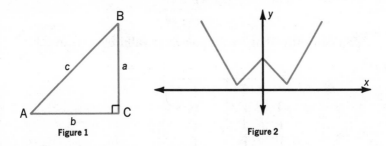

Figure 1   Figure 2

14. The graph in Figure 2 defines a function.

15. $2x + 4 < 6$ is an inequality.

12–8   Rules of Inference

Reasoning from a series of statements, called **premises,** to a final statement, called a **conclusion,** is known in logic as **inference.** The inference is valid if true premises lead to a true conclusion. There are various patterns of inference that are always valid.

Let P and Q denote the following statements.

P: The quadratic equation $x^2 + x - 12 = 0$ has a perfect-square discriminant.

Q: The quadratic equation $x^2 + x - 12 = 0$ has rational roots.

Is $P \rightarrow Q$ a true conditional?   Is P a true statement?   From your work in logic and your earlier work with quadratic equations, you should conclude that both $P \rightarrow Q$ and P are true.   Now without finding the roots of $x^2 + x - 12 = 0$, you can conclude that Q is true; that is, the equation has rational roots.

The truth of this conclusion is determined by **modus ponens,** or the rule of detachment.

Modus ponens   If $p \rightarrow q$ is a true statement and if p is a true statement, then q is a true statement.

Symbolically, *modus ponens* may be expressed as follows.

$$p \to q$$
$$\underline{p }$$
$$\therefore q$$

You can show that *modus ponens* is valid by a truth table.

p	q	$p \to q$	$(p \to q) \wedge p$
T	T	T	T
T	F	F	F
F	T	T	F
F	F	T	F

Hence, $(p \to q) \wedge p$ is true *only* when q is also true.

In an earlier exercise, you proved that $[(p \to q) \wedge (q \to r)] \to (p \to r)$ is a tautology. Then if $(p \to q) \wedge (q \to r)$ is true, $p \to r$ is true by **transitivity.**

Transitivity If $p \to q$ is a true statement and $q \to r$ is a true statement, then $p \to r$ is a true statement.

How is the rule of logic like the transitive property for equality? Symbolically, transitivity is expressed as follows.

$$p \to q$$
$$\underline{q \to r}$$
$$\therefore p \to r$$

EXAMPLE. Draw a valid conclusion from the following statements, P, Q, and R.

P: The weather is good.
Q: I will go to the football game tomorrow.
R: I will spend one dollar tomorrow.

$P \to Q$: If the weather is good, then I will go to the football game tomorrow.

$Q \to R$: If I go to the football game tomorrow, then I will spend one dollar tomorrow.

$P \to R$: If the weather is good, then I will spend one dollar tomorrow.

If you accept the conditionals $P \to Q$ and $Q \to R$ as true, then by transitivity, you can accept $P \to R$ as true.

Consider the statement "For every real number x, $x + 2x = 3x$ is true," or

$$\forall x \in R \quad x + 2x = 3x.$$

Since 6 is a real number, you can replace x by 6 and obtain the true statement

$$6 + 2(6) = 3(6).$$

The right to exchange the general statement $x + 2x = 3x$ for the particular instance $6 + 2(6) = 3(6)$ is due to the **rule of substitution for variables.**

Rule of Substitution for Variables If a statement p is true for all permissible replacements in a given set, then it is true for a particular replacement in the set.

In other words, if p is true for every x, then by the rule of substitution, you can replace x by any particular permissible value for x and obtain a true statement.

This means then that the rule does not apply to a variable x in a statement such as

$$\exists x \in R \quad x + 3 = 7.$$

The quantifier $\exists$ limits the variable to *some* x. If you replaced x by 5, you would get the statement $5 + 3 = 7$, and of course this is not true.

Checkpoint

1. What is meant by *modus ponens*?
2. What is meant by transitivity?
3. What is meant by the rule of substitution for variables?

Exercises

A ▬▬ Use truth tables to determine whether each of the conclusions is true or false. To be true, the conclusion must be true for all cases in which the given statement is true.

1.   *Given:* $\begin{cases} p \rightarrow q \\ \sim q \rightarrow r \end{cases}$

       Conclusion: $\{ p \rightarrow r$

2.   *Given:* $\begin{cases} r \rightarrow s \\ t \rightarrow \sim s \end{cases}$

       Conclusion: $\{ r \rightarrow s$

— Read the following statements. Label the statements in each as p and q, and then show that each argument uses *modus ponens*.

3. If a triangle is isosceles, then it has two congruent sides. It is known that triangle ABC is isosceles. Therefore, triangle ABC has two congruent sides.

4. If a, b, and c are positive integers and $a^2 + b^2 = c^2$ is true, then (a, b, c) is called a *Pythagorean triple*. The integers 5, 12, and 13 are positive and $5^2 + 12^2 = 13^2$ is true. Therefore, $(5, 12, 13)$ is a *Pythagorean triple*.

— Label the statements in the following arguments as p, q, and r, and identify the parts of the argument.

$$p \rightarrow q$$
$$\frac{q \rightarrow r}{\therefore p \rightarrow r}$$

5. If a number is even, then it can be expressed in the form $2n$, where n is an integer. A number of the form $2n$ has a square, $4n^2$, of the form $2(2n^2)$. Therefore, if a number is even, then its square is even.

6. If a number is odd, then it can be expressed in the form $2n + 1$, where n is an integer. A number of the form $2n + 1$ has a square of the form $2(2n^2 + 2n) + 1$. Thus, it follows that if a number is odd, then its square must be odd.

— Study each of the following and determine which, if any, correctly uses the rule of substitution for variables.

7. $\forall x \in R \quad x + 4 = 4 + x$
    $3, 2 \in R$
    $\therefore 3 + 4 = 4 + 2$

8. $\forall x \in R \quad x + 6 = 6 + x$
    $6 \in R$
    $\therefore 2 + 6 = 6 + 2$

9. $\exists x \in R \quad x + 4 = 7$
    $2 \in R$
    $\therefore 2 + 4 = 7$

10. Every rational number can be expressed as the ratio of two integers. The number $0.14\overline{14}$ is a rational number. $\therefore 0.14\overline{14}$ can be expressed as the ratio of two integers.

11.   All girls are beautiful.
    Mary is a girl.
    $\therefore$ Mary is beautiful.

12. $\exists x \in R \quad \frac{x}{6} = 6 \cdot x$

$0 \in R$

$\therefore \frac{0}{6} = 6 \cdot 0$

13. $\forall x \in R \quad 5x = x \cdot 5$

$8 \in R$

$\therefore 5 \cdot 8 = 8 \cdot 5$

14. All numbers that cannot be expressed as the ratio of two integers are irrational numbers. $\sqrt{2}$ cannot be expressed as the ratio of two integers. $\therefore \sqrt{2}$ is an irrational number.

B ——— Use a truth table to determine whether the conclusion in each of the following is true or false.

15.
Given:
$\begin{cases} \text{If I am a careful thinker, then I will make an } A \\ \text{on tomorrow's logic test.} \\ \text{If I am not a careful thinker, then I will have to} \\ \text{study harder.} \end{cases}$

Conclusion:
$\begin{cases} \text{If I do not make an } A \text{ on tomorrow's logic test,} \\ \text{then I will have to study harder.} \end{cases}$

16. *Given:* $\begin{cases} p \to q \\ \sim p \to r \end{cases}$ (*Hint:* Use the contrapositive of $p \to q$.)

Conclusion: $\{ \sim q \to r$

12–9 Direct Proofs

In the last section you learned some general rules, or patterns, of inference that you can use to prove theorems: *modus ponens*, transitivity, substitution for variables. You will frequently use these rules of inference without explicitly mentioning them by name.

A typical proof may look like this.

Hypothesis: p
Conclusion: s

Statements	Reasons
1. $p \to q$	1.
2. $q \to r$	2.
3. $r \to s$	3.
4. $\therefore p \to s$	4.

The *Hypothesis* is the statement(s) that is (are) understood to be true. The *Conclusion* is the statement that is to be proved true.

The proof then consists in establishing the chain of reasoning under the column labeled *Statements*. Each statement on the left must be justified by a reason on the right. The reason may be that the statement is **Given** in the hypothesis or it may be a **definition, postulate,** or previously proved **theorem.**

In order to make your work with proofs easier, the following review list of postulates and theorems is provided as a reference; they hold for all x, y, $z \in$ R, with division by zero excluded.

Postulate

2–2	$x + y$ is one and only one real number.	Closure for addition.
2–3	$x + y = y + x$	Commutativity for addition.
2–4	$(x + y) + z = x + (y + z)$	Associativity for addition.
2–5	$x + 0 = 0 + x = x$	Identity for addition.
2–6	$\exists -x \in$ R such that $x + (-x) = 0.$	Inverse for addition.
2–7	xy is one and only one real number.	Closure for multiplication.
2–8	$xy = yx$	Commutativity for multiplication.
2–9	$(xy)z = x(yz)$	Associativity for multiplication.
2–10	$x \cdot 1 = 1 \cdot x = x$	Identity for multiplication.
2–11	$\exists \frac{1}{x}$ such that $x \cdot \frac{1}{x} = \frac{1}{x} \cdot x = 1$	Inverse for multiplication.
2–12	$x(y + z) = xy + xz$	Distributivity.
3–1	If $x = y$ is true, then $x + z = y + z$ is true.	Addition postulate for equations.
3–2	If $x = y$ is true and $z \neq 0$, then $xz = yz$ is true.	Multiplication postulate for equations.

Theorem

2–3	$x - y = x + (-y)$
2–4	$x \cdot 0 = 0 \cdot x = 0$

The two principal kinds of proof are the direct proof and the indirect proof. In a **direct proof,** you generally begin with a given fact and proceed directly to the desired conclusion by applying the rules of inference previously discussed.

The following examples illustrate this kind of proof.

EXAMPLE 1. Prove Theorem **T–1.**

$$\text{T–1} \quad \forall x \in R \quad \forall y \in R \quad \forall z \in R \quad (x + y)z = xz + yz$$

Hypothesis: x, y, and z are arbitrary real numbers.
Conclusion: $(x + y)z = xz + yz$

Statements	Reasons
1. x, y, and z are arbitrary real numbers.	1. Given.
2. $(x + y)z = z(x + y)$	2. Postulate 2–8.
3. $z(x + y) = zx + zy$	3. Postulate 2–12.
4. $zx + zy = xz + yz$	4. Why?
5. $(x + y)z = xz + yz$	5. Transitivity.

EXAMPLE 2. Prove Theorem **T–2.**

T–2 The sum of two odd numbers is an even number.

To prove the theorem, you need the following definitions.

Definition 1 An even number is a number of the form $2n$, where n is an integer.

Definition 2 An odd number is a number of the form $2n + 1$, where n is an integer.

Definition 3 If n is an integer, then n is either even or odd.

Hypothesis: a and b are arbitrary odd numbers.
Conclusion: $a + b$ is an even number.

Statements	Reasons
1. a and b are odd numbers.	1. Given.
2. Let $a = 2k + 1$, $b = 2p + 1$, and $a + b = 2k + 1 + 2p + 1$.	2. Definition 2.
3. $2k + 1 + 2p + 1 = 2k + 2p + 2$	3. Addition.
4. $2k + 2p + 2 = 2(k + p + 1)$	4. Why?
5. $k + p + 1$ is an integer.	5. Postulate 2–2.
6. $\therefore 2(k + p + 1)$ is an even number.	6. Definition 1.
7. $a + b$ is an even number.	7. Transitivity.

Exercises

A ——— Use the two examples as a guide and prove the following. (These proved statements may be used in later proofs.)

1. T–3 The square of an even number is even.

2. T–4 The square of an odd number is odd.

3. T–5 The sum of two even numbers is an even number. (*Hint:* Let $2n$ be one even number and let $2k$ be the other. Then find $2n + 2k$.)

4. T–6 The sum of an even number and an odd number is an odd number.

5. T–7 The product of two odd numbers is an odd number.

6. T–8 The product of two even numbers is an even number.

7. T–9 The product of an even number and an odd number is an even number.

8. T–10 The sum of two multiples of 3 is a multiple of 3. (*Hint:* A multiple of 3 is a number of the form $3n$, where n is an integer.)

9. T–11 The product of two multiples of 3 is a multiple of 3.

10. T–12 The sum of two multiples of 6 is a multiple of 6.

11. T–13 If a number is divisible by 6, then it is divisible by 2. (*Hint:* Show that a number divisible by 6 is a multiple of 2.)

12. T–14 If a number is divisible by 6, then it is divisible by 3.

13. T–15 The product of two multiples of 5 is a multiple of 5.

14. T–16 If a number is even, the cube of the number is even.

B ——— Prove the following.

15. T–17 $\forall a \in R \quad \forall b \in R$, the values of the expressions $a - b$ and $b - a$ are opposites. (*Hint:* Prove that $\forall a \in R \quad \forall b \in R$ $(a - b) + (b - a) = 0$ is true. Then refer to the meaning of opposites.)

16. T–18 If a number is odd, then the cube of the number is odd. $\left(\textit{Hint:}\ (2n + 1)^3 = (2n + 1)^2(2n + 1) \right)$

17. T–19 If one of two given numbers is even and the other is odd, then the square of their sum is an odd number.

18. T–20 If one of two given numbers is even and the other is odd, then the sum of the square of their sum and the odd number is an even number. $\left(\textit{Hint:}\ \text{Let } x \text{ be the even number and } y \text{ the odd number. Prove that } (x + y)^2 + y \text{ is an even number.} \right)$

19. T–21 If a number is not a multiple of 4, then its square is not a multiple of 8. (*Hint:* Numbers that are not multiples of 4 have the form $4n + 1$, $4n + 2$, $4n + 3$, where n is an integer.)

20. T–22 If a is $2uv$, b is $u^2 - v^2$, and c is $u^2 + v^2$, where u and v are positive integers with $u > v$, then $c^2 = a^2 + b^2$ is true. (*Hint:* Examine $(2uv)^2$, $(u^2 - v^2)^2$, and $(u^2 + v^2)^2$.)

12–10 Indirect Proofs

The second principal method of proof is **indirect proof.** The reasoning pattern in an indirect proof is essentially the following.

First, you assume that the statement to be proven is false. Then using this assumption and other given information, you reason from one statement to another until you reach a contradiction. Upon reaching the contradiction, you conclude that it is false to assume that the original statement is false because it leads to a contradiction. Therefore, the original statement must be true.

EXAMPLE 1. Prove the following.

T–23 If the square of an integer, k, is even, then k is even.

Hypothesis: The square of an integer, k, is even.
Conclusion: k is even.

Statements	Reasons
1. Assume k is not even.	1. Assumption.
2. If k is not even, then it is odd.	2. An integer that is not even must be odd since $2n \neq 2n+1$ for any integer n (Definitions 1 and 2).
3. If k is odd, then k^2 is odd.	3. Theorem T–4.
4. This is a contradiction, since the square of k is even.	4. Why?
5. k is either even or odd.	5. Definition 3.
6. ∴ It is false that k is odd, so k is not odd; that is, *k is even.*	6. If a statement is false, then its negation is true.

EXAMPLE 2. Prove the following.

T–24   The number $\sqrt{2}$ is an irrational number.

Hypothesis: Given the number $\sqrt{2}$.
Conclusion: $\sqrt{2}$ is an irrational number.

Statements	*Reasons*
1. Assume that $\sqrt{2}$ is not irrational, that is, that it is rational.	1. Assumption.
2. Then $\sqrt{2}$ can be expressed as $\frac{a}{b}$, $b \neq 0$, with a and b integers with no common factors other than 1.	2. Definition of rational number.
3. $\frac{a}{b} = \sqrt{2} \rightarrow a = \sqrt{2}b$	3. Why?
4. $a = \sqrt{2}b \rightarrow a^2 = 2b^2$	4. Why?
5. $a^2 = 2b^2 \rightarrow a^2$ is an even number.	5. Definition 1.
6. If a^2 is even, then a is even.	6. Theorem T–23.
7. If a is even, then it can be expressed as $2n$, where n is an integer.	7. Definition 1.
8. $(2n)^2 = 2b^2$, or $4n^2 = 2b^2$	8. Rule of substitution.
9. $4n^2 = 2b^2 \rightarrow 2n^2 = b^2$	9. Why?
10. If b^2 is $2n^2$, then b is an even number and can be expressed as $2p$.	10. Definition 1.
11. Therefore, $\frac{a}{b}$ is $\frac{2n}{2p}$.	11. Why?
12. But $\frac{a}{b} = \frac{2n}{2p}$ is a contradiction.	12. Why?
13. Thus, it is false that $\sqrt{2}$ is a rational number, so it must be an irrational number.	13. If a statement is false, then its negation is true.

Exercises

A —— Prove the following indirectly.

  1. The number $2\sqrt{2}$ is an irrational number.
  2. The number $\frac{1}{4}\sqrt{2}$ is an irrational number.

B **3.** If the square of a number is a multiple of 3, then the number is a multiple of 3. (*Hint:* Assume that the number is not a multiple of 3. Let $3n + 1$ and $3n + 2$ represent numbers that are not multiples of 3. Then examine $(3n + 1)^2$ and $(3n + 2)^2$ and reason to a contradiction.)

4. The number $\sqrt{3}$ is an irrational number.

5. The number $3\sqrt{3}$ is an irrational number.

6. The number $\frac{1}{4}\sqrt{3}$ is an irrational number.

C **7.** If the square of a number is a multiple of 5, then the number is a multiple of 5. (*Hint:* Assume that the number is not a multiple of 5. Let the numbers have the forms $5n + 1$, $5n + 2$, $5n + 3$, $5n + 4$. Then examine the squares of these quantities to reach a contradiction.)

8. The number $\sqrt{5}$ is an irrational number.

9. If a and b are real numbers and $ab = 0$ is true, then $a = 0$ or $b = 0$ is true. (*Hint:* Assume that both a and b are not zero. Then each has a multiplicative inverse. Use this fact with the hypothesis, and reason to a contradiction.)

10. If a is a nonzero real number, then a has exactly one multiplicative inverse. (*Hint:* Assume that a has two distinct multiplicative inverses and reason to a contradiction.)

12–11   Finite Number Fields

So far, you have been proving properties about infinite sets of numbers: the set of even numbers, the set of odd numbers, the set of real numbers. In this section you will examine properties of finite sets of numbers.

An example of a finite set of numbers is the set of numbers on a 12-hour clock.

Suppose you start working at 9 o'clock in the morning and work for 5 hours. You know that you would stop working at 2 o'clock in the afternoon. But suppose you came from some place that did not use a twelve-hour system of time. Then to find out the time you would stop working,  you would have to learn how to add numbers on a clock. Hidden in the table on the following page is the pattern. The numbers across the top and down the left are the addends. The numbers in the table are the sums. Can you uncover the pattern for finding the sums? Cover part of the table and see if you can give the correct sums.

+	1	2	3	4	5	6	7	8	9	10	11	12
1	2	3	4	5	6	7	8	9	10	11	12	1
2	3	4	5	6	7	8	9	10	11	12	1	2
3	4	5	6	7	8	9	10	11	12	1	2	3
4	5	6	7	8	9	10	11	12	1	2	3	4
5	6	7	8	9	10	11	12	1	2	3	4	5
6	7	8	9	10	11	12	1	2	3	4	5	6
7	8	9	10	11	12	1	2	3	4	5	6	7
8	9	10	11	12	1	2	3	4	5	6	7	8
9	10	11	12	1	2	3	4	5	6	7	8	9
10	11	12	1	2	3	4	5	6	7	8	9	10
11	12	1	2	3	4	5	6	7	8	9	10	11
12	1	2	3	4	5	6	7	8	9	10	11	12

You should see that the numbers are continuous through 12 and then start over from 1. If the real-number sum exceeds 12, the clock sum can be quickly found by subtracting 12 from the real-number sum. The real-number sum of 10 and 9 is 19; the clock sum is 19 − 12, or 7.

The following table illustrates clock multiplication. Cover part of the table and see if you can give the correct products.

×	1	2	3	4	5	6	7	8	9	10	11	12
1	1	2	3	4	5	6	7	8	9	10	11	12
2	2	4	6	8	10	12	2	4	6	8	10	12
3	3	6	9	12	3	6	9	12	3	6	9	12
4	4	8	12	4	8	12	4	8	12	4	8	12
5	5	10	3	8	1	6	11	4	9	2	7	12
6	6	12	6	12	6	12	6	12	6	12	6	12
7	7	2	9	4	11	6	1	8	3	10	5	12
8	8	4	12	8	4	12	8	4	12	8	4	12
9	9	6	3	12	9	6	3	12	9	6	3	12
10	10	8	6	4	2	12	10	8	6	4	2	12
11	11	10	9	8	7	6	5	4	3	2	1	12
12	12	12	12	12	12	12	12	12	12	12	12	12

Does the set of clock numbers possess any of the properties of the set of real numbers? For example, are the clock numbers closed under addition and multiplication? Are the clock numbers commutative for addition and multiplication? Do they have identity elements? Do they have inverse elements?

A set of numbers that satisfies Postulates 2–2 through 2–12 (see page 528) is called a **field.**

> **Definition** The set F forms a <u>field</u> with respect to two operations $\oplus$ and $\otimes$ if and only if
> i) the set is closed, commutative, and associative under the two operations,
> ii) there is an identity element z for $\oplus$ and an identity element e for $\otimes$,
> iii) each element has an inverse element under $\oplus$, and each element except z has an inverse element under $\otimes$, and
> iv) $\otimes$ is distributive with respect to $\oplus$.

The set of real numbers is an example of a field. Is the set of clock numbers, C = $\{1, 2, 3, 4, 5, 6, 7, 8, 9, 10, 11, 12\}$, a field? The following discussion will answer the question.

Postulate	Does set C satisfy it?
1. $a + b$ is an element in the set. 2. ab is an element in the set.	1.–2. Yes. The sum or product of any two numbers is in C because every answer in the table is a clock number.
3. $a + b = b + a$ 4. $ab = ba$	3.–4. Yes. Check a few cases. It is easily seen by drawing diagonals on the tables from upper left to lower right. It divides the numbers symmetrically: the pattern on one side is exactly the same as on the other.
5. $(a + b) + c = a + (b + c)$ 6. $(ab)c = a(bc)$	5.–6. Yes. Many cases are required to show that clock numbers do satisfy this. Choose a few examples and try it.
7. There is an identity element for addition.	7. Yes. 12 added to any number gives that number.
8. There is an identity element for multiplication.	8. Yes. 1 times any number gives that number.

(Continued on next page.)

9. Each element has an additive inverse.	9. Yes. The additive identity element, 12, appears in each column. So each number has an additive inverse.
10. Each element has a multiplicative inverse.	10. No. There is no number by which to multiply 2, 3, 4, 6, 8, 9, 10, or 12 to get the identity element, 1; so they do not have multiplicative inverses.
11. $a(b + c) = ab + ac$	11. Yes. All combinations would have to be checked to prove this. Try a few to verify it.

If one postulate is not satisfied, then the set of numbers is not a field. Thus, you could have stopped after finding that postulate 10 did not hold. The set of clock numbers is not a field.

Note that in the finite set C under the operations of clock arithmetic, 12 acts the same as 0 does in the set of real numbers; that is, 12 is the additive identity element and 12 times any number is 12. Therefore, if the clock had been labeled as shown at the right, the pattern for addition and multiplication would be the same with 12 being replaced by 0.

Exercises

A **1.** Complete the following addition and multiplication tables for the set of numbers on a "four-hour clock": {0, 1, 2, 3}.

+	0	1	2	3
0	0	1	2	3
1	1	?	?	?
2	2	3	?	?
3	3	?	?	2

×	0	1	2	3
0	0	0	0	0
1	0	?	?	?
2	0	2	?	?
3	0	?	?	1

2. Does the set of numbers on a "four-hour clock" meet all the requirements to be a field? If not, which postulate(s) is (are) not satisfied? Give examples.

3. Complete the following tables for a "six-hour clock."

+	0	1	2	3	4	5
0	0	1	2	3	4	5
1	1	?	?	?	?	0
2	2	?	4	?	?	?
3	3	?	?	?	?	?
4	4	?	?	?	2	?
5	5	?	1	?	?	?

×	0	1	2	3	4	5
0	0	0	0	0	0	0
1	0	?	2	?	?	?
2	0	?	?	?	?	?
3	0	?	?	?	0	?
4	0	4	?	?	?	2
5	0	?	4	?	?	1

4. Does the set of numbers on a "six-hour clock" meet all the requirements to be a field? Explain.

5. Is any set of numbers on an "even-number clock" a field? Explain.

6. Complete the following tables for a "three-hour clock."

+	0	1	2
0	0	?	?
1	?	2	?
2	?	?	1

×	0	1	2
0	0	0	0
1	0	?	?
2	0	?	?

7. Is the set of numbers on a "three-hour clock" a field?

8. Is the set of numbers on a "five-hour clock" a field?

9. Is the set of numbers on a "nine-hour clock" a field?

10. Is any set of numbers on an "odd-number clock" a field? Explain.

11. Is there any pattern that indicates which sets of "clock numbers" are fields? If so, explain.

12. The following is a finite number system that has two numbers, 0 and 1. The addition and multiplication tables for this system are given below.

+	0	1
0	0	1
1	1	0

×	0	1
0	0	0
1	0	1

Does this finite number system meet the requirements to be a field? Explain.

13. The following finite number system has elements p, a, b, and c, instead of numbers. The operation $*$ for this system is unlike either ordinary addition or multiplication.

$*$	p	a	b	c
p	p	a	b	c
a	a	p	c	b
b	b	c	p	a
c	c	b	a	p

a. Has this system an identity element? If so, what is it?

b. Does each element have an inverse element? If so, what is it for each element?

c. Is the system commutative?

d. Is the system associative?

e. Is the system a field? Explain.

CHAPTER REVIEW

1. Know the meaning of and be able to use each of the following words or phrases. The number shown after each word or phrase indicates where it is introduced, in case you need to review.

statement (*504*)
simple statement (*505*)
compound statement (*505*)
conjunction (*505*)
truth value (*506*)
truth table (*506*)
disjunction (*506*)
conditional statement (*509*)
converse (*510*)
biconditional (*511*)
negation (*513*)
inverse (*513*)
logically equivalent
   statements (*514*)

tautology (*516*)
Law of the Excluded
   Middle (*517*)
quantifiers (*518*)
premise, or hypothesis (*523*)
conclusion (*523*)
inference (*523*)
modus ponens (*523*)
transitivity (*524*)
rule of substitution
   for variables (*525*)
direct proof (*528*)
indirect proof (*531*)
field (*535*)

2. Why is the sentence $3x - 2 = 7$ *not* a statement?

3. Why *is* $\forall x \in R \quad 3(x + y) = 3x + 3y$ a statement?

4. Explain the difference between a compound statement that is a conjunction and one that is a disjunction.

5. Explain why a true conjunction can be represented by the intersection of sets and a true disjunction by the union of sets.

6. Complete this table by inserting the correct truth values.

p	q	$p \rightarrow q$	$q \rightarrow p$	$p \leftrightarrow q$
T	T	?	?	?
T	F	?	?	?
F	T	?	?	?
F	F	?	?	?

7. Write the inverse of this statement: *If a number may be represented by the ratio of two integers, it is a rational number.*
  Is the inverse true? Explain.

8. If you are given that p is true and q is false, then $\sim p$ is false and $\sim q$ is true. Explain why $\sim p \wedge \sim q$ is false.

9. Give an example of a tautology.

10. *All whole numbers are rational numbers.* Is this a true statement? Write the negation of the statement. Is it true?

11. *For any given acute angle, the ratio of the measure of the side opposite the angle to the measure of the side adjacent is called the tangent.* Why is this not a good definition?

12. Represent the following statements symbolically, and explain how the inference is an example of the rule of substitution for variables.

  Drivers of sports cars pay higher insurance premiums.
  Sam drives a sports car.
  ∴ Sam pays a higher insurance premium.

13. Prove: If a number is odd, then the cube of the number is odd.

14. What is the first step in an indirect proof? How do you then establish the conclusion?

15. Is the set of integers a field under addition and multiplication? Explain.

CHAPTER TEST

1. Which of the properties of a good definition does the following definition fail to have? *A rational number is a fraction.*

2. Find the negation of the following statements.

  a. π is an irrational number.

  b. Some triangles are isosceles.

3. Complete the following truth tables.

Conjunction		
p	q	$p \wedge q$
T	T	
T	F	
F	T	
F	F	

Disjunction		
p	q	$p \vee q$
T	T	
T	F	
F	T	
F	F	

Conditional		
p	q	$p \rightarrow q$
T	T	
T	F	
F	T	
F	F	

Biconditional		
p	q	$p \leftrightarrow q$
T	T	
T	F	
F	T	
F	F	

4. Given the conditional $p \rightarrow q$, form its converse.

5. Use a truth table to determine whether or not the following statement is a tautology. $(p \vee q) \rightarrow (p \wedge q)$

6. Indicate the method of proof used in reaching each conclusion.

a. $p \rightarrow q$
$\underline{\quad p \quad}$
$\therefore q$

b. $p \rightarrow q$
$\underline{\quad q \rightarrow r \quad}$
$\therefore p \rightarrow r$

c. $\begin{cases} \forall x \in R & x + x = 2x \\ 3 \in R \end{cases}$
$\underline{\qquad\qquad\qquad}$
$\therefore 3 + 3 = 2 \cdot 3$

—— Prove the following.

7. $\forall x \in R \quad 5(x + 2) = 5x + 10$

8. The sum of three odd numbers is an odd number.

9. If a number is divisible by 2, its square is divisible by 2.

10. $\sqrt{2}$ is irrational.

11. What is the general method used in an indirect proof?

12. Is the set of whole numbers a field under addition and multiplication? Explain your answer.

CUMULATIVE REVIEW

—— Give the letter of the response that best completes the sentence or answers the question.

1. Given that W is the set of whole numbers, ___?___ is true.

a. $\frac{5}{6} \in W$ **b.** $1\frac{1}{2} \in W$ **c.** $\sqrt{2} \in W$ **d.** $3 \in W$

2. If the replacement set for x and y is the set of real numbers, which of the following is true?

a. $\forall x \; \forall y \quad x + 1 = x$

b. $\forall x \; \forall y \quad x \cdot y = x + y$

c. $\forall x \; \forall y \quad (x + y) + x = x + (y + x)$

d. $\forall x \; \forall y \quad x \cdot y > x \cdot x$

3. Which of the following pairs are equivalent?

a. $10 - (-7)$ and $10 + (-7)$

b. $-10 - (-7)$ and $10 - (-7)$

c. $10 - (-7)$ and $10 + (7)$

d. $-10 + (-7)$ and $-10 - (-7)$

4. What is the solution set of the equation $|\, 2x - 3 \,| + 8 = 9$?

a. $\{-2, -1\}$ **b.** $\{2, -1\}$ **c.** $\{2, 1\}$ **d.** $\{-2, 1\}$

5. Which of the following expressions is equivalent to $\frac{2}{3}(a + b) + \frac{3}{4}(2a - b)$?

a. $\dfrac{13a}{6} + \dfrac{b}{12}$ **b.** $\dfrac{26a - b}{12}$

c. $\dfrac{13a - b}{12}$ **d.** $\dfrac{26a + b}{12}$

6. What is the graph of the solution set of $3x - 2 > 15$?

a. A half-plane.   **b.** The coordinate plane.

c. A line segment.   **d.** A ray.

7. Which of the following relations is not a function?

a. $y = \pm\sqrt{x}$ **b.** $x = \pm\sqrt{y}$

c. $3x - 2 = 5y$ **d.** $5x = 2y - 7$

8. What is the equation of the line parallel to the x axis that passes through the intersection of the graph of this system?

$$\begin{cases} -7x + 2y = 10 \\ 5x - 6y = 2 \end{cases}$$

a. $y = 2$ **b.** $y = -2$ **c.** $x = 2$ **d.** $x = -2$

9. What two consecutive integers may replace x and y to make $x < -\sqrt{101} < y$ true?

a. 11 and 10   **b.** 10 and 11

c. -11 and -10 **d.** -10 and -11

10. Which of the following systems of equations is independent?

a. $\begin{cases} 3x - 2y = 7 \\ x + 5y = 1 \end{cases}$ **b.** $\begin{cases} 2x - y = 4 \\ 4x - 2y = 8 \end{cases}$

c. $\begin{cases} 3x - y = 5 \\ 9x - 3y = 2 \end{cases}$ **d.** $\begin{cases} x + 3y = 2 \\ 5x + 15y = -7 \end{cases}$

11. Which of the following is equal to $[x^2(xy^{-2})]^2$?

a. x^4y^0 **b.** x^4y^{-4} **c.** $\dfrac{x^6}{y^4}$ **d.** x^6y^4

12. Consider the trinomial $ax^2 + bx + c$. If a and c are each perfect squares, then which is the correct value of b to make the trinomial a perfect square?

a. $2\sqrt{a} \cdot \sqrt{c}$

b. $(2\sqrt{a})(2\sqrt{c})$

c. $\dfrac{\sqrt{a} \cdot \sqrt{c}}{2}$

d. $\sqrt{a} \cdot \sqrt{c}$

13. The graph of $y = 3x^2 + 5x - 6$ intersects the x axis

    a. at just the origin.   **b.** in two points.

    c. in one point that is not the origin.   **d.** in no points.

14. What are the solutions of the equation $15x^2 + 2\sqrt{2}x - 2 = 0$?

a. $-\dfrac{\sqrt{2}}{5}$ and $\dfrac{\sqrt{2}}{3}$

b. $\dfrac{5}{\sqrt{2}}$ and $\dfrac{3}{\sqrt{2}}$

c. $\dfrac{\sqrt{2}}{5}$ and $-\dfrac{\sqrt{2}}{3}$

d. $-\dfrac{\sqrt{2}}{5}$ and $-\dfrac{\sqrt{2}}{3}$

15. Simplifying $\dfrac{3x^2 - 3y^2}{\dfrac{6(x+y)}{5}}$ gives

a. $\dfrac{18(x^3 + x^2y - xy^2 - y^3)}{5}$.

b. $\dfrac{5(x-y)}{2}$.

c. $\dfrac{5x-y}{2}$.

d. $\dfrac{18(x^2 - y^2)}{5}$.

16. If you are given right triangle ABC with $|\angle B| = 90°$, $|\angle C| = 54°$, and $|\overline{AC}| = 38$ feet, which of the following would you use to find $|\overline{AB}|$?

    a. The tangent ratio.   **b.** The sine ratio.

    c. The cosine ratio.   **d.** The Pythagorean theorem.

17. How may the logarithmic function $y = \log_b x$ be written as an exponential function?

a. $y = b^x$ **b.** $x^b = y$ **c.** $x = b^y$ **d.** $y^b = x$

18. A contractor needs concrete for a construction project. If a large machine can mix the required amount in 12 hours and a small one can mix it in 20 hours, how long will it take both machines running together to mix the required amount of concrete?

    a. 15 hours   **b.** 7.5 hours

    c. 10.3 hours   **d.** 17.5 hours

19. If y varies inversely as x, and y is 5 when x is 3, what is the value of y when x is 6?

    a. 2.5   **b.** 10   **c.** $3\frac{3}{5}$ **d.** 1.25

20. If you are given the statement $\sim p \to q$, then _?_ is its inverse.

    a. $\sim p \wedge q$ **b.** $\sim p \to \sim q$

    c. $p \to q$ **d.** $p \to \sim q$

21. Let the domain of a relation be the automobile license plates in a certain state, and let the range be the automobiles owned by people in that same state. Then mapping of license plates onto automobiles is an example of a

    a. one-to-many mapping.   **b.** one-to-one mapping.

    c. many-to-one mapping.   **d.** linear function.

22. Which of the following is equivalent to $\sim(p \vee q)$?

    a. $\sim p \wedge \sim q$ **b.** $\sim p \vee \sim q$

    c. $\sim p \to \sim q$ **d.** $p \wedge \sim q$

ENRICHMENT

Faulty Logic

If you were asked to solve the equation $3x + 5 - 2x = 3x$, what would you do? Almost certainly you would start applying postulates to collect the x terms on one side of the equals sign and the constants on the other side. Then you would divide by the coefficient of the x terms and arrive at an answer. In the given equation, you get $5 = 2x$, or $x = \frac{5}{2}$. Some of you may check $x = \frac{5}{2}$ in the original equation, but others may feel that the check is unnecessary if you have worked carefully. The goal of this section is to show logically that the check is the most important part of the procedure.

When you are asked to solve the equation $3x + 5 - 2x = 3x$, you are being asked to find a value of x, call it x_1, which makes the equation true; that is, you are to supply some number for x_1. But you do not do this with the usual method of solution. You automatically assume that there is an x such that $3x + 5 - 2x = 3x$ is known to be a true equality when $x = x_1$. In short you are proving that "If $3x + 5 - 2x = 3x$ does have a solution x_1, then x_1 is $\frac{5}{2}$." It is the check that really shows that "If x_1 is $\frac{5}{2}$, then $3x + 5 - 2x = 3x$ does have a solution x_1," which is the converse of the other statement.

Your work will be correct by this method provided that the algebraic equation you started with has a solution. Otherwise, some very strange results occur. For example, $\frac{1}{x} + \frac{2}{x+1} = \frac{3}{x}$ looks innocent enough, but examine the following solution.

$$\frac{1}{x} \quad + \quad \frac{2}{x+1} \quad = \quad \frac{3}{x}$$

$$\frac{x(x+1)1}{x} + \frac{x(x+1)2}{x+1} = \frac{x(x+1)3}{x}$$

$$\begin{array}{rl} (x+1) + \quad 2x \quad & = 3x + 3 \\ 3x \quad + \quad 1 \quad & = 3x + 3 \\ 1 & = 3 \end{array}$$

The result is disturbing, and no amount of checking will tell you what is wrong. What actually has happened is that you have done an indirect "disproof." You assumed that $\frac{1}{x} + \frac{2}{x+1} = \frac{3}{x}$ was a valid equality and derived a contradiction. Therefore, your assumption is invalid, and the equation is not a valid equation.

Here is a slightly different example.

$$\frac{x}{x+2} - \frac{4}{x+1} = \frac{-2}{x+2}$$
$$x(x+1) - 4(x+2) = -2(x+1)$$
$$x^2 - x - 6 = 0$$
$$(x = -2) \lor (x = 3)$$

Again checking reveals trouble, for $x = 3$ is a solution, but $x = -2$ is not. It could have been seen ahead of time that $x = -1$ and $x = -2$ would give zero denominators, but the exception was not made.

Here is a final example.

Since $\sqrt{ab} = \sqrt{a}\sqrt{b}$ is true, you may write $\sqrt{(-1)(-1)} = \sqrt{-1}\sqrt{-1}$. But you know that $\sqrt{(-1)(-1)} = \sqrt{1} = 1$, and by the very definition of square root $\sqrt{-1} \cdot \sqrt{-1} = -1$. Therefore, $1 = -1$ must be true. What went wrong? Check back in Chapter 6 to see if you may assume $\sqrt{ab} = \sqrt{a}\sqrt{b}$ for *any* a and b.

Exercises

1. Solve the following equations and explain the results.

a. $\frac{6}{x+2} + \frac{7}{x} = \frac{13}{x+2}$　　　**b.** $\frac{7}{x-1} - \frac{6}{x^2-1} = 5$

c. $\frac{x^2+5}{x-3} = x+3$　　　**d.** $\frac{2x}{x+2} - \frac{2}{x-2} = \frac{-4}{x+2}$

2. Let x and y be any two real numbers and let $x + y = 2z$. Multiply both sides by $x - y$ to get $x^2 - y^2 = 2zx - 2zy$. Now add $y^2 + z^2 - 2xz$ to both sides to get $x^2 - 2xz + z^2 = y^2 - 2zy + z^2$, or $(x - z)^2 = (y - z)^2$. Then $\sqrt{(x - z)^2} = \sqrt{(x - y)^2}$, or $x - z = y - z$, or $x = y$. Thus, since x and y were any real numbers, any two real numbers are equal. What is wrong? (*Hint:* $\sqrt{5^2}$ and $\sqrt{(-5)^2}$ both equal $\sqrt{25} = 5$ since $\sqrt{a}$ stands for positive square root of $+a$.)

3. The following "proof" assumes that certain laws of exponents hold in certain cases. Explain the erroneous steps.

$$\sqrt{-1} = \sqrt{-1}$$

$$\sqrt{\frac{1}{-1}} = \sqrt{\frac{-1}{1}}$$

$$\frac{\sqrt{1}}{\sqrt{-1}} = \frac{\sqrt{-1}}{\sqrt{1}} \rightarrow \sqrt{1}\sqrt{1} = \sqrt{-1}\sqrt{-1} \rightarrow 1 = -1$$

4. Let $\frac{a}{b} = \frac{c}{d}$ and $a = c$. Then $ad = bc$, and since $a = c$, $ad - bc = 0$ or $ad - ba = 0$. Then $a(d - b) = 0$, so $a = 0$ or $d = b$. This shows that if two fractions are equal and have equal nonzero numerators, then the denominators are also equal.

Now consider the equation $\frac{x}{x - 2} + 2 = \frac{3x - 4}{x - 1}$. If you put the left side over a common denominator, you have $\frac{3x - 4}{x - 2} = \frac{3x - 4}{x - 1}$. But then by the little "theorem" above, $x - 2 = x - 1$, or $2 = 1$. What went wrong?

THE GROWTH OF MATHEMATICS

Vieta

Franciscus Vieta (1540–1603) was a lawyer in France and spent his life in service to the king. He studied mathematics in his leisure time, but he served the king as mathematician, too. Henry IV was challenged to find someone who could solve an equation of the forty-fifth degree that had been solved by a Belgian. Vieta recognized that it could be treated as a trigonometric function and found twenty-three solutions.

Vieta's greatest contribution was that of *inventing* symbolic algebra, although other men made it generally accepted. Whereas Diophantus had used word abbreviations and had only one symbol for the unknown, Vieta used the whole alphabet with numerals and signs. He did not have symbolism for exponents or equality, but he used *x quadratus* and *x cubus* for x^2 and x^3, respectively, rather than different letters as was then the practice. He is truly the father of symbolic algebra.

Table of Squares and Square Roots

No.	Square	Square Root	No.	Square	Square Root	No.	Square	Square Root
1	1	1.000	51	2601	7.141	101	10,201	10.050
2	4	1.414	52	2704	7.211	102	10,404	10.100
3	9	1.732	53	2809	7.280	103	10,609	10.149
4	16	2.000	54	2916	7.348	104	10,816	10.198
5	25	2.236	55	3025	7.416	105	11,025	10.247
6	36	2.449	56	3136	7.483	106	11,236	10,296
7	49	2.646	57	3249	7.550	107	11,449	10.344
8	64	2.828	58	3364	7.616	108	11,664	10.392
9	81	3.000	59	3481	7.681	109	11,881	10.440
10	100	3.162	60	3600	7.746	110	12,100	10.488
11	121	3.317	61	3721	7.810	111	12,321	10.536
12	144	3.464	62	3844	7.874	112	12,544	10.583
13	169	3.606	63	3969	7.937	113	12,769	10.630
14	196	3.742	64	4096	8.000	114	12,996	10.677
15	225	3.873	65	4225	8.062	115	13,225	10.724
16	256	4.000	66	4356	8.124	116	13,456	10.770
17	289	4.123	67	4489	8.185	117	13,689	10.817
18	324	4.243	68	4624	8.246	118	13,924	10.863
19	361	4.359	69	4761	8.307	119	14,161	10.909
20	400	4.472	70	4900	8.367	120	14,400	10.954
21	441	4.583	71	5041	8.426	121	14,641	11.000
22	484	4.690	72	5184	8.485	122	14,884	11.045
23	529	4.796	73	5329	8.544	123	15,129	11.091
24	576	4.899	74	5476	8.602	124	15,376	11.136
25	625	5.000	75	5625	8.660	125	15,625	11.180
26	676	5.099	76	5776	8.718	126	15,876	11.225
27	729	5.196	77	5929	8.775	127	16,129	11.269
28	784	5.292	78	6084	8.832	128	16,384	11.314
29	841	5.385	79	6241	8.888	129	16,641	11.358
30	900	5.477	80	6400	8.944	130	16,900	11.402
31	961	5.568	81	6561	9.000	131	17,161	11.446
32	1024	5.657	82	6724	9.055	132	17,424	11.489
33	1089	5.745	83	6889	9.110	133	17,689	11.533
34	1156	5.831	84	7056	9.165	134	17,956	11.576
35	1225	5.916	85	7225	9.220	135	18,225	11.619
36	1296	6.000	86	7396	9.274	136	18,496	11.662
37	1369	6.083	87	7569	9.327	137	18,769	11.705
38	1444	6.164	88	7744	9.381	138	19,044	11.747
39	1521	6.245	89	7921	9.434	139	19,321	11.790
40	1600	6.325	90	8100	9.487	140	19,600	11.832
41	1681	6.403	91	8281	9.539	141	19,881	11.874
42	1764	6.481	92	8464	9.592	142	20,164	11.916
43	1849	6.557	93	8649	9.644	143	20,449	11.958
44	1936	6.633	94	8836	9.695	144	20,736	12.000
45	2025	6.708	95	9025	9.747	145	21,025	12.042
46	2116	6.782	96	9216	9.798	146	21,316	12.083
47	2209	6.856	97	9409	9.849	147	21,609	12.124
48	2304	6.928	98	9604	9.899	148	21,904	12.166
49	2401	7.000	99	9801	9.950	149	22,201	12.207
50	2500	7.071	100	10,000	10.000	150	22,500	12.247

Table of Sines, Cosines, and Tangents

Angle	Sin	Cos	Tan	Angle	Sin	Cos	Tan
0°	.0000	1.0000	.0000	45°	.7071	.7071	1.0000
1	.0175	.9998	.0175	46	.7193	.6947	1.0355
2	.0349	.9994	.0349	47	.7314	.6820	1.0724
3	.0523	.9986	.0524	48	.7431	.6691	1.1106
4	.0698	.9976	.0699	49	.7547	.6561	1.1504
5	.0872	.9962	.0875	50	.7660	.6428	1.1918
6	.1045	.9945	.1051	51	.7771	.6293	1.2349
7	.1219	.9925	.1228	52	.7880	.6157	1.2799
8	.1392	.9903	.1405	53	.7986	.6018	1.3270
9	.1564	.9877	.1584	54	.8090	.5878	1.3764
10	.1736	.9848	.1763	55	.8192	.5736	1.4281
11	.1908	.9816	.1944	56	.8290	.5592	1.4826
12	.2079	.9781	.2126	57	.8387	.5446	1.5399
13	.2250	.9744	.2309	58	.8480	.5299	1.6003
14	.2419	.9703	.2493	59	.8572	.5150	1.6643
15	.2588	.9659	.2679	60	.8660	.5000	1.7321
16	.2756	.9613	.2867	61	.8746	.4848	1.8040
17	.2924	.9563	.3057	62	.8829	.4695	1.8807
18	.3090	.9511	.3249	63	.8910	.4540	1.9626
19	.3256	.9455	.3443	64	.8988	.4384	2.0503
20	.3420	.9397	.3640	65	.9063	.4226	2.1445
21	.3584	.9336	.3839	66	.9135	.4067	2.2460
22	.3746	.9272	.4040	67	.9205	.3907	2.3559
23	.3907	.9205	.4245	68	.9272	.3746	2.4751
24	.4067	.9135	.4452	69	.9336	.3584	2.6051
25	.4226	.9063	.4663	70	.9397	.3420	2.7475
26	.4384	.8988	.4877	71	.9455	.3256	2.9042
27	.4540	.8910	.5095	72	.9511	.3090	3.0777
28	.4695	.8829	.5317	73	.9563	.2924	3.2709
29	.4848	.8746	.5543	74	.9613	.2756	3.4874
30	.5000	.8660	.5774	75	.9659	.2588	3.7321
31	.5150	.8572	.6009	76	.9703	.2419	4.0108
32	.5299	.8480	.6249	77	.9744	.2250	4.3315
33	.5446	.8387	.6494	78	.9781	.2079	4.7046
34	.5592	.8290	.6745	79	.9816	.1908	5.1446
35	.5736	.8192	.7002	80	.9848	.1736	5.6713
36	.5878	.8090	.7265	81	.9877	.1564	6.3138
37	.6018	.7986	.7536	82	.9903	.1392	7.1154
38	.6157	.7880	.7813	83	.9925	.1219	8.1443
39	.6293	.7771	.8098	84	.9945	.1045	9.5144
40	.6428	.7660	.8391	85	.9962	.0872	11.4301
41	.6561	.7547	.8693	86	.9976	.0698	14.3007
42	.6691	.7431	.9004	87	.9986	.0523	19.0811
43	.6820	.7314	.9325	88	.9994	.0349	28.6363
44	.6947	.7193	.9657	89	.9998	.0175	57.2900
45	.7071	.7071	1.0000	90	1.0000	.0000	

Table of Common Logarithms

N	0	1	2	3	4	5	6	7	8	9
1.0	0000	0043	0086	0128	0170	0212	0253	0294	0334	0374
1.1	0414	0453	0492	0531	0569	0607	0645	0682	0719	0755
1.2	0792	0828	0864	0899	0934	0969	1004	1038	1072	1106
1.3	1139	1173	1206	1239	1271	1303	1335	1367	1399	1430
1.4	1461	1492	1523	1553	1584	1614	1644	1673	1703	1732
1.5	1761	1790	1818	1847	1875	1903	1931	1959	1987	2014
1.6	2041	2068	2095	2122	2148	2175	2201	2227	2253	2279
1.7	2304	2330	2355	2380	2405	2430	2455	2480	2504	2529
1.8	2553	2577	2601	2625	2648	2672	2695	2718	2742	2765
1.9	2788	2810	2833	2856	2878	2900	2923	2945	2967	2989
2.0	3010	3032	3054	3075	3096	3118	3139	3160	3181	3201
2.1	3222	3243	3263	3284	3304	3324	3345	3365	3385	3404
2.2	3424	3444	3464	3483	3502	3522	3541	3560	3579	3598
2.3	3617	3636	3655	3674	3692	3711	3729	3747	3766	3784
2.4	3802	3820	3838	3856	3874	3892	3909	3927	3945	3962
2.5	3979	3997	4014	4031	4048	4065	4082	4099	4116	4133
2.6	4150	4166	4183	4200	4216	4232	4249	4265	4281	4298
2.7	4314	4330	4346	4362	4378	4393	4409	4425	4440	4456
2.8	4472	4487	4502	4518	4533	4548	4564	4579	4594	4609
2.9	4624	4639	4654	4669	4683	4698	4713	4728	4742	4757
3.0	4771	4786	4800	4814	4829	4843	4857	4871	4886	4900
3.1	4914	4928	4942	4955	4969	4983	4997	5011	5024	5038
3.2	5051	5065	5079	5092	5105	5119	5132	5145	5159	5172
3.3	5185	5198	5211	5224	5237	5250	5263	5276	5289	5302
3.4	5315	5328	5340	5353	5366	5378	5391	5403	5416	5428
3.5	5441	5453	5465	5478	5490	5502	5514	5527	5539	5551
3.6	5563	5575	5587	5599	5611	5623	5635	5647	5658	5670
3.7	5682	5694	5705	5717	5729	5740	5752	5763	5775	5786
3.8	5798	5809	5821	5832	5843	5855	5866	5877	5888	5899
3.9	5911	5922	5933	5944	5955	5966	5977	5988	5999	6010
4.0	6021	6031	6042	6053	6064	6075	6085	6096	6107	6117
4.1	6128	6138	6149	6160	6170	6180	6191	6201	6212	6222
4.2	6232	6243	6253	6263	6274	6284	6294	6304	6314	6325
4.3	6335	6345	6355	6365	6375	6385	6395	6405	6415	6425
4.4	6435	6444	6454	6464	6474	6484	6493	6503	6513	6522
4.5	6532	6542	6551	6561	6571	6580	6590	6599	6609	6618
4.6	6628	6637	6646	6656	6665	6675	6684	6693	6702	6712
4.7	6721	6730	6739	6749	6758	6767	6776	6785	6794	6803
4.8	6812	6821	6830	6839	6848	6857	6866	6875	6884	6893
4.9	6902	6911	6920	6928	6937	6946	6955	6964	6972	6981
5.0	6990	6998	7007	7016	7024	7033	7042	7050	7059	7067
5.1	7076	7084	7093	7101	7110	7118	7126	7135	7143	7152
5.2	7160	7168	7177	7185	7193	7202	7210	7218	7226	7235
5.3	7243	7251	7259	7267	7275	7284	7292	7300	7308	7316
5.4	7324	7332	7340	7348	7356	7364	7372	7380	7388	7396

Table of Common Logarithms

N	0	1	2	3	4	5	6	7	8	9
5.5	7404	7412	7419	7427	7435	7443	7451	7459	7466	7474
5.6	7482	7490	7497	7505	7513	7520	7528	7536	7543	7551
5.7	7559	7566	7574	7582	7589	7597	7604	7612	7619	7627
5.8	7634	7642	7649	7657	7664	7672	7679	7686	7694	7701
5.9	7709	7716	7723	7731	7738	7745	7752	7760	7767	7774
6.0	7782	7789	7796	7803	7810	7818	7825	7832	7839	7846
6.1	7853	7860	7868	7875	7882	7889	7896	7903	7910	7917
6.2	7924	7931	7938	7945	7952	7959	7966	7973	7980	7987
6.3	7993	8000	8007	8014	8021	8028	8035	8041	8048	8055
6.4	8062	8069	8075	8082	8089	8096	8102	8109	8116	8122
6.5	8129	8136	8142	8149	8156	8162	8169	8176	8182	8189
6.6	8195	8202	8209	8215	8222	8228	8235	8241	8248	8254
6.7	8261	8267	8274	8280	8287	8293	8299	8306	8312	8319
6.8	8325	8331	8338	8344	8351	8357	8363	8370	8376	8382
6.9	8388	8395	8401	8407	8414	8420	8426	8432	8439	8445
7.0	8451	8457	8463	8470	8476	8482	8488	8494	8500	8506
7.1	8513	8519	8525	8531	8537	8543	8549	8555	8561	8567
7.2	8573	8579	8585	8591	8597	8603	8609	8615	8621	8627
7.3	8633	8639	8645	8651	8657	8663	8669	8675	8681	8686
7.4	8692	8698	8704	8710	8716	8722	8727	8733	8739	8745
7.5	8751	8756	8762	8768	8774	8779	8785	8791	8797	8802
7.6	8808	8814	8820	8825	8831	8837	8842	8848	8854	8859
7.7	8865	8871	8876	8882	8887	8893	8899	8904	8910	8915
7.8	8921	8927	8932	8938	8943	8949	8954	8960	8965	8971
7.9	8976	8982	8987	8993	8998	9004	9009	9015	9020	9025
8.0	9031	9036	9042	9047	9053	9058	9063	9069	9074	9079
8.1	9085	9090	9096	9101	9106	9112	9117	9122	9128	9133
8.2	9138	9143	9149	9154	9159	9165	9170	9175	9180	9186
8.3	9191	9196	9201	9206	9212	9217	9222	9227	9232	9238
8.4	9243	9248	9253	9258	9263	9269	9274	9279	9284	9289
8.5	9294	9299	9304	9309	9315	9320	9325	9330	9335	9340
8.6	9345	9350	9355	9360	9365	9370	9375	9380	9385	9390
8.7	9395	9400	9405	9410	9415	9420	9425	9430	9435	9440
8.8	9445	9450	9455	9460	9465	9469	9474	9479	9484	9489
8.9	9494	9499	9504	9509	9513	9518	9523	9528	9533	9538
9.0	9542	9547	9552	9557	9562	9566	9571	9576	9581	9586
9.1	9590	9595	9600	9605	9609	9614	9619	9624	9628	9633
9.2	9638	9643	9647	9652	9657	9661	9666	9671	9675	9680
9.3	9685	9689	9694	9699	9703	9708	9713	9717	9722	9727
9.4	9731	9736	9741	9745	9750	9754	9759	9763	9768	9773
9.5	9777	9782	9786	9791	9795	9800	9805	9809	9814	9818
9.6	9823	9827	9832	9836	9841	9845	9850	9854	9859	9863
9.7	9868	9872	9877	9881	9886	9890	9894	9899	9903	9908
9.8	9912	9917	9921	9926	9930	9934	9939	9943	9948	9952
9.9	9956	9961	9965	9969	9974	9978	9983	9987	9991	9996

Glossary

The following definitions and statements reflect
the usage of the terms in this textbook.

Abscissa. The first number of the coordinates of a point in a plane is the *abscissa*. In (x, y), x is the abscissa.

Absolute value. The *absolute value* of a real number x is the greater of the two numbers x and $-x$ $(x \neq 0)$. If x is 0, the absolute value of x is 0.

Acute angle. An *acute angle* is an angle whose measure is between $0°$ and $90°$.

Additive identity. The *additive identity* for real numbers is 0; that is, $a + 0 = a$ $(a \in R)$.

Additive inverse. The *additive inverse* of the real number a is $-a$; that is, $a + (-a) = 0$ $(a \in R)$.

Algebraic expression. An *algebraic expression* is any meaningful combination of numerals, variables, and mathematical symbols.

Angle. The union of two noncollinear rays with a common endpoint forms an *angle*.

Associative postulate. The *associative postulate* for addition is $a + (b + c) = (a + b) + c$ and for multiplication is $a(bc) = (ab)c$.

Axes. Two perpendicular lines used for reference in locating points in a coordinate plane are called *axes*.

Biconditional. Two statements joined by *if and only if* form a *biconditional*.

Binomial. A *binomial* is a polynomial of two terms.

Closure postulate. The *closure postulate* states that for a given set, the result of operating on two elements of the set is another member of the set. For $a, b \in R$, $(a + b) \in R$ and $(a \cdot b) \in R$.

Coefficient. Any one of the factors of a term is the *coefficient* of the term. The nonvariable part is its *numerical coefficient*.

Common logarithm. A logarithm to the base 10 is called a *common logarithm*.

Commutative postulate. The *commutative postulate* for addition is $a + b = b + a$ and for multiplication is $a \cdot b = b \cdot a$.

Component sentence. A *component sentence* is one of the sentences that make up a compound sentence.

Compound sentence (statement). A *compound sentence* (*statement*) is formed by two simple sentences (statements) joined by a connective, such as *and* and *or*.

Composite number. A *composite number* is a whole number greater than 1 that is not prime.

Conditional. A *conditional* is a compound statement formed by two statements joined in *if . . . then . . .* form.

Conditional equation. A *conditional equation* is an open equation that is not an identity.

Conjunction. A compound statement with the connective *and* is a *conjunction*.

Consistent system. A system of equations or inequalities whose solution set is one or more ordered pairs is a *consistent system*.

Constant function. A *constant function* is a function defined by $f(x) = b$.

Contradiction. A statement that is always false is a *contradiction*.

Contrapositive. The *contrapositive* of a statement is formed by negating both parts of the converse of the statement.

Converse. The *converse* of a conditional is the statement formed by interchanging the two statements of the conditional.

Coordinate(s). The *coordinate* of a point on a line is the number associated with the point. The *coordinates* of a point in a plane are the ordered pair of numbers associated with the point.

Coordinate plane. A plane with ordered pairs of numbers associated with all points of the plane is called a *coordinate plane*.

Cosine. For any given acute angle of a right triangle, the ratio of the measure of the side adjacent to the angle to the measure of the hypotenuse is called the *cosine*.

Cube root. The *cube root* of a number a is a number b such that $b^3 = a$ is true.

Dependent system. A system of equations or inequalities in which each has the same solution set is a *dependent system*.

Direct variation. *Direct variation* is a relation defined by the equation $y = kx$, where k is a constant.

Discriminant. The *discriminant* of the quadratic equation $ax^2 + bx + c = 0$ is the number $b^2 - 4ac$; this portion of the quadratic formula determines the nature of the solutions.

Disjoint sets. Sets with no elements in common are *disjoint sets*.

Disjunction. The compound statement formed by two simple statements joined by *or* is a *disjunction*.

Distributive postulate. The *distributive postulate* for multiplication over addition is $a(b + c) = ab + ac$.

Domain. The *domain* of a relation is the set of first numbers of the ordered pairs of the relation.

Empty set. The set with no elements is the *empty set*. It is symbolized by $\emptyset$ or $\{\ \}$.

Equation. An *equation* is a mathematical sentence that states that two expressions are equal.

Equivalent algebraic expressions. *Algebraic expressions* are *equivalent* if they name the same number for all replacements for the variables for which the expressions are defined.

Equivalent sentences. Sentences that have the same solution set are *equivalent sentences*.

Expanded notation. Expressing a number as the sum of powers of 10 multiplied by one of the integers 0 through 9 is representing the number in *expanded notation*.

Exponent. The number n in a^n is the *exponent* of the base a; if $n > 1$ and is integral, n is the number of times a is taken as a factor; a^0 is 1; a^1 is a; a^{-n} is $\frac{1}{a^n}$; $a^{\frac{1}{n}}$ is $\sqrt[n]{a}$.

Exponential function. An *exponential function* is a function defined by $f(x) = b^x$ $(b > 0, b \neq 1)$.

Factor. A *factor* is one of the expressions combined by multiplication to form a product.

Field. The set F is a *field* with respect to two operations $\oplus$ and $\otimes$ if and only if
  i) the set is closed, commutative, and associative under the two operations,
  ii) there is an identity element z for $\oplus$ and an identity element e for $\otimes$,
  iii) each element has an inverse element under $\oplus$, and each element except z has an inverse element under $\otimes$, and
  iv) $\otimes$ is distributive with respect to $\oplus$.

Fraction. A *fraction* is the numeral that names a fractional number.

Fractional numbers. The set of *fractional numbers*, F, is the set of numbers that can be named as the ratio $\frac{x}{y}$, $x \in$ W and $y \in$ N.

Function. A *function* is a set of ordered pairs of which no two first elements are the same.

Graph. The *graph* of a sentence is the set of points whose coordinates make the sentence true.

Half-line. A *half-line* is the set of points of a line that is on one side of a point of a line.

Half-plane. A *half-plane* is the set of points of a plane that is on one side of a line.

Identity. An *identity* is an open equation that is true for every replacement of the variable for which the equation has meaning.

Identity element. If there is an element e of a set such that for a second element x under an operation $\odot$, $x \odot e = e \odot x = x$ is true, then e is the *identity element* for the set.

Inconsistent system. A system of equations or inequalities whose solution set is $\emptyset$ is an *inconsistent system*.

Index of a radical. The raised numeral in a radical sign shows the *index* of the radical. It indicates the root to be found. (Since $\sqrt{}$ indicates the square root, the index 2 is usually not expressed.)

Inequality. An *inequality* is a mathematical sentence stating that two expressions are not equal.

Inference. Reasoning from a series of statements, called premises, to a final statement, called a conclusion, is *inference*.

Integers. The set of *integers* is the set, I, consisting of natural numbers, the negatives of the natural numbers, and zero.

Intercept of a graph. The *intercept of a graph* is the point at which it crosses one of the axes.

Intersection of sets. The *intersection* of two sets is the set that contains all the elements common to both sets.

Inverse. The *inverse* of a conditional is the statement formed by negating both parts of the conditional.

Inverse element. If under an operation $\odot$, for an element x of a set, there is a second element i such that $i \odot x = x \odot i = e$ is true, where e is the identity element for the set under $\odot$, then i is the *inverse element* for x.

Inverse of a relation. The *inverse of a relation* S is a relation S⁻¹ that is obtained by interchanging the coordinates of every ordered pair of the given relation S.

Inverse variation. *Inverse variation* is a variation of two related variables such that the product of the variables is a nonzero constant, that is, $xy = k$.

Irrational numbers. The set of *irrational numbers*, Ir, is the set of real numbers that cannot be expressed as a ratio $\frac{x}{y}$ ($x, y \in$ I, $y \neq 0$).

Least common denominator. The least common multiple of the denominators shown by two or more fractions or rational expressions is the *least common denominator*.

Least common multiple. The least number (or polynomial) that is divisible by two or more other numbers (or polynomials) is their *least common multiple*.

Line segment. A *line segment* consists of two points of a line and all the points of the line between them.

Linear function. A *linear function* is a function defined by the equation $f(x) = mx + b$ ($m \neq 0$, $x \in$ R). Its graph is a line.

Logarithmic function. A *logarithmic function* is defined by $y = \log_b x$, which means $x = b^y$ ($b > 0$, $b \neq 1$). The number b is the base.

Logically equivalent statements. If the truth value of two statements is exactly the same, then the statements are *logically equivalent*.

Many-to-one mapping. A mapping is *many-to-one* when at least two elements in the domain are matched with one element in the range.

Mapping. A *mapping* is a rule that associates the elements of one set, called the domain, with elements from a second set. The set of elements associated with the elements in the domain is called the range or image.

Monomial. A *monomial* is a polynomial of one term.

Multiplicative identity. The *multiplicative identity* for the real numbers is 1; that is, $a \cdot 1 = a$.

Multiplicative inverse. The *multiplicative inverse* for the real number a is $\frac{1}{a}$ ($a \neq 0$); that is, $a \cdot \frac{1}{a} = 1$.

Natural, or counting, numbers. The set of *natural numbers* is the set of numbers, N, whose members are 1 and every number found by adding 1 to a member of the set.

Negation. A *negation* of a statement is the statement formed by inserting *It is false that* before the given statement.

Obtuse angle. An *obtuse angle* is an angle whose measure is between 90° and 180°.

One-to-many mapping. A mapping is *one-to-many* when at least one element in the domain is matched with two or more elements in the range.

One-to-one correspondence. Given two sets, if each member of each set is matched with one and only one member of the other set, then the sets are said to be in *one-to-one correspondence*.

One-to-one mapping. A mapping is *one-to-one* when each element in the range is the image of one and only one element in the domain and each element in the domain maps into one and only one image element in the range.

Open sentence. An *open sentence* is one that cannot be classified as true or false until elements of the replacement set are substituted for the variable.

Opposites. Two distinct numbers matched with points on the number line on opposite sides of 0 but the same distance from 0 are *opposites*. The opposite of 0 is 0.

Order of operations. The standard agreement on the *order of operations* is first multiply and/or divide in the order that the operations appear; then add and/or subtract in the order that these operations appear.

Ordered pair. An *ordered pair* is a pair of numbers one of which is designated as first and the other as second.

Ordinate. The second number of the coordinates of a point in a plane is the *ordinate*. In (x, y), y is the ordinate.

Parallel lines. Two lines in a plane that have no points in common are *parallel lines*.

Perfect square trinomial. A *perfect square trinomial* is a trinomial that is the square of a binomial.

Perpendicular lines. Two lines that intersect to form right angles are *perpendicular lines*.

Polygon. A *polygon* is a simple closed path formed by the union of three or more line segments. A polygon separates a plane into three sets of points: the points of the polygon, the points in the interior of the polygon, and the points in the exterior of the polygon.

Polynomial in one variable. A *polynomial in one variable* is an alge-braic expression formed by adding or multiplying numbers and the variable a finite number of times, so that there are only nonnegative integral exponents for the variable.

Postulate. A *postulate* is a statement that is assumed, or accepted without proof.

Power of a number. The nth *power of a number* x is x^n. The third power of 2 is 2^3, or 8.

Prime factorization. The *prime factorization* of a whole number is the product of its prime-number factors or of its factors expressed as powers of prime numbers.

Prime number. A *prime number* is a whole number greater than 1 that has only one pair of whole-number factors, itself and 1.

Prime polynomial. A *polynomial* that has no polynomial factor, except 1, over a set of numbers is a *prime polynomial* with respect to the set of numbers.

Principal root. The *principal root* of a number is the real root if there is only one. If there is more than one root, the principal root is the positive one.

Proper subset. A *proper subset* of a set is any subset of the set other than the set itself.

Proportion. A *proportion* is an equation that shows that two ratios are equal.

Quadrant. A *quadrant* is one of the four regions formed by the axes of a coordinate plane.

Quadratic equation. Any equation of the form $ax^2 + bx + c = 0 \, (a \neq 0,$ a, b, $c \in$ R) is a *quadratic equation*.

Quadratic formula. The *quadratic formula,* $x = \dfrac{-b \pm \sqrt{b^2 - 4ac}}{2a}$, is the general form of the solutions of $ax^2 + bx + c = 0$.

Quadratic function. A *quadratic function* is the function defined by $f(x) = ax^2 + bx + c$ ($a, b, c \in$ R, $a \neq 0$).

Radical. A *radical* is a symbol denoting the root of a number, for example, $\sqrt{a}$, $\sqrt[3]{a}$, $\sqrt[n]{a}$. The radical sign is $\sqrt{}$.

Range. The *range* of a relation is the set of second numbers of the ordered pairs of the relation.

Ratio. A *ratio* is the comparison of two numbers or algebraic expressions by division.

Rational expression. A *rational expression* is one that can be expressed as the ratio of two polynomials, $\dfrac{P}{Q}$, where the numerical coefficients of Q are not all zero.

Rational numbers. The set of *rational numbers* is the set of numbers, Q, that may be expressed in the form $\dfrac{a}{b}$ ($a, b \in$ I, $b \neq 0$).

Rationalizing the denominator. The process of making the denominator of a fraction a rational number is called *rationalizing the denominator.*

Ray. A *ray* is a set of points formed by extending a line segment without bound in one direction only.

Real numbers. The set of *real numbers* is the set, R, formed by the union of the set of rational numbers and the set of irrational numbers.

Reciprocal. The *reciprocal* of a number a is a number b if and only if $ab = 1$. The reciprocal of 7 is $\frac{1}{7}$.

Rectangular-coordinate plane. A coordinate plane in which coordinates of points are determined with reference to a pair of perpendicular number lines is called a *rectangular-coordinate plane.*

Reflexive postulate for equality of real numbers. For all $a \in$ R, $a = a$ is true.

Relation. A *relation* is a set of ordered pairs.

Replacement set. The given set of elements that a variable may represent is called the *replacement set.*

Right angle. A *right angle* is an angle whose measure is 90°.

Scientific notation. When a number is represented as a power of 10 multiplied by a number greater than or equal to 1 and less than 10, it is expressed in *scientific notation.*

Set. A *set* is a well-defined collection of objects called elements.

Similar triangles. Two *triangles* are *similar* if the measures of the corresponding angles are equal and the measures of the corresponding sides are proportional.

Simple statement. A *simple statement* is a statement that has no connective.

Simultaneous, or independent, system. A consistent system of linear equations with one and only one ordered pair in the solution set is a *simultaneous, or independent, system.*

Sine. For any given acute angle of a right triangle, the ratio of the measure of the side opposite the angle to the measure of the hypotenuse is called the *sine.*

Slope of a line. The *slope* of a line is the ratio $\frac{\text{change in } y}{\text{change in } x}$ for any two points on the line. The slope of the graph of $y = mx + b$, $m \neq 0$, is m.

Solution of a sentence. A *solution of a sentence* is a number that makes the sentence true when it replaces the variable.

Solution set. The *solution set* of an open sentence is the set of numbers that replace the variable and make the sentence true.

Square root. A *square root* of a number a ($a \geq 0$) is a number b such that $b^2 = a$ is true.

Statement. In logic, a *statement* is a sentence that makes an assertion that is either true or false.

Subset. If all the members of one set are also members of a second set, then the first set is a *subset* of the second set.

Symmetric postulate for equality of real numbers. For a, $b \in$ R, if $a = b$ is true, then $b = a$ is true.

System of sentences. A *system of sentences* is two or more sentences considered together whose solution set is the intersection of the solution sets of the individual sentences.

Tangent. For any given acute angle of a right triangle, the ratio of the measure of the side opposite the angle to the measure of the side adjacent to the angle is called the *tangent.*

Term. A *term* is a product and/or quotient of numerals and variables that does not involve addition or subtraction.

Theorem. A statement proved from postulates, definitions, and previously proved statements is a *theorem.*

Transitive postulate for equality of real numbers. For a, b, $c \in$ R, if $a = b$ and $b = c$ are true, then $a = c$ is true.

Trigonometry. The study of the properties of the trigonometric functions and their applications, including the solution of triangles, is *trigonometry.*

Trinomial. A *trinomial* is a polynomial of three terms.

Truth table. A *truth table* is a table that shows the truth values of simple statements and the compound statements formed from the simple statements.

Truth values. The truth or falsity of a sentence is its *truth value.*

Union of sets. The *union* of two sets is a set that contains all the elements in either or in both of the sets.

Variable. A *variable* is a symbol that may represent any element in a given set.

Vector. A *vector* is a directed line segment.

Vertex of an angle. The point at which the two rays of an angle meet is called the *vertex.*

Whole numbers. The set of *whole numbers* is the set, W, that is the union of the set of natural numbers and zero.

Zero of a function. The *zero of a function* is a number for x in a set of ordered pairs of the form (x, y) such that y equals 0.

Index

Boldfaced numerals indicate the pages that contain formal or informal
definitions. Numerals in parentheses refer to exercises.

Motion problems, 139–41, 429–30
Muhammad ibn-Musa al-Khwarizmi (A.D. 780–?850), 419
Müller, Johann (1436–1476), 459
Multiple, **6**
  least common, 398–99, 401
Multiplication
  and exponents, 258–60
  of fractional numbers, 27
  of polynomials, 313–14, 322
    of binomials by inspection, 317–18, 320
  of real numbers, 75–77, 78–80
Multiplication postulate for equations, 105–07
  in solving equations, 107–08
Multiplicative identity, 31, 32, 75
  postulate, 31, 32, 75
Multiplicative inverse, 31, 32, 75, 417
  postulate, 31, 32, 75

Natural number(s), 2, 96
  development of, 49
Nature of solutions of a quadratic equation, 377–78
Negation, **513**–14
  of a conditional, 513
  of a conjunction, 514
  of a disjunction, 513–14
  and quantifiers, 518–19
  of a simple statement, 513
Negative of, **56**
Negative integral exponent(s), 267, **268**
Negative number(s), **52,** 56–57
  in addition, 66–69
  in division, 82–83
  and Indians, 347
  in multiplication, 75–77, 79–80
  in subtraction, 71–72, 73–74
Number(s)
  concept of, 49, 217
  fractional, 24–25
  integers, 52
  irrational, 40
  natural, 2
  rational, 53
  real, 53
  whole, 3, 52
Number line, 20, 157

Obtuse angle, **437**
One-to-many mapping, **464**

One-to-one correspondence, **12,** 49, 96–98
  between points on a line and the set of real numbers, 53
One-to-one mapping, **464**
Open interval, **124**
Opposites, **56**
Or (in logic), 506
Order of operations, 18
Ordered pair, **24,** 168, 466
Ordinate, **169**
Origin, **169**

Parabola, 350–53, **351**
  equations of a, 350–53
  vertex of a, 351
Paradoxes, Zeno's, 254
Parallel lines, **164**
Parts of a computer
  input, 300
  operation, 300
    arithmetic, 300
    control, 300
    memory, 300
  output, 300
Perfect square trinomial, **330**–31, 364–65, 367
Perpendicular lines, **164**
Philolaus (Fifth century B.C.), 254
Plane, 163
Plato (427?–347 B.C.), 254, 305
Point, 162
Polar axis, 173
Polar-coordinate plane, 173
Polygon, **164**
  exterior of, 164
  interior of, 164
Polynomial(s), **308**–09
  addition and subtraction of, 310–11
  division of, 341–42
  factors of, 326, 328–29, 330–31, 333–34, 335–36, 338
  multiplication of, 313–14, 317–18, 320, 322
  prime, **326**
  and rational expressions, 386
  types of, 308, 309
Positive integral exponent, **258**
Positive integral power. *See* Positive integral exponent.
Postulate, **31**
Power of a number, 258, 260–62
Premise, **523**

Prime-factorization form, **324**–25
Prime number, **5** (16)
Principal root(s), **271**
  with variables, 279
Proclus, 294
Program for a computer, 250, 300–05
  data, 301
  instructions, 301
Programing, 250–52, 300–05
Proof
  direct, 527–29, **528**
  indirect, **531**–32
Properties of logarithms, 490
Proportion(s), **200**
  in interpolation, 452
  and inverse variation, 476
Pythagoras (569?–?500 B.C.), 217, 346
Pythagorean theorem, **39,** 56, 215, 217,
    346, 435, 445, 500
Pythagorean triple, 346
Pythagoreans, 217, 254

Quadrant, 166, **169**
Quadratic equation, **350**–79
  complete, 350
  discriminant of, **378**
  graph for, 350–51
  incomplete, 350
    solving, 362–63
  solution of, 358–72
    by completing the square, 367–68,
      369
    by computer, 382–83
    by factoring, 358–60
    by graphing, 355–57
    by the quadratic formula, 370–72
Quadratic formula, 370–71, 382
Quadratic function, **350**–79
  graph for, 350–51
Quantifiers, 518–19

Radical(s), 271
  addition of, 287–88
  multiplication of, 282
  and rational exponents, 273–74
  sign, 271
  simplifying, 280–81, 286
Radical equation, **291**
  solving, 291–92
Radical expressions, 283
  addition of, 287–88
  multiplication of, 283
  simplifying, 280–81

Range, **175**, 463, 467
Ratio, **24, 439**
  cosine, 444–**46**
  and Eudoxus, 254
  sine, 444–**46**
  tangent, 439–41, **440**
Rational expressions, **386**–452
  addition of, 400–02
  division of, 396–97
  equality of, **387,** 406–07
  in equations, 422–34
  multiplication of, 393–94
  signs of, 405–07
  simplifying, 389–90, 409
  subtraction of, 400–02
Rational number(s), 52–**53,** 54, 417–18
Rationalizing the denominator, 284–85
Ray, **163**
Real number(s), **53,** 54
  absolute value of, **57**
  addition of, 63–64, 66–69
    postulates for, 63, 64
  division of, **82**–83
  multiplication of, 75–77, 79–80
    postulates for, 75
  subtraction of, 71–**72,** 73–74
  and vectors, 59–60
Reciprocal, **32,** 397
Rectangular-coordinate plane, **169**
Reflection of a curve, 352
  and inverse relations, 483, 487
Reflexive postulate, 34
Regiomontanus. *See* Müller, Johann.
Relation, 174–**175,** 178, 466–93
  domain of a, 175
  graph of a, 175
  inverse of a, 481–83, **482**
  range of a, 175
Resultant force, 214–17, 500
Rhind papyrus, 159
Right angle, **436**
Right triangle, 437
  hypotenuse of a, 437
  sides of a, 437
Romans, 383
Root(s) of numbers, 270–72
  cube, **271**
  *n*th, **272**
  principal, **271**
    with variables, 279
  and rational exponents, 273–74
  square, 2, **270**
    approximations of, 275–77
    table of squares and, 546

Theorem, 39, **67**
Transformation of coordinates, **157–**59
  linear transformation, **158**
  product of, 158
  stretching transformation, **158**
  translation, **158**
Transitive postulate, 34
Transitivity, **524**
Translation, **158**
Trigonometric functions, 492–93
  graphs of, 493–94
Trigonometry, **434**–52, 492–94
  history of, 459
  and resolution of forces, 497–501
Trinomial, **309**
  factoring, 330–31, 333–34, 335–36
  perfect square, **330**–31, 364–65
Truth table, **506**
Truth value, 144, **506**
  and electric circuits, 508–09

Undefined terms, 162
Union of sets, 122–24, **123,** 506–07
Unique factorization theorem, 325
Unit circle, 54
Unit square, 53

Variable(s), 16, 431
  dependent and independent, **178**
Variation
  constant of, 197

direct, 196–97
  and proportions, 200–02
  inverse, 475–76
Vector(s), **59**–60, 71, 214–17, 497–501
  addition of, 60, 215–16, 500
  components of, 215–16, 497, 501
  subtraction of, 71
Vector addition, 215–16, 500
Vector diagram, 215–16, 498–500
Vector rectangle, 215
Venn diagram(s), 122–23
Vertex
  of an angle, 163
  of a parabola, 351
Vieta, Franciscus (1540–1603), 545

Whole number, 3, 52
Work problems, 427–28

x **intercept, 355**

y **intercept, 187, 355**

Zeno of Elea (495–435 B.C.), 254
  paradoxes of, 254
Zero, introduction into number system, 347
Zero exponent, **267**
Zero of a function, 355–57, **356**
Zero ray, 173

Symbols

The following list contains the symbols used in
this book with a brief description of each and
the page where it is first used or explained.

$\ldots$	continues in the same manner	2
$\sqrt{}$	square root	2
$\{a, b\}$	set consisting of elements a, b	3
$\in$	is an element of	3
$\notin$	is not an element of	3
$\emptyset$ or $\{\ \}$	the empty set	3
$\overline{AB}$	line segment AB	4
$\subseteq$	is a subset of	7
$\nsubseteq$	is not a subset of	7
$\subset$	is a proper subset of	8
$\not\subset$	is not a proper subset of	8
$\aleph_0$	aleph-null	14
$=$	is equal to	20
$\neq$	is not equal to	20
$>$	is greater than	20
$<$	is less than	20
$\forall$	for all	23
$0.14\overline{14}$	1 and 4 are the digits that repeat	30
$\approx$	is approximately equal to	40
π	Greek letter pi	53
$\lvert a \rvert$	absolute value of a	57
$\vec{m}$	vector m	59
$:$	such that	110
$\exists$	there exists	111

$\cap$	intersection	123
$\cup$	union	123
$\overleftrightarrow{AB}$	line AB	127
$\overrightarrow{AB}$	ray AB	127
$\triangle ABC$	triangle ABC	127
$\leq$	less than or equal to	145
$\geq$	greater than or equal to	146
$\overrightarrow{AB}$	half-line AB	163
$\nless$	is not less than	206
x^a	x to the ath power	258
$\pm$	plus or minus	272
$\lvert \overline{AB} \rvert$	measure of line segment AB	435
$\angle A$	angle A	436
$\lnot$	right angle	437
$m^\circ\, n'\, p''$	m degrees, n minutes, p seconds	451
$y = f(x)$	y is a function of x	471
f^{-1}	inverse function	482
$\wedge$	and	505
$\vee$	or	506
$\rightarrow$	implies	509
$\leftrightarrow$	if and only if	511
$\sim$	not	513
$\therefore$	therefore	524

Picture Credits

Chapter One Opening: Top left, Werner Wolff from Black Star; top right, Standard Oil Company of New Jersey; bottom right, J. A. Mallegol; background, Lick Observatory.

Chapter Two Opening: Top, Harbrace; center, Ewing Galloway, N.Y.; bottom right, Harbrace map.

Chapter Three Opening: Top left, Three Lions; top right, Brookhaven National Laboratory; bottom left, Ewing Galloway, N.Y.; bottom right, Harbrace.

Chapter Four Opening: Top, Litton Industries, Aero Service Division; bottom, Culver Pictures.

Chapter Five Opening: Top right, NASA; center left, IBM; center right, Harbrace; bottom right, Shea Stadium, Home of the New York Mets.

Chapter Six Opening: Top left, courtesy, the American Museum of Natural History; center left, Photo Researchers.

Chapter Seven Opening: Bottom left, Culver Pictures; bottom right, Harbrace.

Chapter Eight Opening: Top right, Harbrace; center, Photo Researchers.

Chapter Nine Opening: Top left, Harbrace; bottom, Post-Dispatch Pictures from Black Star.

Chapter Ten Opening: Top left, Morris H. Jaffe; top right, Morris H. Jaffe; bottom left, Penn Central Company; background, Culver Pictures.

Chapter Eleven Opening: Top left, Morris H. Jaffe; top right, Harbrace map; center right, Dick McConnaughey from Black Star.

Chapter Twelve Opening: Top left, Waldinger Studios; center, Harbrace; center insert, General Electric.